# Herb-A-Day ☺ ☺ ☺

# Other Books by Dr. James A. Duke

*Anti-aging Prescriptions*

*Dr. Duke's Essential Herbs*

*Handbook of Edible Weeds*

*Handbook of Medicinal Herbs*

*Handbook of Northeastern Indian Medicinal Plants*

*Herbalbum*

*Herbs of the Bible: 2000 Years of Plant Medicine*

*Medicinal Plants of the Bible*

*The Green Pharmacy*

# Herb-A-Day ☺ ☺ ☺

James A. Duke, Ph.D.

**Virginia Beach, Virginia**

Published by:
**ECO IMAGES**

ISBN: 978-0-938423-18-8

Available from:
**Eco Images**
P.O. Box 61413
Virginia Beach, VA 23466-1413
Email: wildfood@cox.net
http://wildfood.home.infionline.net



*Herb-A-Day...* is intended to provide information and recent developments on the use of herbs. Many healthful and even life saving plants, if misidentified or prepared incorrectly can prove dangerous. The responsibility for proper identification and use of plants must remain with the reader.

Printed in the United States of America

First Printing, 2007

# Illustrations

Illustrations by Peggy Duke previously published in *CRC Handbook of Medicinal Herbs* (CRC Press, 2002) or *CRC Handbook of Edible Weeds* (CRC Press, 1992) by James A. Duke.

# Dedicated to the greats –

Portia Mears, Bill and Paula Oliver, and Vickie Shufer, who took my dyslectic, polemic pig's ears of manuscripts and turned them into something worth publishing, maybe even republishing, and to Peggy who tolerated my idiosyncratic writing…

Jim Duke
gratefully, January 2007

# Contents



## Part One: Africa



## Part Two: Australia



## Part Three: Europe



## Part Four: Far East

## Part Five: Latin America



## Part Six: Middle East

## Part Seven: North America – Natives

## Part Eight: North America – Naturalized



## Part Nine: Polynesian Herbs

# Preface

My interest in herbs goes back to my childhood where I grew up on a farm in rural Kentucky, especially the ones you could eat. In college, I took a number of botany classes, including one on "Poisonous and Edible Plants." My interest grew. Then one day someone gave me a video titled "Edible Trees, Shrubs, Berries and Nuts" by Dr. Jim Duke and Jim Meunick. Soon after that Dr. Duke was scheduled to be a presenter at the *Wintergreen Wildflower Symposium* in Virginia. I signed up, went to the conference and came away with a completely new perspective. Dr. Duke's talk was on "Medicinal Plants." It turned out that all those plants I had been eating over the years were not only food, but medicine. The difference was in how they were prepared, the part used, or in some cases, no difference. The concept of food can be medicine and medicine can be food entered my thinking.

That was my first encounter with Jim Duke in May, 1991, almost sixteen years ago as I write this in February, 2007. Since then, I have traveled to the Amazon with him to learn about pharmaceutical plants from the rainforest, taken his mini-course on "Medical Botany" at the University of Maryland, College Park, and his "Ethnobotany" course in Maine. I have toured his Green Farmacy Garden and as a result expanded my own wild herb garden.

In 1994 I took over the publication of *The Wild Foods Forum* newsletter. That was about the same time that the *Business of Herbs*, which featured Jim Duke's Herb-A-Day articles, was discontinuing the publication of their newsletter. I welcomed the opportunity to not only be able to continue to learn from Dr. Duke, but to also be able to share that information with others. Those articles, as well as the ones written for the *Business of Herbs*, are included in this compendium of Herb-A-Day articles. Also included are a number of unpublished articles.

Over the years I have come to realize the importance of eating healthy. Dr. Duke's articles and his phytochemical database have been, and continue to be, a source of guidance and inspiration as I continue to learn about our wild and medicinal herbs.

Vickie Shufer
Editor/Publisher, *The Wild Foods Forum*

# Introduction

Why herb a day ... ? ? ? I believed when I wrote my first Herb A Day... column almost 20 years ago for Portia Mears, that an herb a day... like an apple a day, and today a clove of garlic a day... will keep the doctor away. And more importantly, an herb a day... might keep you away from that most dangerous of non-wartime environs, the hospital. Two million Americans a year acquire infections in hospitals, and 90,000 die from them. Some voices more often heard and powerful than mine even say that pharmaceuticals kill more Americans than any one disease in America.

Meanwhile an herb a day... continues to save a few lives preventitively, sometmes even curatively. And in many cases where they have clinically compared herbs with pharmaceuticals (saffron, saw palmetto, St Johnswort) the herb came out looking better and cheaper.

I wrote my first herb a day column in 1985, more than 20 years ago. As a long standing friend of Portia Mears, it was a small labor of love. And I enjoyed each issue of *The Business of Herbs*, moreso the botanical and herbal issues and less so the economic issues. How well I remember Peggy (Mrs. Duke), my secretary Judi DuCellier and I drove down to southern Virginia to meet with Portia and Dick Mears to discuss the possibility of our taking it over. Portia had other fish to fry. But Portia wanted to get it into good hands. Fortnately for me, we decided against getting into the publishing business, though I continue to write. Then Paula and Bill Oliver took over and did a good job for many years. They too gave it up after so many hard-working years. And the *Business of Herbs* went out of existence. My good friend Vickie was kind enough to add my columns to her newly formed *The Wild Foods Forum*, which took over some of the readers of the *Business of Herbs*. And Vickie, vivacious glutton for punishment that she is, tolerates many hastily written Herb a Day... columns. Still today, I find myself drafting more herb a day columns than get published. There's always news emerging on old herbs, often phytochemical news proving the folkloric medicinals beliefs.

As I write this introduction in early 2007, I have almost convinced myself that the evidence base for the empirical evidence-based herbal medicine is about as strong as the allopathic evidence-based medicine.

The Tai Sophia Institute has inherited all my back issues of *Business of Herbs* and now my *Wild Foods Forum*. They will also inherit my house, my whole library, and my **Green Farmacy Garden**, when Peggy and I move on to even greener pastures in the sunset. Except for my huge databases and nearly thirty years of computer files, Tai has most of my creations. I hope that this way the *Business of Herbs*, the **Green Farmacy Garden**, an *Herb a Day...* will live on, as Peggy and I sublimate or volatize or whatver happens in the rites of passage.

Early 2007, Vickie asked me for an intoduction for the anthology of *Herb a Day...* columns. I was preparing for a lecture on evidence-based medicine in California. I waxed prophetic and repeat now, that I think that within ten years more physicians will take herbs than prescribe them (since herbs are rarely if ever approved medicines, and physicians can lose their license prescribing unapproved drugs.

I often speak of myself as a "psychopathic" practitioner (who fervently believes in the healing power of herbs) in contrast to the allopathic practitioner (who fear the "dangers" of herbs, inspired, if not directly subsidized by a herbiphobic megapharmaceutical industry). Actually, the pharmaceuticial firms have the most to lose, if the power of herbs be fully disclosed, a cause to which I have devoted about three decades, even starting before my relations with the *Business of Herbs* and now *The Wild Foods Forum*. All of the herbiphobes speak of the dangers of herbs, which kill fewer than 100 Americans a year (usually those not following dosage recommendations), while neglecting the dangers of pharmaceuticals, which kill more than 100,000 Americans a year, taking the pharmaceuticals as described. Likewise the allopaths toast and boast of their evidence-base (which is experiencing many flipflops). Loudly and wrongly, they criticize the lack of evidence for herbs as medicines. The more I read and compile, the more I think the evidence for herbs is on average at least as compelling as those for drugs (half of which will be recalled or relabelled for unanticipated side effects within their first decade on the market). Wisely, the FDA cautions that the newest drugs are the most dangerous (usually also the most vigorously advertised and more expensive than its proven pharmaceutical predecessor, and ultimately its herbal predecessor; many pharmaceuticals were derived from herbs). I suppose that the FDA too must expect half of newly approved pharmaceuticals will be recalled, often due to unexpected side effects, that did NOT show up during the $1.7 billion study required to prove that a new drug is "safe" and "efficacious." Once passing these tests, the new evidence-based drug is [temporarily] allowed to market. But 50% of them will prove not to be safe and efficacious, and next thing you know, they are being sold for off-label applications for which there are no efficacy data. So the "evidence" is already more than half wrong. Is that the evidence base of which they boast, more than half wrong?

Allopathic "evidence-based" medicine has reversed itself in this decade, a trend I fear will continue. Many medicines they now recommend as one therapy of choice for a given ailment will turn out to be useless for that ailment, and/or to do more harm than good. The HRT reversal (which costs the public billions of dollars and thousands of cancer deaths, while netting the pharmaceuticals billions of dollars), the vioxx reversal, etc. More recently aggressive treatment with anemia drugs (Epogen, Procrit, and Aranesp; approximately $10 billion in sales worldwide; 2006), proved more likely to kill or cause heart problems than remaining anemic (*NEJM*, 2006). Most notoriously to me, one "evidence-based 2 billion dollar a year drug" was in 2002 shown to be no better than placebo for major depression. Five years later, it still advertises itself in *JAMA*.... I

wish I could list all the flip flops, where the "evidence" proved to be misdirected, misapplied or just plain manipulated. Many fallen pharmaeuticals made billions for the pharmaceutical industry, yet ended up costing society more than the pharmaceuticals earned their producers. Yes, there have been many flipflops in the new millennium.

How weak is the evidence on herbs. Many came to us with the empirical data from trial and errors of our ancestors. Most allopaths have been educated or mal-educated to believe that such empirical folklore is useless, surely the lowest level of evidence. But I have a great respect for the folklore. I like it best when an herb, like the Biblical garlic, has evidence from all fields – the old folkloric field (f); garlic also has animal, epidemilogogical, in vitro, and phytochemical lines of evidence (which score 1) and Commission E approval and/or clinical approval (which score 2 if it applies to an extract of the herb, 3 if it applies to the herb itself). A few herbs like garlic get my highest evidence score (f123).

Though the American Pharmaceutical Industry may say we have the best medicine in the world, I fear they they are dead wrong. We have the most expensive and perhaps the most dangerous. They can't even know that their pharmaceutical is better than the herbal alternative. Until the pharmaceutical has been clinically compared with the competitive herb, neither they, the AMA, the CDC, the FDA nor yours or my allopath, chiropractor, herbalist, mind-body practitioner, naturopath, osteopath or shaman knows which is best. Do we know that interferon is better than the Biblical milk thistle? No, we do not. Until clinically compared we won't know. And using a Biblical food farmacy item like milk thistle adds yet another dimension for my faith-based readers. Those who believe more in a Biblical herb than in a pharmaceutical are often more liable to be helped by that faith-based belief. A case of mind-body interaction enabling the homeostatic human body to heal itself, via homeostatically mining the Biblical food farmacy. Needed phytochemicals bring the ailing unbalanced human body back into the healthy balance as the healing body seeks to attain, via proper herbs, spices and foods.

Although some of these chapters are more than twenty years old, many perennial truths remain. Occasionally I have introduced [[in double brackets]] some new information. Mrs. Duke retains the copyright to those illustrations she generously loaned us to adorn this book.

Part One

# Herb A Day…

# Africa

# Aloe (*Aloe vera*)

*The Business of Herbs* 3(2):12-13, May/June, 1985

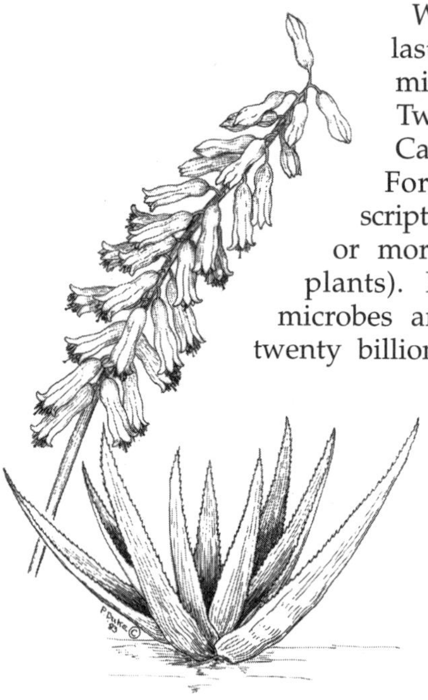

Were you jarred by my suggestion in the last issue that medicinal plants are worth millions of dollars to the world economy? Two fresh quotes are apropos. We read in Caulfield's *New Yorker* article, "The Rain Forests" (1/14/85): "One-fourth of all prescription drugs in the United States contain one or more of those compounds (derived from plants). If drugs derived from animals and microbes are included, Americans in 1960 spent twenty billion dollars on medicines with a natural component." OTC (over the counter) drug remedies run about $16 billion a year in the U.S. (Natural Food Merchandisers). Many of these are also based on natural products, like aloe. A 1965 *Science* article will reveal the exciting development of a new drug from the annual wormwood against malaria, another billion dollar problem. For the seamier side of the economy, we turn to *New Scientist*, (1/17/65) where Christopher Joyce says "in the U.S. alone, quack remedies are a $10 billion-a-year business."

Even though the FDA is challenging some medicinal claims for aloe, I will not call aloe a quack remedy. It is the quack side of the medicinal economy that Rep. Claude Pepper wishes to attack. We presume he shares our enthusiasm for the recent discovery of the mayapple's contribution to the war on testicular cancer and possibly lung cancer (fide Tudge, 1964; also in the *New Scientist*), the latter costing 100,000 American lives a year.

Clearly medicinal plants are important to the World Economy and to the business of herbs. And to the underworld economy? Illicit drug sales (cocaine, heroin, marihuana, etc.) totaled $110 billion in the U.S. in 1984 (*WTOP* radio, Washington, D.C. Mar. 7, 1985). There were more than 150 deaths [[that's more than are killed by herbs in the U.S.]] last year in Washington, D.C. alone, due to drug overdoses, about twice the level in Detroit, three times that of New York. On March 11, 1985, Channel 4 TV, in DC states that alcoholism costs Americans about $120 billion per year.

Plant-derived drugs, licit and illicit are very important in the American economy. I suspect that aloe alone is worth more than $100 million to the American economy. It is extremely difficult to come up with accurate numbers. Published figures vary considerably. The *Chemical Marketing Reporter* (1/16/64) said, "It is estimated that there are approximately

10 to 30 companies in the U.S. which specialize in aloe products, garnering sales between $4 and $5 million in 1962." The *Missouri Botanical Garden Bulletin* (71(1):6, 1983) said, "This year's south Texas crop (1200+ acres), producing approximately 30 million pounds per year, according to the National Aloe Science Council, Inc. (NASC) (where most aloe is grown commercially in this country) will pass $20 million." Alarmed by the disparity in these figures, I wrote to 10 aloe companies. Few responded. One telephoned that her business in aloe products topped $90 million a year.

Foolishly thinking official import figures might be easier to obtain, I found that aloe had been aggregated with other drugs like jalap. In *International Trade Commission* (ITC) jargon, aloe data are in the "basket" with several other drugs. After several circles I was told that aloe made up about 65% of the "basket," which in 1963, contained about 1.1 million pounds crude drugs, worth $1.05 million, 114,747 pounds advanced drugs worth $97,265. Applying our 65% indicates ca $3/4 million worth of aloe. In 1984 the figures calculate out to about $1.1 million for aloe imports, crude and advanced. The ITC assured me, "There is no way to get aloe figures for 1984 and 1963. Maybe in the future! It has to be worth at least a million for disaggregation." We probably do import more than $1 million in aloe and aloe products, grow aloe worth more than $20 million, and sell aloe products worth more $100 million. Aloe is indeed a multimillion dollar plant, important to the U.S. economy and the business of herbs. According to NASC the U.S. imports an estimated 50,000 gallons per year, mostly from Mexico and the Caribbean.

If we can believe the *Chemical Marketing Reporter* (CMR), aloe can return an annual 35 tons of aloe worth ca $200 for a ton, for a healthy $7,000 an acre. "The Rio Grande Valley is the home for an estimated 95 percent of all domestic aloe production, with 3,000 acres under cultivation, producing approximately 70,000 pounds of Aloe Vera gel per acre." (CMR, 1/16/64) There might be 35 tons of biomass per acre on a healthy aloe farm. I doubt that an aloe farm can yield 35 tons of aloe gel annually. The published figures are often less than 1,000 pounds aloe juice per acre, which, at $0.10 a pound, is only $100 per acre. Perhaps the true figure dwells closer to the latter lower figure. The NASC maintains that one can expect 35 tons per acre per year for 10 years with good management. It takes three years between planting and first harvest (NASC).

I'm convinced that aloe is good for burns. I hear so many echoes about its efficacy in skin cancer and indolent ulcers that I would certainly not be afraid to use fresh aloe on such ailments. Peggy, my wife, like many American housewives, has aloe in the kitchen window, first aid for burns. From rather arid environments in nature, aloe seems preadapted to sunny kitchen windows.

Without trying to prove or disprove, let me say that there is a healthy accumulation of folklore about aloe. My computer file alone lists aloe as being reportedly abortive, antiseptic, digestive, emollient, insectide, and larvicide. It is also listed as used in 38 folk remedies, among them amenorrhea, asthma, bruises, burns, and cancer of the stomach, cold, hemorrhage, and radiation burns. [[For a more complete list, see Duke, J.A., Bogenschutz-Godwin, M.J., DuCellier, J. and Duke, P.A. 2002. *CRC Handbook of Medicinal Plants*. 2nd. Ed. CRC Press, Boca Raton, FL. 936 pp.]]

If you want to read more on aloe, read *The Silent Healer-A Modern Study of Aloe Vera*, by B. C. Coats (P.O. Box 46026b, Garland, TX). The author is a pharmacist that is even more convinced than I about the curative powers of aloe. Remember that Coats may be in the Aloe business. The FDA may challenge many of the medicinal claims made for aloe. An *Economic Botany* article in 1981 challenged some claims made for stabilized aloe products. I'll leave these contests to the contestants.

A few recent abstracts that might be of interest to the contestants suggest that:

- *Aloe vahombe* from Madagascar contains an immuno-modulator fraction that significantly protects mice against bacterial, parasitic, and fungal infections.
- Substances in fluid fractions markedly promote attachment of human normal, but not tumor, cells. Growth promotion and wound healing effects of aloe substances in vitro may be analogous to what has been observed in vivo during healing of wounds and burns. In monkeys, water extracts of aloe lowered total cholesterol by more than 60%, triglycerides by more than 35%, phospholipids by more than 50%, and non-esterified fatty acids by more than 45.5%.

I'm foolish enough to speculate that FDA attacks on aloe and evening primrose will stimulate, not hurt, interest and sales in these herbs.

# Bishop's Weed (*Ammi majus*, *A. visnaga*)

(Unpublished)

With the fall hay fever season coming on, just what can *Ammi* do? A member of the celery family, *Ammi* belongs to a genus of 10 species, two of which, *Ammi visnaga*, the "khella," and *Ammi majus*, the "bishop's weed," are both sources of marvelous but marvelously different drugs. Somewhat resembling the Queen Anne's Lace, these similar white-flowered Mediterranean species, easily grown as annuals, even here in Maryland, have given us khellin, which was once prescribed here in the U.S. for hay fever, and 8-MOP, useful in vitiligo.

It's khella that's of interest when people start their allergic sneezing. The story of khellin is well told in the *Reader's Digest* "Magic and Medicine of Plants." Khellin, the compound derived from "khella," is a bronchodilator, expanding the breathing tubes that direct air from the throat to the lungs. "Hence, as the ancient Arabs knew, it can save the life of someone who is suffering from the terrifying bronchial spasm of asthma or severe allergies." (A dear friend of mine died from just such spasms this year. Possibly a few khella seeds could have saved her.) The fruits, or their extracts, also act as diuretics, a characteristic not uncommon among other members of the carrot family. And khellin is a selective coronary vasodilator, expanding only the arteries that feed the heart, quickly relieving angina caused by partially blocked arteries. Unfortunately, khellin has cumulative toxicities building up in the body, resulting in nausea and vomiting. Khellin has an oral LD50 of 80 mg/kg body weight, compared with 192 mg/kg for caffeine, making it roughly twice as toxic as caffeine. Conversely, the 8-MOP is estimated to have an acute LD50 of ca 500 (independent of its phototoxicity) making it less toxic than caffeine, at least in the absence of light. Khellin is no longer employed here in the U.S. But should I find myself with asthma or angina, and without MD and medicine, I would readily take a few of the seeds as emergency first aid, were they available. They are now growing in my garden, dangerous as they may be. Modifications of the compounds derived from the khella and/or khellin are still on sale, by prescription only, under the name cromolyn (or in nasal sprays called "Nasalcrom" or in ampules called "Intal"). [[Remember, this was published in 1985.]]

In the Sigma 1987 catalog, khellin is listed at $74.50 per 100 g, which translate to $338 per pound. Cromolyn (sodium salt) is listed at $141.75 per 25 g, which translates to more than $2,500 per pound.

Bishop's Weed, on the other hand, is one of the richest known sources of linear furocoumarins, containing at least 16 modifications on the psoralen theme. It is these psoralens that were mentioned (See: *Business of Herbs* 5(2):6-7, "Fig Leaf and AIDS," page 6) as being recently used, for the first time, in the treatment of certain types of T-cell lymphomas or leukemias. I have heard more recently from Dr. B. Wintroub, University of California, noting that he is experimentally inactivating the AIDS virus, apparently with the photopheresis and/or psoralen, without inactivating the T-cell. Naturally he's not prematurely releasing many details on his exciting discoveries.

Seeds or fruits of the bishop's weed may contain as much as 2% total psoralen, including 0.2-1.0%$ xanthotoxin (8-methoxypsoralen or 8-MOP), a compound listing at more than $4,000 per pound ($10.70 per gram, $95.10 for 10 g, in the Sigma catalog). With reported yields of ca 150 to 1,500 pounds of fruits per acre, green fruits yielding up to 1% 8-MOP, you might optimistically and correctly say that you can grow more than $60,000 worth of 8-MOP per acre. But your 8-MOP is in the seed and not purified, and there might not even be a market for that much 8-MOP. I cannot obtain demand figures for such esoteric compounds. These psoralens have their dangerous side effects also. When activated by ultraviolet radiation, they may intercalcate with DNA, with phototoxic, mutagenic, and photocarcinogenic consequences. Still they have been used for millennia in the treatment of vitiligo, and more recently in the U.S. for PUVA (psoralen/ultraviolet-A) treatment of psoriasis. Take heart, though, this damage may have a positive side effect. Scientists have developed monoclonal antibodies specific for 8-MOP damaged cells. Researchers can bind powerful toxins, like Ricin A, from castor bean to monoclonal antibodies, so called magic bullets. Monoclonal antibodies can track down cancer cells anywhere in the body. (Donald Robinson, *Washington Post Parade*, June 14, 1987, pp. 14-17, "Are We Winning Against Cancer?")

That special monoclonal antibody can track down 8-MOP-damaged cells, delivering medicine thereto. If you thought the 5-MOP expensive, contemplate the cost of one payload, Ricin A, selling at $135.00 for 5 mg, which translates to more than $12,000,000 per pound, nearly twice as expensive as our vincristine alkaloids for leukemia. Clearly there are dollars in herbal compounds, but not much of it will get to the herb grower.

# Fenugreek (*Trigonella foenum-graecum*)

*The Business of Herbs* 6(1):6-7, March/April, 1988

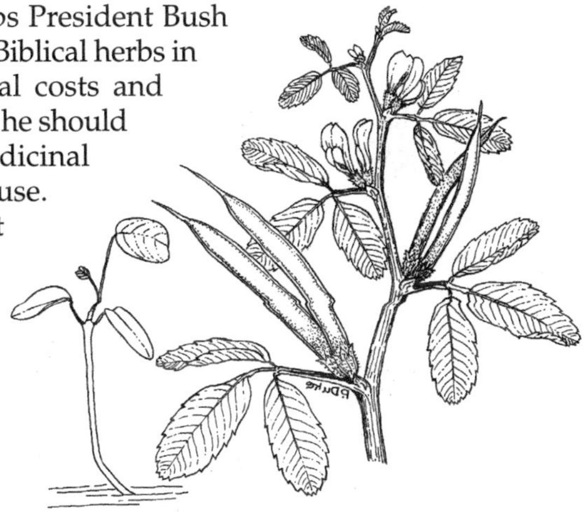

[[Sometimes I think perhaps President Bush should enlist some faith-based Biblical herbs in his efforts to contain medicinal costs and terrorism. Matter of fact, I think he should put a garden of Biblical medicinal species close to the white house. We had a hazardous alert just before Valentine's Day, 2006, down on Congressional Hill. It was a false alarm, but serves to keep the fear of terrorism at high pitch.

[[I was just pretending back during the smallpox scare, wearing a garlic necklace, with oregano air filters stuffed in my nose, and sipping on my "Smallpox-preventiTEA" (fenugreek, garlic, garlic mustard, ginger, leek, lemonbalm, onion, oregano, and turmeric). It's nice that the oregano stuffed in my nostrils diminishes the strong pox-repelling aroma of the garlic hanging round my neck. When my oregano is down, I can use alehoof (*Glechoma*) as a poor man's substitute. But of these I prefer lemonbalm, and suspect it is as potent as the oregano as an antiviral. Both have invaded (with my help) my six acres as welcome weeds. The *Glechoma* was here when I got here. The preventiTEA isn't as strong as straight garlic but it helps, swirling it around your mouth and throat before swallowing. And yes, if the war were being waged, I would consume my version of the "four thieve's vinegar"; two shots of redwine cut with a half shot of vinegar, in which 4 halves walnut and a clove of garlic had steeped. Even though I prefer the taste of white wine, I know that the tannin in the reds have antibacterial and antiviral activities. And yes, I'd eat the walnut and the "pickled" garlic. I'd make up a much bigger batch using roughly the same proportions for daily consumption during attack.

[[Fenugreekine from the fenugreek (*Trigonella*) is said to be antiphlogistic, cardiotonic, diuretic, hypoglycemic, hypotensive, and virostatic, inhibiting replication of vaccinia virus, explaining the use of the seed extract as a prophylactic for chickenpox and smallpox. Yes, fenugreek contains a lot of antiseptic compounds, some antibacterial, some antiseptic, some antiviral, some all three; carpaine, p-coumaric-acid, fenugreekine, gentianine, kaempferol lignin, luteolin, quercetin, rutin and trigonelline. And that's not counting all the ubiquitous vitamins, minerals etc. that this plant shares with all other plants. Still I find few records of the whole plant extracts being very ative as an antiseptic, one extract reported to be active against Micrococcus.]]

## Fenugreek, Biblical Leek?

During the Easter Season, it's nice to ponder a hypothetical question. Could a "bitter herb" of the Bible lower the blood sugar? Many herbs have been identified as "the bitter herbs," taken during some of the fasts of the Easter season. Some people have suggested that the fenugreek might be the "leek" of the Bible, but I am speculating that fenugreek, known as "Helbah" to middle easterners, might indeed be one of the many bitter herbs of the Passover. I doubt we'll ever be sure whether the Biblical "bitter herb" included the fenugreek or not. Surely its seeds have been used for millennia as a cure-all or panacea, from Egypt to India, and probably all around the Mediterranean. Once they were an important ingredient in Lydia Pinkham's compound, which because of its 18% alcohol content could hardly be prescribed for high blood sugar.

But the bittersweet seeds of fenugreek are a pharmaceutical potpourri containing dozens of pharmaceutically proven compounds, diosgenin, a forerunner of the pill, histamines, tryptamine, etc. etc. There are at least five compounds in the seed which are reported to help diabetes, or to lower the blood sugar. As recently as June 2, 1984, *Science News* reported Israeli research with rats that showed that a few fenugreek seeds delayed transfer of glucose from the stomach to the blood, reducing the need for insulin.

As early as 1976, Farnsworth and Cordell reported in the journal *LLOYDIA* that the seeds were used in Israel as an oral insulin substitute. Then they went on to report data on four compounds in the seeds that contributed to this remarkable activity. At levels in experimental animals that would correspond to about 1-4 ounces in a 220-pound man, the compounds coumarin and scopoletin showed marked hypoglycemic (lowering the blood sugar) activity in normal and diabetic rats. Two unrelated compounds, nitrogen-containing nicotinic acid and trigonelline, also lowered the blood sugar. The nicotinic acid had a stronger but shorter-lived activity while the trigonelline exerted a milder but longer-lived activity. So these compounds, in different ways, affect the normal and diabetic experimental animals lowering the blood sugar.

Meanwhile Indian researchers reported yet a fifth compound, fenugreekine, which in addition to anti-inflammatory, cardiotonic, diuretic, hypotensive, and viricidal activities, showed hypoglycemic activity. Clearly fenugreek seeds contain compounds which will lower blood sugar.

In countries poorer than the United States (where it costs ca 600 million [[2005]] to prove a drug is safe and efficacious) studies continue on the fenugreek. If these seeds, already on the FDA's GRAS or "Generally Recognized as Safe" list, contain compounds that are hypoglycemic and safe and can reduce the need for insulin, poorer countries might be on the verge of discovering a dietary approach to diabetes. Here in the U.S., it would not profit the drug companies to prove that the seeds were safe and efficacious for lowering blood sugar. How would they get their money back if you and I grew this legume and harvested and used our backyard fenugreek seed?

If you don't consider a dietary approach to diabetes good herbal business, how about an herbal dietary approach to enlarge the bosom. There have been more than 2,000,000 breasts enlarged by operations here in the U.S. Rumors floated out of the Middle East for centuries that harem women were fed the fenugreek seed to make them more buxom. This turned out to be more than rumor. The seeds, in addition to female steroid precursors, also contain a compound that increases the production of milk. Ironically, both fenugreek and marijuana, said to enlarge the breasts, contain the biologically active compound trigonelline. Since the seeds, sprouts and seedlings, like those of other legumes, have been used for food by various ethnic groups in various countries, I have not hesitated to use these bittersweet seeds to add a hint of caramel or butterscotch aroma to some of my herbal teas and liqueurs. My breasts are a bit larger since I started indulging in fenugreek, but then so are my waistline, hip line, upper arm, thighs, etc.! [[All that has since reversed; in old age I am shrinking a bit.]]

This herb merits much closer attention by herbalists, naturopaths and medical doctors. I'll wager that if the mucilages of the seeds were studied, they would prove about as beneficial at lowering cholesterol levels, blood pressure, and coronary heart failure, safer and cheaper than some of the synthetics finding their way to more lucrative markets.

Here's what I said in my *Medicinal Plants of the Bible* in 1983:

***Trigonella Foenum-graecum* L.; Fenugreek Leek (Biblical)**

*...We remember the fish...and the leeks...* Numbers 11

Some scholars consider the fenugreek more likely than *Allium porrum* to be the leek of the Bible. According to Tyler, Lydia Pinkham's "Vegetable Compound" contained 12 ounces fenugreek seed, 8 ounces unicorn root (*Aletris*), and 6 ounces each of life root (*Senecio*), black cohosh (*Cimicifuga*) and pleurisy root (*Asclepias*) in enough alcohol to make 100 pints of compound (58). In India, the seeds are used as a condiment and in perfumery. Europeans add them to hay, especially old hay, to make it more appealing to the animals. Seeds are used as an adulterant in, or substitute for coffee. They are also the source of a yellow dye. Fenugreek has wide use in the Middle and Near East today. According to Phillips, the Fenugreek is almost as popular in Lebanon today as the peanut is in America as a snack. In Beirut, they make a mush from the green seed after soaking, forming a fenugreek "milkshake."

The "milkshake" is prescribed in Lebanon for hypertension. In the Middle East, fenugreek is often believed to be both preventive and panacea. At a Lebanese clinic, patients reported using it as a poultice, and for diabetes, dyspepsia, fever and heart trouble. The root is more often used than the herb for pain and rheumatism. A fenugreek diet was reported (by only one informant) to speed the healing of broken bones, and to help convalescents, especially those suffering from chest inflammations, and recovering from typhoid. The mucilaginous seeds, emollient, tonic, and vermifugal, used for chapped lips, oral ulcers, and stomach irritation. Crushed leaves were taken for dyspepsia. The seeds were used for alactia, diarrhea, dyspepsia, fistula, glands, gout, neuralgia, rheumatism, sciatica, skin, sores, stomachache, tumors and wounds. Containing up to 40% mucilage, they are used in ointments and poultices. The plant is also suggested to be aphrodisiac, astringent, carminative, demulcent, diuretic, emmenagogue, emollient, expectorant, lactogogue, restorative and tonic. Iranians infuse the seed for menorrhagia.

# Fig (*Ficus carica*)

(Unpublished, written ca July 21, 2001)

Perhaps I am too excitable, two decades ago, I got all excited about the potential of the common fig as a food farmacy cancer remedy. Then a decade ago, I got excited about the possibility of figs and photophoresis for AIDs. I'll recite a couple paragraphs from that decade-old *Herb a Day* column. But this final week of July, 2001, my last issue of the *Journal of Natural Products* re-whetted my enthusiasm for the fig as an anticancer remedy. Fresh, dried or preserved, figs are food farmaceuticals, containing several compounds that have anticancer activity. And since the figs have been with us at least since Biblical times, I suspect our genes are well familiar with the phtyochemicals in figs. Perhaps a bit flakily, I believe that when we offer our bodies a food farmaceutical like figs, with which our genes have long familiarity, it's like offering it a menu of mild medicines. More flakily, I believe, that through homeostasis, the body, managed by those genes that coevolved for millions of years with many of these phytochemcials, sifts through that menu and grabs what it needs. That's what I mean by the herbal shotgun as opposed to the synthetic silver bullet. The pharmaceutical silver bullet usually offers you only one or very few, usually synthetic medicines; the herbal shotgun offers thousands of natural bioactive compounds.

Rubnov, et al. (2001) discussed chemicals in the Biblical fig, used even by Solomon to treat his boils (if you believe the Bible more than the other folklore). They stated that the first scientific investigation of fig latex was back in the 1940s. Large doses of the latex injected in rats were lethal. But smaller doses injected in mice infected with a benzapyrene-induced sarcoma inhibited growth of the tumor and some smaller tumors disappeared. I'd be more inclined to use it for cancer prevention than for worm treatment. "Fig latex has also been tested for anthelminthic activity, but is acutely toxic, inducing hemorrhagic enterosis." The leaf decoction affected lipid catabolism in hypertrigly-ceridimic rats and lowered blood sugar in type-1 diabetes patients (Rubnov et al., 2001). So yes, there is some scientific evidence for its antidiabetic as well as its anticancer activity.

But Runnov, et al.'s work adds 6 more anticancer chemicals, with names a full line long each, to join a dozen other antitumor phytochemicals in the Biblical fig. If you want their names, click on PubMed abstract PMID 11473446. The mix of 6-ACS compounds are potent cytotoxic agents, here from fig (*Ficus carica*) latex. But they also occur in soybeans. I'll wager they'll also find 6-AGS in the Biblical chickpea (*Cicer arietinum*) and I'll bet you'll find them in the Biblical broad beans and American black beans as well. And they are in edible parts of those plants. Some of the AGS phytochemicals occur in the milk (latex) of the fig, so you get some of these phytochemcials deserting on figs. For what it's worth, ACS compounds occur also in chicken skins and I presume chicken soup as well, if you make the soup with the skin intact. Adding this activity to the other anticancer compounds in fig latex makes it an even more interesting potential medicine. Maybe it could stop or sequester Solomon's sarcoma as well as arrest his boils???

My insulin-dependent diabetic niece might be interested in the diabetes work, e.g. that was reported by Serracalra, et al. (1998). Six males and 4 females, Type I diabetics, aged 22 to 38, with a mean duration of diabetes of 9 years were given a decoction of fig leaf (*Ficus carica*) with meals for one month. Then they were crossed over to a non-sweet commercial tea for the next month. Postprandial glycemia was significantly lower during the month when *Ficus* was given as compared to the commercial tea (156.6 vs. 293.7 mg/dl) without preprandial differences. The average insulin dose was 12% lower during the ficus treatment (Serracalra et al., 1998). I might also add the Biblical mulberry leaf to my Biblical fig leaf, sweetened with stevia leaf, were I suffering diabetes or Syndrome X. But since neither leaf is normally considered a food, I would not normally recommend them to others, unless they were under the guidance of a qualified health care professional.

*Hager's Handbook* (Ed.3) even suggests a Biblical aphrodisiac, Biblical in that all but the cardamom among the components are mentioned in the Bible: almond, fig, pistacia, saffron and sugar in milk (HH3). That after a Biblical bean dish with onions and garlic just might do the trick, with the unfermented fruit of the vine.

Let's refresh ouselves on the potential of figs in AIDS. I don't think we are any closer to a cure today than we were back in the late 80s when I wrote the following words:

## The Fig Leaf – and AIDS

*The Business of Herbs* 5(2):6-7, May/June, 1987

Wouldn't it be ironic if the Biblical fig leaf from the Holy Land contained a cure for that unholy disease known as AIDS? The "Valentine's Day" issue of *Science News* this year didn't suggest that. It did, however, suggest that treatment with variants of psoralen followed by ultraviolet radiation, a treatment already in use for psoriasis, might also, with some modification, be of use in AIDS.

Here's exactly what *Science News* said, "photopheresis somehow inactivates the AIDS virus in human white blood cells." Psoralen, the drug administered before photopheresis, does occur in the fig leaf, leaves of the same fig that cured Biblical boils. (Russians, who report no AIDS, are extracting psoralens from fig leaves.)

I never heard of photopheresis until this year. It is claimed to be the best way to deal with a leukemia known as "cutaneous T-cell lymphoma." Patients swallow an inactive form of psoralen. Apparently the blood cells ultimately absorb the orally-ingested psoralen. Then some blood is withdrawn from the patient, and the white blood cells are separated out, then exposed to ultraviolet light. The light activates the psoralen, which lethally damages the cancerous white cells, which are then re-injected into the patient, setting off an immune-system reaction against other cancer cells. Unless we have leukemia, we want all our white blood cells, but in AIDS, a virus attacks our white blood cells, vitally draining our defense mechanisms. With these T-cells under attack, the AIDS patient is swamped by alien invaders resulting in infections which finally overcome the patient.

If photopheresis inactivates both the T-cell and the AIDS virus, we haven't gained much. But there are many types of these photoactive compounds called coumarins. Many plant species contain many kinds of photoactive compounds with different phototoxicities. Some are doubtless relatively more toxic to the virus, others relatively more toxic to the white cells we wish to protect. The only significant photoactive furocoumarins in fig leaf "milk" are psoralen and bergapten, according to Lebanese researchers. Psoralen also occurs in several other edible plants and herbs: angelica, bishop's weed, carrot, celery, citrus, coriander, cow parsnip, parsley, and parsnip, for example. An article in the September issue of *Economic Botany* is scheduled to contain my brief on another plant, *Psoralea,* also known to contain psoralens, in the PUVA (psoralen/ultraviolet) treatment for psoriasis.

I have great respect for the Ayurvedic system of medicine and was pleased to read that they employed the fig to treat blood disorders. And today there is probably no more frightening blood disorder than AIDS. Of the 32,000 cases diagnosed in the U.S., 18,000 have already died (*Discover*, April 1987, p. 41). Now they are about to offer the synthetic drug AZT to a select few of the AIDS patients, but it may cost them $200 a week. And for over half of those who try the AZT, the side effects are described as about as bad as AIDS.

There are easy tests for the AZT in vitro, showing how the AZT protects the T-cells. Without AZT, the T-cell is eradicated by the virus (*Science*, March 20, 1987). I'd like to see the milky juice from the Biblical fig leaves tried in similar tests. Fig "milk," world famous as a folk remedy for other types of cancers, and containing the anti-cancer compound, benzaldehyde, in addition to the psoralen, might possibly be as effective as AZT.

And here's what I said about the fig a few years earlier (Duke, 1983), with a little bit of editorial embellishment.

***Ficus carica* L. Fig Tree**

> *And Isaiah said, take a lump of figs. And he took and laid it on the boil and he recovered...* II Kings 20

The leaves of the fig, first fruit recorded in the Bible, were used to make a covering for Adam and Eve. I don't know about Adam and Eve but, with me, the leaves cause violent itching when in contact with my bare skin. To sit under one's own vine and fig tree was the Jewish concept of peace and prosperity as indicated in I Kings 4:25. Figs are eaten fresh or dried and threaded on long strings. "Cakes of Figs" are mentioned in I Samuel 25:18, and these were also for travel. Fig leaves are still sewn together and used as wrappings for fresh fruit. To Egyptians the fig represented the Tree of Life. Some suggest that the fig was the forbidden fruit of the Garden of Eden. The fruit is said to be poisonous when green, the poison being replaced by sugar in ripening (Moldenke & Moldenke, 1952). Ficin, a proteinase, is used in meat tenderizers, and in the preparation of protein hydrolysates, edible collagen films, and sausage casings, in cheese making (as rennet) and in chill-proofing beer. Africans drop the latex in ant holes to drive them away. They believe that eating the fruits, dried, facilitates conception (Watt & Breyer-Brandwijk, 1962). Boulos states, "decoction of leaves erases freckles" (Boulos, 1983). That could be worth a lot if true. Boulos also recommends a tonic anise-flavored fig brandy.

Regarded as aperient, demulcent, digestive, disinfectant, diuretic, emollient, expectorant, laxative, pectoral, restorative, stomachic, and vermifuge, figs find their way into folk medicines for abscess, asthma, boils, cancer, carbuncles, catarrh, condylomata, corns, cough, diptheria, flu, gingivitis, inflammation, measles, pertussis, piles, pimples, polyps, scrofula, sorethroat, tumors, warts, and worms (Duke & Wain, 1981; Kirtikar & Basu, 1975). K.P. Hong, in the *Jerusalem Post* (Nov. 14, 1979), recalls that a Japanese bacteriologist, Dr. Kochi, reported "permanent cures" (no further cancer cell divisions were seen). Benzaldehyde, the active ingredient, was effective in experiments on mice afflicted with Ehrlich carcinoma. "Malignant tumours are changed into foreign matter and cease growing." Small wonder the fig has such an anecdotal repertoire for cancer remedies. Hartwell in his monumental *Plants Used Against Cancer*, lists the fig as a treatment for cancer of the gums and uterus, calluses, condylomata, corns, exacerbations, excrescences of the eyelids, vulva or uterus, fibroids, impostumes, moles, myrmecia, neoplasms, polyps, scleroses of the cervix, kidney, limbs, liver, sinews, spleen, stomach, testicles, and uterus; thymi; tumors of the abdomen, bladder, fauces, feet, glands, liver, neck, parotid, uterus, and wind-pipe; warts and wens (Hartwell, 1967-1971). Ayuvedics use the fruit for epistaxis, leprosy and diseases of the blood and head. Unani use the root for leucoderma and ringworm, the alexiteric, aphrodisiac, lithontryptic, purgative, tonic, fruit for alopecia, chest pains, hepatosis, fever, inflammations, paralysis, piles, splenosis and thirst. They regard the milky juice as diuretic, expectorant, yet dangerous to the eyes (Kirtikar & Basu, 1975). Contrarily, North Africans rub red and painful conjunctiva with the leaves, then bathing them in a rose water infusion of almonds. Africans use the fresh root in a lotion for thrush. Chinese apply the leaves to hemorrhoids (Watt & Breyer-Brandwijk, 1962). Let me quote from one of hundreds of letters I received last year relating to medicinal plants (Duke & Duke, 1983).

> "I have just read your article about searching for plants that contain anticancer chemicals. For a long time I have believed that figs would be used in the treatment of cancer. My reason – in II Kings Chap. 20 in the King James Version of the Bible beginning with the 1st verse through 7. Please read it and see what you think. I do pray to God that something will come through soon."

Maybe she's right. Maybe an ounce of fig phytoprevention could do more good AND less harm than a pound of chemotherapy.

## References

Duke, J.A. 1983. *Medicinal Plants of the Bible*. Conch Publications. NY. 233 pp.

Duke, J.A. 1987. "An Herb a Day…The Fig Leaf – and AIDS. *The Business of Herbs* 5(2):6-7, May/June.

Rubnov S., Kashman Y., Rabinowitz R., Schlesinger M., Mechoulam R. 2001. "Suppressors of Cancer Cell Proliferation from Fig (*Ficus carica*) Resin: Isolation and Structure Elucidation." *J Nat Prod,* 2001 Jul 27; 64(7): 993-996.

Serracalra A, et al. 1998. "Hypoglycemic action of an oral fig-leaf decoction in Type-I diabetic patients." *Diabetes Research and Clinical Practice* 39, 19-22.

# Khat (*Catha edulis*)

*The Business of Herbs* 11(1):10-11. March/April, 1993

## New Drug on the Scene

In 1992, the yew (*Taxus* spp.) probably made more headlines than any tree. It is a source of taxol, the most promising anti-cancer drug in a decade or so, likely to become a billion-dollar medicine by the year 2000. [[It became a billion dollar a year drug by 1998.]] But as 1993 got underway, an eastern African shrub or small tree replaced yew as the headline-getter. It is what I have seen called the "Somalian coke" [[Dan Rather, *CBS News*]]. No, it's not really "coke" or coca (*Erythroxylum coca*), the source of cocaine. But it has recently been listed by the United Nations (UN) as a narcotic. It is probably illegal for me to keep the specimen I have had in the greenhouse for several years, without getting a permit to handle narcotics.

The plant is khat (*Catha edulis*). Khat is one of a host of spellings I've seen, including qat, cat, gat, kat and chat.

Why is it called Somalian coke? There are several parallels in my old files, where you read about "coke-crazed" Indians in Latin America. Each night during the first week of the Somalia adventure, U.S. news commentators talked about khat-crazed natives, liable to do anything, including shooting Americans. Well, after four years of travel in Latin America, I've seen a lot of coke-chewing Native Americans, but I've never seen any signs of coca intoxication.

Chewing coca does seem to postpone symptoms of hunger and weariness. In my own case, the maté de coca (coca herbal tea) certainly helped when I suffered high altitude sickness, called "soroche" in Bolivia. (The city of La Paz is at about 12,000 feet, the airport closer to 13,000.) So I consider the coca leaf, as chewed and consumed as tea by Native Americans, a relatively healthy item, even a bit nutritious.

## A holy plant?

As with the Amerindian coca, "divine plant of the Incas," there are Muslim traditions which emphasize that khat is holy. As Abraham Krikorian (1983) tells us, khat is still believed to effect 501 different kinds of "cures." These equal the numerical value of its Arabic name Ga-a-t (400+100+1). What are some of these 501 uses? I've seen reference to anorexic (appetite suppressing), antiasthmatic, CNS-stimulant and aphrodisiac properties and its folk usage for bubonic plague, chest ailments, circumcision, cough, debility, dental ailments, diabetes, flu, lethargy, stomach problems and ulcers.

Legend tells us the plant was discovered by a shepherd named Alexander who noticed his goats were affected by it. When he tried it himself, he seemed stronger and more wakeful. Consuming some before bed that night, he was unable to sleep, and hence stayed up and prayed and meditated. Many Muslims have always been and still are avid users of khat.

Reportedly aphrodisiac, like so many stimulants, it is better regarded as anaphrodisiac. One botanical explorer (Schweinfurth) said that he had never seen so many bachelors in the Mohammedan East as he saw in Yemen, where it was openly stated that chronic consumers of khat were indifferent to sexual excitation. Krikorian (1983) concluded on this issue: "Khat has, therefore, generally but not invariably been seen in the context of heightening desire but actually depressing sexual performance... Chronic users may develop impotence." Watt and Breyer-Brandwijk make it sound a bit better: "Occasional use is said, however, to produce sexual stimulation but habituation the opposite."

## Parallels in usage

One sees in Krikorian's description of an Ethiopian farmer, the parallel I am drawing with the Andean farmer chewing coke: "The farmer typically rises early in the morning and eats a light breakfast. He then goes to the fields, often unaccompanied, and chews khat. By mid-morning, the effects are apparent, and the farmer can work vigorously until mid-afternoon, at which time he may chew khat again. He will often continue to work until late in the evening...It is obvious that such a routine could easily absorb any tendency for vigorous activity. A stimulant anorexiant such as khat is, in some ways, as much a boon to this sort of poor Ethiopian farmer as coca leaf is to the Peruvian Indians living in the thin atmosphere of the high Andes...An image of khat as an addicting agent which makes one poor, malnourished or otherwise debilitated or unfit for labor is not per se surprising. Such an image, however, takes khat chewing to be a cause rather than an effect of certain conditions designated as undesirable...Urban users are the main abusers" (Krikorian, 1983).

There are other parallels in usage. Bushmen in South Africa make a tea of khat leaves and chew the young shoots. In Arabia, dried khat leaves are smoked like tobacco. In Ethiopia they are eaten with sugar or honey. Both coca and khat leaves are anorexics. Years ago, I chewed coca leaves in Latin America and learned that they do curb the appetite. Andy Weil tells me he suspects that there are more than 10 anorexic alkaloids in coca, in addition to the cocaine, which is an ant repellant. I speculate that, if all these alkaloids evolved to protect the coca plants from their predators, then they are probably synergic in repellant, if not anorexic, properties.

Scientists at the University of Mississippi have a patent for an anorexic extract of coca leaf, devoid of cocaine. The anorexic, speed-like properties of khat prompted me to say in my CRC *Handbook of Medicinal Plants* (CRC Press, Boca Raton, 1985): "Would that the obese Jim Duke could chew khat and coca, dare I call it, coca cata, instead of lunch."

## Undesirable effects

Unpleasant side effects are possible. After listing a number of undesirable effects, the *Bulletin of Narcotics Special Issue on Khat* (1980) says: "Toxic psychosis occurs very rarely, if at all." The UN Narcotic Laboratory has isolated several substances from this plant. Investigating the pharmacological properties of cathine and cathinone, the World Health Organization (WHO) recommended them for control under the 1971 Convention of Psychotropic Substances. The UN Committee accepted the recommendation. But, the dilemma whether and when to control khat as a plant still remains for the authorities in individual countries to decide (Khan, J. *Ethno-pharmacol*, 1991).

Cathinone is an anorexic drug, and can become addictive, with cross tolerance to amphetamine. Cathinone is eight times more potent than cathine with addicted rats. "In selecting a phenylalkylamine to confer stimulant properties to khat leaf, Nature chose a highly potent one, and thus had its own amphetamine long before the advent of pharmaceutical chemistry. It is not surprising, therefore, that the mood-elevating and hunger suppressing effects of khat have been described as early as 1237 in an Arabic medical book" (Kalix, 1992).

How bad is the addiction? Here's the way the chronic user is described in Watt and Breyer-Brandwijk: "The habitue lives in a dream world... mentally divorced from reality and develops deterioration of character. He becomes increasingly apathetic, dull in intellect and unable to concentrate; he is no longer able to work and becomes a burden on his family and friends. He also becomes a liar and acquires an attitude of irresponsible fearlessness."

Sounds like alcohol, cocaine, heroin, marijuana, opium, speed and all the other drugs of addiction. I'm told you can already buy khat on the streets of New York and Washington. Don't we already have enough escape hatches?

Part Two

# Herb A Day…

# Australia

# Black Bean Tree, Moreton Bay Chestnut (*Castanospermum australe*)

(Unpublished

I first heard of this tree when I was starting a CRC *Handbook of Nuts*. It is an obscure Australian nut tree in the legume family. It was processed by the Aborigines for food, relatively rich in starch. The timber was also useful, and so resistant to the passage of electricity that it was used in making electrical switchboards. As a legume, it probably takes nitrogen from the air and "fixes" it in the soil. There wasn't much mentioned in the way of folk medicine, but some ominous notes cropped up in the literature. Some fatalities were reported among cattle grazing the seeds in the dry season. One report even suggested that cattle might get addicted to the leaves and seeds, pining away and dying when deprived of them, once hooked. Military personnel, on survival maneuvers in Australia, were hospitalized after ingesting the seed. Clearly, there are warning signals out about this nut.

At the Second Herb Conference in Indianapolis, I went so far as to speculate that this species would contain four million-dollar-plus compounds. It will surprise me if the leaves don't contain chlorophyll b, which trades at $178.70 per 10 mg in the Sigma catalog, which figures out to ca $8 million per pound, broadly rounded. Similarly, I'll bet the seed oils will contain traces of beta-sitosterol and campesterol, both of which sell at the milligram level at what translates to ca $4 million per pound.

But it is the unique compound, castanospermine, which prompted this article. In the Sigma catalog, it was listed at around $23 a milligram, or 90 to 95 for 5 mg, which translates to ca $8 to $10 million per pound. A year ago I saw an item in the *Threatened Plant Newsletter* hinting that the species was being studied for AIDS and/or cancer, and that 100 pounds of seeds had been sent to our National Cancer Institute (NCI). I quizzed friends at the NCI, but they denied any knowledge of it.

I learned just before I left for the Indianapolis meeting though, that the NCI was having a meeting on castanospermine, July 17, 1987. Dr. Kenneth Snader, of NCI, wrote me on July 22, "I do not at this moment know if castanospermine will become an AIDS treatment but it is showing some activity in our screening systems... There is enough interest to want to look farther at the pharmacology and to explore other products with either similar structures or with the same mechanism of action."

As anticipated by reports of diarrhea in cattle and survivalists who had eaten the seed, rats experienced diarrhea... Other biological activities surfaced, e.g., decreasing alpha-glucosidase activity in brain, kidney, liver, and spleen, 48-55% happen at 50-250 ug. More importantly, at 50 micrograms per milliliter, it inhibits death of AIDS-infected cells, and decreases so-called "syncytium formation." At 100 micrograms per milliliter, it completely inhibits the AIDS virus. Other items mentioned by Dr. Snader are more difficult to fathom.

The tree grows in a subtropical arid climate and apparently survives milder Mediterranean climates. I'm told that outside its native Tablelands of Australia, it is growing in India; Sri Lanka; Pretoria, South Africa; Miami, Florida; and San Marino, California. Oddly, it does not always set seed outside its home territory, even after 20 years' growth. I suspect the "nonvitalists" will synthesize castanospermine if the price doesn't come down substantially. New procedures can produce 100 mg castanospermine and four of its isomers for $10,000. Sigma's price has already come down to $12,500 per gram, which translates to less than $6 million per pound. (Swainsonine, a related compound, was recently offered at milligram prices that would translate to nearly 50 million a pound).

Whether herbal or botanical, there are some high priced compounds out there.

# Eucalyptus (*Eucalyptos globulus*)

(Unpublished)

I must confess I'm abusing my title and won't be talking only about eucalyptus, clearly a very important medicinal genus of perhaps 500 species, mostly fast-growing (and among the biggest) trees in Australia, some of their products perhaps finding their way into your cough drops as eucalyptol. Nor will I be talking just about eucalyptol, alias cineole, but rather about a suite of aromatic volatile compounds which make eucalyptus, mints, and other aromatic plants smell so good.

I will start with eucalyptol, which really can have two meanings: oil of eucalyptus, which is often dominated by cineole, or just pure cineole. Eucalyptol is in many of the over-the-counter (OTC) preparations for colds, coughs, and sore throat. As cineole, it's one of the major compounds in the aromatic essential oil of rosemary, long known as the "Herb of Remembrance" (if I remember correctly). It is these aromatic compounds that underpin the rapidly growing rage of aromatherapy. On the Board of Advisers for the *International Journal of Aromatherapy*, I recently reread many of the recent issues. It was most interesting, full of potential promise and the ever-present flip side, potential peril.

## Purists vs. Impurists

Cineole has been shown to stimulate the motor activities, coordination, and presumed cerebral functioning (thought processes) of mice, if not men, just from inhaling the cineole. A recent controversy has erupted in the aromatherapy community. The purists say that aromatherapy should be restricted to inhalation of these aromatic compounds, while the "impurists" believe that essential oils should be used in aromatherapeutic massage as well.

Such use results in a double whammy. You get results both from inhaling these compounds and from what passes through the skin, a mode of drug administration familiar to you in the form of transdermal (or percutaneous) patches of capsaicin, nicotine, or scopolamine (all incidentally from the potato family). The literature I read tells me that 100 times more of the chemical passes through the skin, especially hairy skin, into the blood stream, than gets through to the bloodstream from the lungs via inhalation. Further, these massaged compounds not only enter the bloodstream, they sometimes do it so rapidly that they can be detected in exhaled air in a matter of minutes, if not seconds. And, reportedly, they can pass into the brain from the bloodstream.

Alzheimer's Disease is sometimes characterized by too little of a chemical called acetylcholine or its simpler sister compound choline in the brain. There are enzymes in the brain (cholinesterase and acetylcholinesterase) that break down these compounds, which are, at least in normally functioning people, being constantly replenished, some coming into the brain from dietary choline, e.g., from choline-rich legumes. Scientists are mounting two attacks on the prevention or deceleration of the ravages of Alzheimeran acetylcholine depletion, increasing that coming into the brain, by dietary approaches, and decreasing the breakdown of these essential chemicals in the brain.

I simplify as much as possible by calling the chemicals that prevent the breakdown anticholinesterase compounds. I can finally pronounce this word, used as a buzz word today for anti-Alzheimeran potential. Tacrine is a synthetic anticholinesterase drug, approved by the FDA within the last year for Alzheimer's disease, even though it seems to help, only a little, about a quarter of the experimental subjects. It also damages a few livers in the process.

## Anticholinesterase Compounds

Several of our mint compounds, including cineole, are reported to possess anticholinesterase activity; there are also carvacrol, fenchone, pulegone, and thymol. If, and I emphasize if, all of these compounds get through the skin, especially rapidly through the hair follicles, and then pass through the blood-brain barrier unchanged, retaining their anticholinesterase activity, can they slow the ravages of Alzheimer's disease as well as tacrine? That's a question I fear we will never see answered as long as it costs $359 million to prove a eucalyptus /rosemary/nettle (ERN) shampoo safe and efficacious against Alzheimer's. Who is willing to spend that much on a product they could scarcely monopolize, much less patent?

Tacrine may damage the liver. So might pulegone, which I have been using as a topical tick repellent for years. Some scientists say it is rapidly absorbed through the skin and converted in the liver to menthofuran, which damages the liver, some cells irreversibly. So, should I die of cirrhosis, readers will never know whether it was the mint juleps or menthofurans that did me in. I'll never know whether the risk of dermally applied pulegone is sufficient to justify its benefits: the possible prevention of Rocky Mountain Spotted Fever or Lyme Disease (or Alzheimer's?).

Eucalyptus and rosemary are both good sources of cineole; oregano and horsebalm, of carvacrol and thymol; mountain mint, pennyroyal, and peppermint, of pulegone; fennel and rosemary, of fenchone. Nettle is a reasonable source of choline and acetylcholine, which may be broken down if ingested (eaten) or injected. Each hair of the stinging nettle is capable of giving you microinjections of acetylcholine, choline, and histamine.

## Alzheimer's Treatments?

Here are some questionable procedures we might see recommended for prevention or deceleration of Alzheimer's:

1. One could eat plenty of beans, excellent and tasty sources of dietary choline. This is safe for anyone not allergic to the bean. But some beans cause anaphylactic shock in susceptible people when ingested. (Relatively safe.)
2. One could eat cooked stinging nettles as a potherb. (Relatively safe.)

**Option A:** One could sting oneself on the carotid artery with the nettle; VERY DANGEROUS, causes a histaminic reaction in most individuals. (No fatalities reported yet!)

3. One could use GRAS (Generally Recognized as Safe) herbs in one's baths, hair tonics, underarm deodorants, massage oils, and/or choline-rich shampoos (eucalyptus, fennel, oregano, peppermint, rosemary, sage, and/or thyme). No fatalities reported yet! The GRAS list of the FDA is a moving target. At one time or another some or all of these herbs were GRAS.

I do not recommend step three, even though masseuses who have worked with these herbal oils for years have reportedly not suffered any ill consequences from dermal absorption of the anticholinesterase compounds, which will go through the palms of the hand and soles of the feet, in spite of the absence or near absence of hair follicles there. I have consumed all the herbs suggested under (3) in pleasant herb teas, inhaling some of the essential oil ingredients as I savored my tea. But then, I may have become a bit flaky from this overexposure to anticholinesterase compounds. If an aroma compound can mess with your cerebral acetylcholine, it might also mess up your mind.

Part Three

# Herb A Day…

# Europe

# Angelica (*Angelica archangelica*)

Originally printed in *The Raleigh Reporter*, August 14, 1993

### A Chemical Powerhouse

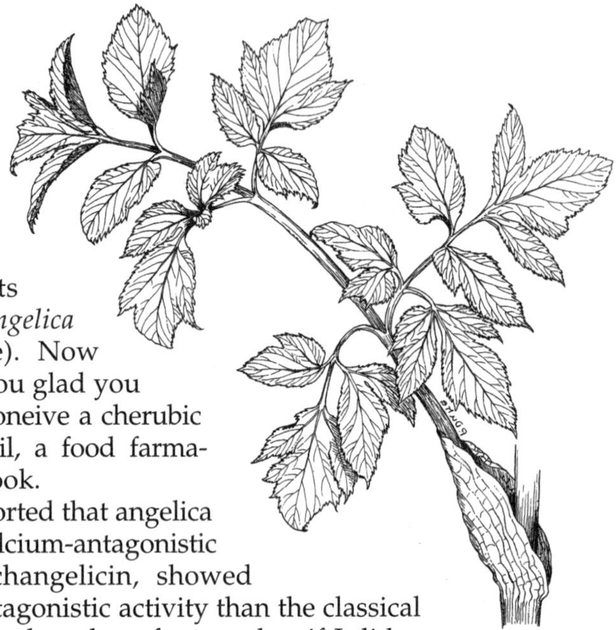

Some of you will have heard of the herb angelica, stalks of which are eaten raw, candied, or cooked. You probably haven't heard that its scientific name is *Angelica archangelica* (Apiaceae). Now that you have, aren't you glad you tuned in? You could coneive a cherubic cardioprotective cocktail, a food farmaceutical in my weird book.

A recent article reported that angelica roots contain fifteen calcium-antagonistic compounds. One, archangelicin, showed significantly higher antagonistic activity than the classical drug verapamil. I'd list the others for you, but if I did, my typist might ask for a raise. Anyway, angelica is a real chemical powerhouse. Those [15] compounds are enough to unnerve the California chemophobes. But there is little in the classical folklore to suggest angelica's potential as a heart disease preventive. In fact, some of its compounds can be toxic in concentrated sunlight or ultraviolet. They are even used in modern medicine with ultraviolet for treating psoriasis. I'm not about to suggest ingestion of phototoxic coumarins as calcium-antagonists. Nor do I know how archangelicin compares with the other more widely distributed coumarins. But if archangelicin is comparable to verapamil, shouldn't our FDA and/or HHS and/or NIH compare them? Verapamil is, according to the Merck Index, a coronary vasodilator with calcium-blocking activity [[not necessaily benign]], used for angina and other coronary problems, like arrhythmia and hypertension.

I want the best medicine for me and my family. Is synthetic verapamil safer and/or more efficacious and/or cheaper than archangelicin? Ask your pharmaceutical manufacturer. I don't think you'll get an answer. Ask your physician if Angelica is right for you. Again, you may not get an answer. But you and America deserve an answer.

Angelica is GRAS (Generally Recognized As Safe) by our FDA at levels up to 2,000 ppms. The rather expensive root is used in liqueurs and cordials and can be grown easily in your backyard. I suspect that one (no more than one) angelica cordial might be useful for people approaching the age and incidence of heart problems, perhaps even a bit preventive. But I don't have the $ millions it would cost to prove a new drug safe or effective in preventing or settling arrhythmia or angina. And the drug companies have no interest in validating an herb like angelica, and displacing the profitable verapamil.

Write a letter to your congressional creature and one to the Secretary of HHS, noting that many, if not most of our senior citizens can't afford the verapamil and/or the doctor to write the prescription. Tell them that you want to know if verapamil is better than angelica liqueur for coronary health. And anytime you see a television commercial touting a calcium blocker for one ailment or another, write to the advertiser and challenge him on angelica.

Heart failure kills more Americans than any other disease. Angelica could conceivably be an angel of mercy.

## P.S. 2006

Ask your doctor if angelica is right for you. He/she might send you to a psychiatrist, or advise you to stay away from those evidence-lacking dangerous herbs, and recommend you try an evidence-based FDA approved ACE-Inhibitor, and/or a Beta-Blocker, and or a Calcium Channel Blocker and/or a diuretic. Ask him/her if all those are still considered to be solid evidence-based recommendations for cardiopathy? If he/she says yes, tell him/ her to reread the last decade of *JAMA* articles. Ask him/her how much all four would cost for a month. His/her answer, if correct will be a three digit number. Tell him/her you know a GRAS-herb, used in liqueurs and candies that contains at least three dozen compounds that have been shown to be useful in cardiopathy. Ask him/her for the proof that the pharmacological cocktail is good and safe and efficacious, and better than your herbal cocktail. He/she can't honestly provide proof, until they have been cliniclly compared. Walk on home, relax, have some carrot and celery stalks with hummus and one delicious angelica cordial. And for breakfast next AM try an "Archangelade" (juiced angelica, carrot, celery, plus or minus fennel and parsley juice) and take another walk. Keep it up, and you'll probably outlive your physician. And the hundreds of dollars saved each month will make it easier to afford a second opinion.

# Chamomile, Roman (*Chamaemelum nobile*)
# Chamomile, German (*Matricaria recutita*)

*The Business of Herbs* 4(3):10-11, July/August, 1986

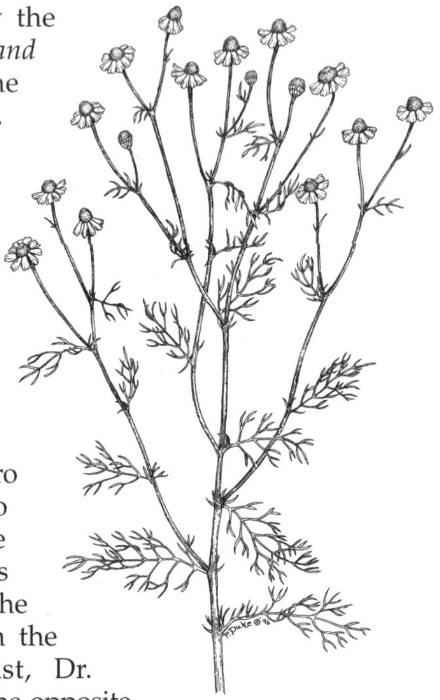

Recently, I was invited to review the premier volume of *Herbs, Spices, and Medicinal Plants*. The invitation came from famed medical botanist, Dr. Walter Lewis, who is the book review editor of the journal "Economic Botany," a journal with which herbalists who mean business should become familiar. Printed by the New York Botanical Garden, the quarterly "Economic Botany" often has detailed articles on medicinal plants and/or herbs and spices. I mention Dr. Lewis (who traveled with me to China in 1978 to study eleuthero ginseng) because he is very sensitive to ragweed pollen. As a hypersensitive scientist, he has, perhaps as loudly as anyone, sounded the alarm about the allergenic potential of chamomile. On the other hand, famed pharmacognosist, Dr. Farnsworth, has done as much to take the opposite stance, muting the argument about allergenicity. Not being sensitive to ragweed pollen, I won't take a stand, I'll just summarize by saying that those who are sensitive to ragweed pollen had best be careful with chamomile, which contains pollen from the same biological family as ragweed.

Connie Mann and John Staba wrote the chapter, "The Chemistry, Pharmacology, and Commercial Formulations of Chamomile," (pp. 235-280) in *Herbs, Spices, and Medicinal Plants*, Vol 1. Their article was, to me, the most interesting in this premier volume. With nearly 25% of their pages devoted to the citation of 220 references, Mann and Staba summarize the differences between the Roman Chamomile, *Chamaemelum nobile* and the German Chamomile, *Matricaria recutita*, without mentioning the perenniality of the former. I cite the scientific names here, because if you are as old as I am, you may have known these plants as *Anthemis nobilis* and *Matricaria chamomilla* back in the old days. And the common names have suffered their vicissitudes as well.

When you consider that chamomiles are small hand-picked flower heads, the annual production of more than 4,000 tons seems pretty impressive.* But it is widely used. My first introduction was in Panama where, instead of coffee, "te de manzanilla" was offered after dinner, both to facilitate digestion and to lead to a relaxed and sleepy evening, via carminative and sedative properties of the tea.

Mann and Staba devote more than 25% of their chamomile space to tabulating the chemical compounds, their structures, etc., with 60 terpenoids, 37 flavonoids, and more than 100 "other organics" listed in their tables.

Herb business people will be interested to read that commercial chamomile products have been formulated for cystitis, dental afflictions, shaving emulsions, veterinary uses, and cosmetic applications, not to mention their wider usage in herb teas, cosmetics, shampoos, and pillows.

Since I am building a computerized data base on the pharmacological activities of herbs, I was most interested in their short sections on pharmacology and pharmacodynamics. Ironically, the first mentioned is the antiallergenic (and anti-inflammatory) activity of the azulene compounds, suggesting that possibly azulene might antihistaminically cure rather than cause hay-fever. The essential oil, and the azulene, guaiazulene, and bisabolol, have some anti-inflammatory activity. Azulene compounds "stimulate liver regeneration." Alpha-bisabolol is said to have anti-inflammatory, antibacterial, antimycotic, and ulcer-protective properties, especially with alcohol-induced ulceration. Alpha-bisabolol and alpha-bisabol oxides are believed to relax the smooth muscles. The sesquiterpenoids nobilin, 1,10-epoxynobilin, and 3-dehydro-nobilin have demonstrated antitumor activity in vitro. Flavonoid glycosides and the flavones apigenin, luteolin, patuletin, quercetin, and apigenin monoglucosides are smooth muscle relaxants. The coumarins, herniarin and umbelliferone, have minor smooth muscle relaxant activity. Many flavonoids have antiviral activity and coumarins have demonstrated anti-bacterial activity. Extracts of *Matricaria* are reported to enhance uterine tonus, and can be used to help healing after surgery on the large intestine and urogenital system, though excessive doses may result in emesis and stomach muscle flaccidity. The extracts are said to have anti-inflammatory, antiseptic, myorelaxant, and sedative effects, the latter perhaps due to tryptophan.

[[Since Mann and Staba's excellent chapter, synthetic COX-2-Inhibitors have risen and fallen, but natural COX-2-Inhibitors like apigenin in chamomile and celery remain a natural option. You can read about all these and many more activities on the searchable database at the USDA, www.ars-grin.gov/duke/.]]

Mann and Staba's sections on "Toxicology" and "Allergenicity" lead me to conclude that chamomile tea is probably much safer than coffee or tea, unless you are one of the very few people who might be hypersensitive to chamomile pollen, like ragweed pollen. With that caveat, I would recommend it as an after-dinner tea or perhaps even a chamomile liqueur.

I've been properly criticized for my lack of sensitivity to nomenclatorial problems. But thanks to nomenclatorial changes, I will forever have to look up both the scientific and the common names of the perennial and annual chamomiles, and will gradually tend to spell the herbs camomile instead of chamomile. But I will perennially enjoy the tea, without even thinking about the dozens of chemicals it contains.

# Christmas Rose (*Helleborus niger*)

*The Business of Herbs* 3(5):6. November/December, 1985

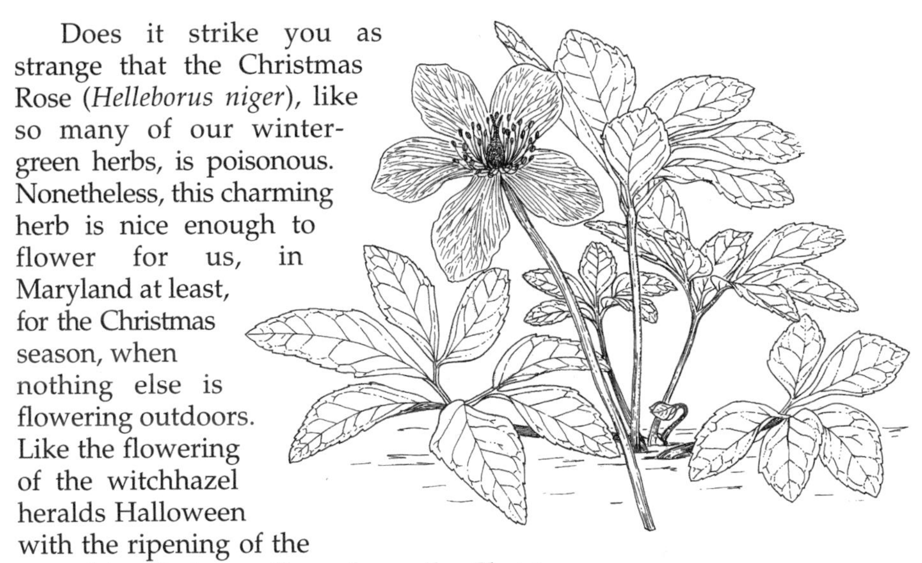

Does it strike you as strange that the Christmas Rose (*Helleborus niger*), like so many of our wintergreen herbs, is poisonous. Nonetheless, this charming herb is nice enough to flower for us, in Maryland at least, for the Christmas season, when nothing else is flowering outdoors. Like the flowering of the witchhazel heralds Halloween with the ripening of the pumpkin, Christmas Rose cheers the Christmas season.

True, there are many evergreen or wintergreen species around, some appropriately adorned with red berries, like the holly, the partridge berry, the wintergreen, and the yew. But none in flower save the Christmas rose! Small wonder then that it was supposed to have magical powers, making magicians invisible, and protecting animals from evil spirits.

One legend tells that the flowers of the black (niger) hellebore were originally black but miraculously turned white as snow when Christ was born. Early Christians used the white flowers as symbols of purity and humility. Another legend says that Gabriel led a tearful young shepherdess, distraught because she had no gift for Jesus, to discover the flowers of the Christmas rose, which she then delivered cheerfully to the Holy Child (Tyrell, *The Herbarist*, No. 34).

As many as 1,400 years before the birth of Christ, the Christmas Rose was used for mania. It contains the poisonous but strongly cardioactive alkaloid, hellebrin, which is similar in its activities to the glycosides of *Digitalis* and *Strophanthus* but less toxic. It is also diuretic. Large doses can paralyze the Central Nervous System. The herb (rhizome) has been used, albeit dangerously, as an abortive, anthelmintic, emetic, emmenagogue, and purgative. It has been regarded, in the past at least, as a specific for nephritis. But even European doctors are afraid of the side effects of this herb, so probably it should not be used as a medicine at all, merely as a refreshing outdoor flower for Christmas.

In homeopathic doses, which by definition contain almost infinitesimal quantities of hellebore, I presume that this, like other poisonous herbs, is safe. But I'm skeptical of any except placebo benefits from homeopathic dilutions of any herb. Nonetheless, Europeans use homeopathic tinctures of hellebore for cardiac insufficiency, collapse, dementia, encephalitis, epilepsy, hydrocephaly, melancholy, meningitis, etc. Though skeptical, I add that minute doses of toxins might help immunize the body against larger insults later. But let's not play with toxins at Christmas.

Even though I personally have eaten holly berries, poinsettia petals, and even yew berries, and consumed several mistletoe teas, I don't recommend such tomfoolery. These are some of the wintergreen species often mentioned in the literature as poisonous plants that might be found around the house at Christmas. Out in the woods, there are several wintergreens, the very poisonous mountain laurel, the medicinal pipsissewa, wintergreen, leatherleaf, puttyroot, honeysuckle, and then the thorny evergreens (stems at least) like the multiflora rose and greenbriars.

Probably the poisonous and/or medicinal attributes, like thorns, protect these conspicuous evergreens from overgrazing by hungry herbivores. But the wintergreens represent a nice respite from the drab of winter. That's why they've been brought indoors as decorations for millennia in the middle of winter.

Holmes, P. 1997. (3rd edition). *The Energetics of Western Herbs*. 2 vols. Snow Lotus Press, Boulder Colorado. 960 pp.

# Feverfew (*Tanacetum parthenium*)

*The Business of Herbs* 4(2):8-9, May/June, 1986

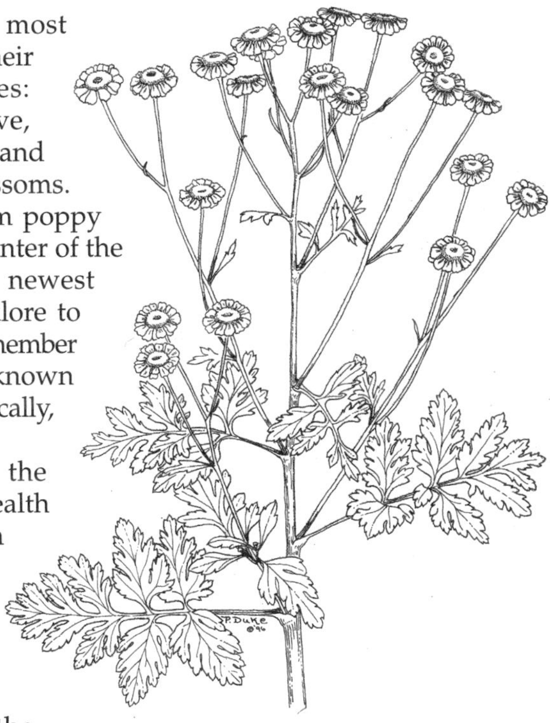

"Some of the world's most effective medicines began their careers as herbal remedies: digitalis came from foxglove, aspirin from willow bark, and morphine from poppy blossoms. [[Morphine really comes from poppy pods, which develop at the center of the blossoms.]] Potentially the newest plant to cross over from folklore to mainstream treatment is a member of the chrysanthemum family, known as common feverfew, or botanically, *Tanecetum parthenium*."

That's a quote from the Harvard Medical School "Health Letter" of April 1986, not Jim Duke. It's a pleasure to find such support for herbal medicines in such a conservative institution.

My sister-in-law, visiting from Hawaii, suffers, on the average, one migraine headache per week. To cope with her pain she's into some heavy and expensive medication. She estimates her migraine medication costs her $200 per year.

Somewhere between three and thirty percent of Americans suffer from migraine. If we assumed that just 12 million Americans experience the same problems that my sister-in-law does, their outlay from medicine would be almost 2¼ billion dollars a year, not to mention lost work days. I don't think the purveyors of pharmaceuticals would be pleased to see feverfew replace the drugs now used for migraine.

According to the Harvard letter whose source was *The British Medical Journal*, "Eating feverfew leaves has become a familiar method for preventing migraine attacks in modern England. Some people for whom conventional treatments for migraine have not worked have turned to feverfew with good results." The typical "feverfew eater" eats one to four fresh leaves a day, often with food to mask the bitter taste.

To evaluate this folk remedy British scientists designed a controlled study. Since feverfew had not gone through animal studies as is appropriate before a drug is tested on people, they decided on an unusual human test that was both human and ethical. Rather than give the herb to subjects who were inexperienced with the drug, they chose people who had used feverfew for years. Half the chosen group was given a capsule containing freeze-dried feverfew, the other half received a look-alike capsule containing only a placebo. Those receiving the freeze-dried feverfew experienced no increase in their migraine symptoms while those who received the placebo experienced considerable increase.

The Harvard letter went on to say that the name feverfew indicates a belief dating from the Middle Ages that the herb was a good treatment for fever and certain other ailments including arthritis, headaches and psoriasis. Like other of the numerous reports coming out on feverfew the Harvard newsletter cautioned that feverfew, like conventional drugs can have side effects. "Feverfew is capable of producing rather marked allergic reactions; some people who try it develop sores in their mouth, or, less commonly, a generalized inflammation of the mouth and tongue." I have tried feverfew myself and have not experienced such inflammation. [[Once during a lecture, I chewed some and had to have a drink, it was so bitter, before resuming my talk, to a Maharishi Ayurevedic Group.]]

Although the article does not specify the side effects as coming from leaves or capsules, they are probably talking about people who have been eating the leaves. I think it would be almost impossible for the capsules to have such an effect.

Arthritis probably affects more people than does migraine. Preliminary studies suggest that the feverfew does indeed have some anti-inflammatory activity via the complex prostaglandin inhibition. We hope that further studies on this herb will prove as successful as the migraine study was.

However, arthritis is more complicated. Many of the herbal approaches to arthritis, including evening primrose, are aimed at things that seem to inhibit prostaglandins synthesis. In an article on Feverfew appearing in Vol 4, No. 2, of *The American Herb Association Newsletter*, Christopher Hobbs indicates that there is such inhibition activity in feverfew, which means we should look at it more closely for arthritis.

Feverfew has anti-inflammatory properties unquestionably. Antiinflammatories are useful in certain types of arthritis. Perhaps there are enough people in the U.S. who have taken feverfew for migraine who also suffer from arthritis who would be willing to provide anecdotal evidence against arthritis that could be checked out with the same methodology as was used in the British migraine study.

People in the U.S. who are sympathetic to medicinal herbs might find this a novel method of testing other herbal therapies. Such a test could sidestep F.D.A. requirements. There may be ethnic groups (one would need a group of 50 or so) willing to take part who have been using a given herbal treatment for many years on a regular basis.

As for feverfew, based on what I've read in Hobbs and elsewhere, it seems the single flowered variety is medically more efficacious than double-flowered varieties. [Also from a British newsclipping sent me some time ago, it seems that relief from migraine symptoms using feverfew happens gradually, taking up to three months of daily doses. The Ed.]

I'd like to close quoting the British Medical Journal, "This provides evidence that feverfew, taken prophylactically prevents attacks of migraine..."

## Postscript

Late in February, I got some privileged information about one drug company and a very important drug. I can't tell you the exact details until the news has broken officially. Over 4 million prescriptions containing the drug are sold in the U.S. each year. The drug has not yet been synthesized and is available only from three species of shrubs which occur only in "Banalandia" (real name withheld to protect the millions of people who need the drug). There are no plants growing outside "Banalandia," as far as I can determine. One European drug company, perhaps realizing this, bought up all the plantations in "Banalandia" about 8 years ago, getting a monopoly on the shrubs, the only known source of this natural drug. Now the cost of the drug has increased almost tenfold ($200 to $2000 per kilo). This drug company may be gouging the people who need the drug, largely senior citizens. One MD specialist, sharing my disgust with such a situation, has enlisted my help in trying to find an alternative source for the drug, either a related species with similar compounds, or an overlooked specimen outside the borders of "Banalandia." I have accepted the challenge with great gusto. Not only do the drug companies steer us away from the naturals and to their new synthetics, to which our genes have not yet been exposed, they try to monopolize the source of the natural drug when they can't make a synthetic, at least in this case. I predict that we will break the "Banalandia" monopoly. When the news breaks, remember you read it first in *The Business of Herbs*. [[2006 – Actually nothing came of it. I now have the tropical shrub growing in the green house. My sponsor passed away. But I enjoyed a nice trip to Banalandia]]

Feverfew now is almost cosmopolitan, growing in most, if not all, temperate climate countries and some subtropical and tropical countries. [[Even as I write this, following a 15-inch snow on **The Green Farmacy Garden**, the feverfew is a vigorous weed in my garden, some peeking out as semi-evergreen in the white snow.]] If feverfew were confined to "Banalandia," and nobody had it growing in their gardens, I suspect the drug companies would rush to monopolize it. As it is, there is already a rush here in the U.S. by migraine sufferers, trying to get living plants and/or an adequate supply of feverfew to avert their migraine headaches. Some of our local dealers cannot keep up with the demand. If I had suffered the way migraine sufferers do, I would certainly indulge in a little self experimentation with feverfew. If you must self-diagnose and self-medicate, be careful. We will probably never know whether feverfew is more or less safe and efficacious than the synthetics being offered us.

# Flax (*Linum usitatissimum*)

*The Business of Herbs* 7(1):10-11, March/April, 1989

In the seventh line of the ingredients of my loaf of Roman Meal bread a decade ago at least, it said "DEFATTED FLAXSEED MEAL." Where did the fat go? The flax fat contains alpha-linolenic acid (ALA) which has been getting a lot of attention lately as "Omega-3: the missing ingredient." Research by Donald Rubin, published in *The Omega-3 Phenomenon* (1987) indicated "the dietary availability of Omega-3 declining to only 20% of the level it held in traditional diets a hundred years ago." Rudin goes on to implicate Omega-3 deficiency loosely with more ailments than the 44 patients who participated in his non-blind, laxly controlled "clinical studies." People who are gullible, hypochondriac or placebo prone and suffer from any of the more than 50 ailments mentioned by Rudin are likely to consider buying linseed oil (flaxseed oil) to see if the ALA will help them. I, too, would not hesitate to modify my diet to increase alpha-linolenic acid were I suffering from any of these ailments; but I would approach my self-medication with skepticism. [[In 2006, after hearing Jerry Cott of the FDA give two presentations, my skepticism has evaporated for omega-3 fatty acids in fish oil if not also the phytochemical, ALA.]]

Like some other authors, Rudin makes it sound as though linseed oil is the best source of ALA. For example, Dyerberg (*Nutrition Reviews* 44(4):125. 1986) goes off the deep end, wrongly stating that the only plant source of linolenic acid is linseed oil. Rudin's own tables show that, in fact, the beefsteak plant, Perilla, is a better source of ALA. Following Perilla, the list includes linseed, hempseed, English walnut, black walnut, soybean, wheat germ, and chestnut, in order of decreasing ALA content. Recently scientists have also found kiwi seed to be a good source.

Perilla is a weed here at the **Green Pharmacy Garden**, competing with my favorite weed, the evening primrose, source of omega-6, gamma-linolenic acid. As a matter of fact, I could mix up a pretty good non-Roman meal using the Perilla and evening primrose seed. I would not hesitate to add flax or Perilla seed to my bran flakes were I convinced that ALA would do me some good. We'll talk about Perilla another time.

Today, in 2001, the label on my "6-Grain Round Rye Bread" says Wheat, Barley, Rye, Sunflower, Caraway, Sesame, Oat, Soy Oil and Grits, Corn, Triticale, Flax Seed, Brown Rice, (Cottonseed Oil), and Fennel. Today that's my bread of choice in my Struggle for 7 campaign, i.e. daily seven beans, seven fruits, seven herbs, seven nuts, seven spices, seven veggies, seven whole grains; Don't go for more calories; go for more variety.

If the seed is going to be promoted by the health food industry, it seems prudent to document its long use as food. For that I quote "USDA Technical Bulletin #938" (1947):

> "Primitive man was more interested in food than in clothing. Wild flax was probably first gathered for its seed as a source of food... Today the use of flaxseed in food is not important, but linseed oil is used for food in Russia, India, and some other countries. The flax plant supplies clothing [linen fabric] and food for man and feed for animals."

Seeds of native prairie flax, *Linum lewisii*, were eaten by Amerindians in the Dakotas and Nebraska according to USDA Miscellaneous Publication #237 (1936). Asian Indians eat the seeds in candies and chutneys (*The Wealth of India*, 1948-1976).

But is it nutritious? On a zero-moisture basis 100 grams of flax seed would furnish more of most nutrients than our flax-containing bread. More importantly, that flax seed would contain 17 grams of ALA, much more than the 2 grams Rudin suggests as a minimum daily allowance. An ounce of seed would be more than adequate for ALA, providing, as well, one or two grams of fiber.

So, where did the fat in the defatted flaxseed meal go? The oil and ALA from that flaxseed may have ended up at the health food store, or in the linseed oil destined for the paint industry. Heretofore, linseed oil has been considered more suitable for painting than for health food, and not all linseed oil may be suitable for human consumption. There is a remote possibility of getting cyanide in cold-pressed oil. Cyanide seems to prevail in flowering plants with unripe seed. The processed linseed oil found at the hardware store is, of course, not a food product.

Besides the historical use of flax for food and fiber, there is a long list of medical folklore involving flax seed, including the treatment of cancer and cancer-related maladies. The genus *Linum* does, in fact, contain three known anticancer agents, traces of which may be found in the oil. Linseed seed, often mixed with honey and lemon juice, has been widely used for colds, coughs, and other conditions. Contradictorily, Ayurvedic medicine suggests that seed usage may lead to impotency, while the Unani system views them as aphrodisiac. Just because of that contradiction, I'll not repeat the lengthy, computerized list of ailments for which flax is a folk remedy. [[You can use the ethnobotancy query in the phytochemcial database at USDA – http://www.ars-grin.gov/duke/.]] With two long lists there's naturally some overlap. Many of Rudin's diseases reputedly helped by ALA are those already in the folk repertoire of the Biblical linen. Luke 23 mentions linen, then, as now, a classical textile, and Duke (*Medicinal Plants of the Bible*, 1983) mentions the flax. Both of these fibers, like both linseed and flax seed oil, are obtained from one species, *Linum usitatissimum*. Linseed fiber is even used in making Bibles; so somewhere there are a few linen Bibles mentioning the Biblical linen.

Working with Dr. Chris Beecher of NAPRALERT and Dr. Herb Pierson of NCI, Paul Stitt concentrated on cancer as the reason why George should eat his broccoli. But when it comes to flax and ALENA, his melodic name for alpha-linolenic-acid (interestingly called simply linolenic-acid in his food tables), he rekindles several of the health claims made, many with good reasons, for stabilized flax and its ALENA. Most of these I have discussed elsewhere in a paper called "Orthomegalomania" (*Organica* 8{28}: 12-3. 1989), detailing some of the claims made for omega-3 fatty acids, especially with prostaglandin-related ailments.

Flax, which Stitt clearly and deservedly promotes, had 27 cancer-preventives listed.

## Flax Linen

"The transition from the hunter-gatherer culture began with the practices of seeding and harvesting in fertile river valleys. Human settlement in such regions followed the Biblical story of Joseph, whose coat of many colors was said to have been made of linen, illustrates the importance of the ability to store surplus grain in years of plenty to withstand the periodic drought cycle that otherwise devastates nomadic societies. The earliest agrarian societies developed in the Tigris and Euphrates valleys in Mesopotamia. By around 6000 BC virtually all staple crops were being grown. Evidence for flax cultivation was already present. The earliest fragment of cloth ever identified was from Eastern Turkey (Cayonu in 1988 in the upper Tigris River valley), carbon dated to 9,000 years ago, and is considered to be of linen. Prepottery Neolithic finds at Jericho include similar flax artifacts." (Cunnane and Thompson, eds. 1995)

Ancient Egyptians depicted the growth of flax on papyri, the spinning of flax thread in murals, and the weaving of that thread into linen. Remains of the Pharaohs are bound in fine and delicate linen, woven with an expertise that is still today difficult to repeat 3-4,000 years later. Not only was the linen used in mummy cases, the oil was used in embalming. "Flaxseed oil is traditionally used in Egyptian cuisine in the dish 'ful medames,' a stewed (faba) bean dish served with garlic, onions, and cumins." Talk about food "farmacy," I'd recommend that as a food pharmacy approach, replacing a fatty meat dish, for all the major "civilized" diseases of civilization, cancer, coronary, diabetes, even impotence and parkinson's disease! (Faba beans are said to be the beans that incited Cicero to passion.) Recent clinical studies suggest that flax' ALA is of substantial value in reducing mortality from cancer and cardiopathy

| Nutrient | Flax-Containing Bread 4 slices (ca 96 g) | Flax Seed 100 g |
|---|---|---|
| Calories | 240 | 531 |
| Protein | 8 grams | 19-29 grams |
| Carbohydrate | 44 grams | 30-40 grams |
| Fat | 4 grams | 36-40 grams |
| Sodium | 460 mg | ? |
| Thiamine | 24% of RDA | 10% of RDA |
| Riboflavin | 16% of RDA | 10% of RDA |
| Niacin | 16% of RDA | 3% of RDA |
| Calcium | 8% of RDA | 18-39% of RDA |
| Iron | 16% of RDA | 20-300% of RDA |

(Cunnane and Thompson, 1995 and Judd, 1995).

From time to time a new book prompts me to move an herb to the top of the herb-a-day heap, and that's what prompts this second HAD column on flax. I cite the title, *Flaxseed in Human Nutrition*, and that introductory quote, because I want the FDA to know that flaxseed is and has been food for a long time. Every now and then they attack a food "farmaceutical," saying that it's not a food. Flax is clearly food and has been for millennia. Traditionally, flaxseed has been consumed in various forms for more than 5,000 years. And the three principal components of nutritional significance – alpha-linolenic acid (ALA), dietary fiber, and polyphenolics (particularly lignans) – have certainly gotten their share of good press lately.

Here's what I said in 1983:

***Linum Usitatissimum* L.; Flax Linen (Biblical)**
*...And he took it down, and wrapped it in Linen...* Luke 23

The flax plant is commonly used to make linen, the most ancient of all textile fibers. Linen is the most important product made from the fiber of the flax plant. Flax fibers are soft, lustrous and flexible, although not so flexible or elastic as those of cotton or wool. Seeds contain 24% protein, and also are the source of linseed oil. In some countries it is also used as edible oil and in soap manufacture. Linseed is often employed with other seeds as food for small birds.

## A Long History

Those of you interested in the origin of words will delight in the historical chapter by Andrew Judd, Faculty of Medicine, University of Saskatchewan. He leans on the Compact Oxford Dictionary as "the most reliable source on the linguistic origin of words." The surprise: Judd blames the word "line" on linen or *Linum*, scientific generic name of flax. "The word line has many linguistic roots-Old English, Old High German, Middle High German, Old Norse, Swedish, and Gothic-all implying its descendance from a Latin or Greek ancestor, linum, meaning 'flax.' A common origin and antiquity are clearly implied." The words linen, lining, linear, and lineage all derive from the word "line." Even the plumb line for the spun thread used in construction may have Biblical origin. See, for example, Ezekiel 40:3, "with a line of flax in his hand and a measuring reed."

There's even some early phenology in the Bible: "For the barley was in the ear and the flax was bolled" (had developed seed heads). "...and when Joseph had taken the body, he wrapped it in a clean linen cloth" (at the burial of Christ). The word liniment also derives from linum.

"Linen was the principal sailcloth during the great sea voyages of discovery." (Others attribute such sails to another source of GLA, *Cannabis*, from which the word canvas is said to derive.) "However, to this day, the finest artist's canvases are linen in origin." And linseed oil is often used as a vehicle for the pigments in painting. In one of the first mechanically reproduced Biblical efforts (Johannes Gutenberg's), the "pigment" was lampblack, and the drying agent was predominantly boiled linseed oil. Early rugs were made of flax (though often replaced with wool in the famous Middle Eastern weavings), but then too often replaced with linoleum (linum=flax; oleum=oil). In 1847, Michael Narin in Scotland developed the first prototype linoleum from oil paint. Then Frederick Walton in Britain developed a technique for oxidizing linseed oil with a flax weave backing known as the "resilient floor." He patented his product in 1860, the same year that American Thomas Armstrong developed linoleum with patterns and colors which "beautified the plain floor."

Stretching the lines of imagination, Judd notes that there are few if any straight or linear constructs among primitive hunter-gatherers. "Did the concept of a straight line and its application occur to primitive societies as a consequence of the utility of a flaxen thread? ...To what extent has the utilization of flax fiber and flaxseed oil characterized Western civilization ...Studies in China indicate that flax has been in use for at least 2,000 years, both for its fiber and its medicinal properties...Most Chinese flaxseed is consumed in the diet as oil. Speculation of a much longer Chinese heritage of up to 5,000 years is also recorded."

## Activities

Considered anodyne, astringent, cyanogenetic, demulcent, diuretic, emollient, expectorant, laxative, suppurative and vulnerary. In Ethiopia, the seeds are used for amebic dysentery. *Linum* finds its way into folk remedies for boils, bronchitis, burns, cancer, carbuncles, cold, conjunctivitis, corns, coughs, cystitis, diarrhea, gallstones, gonor- rhea, gravel, gout, hepatitis, inflammation, intoxication, labor, rheumatism, scalds, sclerosis, sores, spasms, swellings, and tumors. Since linen has long anticancer folk history, it is interesting to see that *Linum* contains the anticancer agents 3'-demethylpodophyllotoxin podophylotoxin and beta-sitosterol. L-glutamic acid is used to treat adolescent mental deficiencies. Seeds are considered emollient, demulcent, pectoral, diuretic, and astringent. Crushed seeds make a good poultice (for colds, pleurisy, etc.), either alone or with mustard; lobelia or hollyhock seed added to the poultice for boils. Sometimes seeds are roasted and used in a poultice. Hot seeds are applied to abscesses and rheumatism. Sometimes employed as an addition to cough medicines. Linseed tea used for colds, coughs, irritation of the urinary tract (when honey and lemon juice may be added). With lemon, it is used in Lebanon for cystitis, gallstones, gravel, hepatitis, and kidney stones. Internally, oil given as a laxative. Linseed oil mixed with equal quantity of lime water, known as Carron oil, is an excellent application for burns and scalds. Flowers with immature seeds contain 0.69% HCN, 0.22 kg (half pound) of flowers will cause death of bullocks. Oil mixed wth honey is used as a cosmetic for removing spots from the face. In veterinary medicine, oil is used as a purgative for sheep and horses, and a jelly formed by boiling seeds is used as a purgative for sheep and horses, and ajelly formed by boiling seeds is often given to calves. Flax is a folk remedy for such cancerous conditions as apostemes, cancer of the breast, and mouth; condylomata, indurations of the breast, cervix, limbs, liver, spleen, stomach, testicles, uterus, and viscera; sycosis; tumors of the abdomen, fauces, feet, glands, intestines, neck, parotids, testicles, uterus, and uvula; warts and whitlows. Ayurvedics use the leaves for asthma and cough, the seeds (considered harmful to the eyes and leading to impotency) for backache, biliousness, consumption, inflammation, leprosy, ulcers and urinary discharges. Unani use the oil from the seed also for "bad blood," internal wound, and ringworm; the burnt bark for wounds as a styptic. They use the bark and leaves for gonorrhea; the seeds, considered aphrodisiac, diuretic, emmenagogue, and lactagogue, for cough and kidney ailments.

Livestock owners have long known that adding flaxseed to food rations improved the quality of the animal's coat, particularly in horses and show animals. That might lead to the addition of linseed oil to the diets and hair products of humans. Flaxseed was eaten by ancient Greeks and Romans. Egyptians, from the Pharaohs to the present Ethiopians on the southern Nile, consume the oil. Asian Indians consume flaxseed oil in cooking. Chinese consume flax domestically, primarily as oil.

## Modern Medicinal Benefits

Smithkline Beecham patented a flaxseed mucilage cosmetic preparation claiming utility as an artificial mucus and/or lubricant for the skin surface and the anal, nasal, ocular, oral, and vaginal cavities. The preparation is suggested for dry-eye, xerostomia, and radiotherapy-induced secretory cell disorders. Frankly, not all these uses are too far removed from its folk uses in acne, dry skin, eczema, and internal ulcers (Kolod-ziejczyk and Fedec, 1995). Commission E approves flaxseed (30 to 50g linseed meal as a hot poultice) externally as a hot, moist poultice for local inflammatory lesions (Bisset, 1994), such as boils, carbuncles, festering sores, and other skin afflictions. As I was concluding this flax paper, a DC cosmotologist

(Channel 9, 5:00 news) was recommending linseed as the best possible application for the horrible, itchy, wintertime dry skin, that usually starts bothering me about a week after we turn the heat on for the winter. [[The first year I thought it was psoriasis; I suspect it would help that as well as the winter dry-skin syndrome.]]

Why have Europeans incorporated it less frequently into their diet? Maybe they do so to their detriment. My colleague C. Leigh Broadhurst recommends supplementation with flaxseed oil and evening primrose oil to solve many of the problems of mankind. Epidemiological studies show lower incidences of inflammatory and autoimmune diseases in populations consuming much fish oil, probably due to their n-3-fatty acids, EPA and DHA. Flaxseed oil and perilla seed oil contain about 60% ALA. As little as 0.12 ml per day ALA has doubled the percent of T-helper cells in circulation (Kelley, 1995).

In Leigh Broadhurst's upcoming technical paper, "Balanced Intakes of Natural Triglycerides for Optimum Nutrition: An Evolutionary and Phytochemical Perspective," scheduled for the September 1997 issue of *Medical Hypotheses*, you'll find an excellent summary of the health benefits of ALA (alpha-linolenic acid).

## References

Cunnane, S.C. and Thompson, L. U., eds. 1995. *Flaxseed in Human Nutrition*. AOCS Press, Champaign IL.

Judd, A. 1995. *Flax - Some Historical Considerations*.

# Garlic (*Allium sativum*)

*The Business of Herbs* 9(1):12. March/April, 1991

## Allium and Anthrax – Garlic vs Cipro???

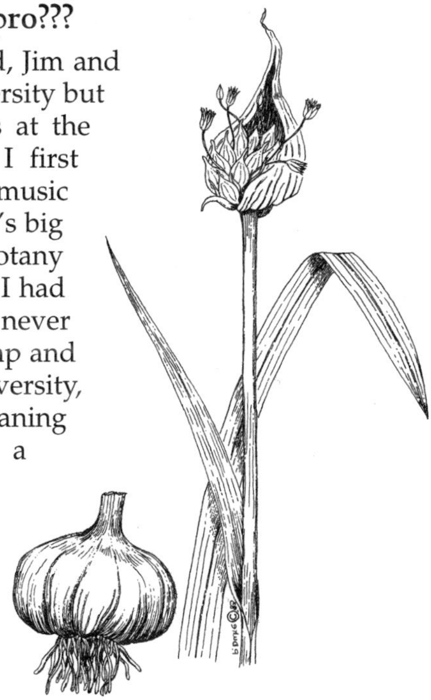

We three Duke boys, chronologically, Ed, Jim and Dan, couldn't readily afford Duke University but we between us accumulated 8 degrees at the University of North Carolina (UNC). I first started UNC at Chapel Hill in 1948, as a music major, playing jazz with John Satterfield's big jazz band. I quickly switched to a botany major. By the time I finally left, in 1960, I had taken three degrees there. But I had never worn a cap and gown. I wore my first cap and gown at the 208th birthday of the University, October 12, 2001. Fortunately, for my waning career, I had been designated as a Distinguished Alumnus, sharing the podium and honors that day with three other distinguished alumni. They were: Hugh Leon McColl, a very distinguished financeer; Anthony Eden Rand, a very distinguished politician, Dr. P. Kay Wagoner, a very distinguished medical researcher, and me, Dr. James A. Duke, a nearly extinguished herbal advocate. North Carolina's governor, also a distinguished alumnus, helped with the presentation.

It was so nice to see Dr. and Mrs. John Satterfield following the ceremonies at a celebratory barbecue in Lowe's Grove. John recounted how he was infuriated by the glowing advertisements for Zocor for high cholesterol. Matter of fact, John had a hypocomplimentary opinion of this hypocholesterolemic drug, one of the many statins, many of them in the billion dollar pharmaceutical category (sales over a billion a year). And he had not even read what the *Felix Letter* (No. 116 & 117, p. 4, 2001) had to say about the statins. "The statin story is not improving. In August the German drug-maker Bayer AG withdrew its statin drug from the market after Baycol (cervistatin) was found responsible for 31 deaths from a muscle-destroying side effect. Soon afterward, consumer watchdog Public Citizens petitioned our government 'to require manufacturers to give warning brochures to the 12 million Americans who take those medicines – statins – telling them to quit the pills at the first sign of muscle pain or weakness" (*Felix Letter*, 2001). [It is Bayer who may have tried to stifle competition with its patent on Cipro. That will bear watching in the months ahead. But suppose garlic juice were almost as efficacious and had fewer side effects and cost significantly less than Cipro.]

But shortly after 9/11, irrationally, we were more worried about anthrax than cardiopathy. Yes, illogical anthraciphobia prevailed then, consuming 90% of our TV news specials. I voiced my controversial personal opinion: antiseptic and immunostimulant garlic, in combination with antiseptic and immunostimulant echinacea, could possibly do more for the prevention of anthrax than Cipro. We won't really know until they have been clinically compared. That year, scientists said on TV that there was no statistical proof that Cipro could prevent X percent of anthrax (X could of course be 0% or 100%. I had no proof either that garlic could prevent X percent of anthrax. BUT! Garlic and echinacea will not lead to antibiotic resistance as will prolonged prophylactic use of Cipro. I wagered that many well-heeled and politically attached Americans were already hoarding Cipro for prophylactic use. Surprisingly, a PubMed search for Cipro and Anthrax turned up only 3 abstracts, none stating that Cipro could clinically cure anthrax. True confessions: a PubMed search for garlic and anthrax turned up no abstracts at all, at least back in 2002. Still I felt that garlic would be better than nothing for treating anthrax.

In the contagious unit at Breslau, gravediggers chewed garlic every day. Cerca 1540, Hieronymus Bock wrote, "Eating garlic prevents all poisoning all tired field workers who in the heat would drink polluted soft water and therefore many a germ grow which can be overcome by garlic." When Basle suffered the great plague, the Jewish population who regularly consumed garlic, had a lower incidence of fatalities. During a breakout in Marseilles (1721), thieves robbed the sick and dead without themselves becoming sick. Four prisoners who were caught attributed their survival to regular consumption of wine, garlic, and vinegar, the so-called "Four Thieve's Vinegar." This also proved useful in a Bulgarian cholera epidemic in 1848. I regularly serve my **Green Farmacy Garden** (GFG) volunteers an olive-oil enrichened version of the "Four Thieve's Vinegar."

Yes, if garlic could prophylactically protect thieves from the plague, it might possibly help prevent successes of the bungling efforts of copy-cat terrorists trying to scare us to death with anthrax mailings, and/or public relations experts selling more of their books and newscasts by frightening the gullible American public. I hope but doubt that our anthrax tests are perfect, maybe somewhere between the accuracy of the tests for lyme disease and thyroid. But still today they talk about "presumptive positives" for anthrax, whatever that means. Makes me presume they may be right or wrong. And I fear it is equally "presumptive" that Cipro will help. I have seen no clinical data to prove that Cipro has helped anthrax in humans. Still, I too would resort to both Cipro and garlic if both were available to me.

Back in the days of the anthrax scares, the herbal associations advised me NOT to recommend garlic as there was no proof that it could help. I waved the immune-boosting flag to no avail. Garlic contains more than a dozen immunostimulating phytochemicals. But since then, Sasaki and

Kita (2003) showed that 1-5% garlic powder reduces in vitro growth of *Bacillus anthracis,* and reduces the number of intestinal bacteria in a mouse (1 ml of 1%, garlic powder solution/orally once a day for 3 days). Their results surely suggest that oral garlic powder is effective against pathogenic bacterial invasion of the intestine (Sasaki and Kita, 2003).

Does garlic boost the immune system? Garlic tablets enhance natural killer cells in vitro which are important in fighting certain bacteria. Aqueous extracts and polar fractions increase interleukin-1 production. The thiosulfinate fraction enhances natural killer cell activity. All three fractions increase interleukin-2 production. Echinacea is even better known as an immune booster, but not so well known as an antianthrax herb. The early eclectics used echinacea for anthrax. Today, as we discuss Biblical garlic, this herb (or spice depending on your definition) may assume more importance in the unholy holy war hovering on the horizon. The related onion might also help against anthrax, both by boosting the immune system and by a battery of antibacterial compounds.

Anyone interested in learning more about the antibacillary activities of garlic should visit Koch and Lawson's great book. Though there is nothing there that specifically mentions anthrax, there are several interesting comments. "[E]limination from crushed garlic of a class of volatile compounds called thiosulfinates, of which allicin is the most abundant, results in the removal of all or most of garlic's antibacterial effects... Since the thiosulfinates are very effective antibacterial and antifungal agents, it has been proposed that they 'offer the plant protection against the bulb decay induced by fungi.'..." Garlic can contain up to 27,800 ppms allicin, and 40,000 ppms of its precursor alliin, as well as 278 ppms ajoene, on a zero-moisture basis.

Koch and Lawson also mention the Brazilian "garlicina" alias "Machado's garlicin" but that is just one of dozens of garlic products, poorly defined, among many well defined garlic products that have proven antibacterial activity. I still think most highly of the whole fresh garlic than any of the derivative products. Pickled garlic is my favorite as a finger food. But I do enjoy raw garlic abraded onto hot bread or cooked garlic squeezed onto olive-oil soaked whole grain bread, a real holistic wholesome heart healthy hypocholesterolemic habit. And yes, garlic is probably better at preventing heart disease than preventing anthrax. But when it comes to antisepsis and immunostimulation, perhaps every little bit helps.

I'm not sure that Escherichia and Staph are any more (or less) sensitive than anthrax and plague to garlic and its compounds. There is an interesting comparison of the MIC (Minimum Inhibitory Concentration) levels of garlic oil and some garlic constituents. I'd still bet that whole garlic (with comparable levels of allicin) would excel an equivalent amount of pure allicin for these and other bacteria, including anthrax.

## Antibacterial Compounds In Garlic (after Koch and Lawson, 1996)

Antibacterial and antifungal effects of aqueous garlic extracts are abolished when thiosulfinates are removed (with chloroform at least). Since antibiotic activity parallels allicin stability, chemical stabilization (e.g. storage in 2% vinegar) preserves the activity undiminished for up to 4 months. Even at dilutions of 1:85,000 to 1:125,000 allicin inhibits a variety of Gram(+) and Gram(-) bacteria. The antibiotic activity of one milligram allicin equals that of 15 IU penicillin.

No wonder it has been called Russian penicillin. [[Regrettably, one of the three Cipro abstracts says: "Despite the sensitivity of B. anthracis to penicillin, treatment is rarely successful." Debord and Vidal, 1998)]] Ajoene is almost as active as allicin, and both occur in garlic and onion. The activity of the steam-distilled oil is significant against *S. aureus*, ca 4 times more than expected from the individual activities of the individual components, suggesting synergism. That tells me that "The whole garlic is better than isolated silver bullets derived therefrom!" If I knew I had been hit with anthrax, and was being given Cipro, I'd still also take my garlic and onion [and walnut extract (said to be more effective against *Bacillus anthrax* than *B. subtilis*)]. Why? Koch and Lawson tells us that "The combination of garlic extracts with antibiotics leads to partial or total synergism, mainly against aerobic bacteria...This is true also for other *Allium* species, such as wild garlic (*A. ursinum*), elephant garlic (*A. ampeloprasum*), shallots (*A. ascalonium*), Chinese chives (*A. tuberosum*) and Japanese bunching onions (*A. fistulosum*) and others. Allicin also enhances "in a synergistic manner, the effectiveness of antibiotics such as streptomycin or chloroamphenicol, against, for instance, *Mycobacterium tuberculosis*." Pediatric cases of dyspepsia, gastroenterosis, nephrosis, pneumonia and sepsis have responded to garlic preparations. Merely eating garlic lowered the incidence of dysentery in Soviet soldiers (LAW).

Not to minimize onion. It shares many of these antibiotic phytochemicals and others too. There is no epidemic of anthrax, just an epidemic of anthraxophobia.

Pasteur was the first to demonstrate the antibacterial effects of onion and garlic juices. Schweitzer first treated amebic dysentery with garlic. Even acid fast bacteria, like *Mycobacterium tuberculosis* and *M. leprae* are not resistant to the antibiotic action of garlic. Raw juices of garlic and onion were highly effective against *Bacillus subtilis, Candida, Escherichia coli, Klebsiella, Micrococcus, Pseudomonas, Salmonella*, and *Staphylo-coccus aureus*. Remarkably, pathogenic intestinal bacteria are more easily inhibited by garlic than those bacteria which are part of the normal intestinal flora. The IC50 values of a garlic extract ranged from 1.34-3.35 mg/ml in 30 mycobacteria strains. The IC50 for six strains of *M. tuberculosis* was 1.34 mg/ml. Not only does garlic have "strong antibiotic properties, the complete lack of resistance of germs to garlic has been found repeatedly" (LAW). Unlike Cipro, the broad spectrum antibiotic garlic does not lead to antibiotic resistance. How many bactericides does garlic contain, in addition to those tabulated above: ajoene; allicin; alliin; allistatin-i; allistatin-ii; ascorbic-acid; beta-sitosterol; caffeic-acid; chlorogenic-acid; chlorophyll; citral; diallyl-disulfide; diallyl-trisulfide; ferulic-acid; geraniol; kaempferol; lignin; p-coumaric-acid; p-hydroxybenzoic-acid; pectin; quercetin; rutin; salicylic-acid; sinapic-acid; and vanillic-acid, to name just a few in my updated database.

Saliva and blood do not seem to deactivate garlic phytochemicals, while other body fluids (gall, gastric juices, and urine) seem to enhance the activity of the garlic constituents. Excretion of the active ingredients in urine does not occur until at least 6 hours after oral administration.

Not too long ago, *People* magazine faxed me in the Peruvian Amazon asking me 13 questions about the 13 herbs I take most regularly. I decided at that point that these were the questions that the *People*-reading people or should I have said the people reading *People*, would be most likely to ask. That's why I took the arrival of the 13 questions as a good omen, guiding me to 13 questions, which American people are most likely to ask about the 13 herbs I take most frequently, the so-called Duke's Dozen. Here are my responses for garlic:

1. *What plant part(s) is(are) used?*
   The bulbs, individually known as cloves, not to be confused with the spice called cloves. All parts of the garlic contain some active sulfureous phytochemicals, and the seeds, not usually used in modern herbalism, may be proportionately richer in phytosterols (useful against hypercholesterolemia, the iatrogenic disease of the month in July, 2004), when the lowers target levels down to 100-70.

2. *Where is the plant found?*
   Now grown by serious gardeners around the world, garlic is probably native to the Middle East, certainly not known in America before Columbus. Garlic and onion were mentioned in the Bible.

3. *What have been the traditional uses?*
   Few herbs have more folklore attached to them, and few herbs have more phytochemicals that can rationalize the folklore.

4. *What ailments does it help alleviate, cure or prevent?*
   Cancer, candidiasis, cardiopathy, colds, flu, high blood pressure, high cholesterol, high triglycerides, impotence, sepsis, etc. etc. ad nauseum, maybe even anthrax.

5. *How is it beneficial?*
   The sulfureous compounds can explain most of the proven biological activities of this marvelous, food, herb, medicine, spice.

6. *Do scientists generally agree that it works?*
   This one, still heavily accepted in Europe as a phytomedicinal, probably has a slight edge over echinacea among American allopathic physicians.

Herbalists, nurses, pharmacists, and European physicians are much more inclined to accept the credible studies on garlic than American allopaths. Of all the herbs mentioned in my Duke's Dozen, I think the garlic and the ginkgo have made the biggest dent in the fixed fortress of physicians. But we have a long way to go.

7. *Do you think it works?*
   I take the echinacea and the garlic everytime I feel my immune system needs a little help, like when the grandchildren come, or when I am travelling (although I may shy from the aromatic garlic and stress the echinacea on the road to meetings, not wanting to offend my co-conventioneers. And now, I'd boost my immune system if I suspected anthrax attacks, bubonic plague, smallpox or west nile virus.

8. *Why is it so popular now?*
   It's been popular for more than 2 millennia. Some say garlic built the pyramids. None of the synthetic medicines have been with us 200 years, yet, much less 2,000 years.

9. *Does it deserve such popularity?*
   Yes. Russian penicillin isn't a bad name at all.

10. *Who should take it? Who should not?*
    I think of it as a safe immune boosting gentle antibiotic that should be taken before the hardline antibiotics of last resort. A daily clove of garlic would do more good for Americans than any one 5 g dose of veggie I can think of, except maybe onion. That includes many hyper-cholesterolemics, hyperglycemics, and hypertensives. I know people allergic to garlic and they know better than I that they should not take it.

11. *How should one take it (pill, tea, tincture)?*
    This one I prefer to take as food at home, in juices, soups and stews, and even as a spread, baked, on bread, as a food farmaceutical. On the road though, I'll take the capsules or tablets, deodorized if I have too many social obligations. I strongly believe, unlike the makers of deodorized garlic, the more it stinks, the more antiseptic it is. Hence raw is best.

12. *Are there side effects? Any risk of overdosing?*
    Some people will react to overdoses of garlic. You can overdose on anything, even a good food farmaceutical like garlic.

13. *Anything surprising or unusual?*
    Not that I know of.

And while I am talking herbal alternatives, I still believe that Americans, especially we senior citizens, should try whole natural garlic before we resort to statin drugs for lowering cholesterol. Yes the statins almost killed Dr. Satterfield and his wife, already in their 70s, when their doctor suggested they lower their cholesterol to lower their incidence of heart attack. But this year we learn anew, that too low cholesterol is associated with a higher, not a lower incidence of cardiopathy (Schatz et al., 2001).

I don't think that natural polychemical drugs like garlic in their evolutionary context, having long coevolved with man, are as liable to develop antibiotic resistance or to have harmful side effects, as compared to synthetic monochemicals. The latter may be significantly more active for a year or two, but then comes resistance.

Here's what I said about garlic in my *Medicinal Plants of the Bible* (1983):

### *Allium sativum* L.; Garlic

*...We remember the fish...and the onion, and the garlick...*
Numbers 11

Garlic is cultivated for the underground bulb which has a strong flavor and pungent odor. It is used fresh, dried or powdered as a seasoning, rather than as a vegetable. For most purposes it should be crushed very finely and used in moderation. If fried in fat or oil too hot, it develops an acrid flavor. Bulbs yield 0.6-0.1% of an essential oil containing allyl propyl disulphide, diallyl disulphide and two other sulfur compounds, allicin and allisatin Hippocrates prescribed eating garlic as treatment for uterine tumors. The Bower manuscript, dating about AD 450 in India, recommended garlic for abdominal tumors. The NCI files report that cancer incidence in France is supposedly lowest where garlic consumption is greatest, that garlic eaters in Bulgaria do not have cancer, and that a physician in Victoria, British Columbia, related that he has successfully treated malignancies by prescribing garlic eating. Garlic extracts contain a powerful bactericide, allyl thiosulfinic allyl ester or allicin, formed by the interaction of a garlic enzyme alliinase and the substrate S ethyl L-cysteine sulfoxide. When enzyme or substrate was inoculated into mice with sarcoma, all animals died within 16 days; when enzyme was allowed to react with substrate, followed by administration to the tumor-bearing animals, no tumor growth occurred and the animals remained alive during a six-month observation period. Recent Italian studies suggest that feeding garlic to pigs instead of zinc bacitracin is better because its antibiotic activity is as great while it stimulates growth without affecting the organoleptic qualities of the pork.

Said to be alexiteric, amebicidal, antiseptic, ascaricidal, bactericide, carminative, cholagogue, demulcent, diaphoretic, digestive, diuretic, emmemagogue, expectorant, rubefacient, sedative, stimulant, stomachic, tonic, and vermifuge, garlic is one of the most versatile of folk medicines. It is said to be useful in alopecia, angina, anthrax, arteriosclerosis, arthritis, asthma, baldness, bilious ailments, bronchitis, bronchiectasis, bugbite, burns, calluses, cancer, catarrh, cholera, cold, colic, consumption, corns, coughs, cramps, dandruff, diabetes, diarrhea, diptheria, dropsy, dysentery, dysmenorrhea, dyspepsia, earache, eczema, egilops, epilepsy, felons, fever, flatulence, gallbladder, gangrene, gastroenteritis, heart, hematuria, hepatitis, hoarseness, hypertension, hypotension, hysteria, indigestion, itch, jaundice, leprosy, leukemia, lungs, lupus, malaria, melancholy, neurosis, oliguria, paratyphoid, parturition, phthisis, piles, pinworms, plague, polyps, prostatitis, rabies, rheumatism, ringworm, scabies, sclerosis, scrofula, senescence, sinusitis, skin, smallpox, snakebite, sores, spasms, splenitis, stings, stomach, stomachache, stones, sunstroke, thirst, thrush, tinea, toothache, trichomoniasis, tuberculosis, tumors, typhoid, ulcers, vaginitis, warts, wens, whitlow, whooping cough, worms, and wounds. Extracts of garlic have shown marked larvicidal activity. It is believed by some to be a cancer preventative. Its reputed action in alleviating problems caused by putrefactive intestinal bacteria might be useful in preventing cancer of the colon. Garlic is rather highly regarded for lowering blood pressure and counteracting arteriosclerosis. Among cancerous ailments, Hartwell mentions the following as treated by garlic in home remedies: cancer of the skin, uterus, fibroids, and neoplasms, sclerosis of the uterus, seed warts, tumor of the abdomen, bladder, glands, and uterus. Inhalations of the stalk are said to be a folk rememdy for uterine tumors, fibroids, polyps and neoplasms. A poultice of the bulb is said to help tumors (bladder, uterus), an ointment of the root to remedy cold tumors and corns. An ointment of the juice is said to correct hard swellings and skin cancer. Contains the antibiotic and antifungal allicin and has shown anti-tumor activity. Without citing all the evidence, M. Walker says that garlic is successful in treatment of anemia, arthritis, asthma, colds, cough, diabetes, diptheria, dysentery, gas, gastrointestinal disorder, hypotension, hypertension, intestinal putrefaction, intestinal worms, pneumonia, tuberculosis, typhus, and whooping cough. Recent studies document the fungicidal activity of garlic extracts against *Candida albicans*, show that low concentrations of garlic extract are both lethal and inhibitory to numerous strains of *Cvyptococcus neoformans*, and document a hypocholesterolaemic effect. In *Science* 204(20):293 (1978) we read that garlic and onions have long been reputed to have such mystical powers as the ability to stimulate bile production, lower blood sugar, alleviate hypertension, speed healing of gunshot wounds, cure scorpion bites, freckles, and the common cold. Garlic is considered aphrodisiac, carminative, diaphoretic, diuretic, expectorant, stimulant, and stomachic. It is used in cough, fevers, and intermittent fever. The juice is rubefacient, mixed with oil, it is useful for curing skin diseases, ulcers, wounds, insect bites, and as eardrops for earache. As an expectorant, it is useful as a potent remedial agent in the treatment of TB. As an anthelmintic for tapeworms, garlic is eaten along with prescribed medicine. It acts as an anodyne in headaches, earaches and rheumatic pains. Oil of garlic is used for flavorings and medicinal uses, being known for these purposes by the ancient Hindus. Lebanese believe that eating garlic freely prevents infection, malaria and typhoid, and cures tuberculosis, mitigates stroke, and reduces blood clots, promoting virility all the while. Seeds are sold in Iranian bazaars for use as a demulcent, purgative and stimulant, especially in cases of typhoid fever.

## The Rest of the Story

Recently CNN approached me about a *JAMA* article which they said showed that garlic was useless for lowering cholesterol. The article by Berthold only showed that the poor brand of garlic oil they used did not lower cholesterol.

## Citation:

Berthold, H.K., Sudhop. T. von Bergmann, K. 1998. "Effects of a garlic oil preparation on serum lipoproteins and cholesterol metabolism." *JAMA* 279(23): 1900-2.

I'll bet my wild garlics and ramps would do better than expensive coated (and poorly absorbed) steam-expresed garlic oil. Their product not only was poorly absorbed (see letter from Larry Lawson), it was also devoid of the most important active ingredients. But at least *JAMA* and other medical journals weren't being partial to the natural alternatives for cardiopathy. In the last year, they have questioned the value of the ABC's of cardiopathy, Angiotensin-converting-enzyme inhibitors, Beta-Blockers, and Calcium Channel Blockers. Back to back with the garlic-oil-buster was a beta-blocker-buster, so *JAMA* is not being impartial. First let me chastise the writers and reviewers of the Berthold article for (1) not recommending diet (except for tending to drive people away from one of the best dietary approaches to high cholesterol, whole garlic or garlic powder), (2) not recommending exercise, and (3) more importantly, not telling what the hyperchole [[sterolemics]] should take, if not garlic. Berthold et al. were negative on one good thing, and omitted reference to the other good things. They should have compared whole garlic and standardized garlic powder against the pharmaceutical hypocho [[lesterolemic]] pharmaceuticals, not garlic oil (devoid of alliin, allicin and diallyl sulfide, the major active ingredients, well known to all). Messerli et al. (1998) conclude, flying in the face of earlier *JAMA* articles, that B-blockers, until proven otherwise, should no longer be considered appropriate first-line therapy of uncomplicated hypertension in the elderly hypertensive. They remain an important treatment for patients after myocardial infarctions, regardless of their age, and in other clinical situations. Studying retrospectively ten trials (out of 791 identified articles) involving 16,164 elderly patients (59 years old), they found that two thirds of patients on diuretics fared well on monotherapy, while less than one third of patients on beta-blocker monotherapy were well controlled. Diuretics reduced cerebrovascular events by 39%, beta-blockers by 26%. Odds for CHD were reduced by 26% with diuretics, beta-blockers did not reduce them at all. (I'd like to see CNN take this last clause for their spin, as they took garlic- doesn't-lower-cholesterol spin.)

Diuretics reduced likelihood of cardiovascular mortality 25%, beta-blockers 0%. Hence diuretics "remain the standard therapy," and there are plenty of gentle herbal diuretics.

So *JAMA* tells us and I quote Messerli et al. (1998) that beta-blockers "have been used for the treatment of hypertension for more than 3 decades...No study shows that their use as a single hypertensive therapy in the elderly reduces mortality...B-blockers do not reduce CHD morbidity and cardiovascular and all-cause mortality." In one case control study, risk of sudden cardiac death was higher in elderly patients receiving either B-blocker as monotherapy or in combination with thiazide diuretic compared with patients receiving other antihypertensive therapy (calcium-antagonists, angiotensin converting enzyme inhibiting or potassium sparing diuretics (Messerli et al., 1998).

Do we believe *JAMA* this year or last year when Larson and Sheffield (1997) say: "...Lowering cholesterol level in middle-aged men with hypercholesterolemia reduced all-cause mortality by 22% after 5 years." "Until randomized trials demonstrate that calcium channel blockers improve mortality, diuretics and B-blockers should remain front-line agents in the treatment of hypertension."

And during that same week we hear also from the *New England Journal of Medicine* (NEJM, Boden et al., 1998), which published an interesting article that was picked up by the media as well. This same week (*CBS*, Channel 4; Washington DC; ca 12:30 PM, June 18th) CBS carried news from the *New England Journal of Medicine* showing that aggressive therapy following a first heart attack caused more fatalities than non-invasive less aggressive therapies. They were actively studying 920 patients. During an average follow-up of 23 months, 152 events (80 deaths and 72 nonfatal infarctions) occurred in 138 patients who had been randomly assigned to the invasive strategy, and 139 events (59 deaths and 80 nonfatal infarctions) in 123 patients assigned to the conservative strategy (P=0.35). I bring all this out to show that they used close to 1,000 people in studies to show that their aggressive therapies did more harm than the non-aggressive. They used more than 10,000 when they retroactively bad mouthed three decades of recommending beta-blockers. But Berthold et al., in *JAMA*, bad mouthed garlic based on 12 week studies on 25 people. Too bad we don't have three decades of study on hawthorn and garlic as ACE-inhibitor and hypertensive, and dandelion as a potassium sparing diuretic.

## References

Boden et al. 1998. "Outcomes in Patients with Acute Non-Q-Wave Myocardial Infarction Randomly Assigned to an Invasive as Compared with a Conservative Management Strategy." *NE J. Med* 338(25): 1785-92.

Larson, E. B. and Sheffield, J. V. L. 1997. "General Internal Medicine." *JAMA*, Vol. 277, No. 23, June 18, 1997, pp. 1860-1861 (Annual Contempo Issue).

Messerli, F.H. and Grossman E, Goldbourt, U. 1998. "Review – Are beta-blockers efficacious as first-line therapy for hypertension in the elderly?"

My letter to *JAMA* following their harshly critical article on garlic was unpublished. Here's my note to CNN who failed to air the criticisms I accurately leveled at the Berthold paper when they interviewed me in the backyard and filmed me blending garlic and carrots in the kitchen.

"(CNN) Reckon I bombed. Please ask your supporters of Berthold if the product studied in the *JAMA* study contained any alliin, allicin, or diallyl sulfide (If it did, it was not reported). And then ask any garlic researcher what are the major active ingredients. And the study did not recommend diet and exercise to my recollection. Those intelligent alternatives are more often made by the quacks than by the AMA. We never even got around to the Viagra spin, much less probable than the proven hypocholesterolemic activity of whole garlic (10-16% reduction), garlic powder (standardized) (10-13% reduction) alliin, allicin, and diallyl sulfide, expressed oil, not steam distilled (14%), and to a much lesser extent steam-distilled garlic oil (4% in Koch Lawson's book; 0% in Berthold et al., per *JAMA* game). Berthold et al. did not mention any of the important data in the Koch and Lawson book.

## The Berthold Study

Berthold et al. (1998) concluded and I quote exactly BECAUSE THEIR FINAL CLAUSE WAS MISQUOTED WIDELY, dropping as did I the qualifying clause "based on the results of the present study." But here's what the allopathic world was quoting, the second half, "there is no evidence to recommend garlic therapy for lowering serum lipid levels." Theirs was a a 12 week study of 25 patients dosed twice daily with enteric coated "Tegra" containing 5 mg of steam-distilled garlic oil bound to a matrix of beta cyclodextrin or matching placebos whose coatings tasted like garlic. The authors equate this 10 mg garlic oil with 4 g to 5 g of fresh garlic cloves or 4000 units of allicin equivalents per day. "The active ingredients are the stable compounds diallyl disulfide (30%) and diallyl trisulfide (25%) which are formed from alliin and allicin upsteam." Patients were randomly garlic-placebo or placebo-garlic in blocks of 10 for the first 20 patients, blocks of 2 for the remainder. Patients were randomly given placebo for 4 weeks in a single-blind fashion. The garlic-placebo or placebo-garlic was given double blind, for 12 weeks, followed by a 4-week, single blind placebo washout, then the 12-week double blind cross over. Lipoproteins from appropriately drawn blood samples were enzymatically measured. HDL- and LDL-cholesterol were also measured. Furthermore, during the last week of each 12-week period, patients were given a capsule containg D5 cholesterol and D4 sitastanol thrice daily for that final week (quantity not obvious, JAD). Patients during this period kept a 7-day dietary protocol to determine their intake of nutrients (dietary recall) and cholesterol. A 24-hour excretion of mevalonic acid was monitored, as was the cholesterol precursor lathosterol.

Macronutrients, alcohol, cholesterol, and fiber consumption was similar during the two terminal week's observations. Body weights remained constant. "There was a slight increase in all lipoprotein fractions during active drug (garlic) treatment compared with placebo, none statistically significant."

If we can believe the authors, all three studies (including this one) that showed no influence of garlic on cholesterol were well designed, while they seemed to think they have trashed, as poorly designed, the 2 meta-analyses (including one that included 1365 individuals) and a recent study that showed small but significant effects on serum lipoprotein levels. Strangely Berthold et al. (1998) admit that "few studies have used steam-distilled garlic oils or oil-macerated garlic. These preparations contain only polysulfides and other volatile thioallyls." This is hyperbole, but if correct, confesses that many of the important hypocholesterolemic compounds (Ajoene IC37-72=234 g/ml; allicin IC37-72=162 ug/ml); alliin; s-allyl-cysteine-sulfoxide; caffeic-acid; chlorogenic acid; diallyl sulfide; IC37-72=146 g/ml; nicotinic-acid (1-6 g/man/day); ornithine; rutin; and taurine from my first Multiple Activity Table from my database may not be present in their product. Still they say, "Based on comparison of the content of active ingredients, the dosage of our study medication would be relatively high." But they as MDs and pharmacists will know better than this botanist how many of the above hypocholesterolemic compounds were eliminated in steam distillation. I read their article and interpret them as saying that their steam distilled oil did not contain the most important ingredients, alliin, allicin, ajoene, and diallyl sulfide. The following are the only compounds they name as suspected actives. "In vitro data in rat hepatocytes suggest that allicin and ajoene inhibit cholesterol synthesis at various steps or inhibit acetate uptake into liver cells respectively." Having reread their paper a second time, I'd like to restate their conclusions in their words.

"Absorption of cholesterol was not affected by garlic," i.e. "10 mg (Tegra's) steam-distilled oil" which "contains only polysulfides and other volatile thioallyls."

**THEIR CONCLUSION**

That's not exactly how they conclude: "(T)here is no evidence to recommend garlic therapy for lowering serum lipid levels." What they should have concluded is that, under their 12 week study of 25 moderately hyper-cholesterolemic people "10 mg/day (Tegra's) steam-distilled garlic oil (minus many of garlic's active ingredients) did not lower serum lipid levels."

I'll go with that rephrased conclusion. And I'll stick with my whole garlic, believing as I did before that a clove of garlic a day will keep the hypocholesterolemic hucksters away. And I'll believe the data presented by Koch and Lawson retabulated here. Reviewing 40 clinical garlic studies in their Table 5.1, Reuter et al. (1996) found 12 in which cholesterol was highly significantly lowered (P<0.001), and none in which the cholesterol was significantly raised. The average reduction for all 40 studies was 10.6% (more than 4,000 subjects).

| | | | |
|---|---|---|---|
| Beck, 1993 | 16% | Holzgartner, 1992 | 5% |
| Bhushani, 1979 | 15% | Kiesewetter, 1993 | 12% |
| Brewitt, 1991 | 16% | Mader, 1990 | 12% |
| Brosche, 1989/90 | 8% | Vorverg, 1990 | 21% |
| Gadkari, 1991 | 15% | Walper, 1994 | 3% |
| Grunwald, 1992 | 8% | Zhejiang, 1986 | 14% |
| **AVERAGE –** | 14% | | |

## References

Reuter, H. D., Koch, H. P. and Lawson, L. D. "Therapeutic effects and applications of garlic and its preparations." Chap. 5, pp. 135-212.

Koch, H. P. and Lawson, L. D., eds. 1996. "Garlic – The Science and therapeutic application of Allium sativum L. and related species." Williams & Wilkins, Baltimore. 329 pp.

For all 40 studies on 43 groups of people (more than 4,000 people), the mean decrease was 10.6% (treatments lasting 3 weeks to several months).

Of the 7 studies giving 3-10 g fresh garlic to 301 people, the average decrease was 16%. The 13 placebo-controlled studies (427 x) with standardzied alliin/allicin (0.3-1.2 g powder), loss was 10.3%. This compares with the open (not-placebo controlled) (4179 x) with powder/ tablets, it was 11.3% per study or 12.9% per patients. The average decrease for the steam-distilled oil studies (4-120 mg) was only 4%, but was dose dependent. Ether extracted or macerated oil extracts was 14.3%.

## National Public Radio Service Announcement:

**Opening:**

Don't believe all that hype the herbalists are spreading about garlic, that it will thin the blood, lower blood pressure and cholesterol, and kill all those germs out there. Pure hype!!!

**Closing:**

Don't take garlic when you are taking aspirin as they both might thin the blood to the point that you will have coagulation difficulties.

**In Truth:**

Many herbs, like garlic, can thin the blood, contributing to epistaxis but preventing cardiopathy.

### Garlic Studies

| | |
|---|---|
| Fresh garlic (3-10 g) (301 x) | 16.0% |
| Alliin/Allicin STX open (4179 x) | 12.9% |
| Alliin/Allicin STX pc (427 x) | 10.3% |
| Garlic Oil non/distilled) (103 x) | 14.3% |
| Steam-Distilled Oil (204 x) | 4.0% |
| Berthold (25) 10mg/d/12 wk | 0.0% |

(x = number of cases)

## Grape (*Vitis vinifera*)

(Unpublished)

Grape, often called vine in the Bible, was one of the more important of more than 100 medicinal plants in the Bible. The green seedless grapes were twice as expensive as the red grapes with seeds. But probably the green seedless lacked many of the health-giving benefits of the red grape which had more polyphenols, and the seeds which were chewed up in my fruit juice blender this morning. Yes, the health food companies are going to great lengths to tell you about and sell you on their grapeseed products. I believe that the grape seeds do contain many phytochemicals that our paleolithic ancestors consumed in larger quantities than does modern man and woman.

Too often American consumers are duped into buying seedless grapes (often much more expensive than seeded grapes) and then walking into the health food store next door to buy grapeseed extracts, which admittedly have many health giving attributes. But in the process the consumer is paying twice as much as would have been paid for seeded grapes (which are not quite so pesticide-dependent. So the genetically selected seedless grapes are environmentally and economically more costly, and the seed extract, usually produced in concert with wineries or other grape industries, have their energetic costs as well. I'm saying that the natural seeded grape contains more natural pesticides and hence requires fewer synthetic pesticides. They are then friendlier to your health and that of your environment.

So if you want these paleolithic phytochemicals, you can buy the grapeseed extracts, or you can grind up the seeds in your fruit juice, or go out in autumn and eat those small fox grapes, which probably more closely resemble what your paleolithic ancestors consumed. I sometimes chew up those seeds, or like the raccoons and possums, swallow them whole, suspecting that I too, like the other animals, pass them whole, and perhaps better prepared to germinate next spring, better fertilized. Or you can, as do I, enjoy eating the young new shoots of grapes raw, or rolled around rice in olive oil in dolmas. That's the best way to get my resveratrol.

I'm such a cheapskate that I'd rather eat my grapeseeds, if my fillings will tolerate such, than pay big bucks for a grapeseed extract, highly praised though they be. E.g. Gabetta et al. (2000) reported that one brand of grapeseed (Leucoselect) has 80% (-)-epicatechin-3- O-gallate and its dimers, trimers, tetramers and their gallates. (-)-Epicatechin-3-O-gallate may be the isomer reported synergistically thermogenic by Dulloo et al. Gabetta et al. (2000) also reported 9.2% (+)-catechin, the isomer that reportedly has COX-2-Inhibitory activity, possibly implying antialzheimeran, antiarthritic, antiinflammatory, and anticolon-cancer activities, the latter three of especial interest to me. If the leucoselect reflects the whole seeds, then it would fall at 92,000 in the following table (Zero Moisture Basis). But that's a big if! It's for sure though that the capsules would contain up to 92,000 ppms (+)-catechol and lots of (-)-epicatechin-3-O-gallate and its dimers, trimers, tetramers and their gallates, possibly making it more promising for obesity than green tea (and pine bark, and other things pushed for their OPC's ).

What's been said about tea, then, might be said in part about grape, but for the lack of caffeine...*Science News* on New Years Day, 2000, commented on tea as "the brew for a slimmer you" based on the work of Abdul G. Dulloo, U. Fribourg. Switzerland. Like capsaicin and fish oil, epigallocatechin gallate, a flavonoid in green tea, has a thermogenic effect, speeding the conversion of flabby fat to heat. Men burned some 4% more energy (~80 additional calories) on days they took tea capsules and the tea made the body burn fat preferentially. The *Science News* article (Raloff, 2000) blamed the thermogenic effect on epigallocatechin gallate but a Reuter's "Health Review" stated simply epigallocatechin. Perhaps both are right. So instead of my morning coffee with fatty cream and sugar, I popped the contents of two of Nature's Herbs' green tea capsules into a cup of water, added some hot pepper sauce, and half a capsule of Stevia. That mix probably contains at least 5 thermogenic compounds with no ephedrine or synephrine. I still think some rich company should challenge the FDA and put the Stevia in more convenient green packets along the blue and pink and white (sugar) and tan (brown sugar) in the restaurant sugar bowls (Raloff, 2000). Already praised as a powerful antioxidant, green tea extract may also help dieters lose wight, say researchers in the *American Journal of Clinical Nutrition* (Dec., 1999). The green tea extract may be a safe improvement on traditional diet pills because its does not generate an increase in heart rate, according to Dr. Abdul Dulloo, University of Geneva in Switzerland, and his colleagues. In their study, the investigators measured the 24-hour energy expenditure of 10 healthy men receiving daily three doses of caffeine (50 mg), green tea extract (containing 50 mg caffeine and 90 mg epigallocatechin), or a placebo. Compared with placebo, green tea induced significant increases (~ 4%) in energy expenditure. The thermogenesis was not linked to the small quantity of caffeine found in tea. Subjects receiving similar amounts of caffeine derived not from tea displayed no change in daily energy output. Dulloo's team emphasizes that to treat obesity, one must reduce energy intake (i.e., dieting), or increase energy output. Green tea extracts may accomplish the latter function, but mechanisms for the action remain unclear. The extract contains a high amount of catechin polyphenols, which may work with other phytochemicals to speed up fat oxidation and thermogenesis, where the body burns fat fuels to generate heat. This stimulated thermogenesis and fat oxidation did not raise subjects' heart rates, perhaps making green tea better than stimulant diet drugs, which may have adverse cardiac effects, especially in obese subjects with hypertension and other cardiovascular problems, e.g. those associated with syndrome X (*American Journal of Clinical Nutrition* 1999; 70:1040-1045).

So this morning instead of green tea, I had grape leaf tea. I can grow grape leaves but I'm not so good at growing tea leaves. Not bad. And I ate the "tea" grounds, getting some free resveratrol, catechin, and epigallocatehcin, sans caffeine. Grapeseed extracts show many activities, e.g. antioxidant and antiulcer activities. But grapeseed oil contains 1000-fold more tannins than other conventional seed oils. Additionally, they contain epicatechin and epicatechin-gallate which may underlie the recently reported thermogenic activities of tea. Seed fractions containing campesterol, catechin, 2-trans-4-cis-decadienal, 2- trans-decenal, epicatechin, 2-trans-heptenal, linoleic-acid, linoleic acid ethyl ester, linoleic acid methyl ester, nonanal, oleic-acid, palmitic-acid, palmitic-acid butyl ester, beta-sitosterol, stearic- acid butyl ester, and stigmasterol, were biologically active.

Cranberry (and probably other related berries, rich in anthocyanidins, anthocyanosides, condensed tannins, oligomeric procyanidins (OPCs), alias proanthocyanidins, alias procyanidins, alias tannins), can both prevent and treat P- fimbriated *E. coli* associated with UTIs (*The New England Journal of Medicine*, Oct. 8, 1998). But grapes too contain anthocyanins and many *Escherichia coli* killers. So cutting and sweetening your cranberry juice with grapejuice (with seed macerate) might be even better for those pesky UTI's. Seed fractions containing campesterol, catechin, 2-trans-4-cis-decadienal, 2- trans-decenal, epicatechin, 2-trans-heptenal, linoleic-acid, linoleic acid ethyl ester, linoleic acid methyl ester, nonanal, oleic-acid, palmitic-acid, palmitic-acid butyl ester, beta-sitosterol, stearic- acid butyl ester, and stigmasterol, were active against some gram (+) and (-) bacteria, *Citrobacter freundii* (-), *Escherichi coli* (-), *Escherichia cloaca* (-), *Staphylococcus aureus* (+), *Staphylococcus coagulans*. Catechin showed modest activity against *E coli*. Epicatechin was active against all the bacteria (Palma and Taylor, 1999). As one of the better sources of COX-2-Inhibitor, resveratrol, grape leaves, like grapes, may be important cancer fighters. I don't recommend a straight grape diet. Instead, increase your uptake of grape and grape leaves and seeds (always striving for 7, 7, 7, 7, 7, 7, 7 [beans, culinary herbs, fruits, grains, nuts, spices, veggies]), increasing your dietary diversity but not your calorie count. I didn't mention meat, but feel that Jeffersonian use of red meats (as spices) and more generous use of cold water fish and fowl are OK, if not desirable. It may depend on what your ancestors ate millennia ago what's best for you. There is so much for your good health in the good Biblical grape, that I thought you should see what I had to say about the grape back in 1985:

"In general agricultural selection breeds out some of the natural pesticides, like resveratrol, which also have many interesting biological activities. The recent ACS book *Wine, Nutritional and Therapeutic Benefits*, heaps praise on resveratrol, failing to tell us that there is 10-100 times more in the leaves, and I suspect seeds, than in the fruit pulp and wines. Ironically, leaves stressed by disease, insects, physical damage are liable to be richer with resveratrol. The seeds have only recently come to the market and clinical trials are few and far between. On the other hand the fruits contain more than 30 types of anthocyanins. Small wonder that grape juice has 4 times the antioxidant ORAC score of any other fruit juice studied (JNU). Resveratrol has gotten much press for cancer prevention. E. G. Stewart at al. (2003), commenting on resveratrol as a candidate for prostate cancer prevention, comments that it may constitute 5-10% of grapeskin. 'Resveratrol may represent the tip of the iceberg of a broad class of stilbene and related polyphenolic natural products,' possibly safe and effective agents for cancer prevention. They look to resveratrol as a lead agent for prostate cancer prevention since it inhibits each stage of multistage carcinogenesis, and scavenges incipient populations of androgen-dependent and androgen-independent prostate cancer cells (X12840221). Resveratrol protects against colitis, and has antioxidant and apoptotic actvities. At levels of 5-10 mg/kg/day (equivalent to one gram a day if I were the 100 kg rat), resveratrol reduced colonic injury, index of neutrophil infiltration and levels of cytokine (Martin et al., 2204, X15013856). But I like to remind us that it is a cocktail of closely related compounds, piceatannol and pterostilbene deserving almost as much praise as the resveratrol (X15309446). Many other anticancer activities are listed in the USDA datbase. Pycnogenol in grape seeds (and the patented pycnogenol form pine bark) has received almost as much academic praise as resveratrol. Cesarone et al., report the prevention of edema on long flights with pycnogenol((r)) (X16015414). Reading that study, I'd be inclined to chew up and eat my grape seeds on long flights. I've heard the famed pharmacological author, Varro Tyler, was killed by just such edema. Peng et al. (2005) reported antihypertensive activities of grape polyphenols (e.g., proanthocyanidins, which lack appreciable estrogenic receptor binding) in estrogen-depleted, female, spontaneously hypertensive rats, probably via an antioxidant mechanism (X16105821). A study by Fernandez-Pachon et al (2005) confirms what I had long heard, red wine increases uric acid levels. That can be good in normouricemic humans, but may induce a gout crisis in hyperuricemic individuals. Maximum concentrations of maximum antioxidant capacity (and uric acid) occurred after about an hour. Uric acid, like albumin and bilirubin, is an endogenous antioxidant as well (X15941351)."

And here's what I said more than 2 decades earlier in that first Bible book of mine:

*Ficus carica* L. **Fig Tree**

> *...But they shall sit every man under his vine and under his fig tree...* Micah 4

"Cultured for fruit, eaten fresh or processed into wine, raisins, juice, with some cultivars adapted for the canning industry. Even Noah planted the grape after the flood and made wine therefrom. Grape seeds contain 6-20% oil, used for edible purposes, soaps, and as a linseed substitute. The leaves of this and other species are eaten in other cultures. Sap of young branches used as remedy for skin diseases. Leaves astringent, used in diarrhea. Juice of unripe fruit astringent, used in throat affections. Dried fruit cooling, demulcent, laxative, stomachic (31). Regarded as apertif, astringent, demulcent, diuretic, expectorant, hemostat, laxative, lithontryptic, refrigerant, restorative, stomachic, and tonic, the grape is a folk treatment for cachexia, cancer, cholera, consumption, diarrhea, dropsy, heart, hoarseness, kidney, nausea, ophthalmia, seasickness, skin, smallpox, sorethroat, thirst, tuberculosis, and warts. Grapes figure into several anticancer 'remedies': cancer, condylomata, corns, fibroids, impostumes, moles, neoplasms, polyps, scirrhus, sclerosis of the liver, testicles, and uterus; tumors of the ear, fauces, neck, testicles, throat, tonsils, uterus, and uvula; and warts. In the Transvaal, grape syrup is used for diptheria. Lebanese have a grape 'cure' for fever, liver, nervousness, smallpox and tuberculosis. Small young leaves and/or tendrils are fed to infants to prevent scurvy and iron deficiency, (the seeds and roots are ground for an anemia treatment, and wine itself is suggested for anemia). The expressed leaf juice is applied to various skin conditions, including 'cancer.' Wine or its distillate is used by Lebanese for cramps, stomachache, toothache, and for any pain for that matter. More recent headlines in the U.S. proclaim that red wine (perhaps due to tannin) show some viricidal activity against herpes, more so than white wine. Ayurvedics regard the fruits, especially the black fruits, as aphrodisiac, diuretic, laxative, purgative and refrigerant, and use them for asthma, biliousness, blood disorders, burning, eye ailments, fever, hangover, jaundice, sore throat and strangury. Unani use the leaves, or their juice, for bleeding at the mouth, headache, nausea, piles, scabies, splenitis, and syphilis, the ashes of the stem for arthritis, bladder stones, orchitis and piles, the fruit for fever, the seed ash for inflammation. They consider the seeds aphrodisiac, astringent and refrigerant, the fruit as depurative, digestive, expectorant, and stomachic (Duke, *Medicinal Plants of the Bible*, 1985)."

# Hawthorn (*Crataegus* spp.)

*The Wild Foods Forum* 11(1):8-9, January/February, 2000

*The fact that scientists had the nerve to say that isolated compounds were better than the whole, synergistic miracle that nature created was a tremendous disservice to the public... Plants in their whole state adapt to the body's need at that specific time and then work with the body to cleanse, nourish and rebuild whatever needs to be restored* (Laurel Dewey, May 1999).

Simplistic, or "complexitic," I like the sentiments of holism expressed in Laurel's "Introduction" to her latest book. But I must confess that this review was triggered by my hawthorn "hip" tea or should I call it hippy hawthorn hooch (if I spike it with Vodka). I think that garlic and hawthorn together may make a naturalistic holistic pair that might be more heartwise than lipitor and zocor. I don't know which is better for lowering cholesterol. I want to know. And this is the first time I referred to the fruit of the hawthorn as a "hip." But it is similar, in some regards to the fruits (hips) of the related rose. I won't go into the technicalities of the structures of the fruits and seeds, nor labor you with the fact that many roses and more hawthorns are very difficult to identify to species.

And of those you buy at the nursery shop, an estimated 40% are mislabelled. I've been living with the hawthorn I purchased as *Crataegus oxyacantha* for two years, and I still haven't figured out for sure what species it is. It rather consistenly has 4 seeds, rarely 3, and even more rarely five. If I don't know my hawthorn, after two years with full knowledge of its flowers and fruits, how do you know what's in your hawthorn capsule? Rhetorical question for which I have no answer. It's my usual complaint. Few of the chemical studies are backed up by voucher specimens authenticated by a specialist in the genus *Crataegus*, of which there are very few. So the chemistry is no more reliable than those few, if any, studies that are backed up by such voucher specimens.

Normally when contemplating my own now stress-ridden heart which survived 3 decades of hard drinking and hard smoking, I'll take the standardized capsules of garlic and hawthorn. Quick and easy. But then on relaxed weekends at the **Green Farmacy Garden**, I'll dabble with the even more holistic approach, the food farmaceuticals. And that's why I blended up a fresh batch of "HeartADE."

Laurel's only indexed item to a heart tonic was to her "Rose Petal Tea" on page 245, which might even have prurient appeal for the placebo-prone: "That rose petal tea might have aphrodisiac qualities...hasn't been proven by science...yet. It is known that one cup of rose petal tea can be beneficial for a woman to drink after going through labor since it tends to ease residual pain and calm both mind and body." If we can get our easterners indulging in the flowers and the fruits of our weedy *Rosa multiflora*, not covered by Laurel, we might make a dent in its inroads on our farms and fields. It's popping up everywhere on my farm, forest and pasture.

> ### *HeartADE*
>
> 7 hawthorn hips
> 7 rosehips
> 1 clove of homegrown garlic
> 1 stalk of homegrown celery
> ½ onion
> ½ bell pepper
> 2 carrots
>
> This strange tasting beverage contains some of the better heartwise foods and herbs. But it will be tougher for some people to take than the equivalent garlic and hawthorn capsules.

Like so many books that don't list its sources, it is difficult to know where she got the information that makes her so positive that a single rose hip an inch wide is equivalent to 500 mg vitamin C, or that one cup of fresh rose hips equals the vitamin C content of 12 oranges. Citrus is not notably high in ascorbic acid. And rose hips do seem to look a bit better, the petals perhaps even better, as far as ascorbic acid is concerned. And all this is important to HeartADES, the cumulative antioxidant hypothesis suggesting that cardioactivity is equivalent to the multiplied aggregate of vitamins E, C and A and selenium, divided by the cholesterol. If you'd like to read more about this hypothesis see my 1992 review [Duke, J.A. 1992. "Mint tease and the cumulative antioxidant index." *Trends in Food Science & Technology* 3:120, May. (Letter)].

That would argue for blending the rose hips and hawthorn seeds, as most of the E (although not a great deal) is in the seeds, and there are clearly carotenoids in the red fruits with the ascorbic acid. Our paleolithic ancestors probably ingested many fruits that were half seed, giving them a much higher vitamin E/vitamin C ratio than our watered-down agriculturally derived fruits, like apple and citrus. I hope the rose hip and hawthorn hips, like those consumed by my paleolithic and maybe even Neanderthal ancestors, will prove to be a better source of vitamin C than the citrus, which, highly bred commercially is 95% water anyhow. Even on a dry weight basis (in my **Father Nature's Farmacy** database) *Rosa* is richer than *Citrus*. On the lowest fresh-weight basis, I find figures as low as 25 mg/100 (half a cup) of rosehips, but up to 300 for fresh rose petals, as compared with some 31-88 in *Citrus*. And that's on a fresh-weight basis (citrus might look a bit better on a dry wight basis). I'll cite my sources (Duke, J.A. and Atchley, A.A. 1986. *Handbook of Proximate Analysis Tables of Higher Plants*. CRC Press, Inc. Boca Raton, FL. 389 pp.; **Father Nature's Farmacy:** http://www.ars-grin.gov/duke) and wager they are a bit more reliable than Laurels' source. This is not to argue with Laurel, just to question the hyperbolic numbers she has selected.

Long a grazer on wild rose relatives, crabapple, hawthorn and rosehips (incidentally ingesting peel and seed with the scanty relatively dry fruit), much more like the fruits my ancestors had than the modernized watered down apples, peaches, pears, and plums, of which too many of us discard the peels and seeds (sure I know the seeds contain traces of cyanides, and my ancestors consumed those cyanide-containing seeds). Yes, primitive homo (sounds bad but it's less sexist, I think, than primitive man and woman) probably ate many more fruits like the crabapple, hawthorn and wild rose, by the dozens, seeds and all, and didn't have that big juicy horticultural apple a day, packed with water and fewer nutrients. Since primitive man didn't have a gizzard like the birds with whom he competed for fruits, he probably did not digest many of these seeds. But I'll wager that primitive homo, like modern Native Americans, had learned to pound and sun dry fruits during times of plenty. They would have smashed some of those hard seeds, like those of my hawthorn, most of which even survived their trip through my blender. Those smashed seeds would have been a much likelier source of vitamin E, the premier antioxidant, and the one in which modern man is most likely to be deficient. I'm looking for someone who can analyze my hawthorn seed for vitamin E. Then maybe I'll pound my seed instead of spitting them out or swallowing them whole. I've only seen one ascorbic analysis for the fruit, and that's much lower than I would have guessed, only 85 ppms. The leaves are closer to 1,800 ppm, or 180 mg/100 g. I don't have any chemical analyses for seeds of any *Crataegus*. I'll bet they would be just as medicinally useful as the grapeseed and grapefruit seed. I see a pound of fruits on my hawthorn, and estimate that half of that is seed. Anybody want to analyze them, let me know.

As I contemplated these ideas I e-mailed that great resource, anthropologist Dan Moerman, and posed the following questions:

> "Hi Dan: Even when I write book reviews, I get diverted, better derailed, but interestingly so, from the main thesis of the review. This morning fresh in from consuming my hawthorn hips with their osseous 3-5 (usually 4) seeds, I reasoned that this is much more the type of fruit that paleolithic homo ingested. And knowing that even tender seeds like tomatoes pass through undigested and viable into the feces, and remembering the wild cherry and persimmon seeds in possum feces, I thought more about the pounded fruit pemmicans that the Native Americans made. In how many species do you recall Native Americans pounding the fruits such that the seeds, like those of the HCN-rich wild cherries, are pounded? I remember blueberry and cranberry pounding too, perhaps sundried, but those

have more delicate seeds that may have been digested. Did the Native Americans make fruit "leathers," maybe even invent them?"

He answered with an e-mail containing more than 20 pages of citations from his super database. He had data on the three rosaceous members that I mentioned above: crabapple, hawthorn, rose. Here's what he had on hawthorns:

> "Of *Crataegus columbiana*, the Okanagan-Colville NAs mashed berries and formed them into cakes, dried and eaten like cookies. Nothing was said about removing the seed. The Sanpoil and Nespelem use whole berries, fresh or mashed in a mortar. Of the black hawthorn, *Crataegus douglasii* Lindl, the Okanagan-Colville used the berries, mashed and dried into thin, hard cakes. The dried cakes were eaten for snacks on winter evenings. They were also used like crackers to dip in deer marrow soup to soak up the fat. Of the waxy fruit hawthorn, *Crataegus pruinosa* (Wendl. f.) K. Koch, and the Quebec Hawthorn, *Crataegus submollis* Sarg., the Iroquois used the fruit mashed, made into small cakes, and dried for future use. An unidentified species, like mine, *Crataegus* sp. was consumed by the "Coeur d'Alene," the berries mashed, made into cakes, dried and used for food."

Other rosaceous genera he mentioned as used pemmican style were serviceberry (*Amelanchier*), strawberry (*Fragaria*), cherry (*Prunus*), pear (*Pyrus*) and the blackberry/raspberry genus (*Rubus*). In the heather family he mentioned among others bearberry (*Arctostaphylos*), teaberry/ wintergreen (*Gaultheria*) and the bilberry /blueberry/cranberry genus (*Vaccinium*). In other families he mentioned the pawpaw (*Asimina*), barberry (*Berberis*), cactus (*Carnegeia* et al.), hackberry (*Celtis*), dogwood (*Cornus*), squash (*Cucurbita*), juniper (*Juniperus*), wolfberry (*Lycium*), oregon grape (*Mahonia*), partridgeberry (*Mitchella*), husk tomato (*Physalis*), mayapple (*Podophyllum*), sumach (*Rhus*), currrant /gooseberry (*Ribes*), elderberry (*Sambucus*), buffaloberry (*Shepherdia*), snowberry (*Symphoricarpus*), nannyberry (*Viburnum*), wild grapes (*Vitis*), yucca (*Yucca*) and desert date (*Ziziphus*).

Native Americans managed to learn about all these in their limited span of time here in America, some say 15 millennia, some say 25,000, some say more... I feel sure that ancestral paleolithic homo was similarly inquistive on how to improve the scrawny unimproved fruits with which they subsisted. I maintain we, and our modern Native American neighbors, would have less cancer and cardiopathy and diabetes, if we ate a cup of those smashed primitive nutrient and phytochemical dense fruits (at least the rose relatives I discuss herein) than if we ate the STRIVE FOR 5 modern watered down horticultural varieties.

## Reference

Dewey, Laurel. 1999. *Plant Power – The Humorous Herbalist's Guide to Finding, Growing, Gathering & Using 30 Great Medicinal Herbs.* ATN/Safe Goods, New Canaan, CT.

## Hawthorn and Syndrome X

A registered nurse who has accompanied our Peruvian ecotours frequently claims to have really changed her family with hawthorn. She weaned her husband off Vasotec and on to Linden/Hawthorn, she has her father on Hawthorn for cardiomyopathy, and her younger sister (IDDM) on Hawthorn after she recently had an awful reaction to the diuretic the MD put her on. I cannot vouch for the latter indication, but did have my IDDM niece sample my smoothie. She agreed; not bad; not good; like a fluffy applesauce. She normally takes an apple a day.

Having read this, and enjoying my first crop of hawthorn, I am happy to report a serendipitous discovery re hawthorn, realized at noon on Thanksgiving Day, 1999. I had juiced (blended, slurried) a small experimental portion of my first hawthorn crop a day or two before. Had to add water to make the slurry as the hawthorn was half seed, half pulp. To my pleasant surprise the mixture jelled in the blender, indicating to me that the hawthorn is loaded with pectin. And that makes it even more like the apple a day...add an herb a day...to keep you off the awful path of the allopath. Adding a little artificial lemon and sweetener made it taste like a lemon-apple smoothie, too full of gritty seeds. Those gritty seeds make it an unpleasing HeartADE, almost as unpleasing as a hawthorn capsule to take with no liquid to chase it down. I'm planting some to see if the trip through the blender scarified them or not. But for now, hawthorn looks like a good candidate for syndrome X, if you believe in the virtues of dietary pectin. (And for me, a colon cancer candidate, the benefits of modified citrus pectin for preventing colon cancer.)

# Lemonbalm (*Melissa officinalis*)

*The Wild Foods Forum* 12(5):8-9, September/October, 2001

## A Book Review, and then some

Tucker, AO and; Debaggio, T. 2000. *The Big Book of Herbs*. Interweave Press, Inc., Loveland, CO. 688 pp.

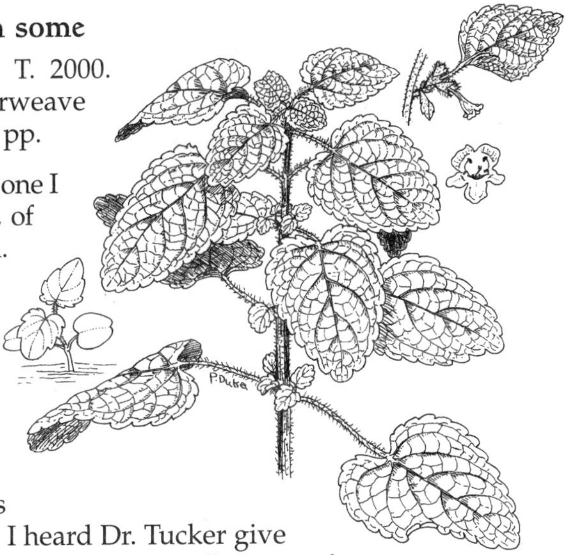

Wow, this is a great book, one I recommend for all herbalists, of whatever herbal persuasion. They have skillfully steered away from the medicinal uses of herbs, even excluding them from their definition of herbs. But they have mentioned some medicinal applications of the culinary herbs they cover. October 19, 2000, I heard Dr. Tucker give a very stimulating talk on the stimulating influences of aromatherapy (including a comment that primates, not necessarily man, start to masturbate immediately after sniffing androstendione (I think that's the hormone reported to have helped one home run hitter better manipulate his bat too). Today I have the pleasure of a quick review of his great book.

My cover blurb says it well, I think. "What synergy. The best aroma botanist and the best rosmariologist get together to bring us agronomically, chemically, and taxonomically precise information on the most popular herbs grown in the U.S. A book as refreshing and stimulating as the herbs themselves."

I'll concentrate on just one of the herbs covered in the book. As I count it, there are 103 herb profiles, but many species in the same genus are covered in some of the profiles, perhaps justifying the introductory comment that this book "provides accurate information to help you identify, grow and use hundreds of herbs." I was puzzled by their inclusion of the mioga ginger, *Zingiber mioga*, and the exclusion of ginger, *Zingiber officinale*, and turmeric, *Curcuma longa*, so I e-mailed Art. His answer is worth including in the review. "*The Big Book of Herbs* emphasizes the common species being grown by North American gardeners and hardy outside in most zones; it also includes a few species which are not hardy but can be conveniently (and economically) grown in pots. Thus, *Zingiber mioga* is hardy to Zone 7 and found now even in perennial catalogs, but other species of *Zingiber – Alpinia, Kaempferia, Curcuma*, etc. were omitted as being less common and hardy…"

I'm rather more positive on *Melissa* than were Tucker and DeBaggio

(2000), at least from the medicinal point of view. They say (p. 353): "lemon balm, or simply balm, was once medicinal. The Swiss-born alchemist and physician Paracelsus (1493-1541) selected lemon balm to prepare his elixir vitae, "primum ens melissa," by which he professed to regenerate the strength of man and render him nearly immortal." (At age 71, this sent me out to harvest more *Melissa* for the winter.) "Lemon balm has been employed in tisanes, wines and cordials, and we still find it in liqueurs. The essential oil of lemon balm is considered GRAS (generally recognized as safe) at 1-60 ppm, while the leaf extract is GRAS at 2,000-5,000 ppm. Lemon balm is also antioxidant and antimutagenic. A cream formulated with 1 percent dried lemon balm significantly accelerated the healing of herpes infections. That's all they have to say about medicinal virtues of the lemon balm. But this book was not about herbal medicine, it was about culinary herbs. And a good one indeed, commenting on the growth form, hardiness, light requirements, soils' requirements, propagation, culinary uses, uses in crafts, and use in landscaping. And there are some very interesting tidbits scattered here and there. "The chemical composition of lemon balm oil is remarkably similar to the content of the worker honeybee's Nasonov gland, which the bees use for chemical communication about food sources." And there are details on how to grow the herb, on taxonomic variants, with keys for distinguishing the bush variety from the official variety. And a morphologic terse description of the herb. Where commercial sources and cultivation data were available to the authors, they included them. There are also useful comments on GRAS status and LD50's.

Lamentably for me, the authors do not quantify the essential oil, i.e. tell me how much of the oil there is. That's critical for me in converting their percentages to ppms in my database. Fortunately the Sorensen paper discussed later tells me that the plants can contain 0.01 to 0.4% essential oil (100 to 4000 ppm). That enables me to convert the percentages offered by Tucker and DeBaggio, such that I can add their data, converted to ppms, to my database. Here's what they say about the chemistry of lemon balm: "dominated by 1 to 40 percent geranial, trace to 39 percent citronellal, 0 to 36 percent neral, 0 to 23 percent geraniol, and trace to 20 percent beta-caryophyllene. The essential oil of bush balm from New Zealand, sub sp. altissima, is dominated by 39 percent beta-cubebene and 10 percent terpinolene. Bush-balm from Europe has 32 to 54 percent germacrene D and 7 to 22 percent beta-caryophyllene. The authors only attempt to name those active constitients which comprise more than 10% of extracts or essential oils. My database lists more than 50 other chemicals in lemonbalm as well.

This will be my herbal reference of choice for its generous mix of botanical, chemical, culinary and cultural information on the major culinary and crafting herbs often grown in the U.S. Unlike these herbal authors, this more medicinally oriented reviewer, Jim Duke, thinks lemonbalm is still medicinally important today, and I recommend it (only to close friends and family who won't report me to the FDA) for herpes, insomnia and possibly prevention of Alzheimer's.

[[ With lemonbalm the herb of the year 2007, I have submitted a long draft on that super herb to IHG.]]

# Licorice (*Glycyrrhiza glabra*)

*The Business of Herbs* 8(1):6-7, March/April, 1990

Let's compare quotes from one of my favorite scientific herbal writers, D. B. Mowrey. In 1988 (*Let's Live*, October, p. 64) Dan said of licorice, "this root is potentially toxic and must be administered cautiously." This does not necessarily conflict with *The Scientific Validation of Herbal Medicine* (Cormorant Books, 1986), "The use of whole licorice root (powdered or otherwise prepared) has not poisoned anyone." He calls it "one of the most beneficial herbs known" and its detractors "bumbling eager-beaver go-tell-em-like-it-is herbalists and authors."

## Ulcers

Dan is clearly pro-licorice: "I recommend whole deglycyrrhizinated licorice for it is effective in treating ulcers, but without the side effects." Some might consider whole and deglycyrrhizinated as contradictory terms, but here's another beautiful example of synergies among herbal compounds. There's more than one antiulcer compound in licorice. Quoting Dan, "...licorice root promotes the healing of peptic, gastric, and duodenal ulcers." Nearly three decades ago a British scientist put the spotlight on the primary licorice constituent, glycyrrhetinic acid (GLA-not to be confused with gamma-linolenic acid), which was more effective (speedier) and had worse side effects than licorice extract. Distancing itself from the word Glycyrrhiza, GLA became known as carbenoxolone sodium, which by 1964 was the top drug for treating ulcers. The choice of code name, carbenoxolone sodium, was ironic in that one of the side effects was retention of sodium.

GLA had so many side effects that scientists sought alternatives. Roots from which 97% GLA had been removed were still capable of healing ulcers, but without side effects, according to Mowrey, reducing ulcer severity 75-80%.

I would certainly give the licorice root a try if I had an ulcer and did not have high blood pressure or high sodium.

## Addison's Disease

Defined by Mowrey (1986) as "complete adrenal exhaustion," Addison's disease is often accompanied by chilliness, dizziness, headache, numbness and weakness, the adrenals unable to keep up with the demand for corticoids and sex hormones. Licorice root helps prevent adrenal failure by maintaining electrolyte balance and preventing enzymatic digestion of existing corticoids. According to Pizzorno and Murray (1985), active ingredients in licorice suppress an enzyme which inactivates products of the adrenal gland. Perhaps more importantly, licorice preserves the adrenals against atrophy. Rather than contributing to adrenal atrophy as do synthetics, licorice tends to preserve adrenal integrity.

## Detoxicant

In Leung's *Encyclopedia of Common Natural Ingredients* (John Wiley Sc Sons, 1980), decoctions of equal amounts of licorice and black or mung beans are suggested as antidotes to unspecified poisons and food poisoning. As a preventive, GLA inhibits carbon-tetrachloride- and galactosamine-induced liver damage. Considering licorice the great detoxifier, the Chinese have included it in herbal formulae for centuries.

## Hepatitis

Pizzorno and Murray (1985) mention double-blind trials showing glycyrrhizin quite effective in treating viral hepatitis. One product (with 0.2% glycyrrhizin, 0.1% cysteine and 2.0% glycine) is used intravenously in lap en for hepatitis. Glycine and cysteine appear to modulate glycyrrhizin's activities, glycine preventing the aldosterone effects, cysteine aiding in detoxification via increased glutathione synthesis and cystine conjugation.

## Immune System

Glycyrrhizin is immunostimulant. Preparations containing glycyrrhizin induce interferon formation in mice and man (Hikino, 1985) and according to Pizzorno and Murray (1985), "activation of macrophages and augmentation of natural killer cell activity." But licorice extracts also exhibit immuno-suppressive activity, while glycyrrhizin inhibits the immunosuppressive action of cortisone. That's why wordsmiths resorted to the better term immunomodulator.

## Skin Ailments

Mowrey (1986) cites studies showing the effectiveness of topical applications of licorice derivatives for anal piles, atopic eczema, conjunctivitis, dermatitis, eczema, herpes, impetigo (with neomycin), itch, lichen simplex and neurodermatitis. He adds that the licorice derivatives compare favorably with hycirocortisone.

## Sore Throat

Hikino (*Econ & Med. Pl. Res.* 1:53, 1985) attributes most licorice activity to saponins, flavonoids and polysaccharides. "The licorice saponins consist of one major component, glycyrrhizin (glycyrrhizic acid) and 13 minor components." Licorice may be effective on a sore throat due to its sweetness (glycyrrhizin is 50 times sweeter than sucrose) and tracheal mucogenesis. "This also explains its use as an expectorant and an anti-tussive. On the other hand, it is claimed that a mechanism involving the central nervous system participates in the antitussive action of glycyrrhizin." According to Mowrey (1986), "Licorice root derivatives have been shown to be as effective as codeine in terms of suppressing coughs." Licorice may curb inflammation throughout the body including lungs and throat. We read in Duke's *Handbook of Legumes of World Economic Importance* that singers even chew the root to strengthen the throat.

The list goes on... How about a natural deodorant to go with your natural sweetener. In India a poultice of the leaves is recommended for "foul perspiration of the armpits" (WOI). Not only is it sweet, glycyrrhizin is being touted by the Israelis as preventing tooth decay by killing bacteria that cause cavity-producing plaque (*Chem. Bus.* May 1987. p. 23). Phone calls I receive hint that chewing on a licorice root helps alleviate the pangs of those trying to quit smoking. [[And chewing on the root like a well chewed cheroot might help the oral fixations.]] The root or the glycyrrhizin, in addition to replacing sugar as a sweetener, may also help placate the pangs of hunger in dieters.

"Glycyrrhizic acid completely inhibits the growth of several DNA and RNA viruses at concentrations well tolerated by uninfected cell cultures." (*Pompei, Riv. Farm. e Terapia* 10:281. 1979). Pizzorno and Murray (1985) state that "when estrogen levels are too high, it will inhibit estrogen action, and when estrogens are too low, it will potentiate estrogen action. Administration of glycyrrhiza during the midluteal phase may reduce PMS symptomatology." The surfactant activity of licorice saponins facilitates the absorption of poorly absorbed compounds like carotenes and anthraquinone glycosides.

# Oregano (*Origanum vulgare*)

(Unpublished)

There's no proof that garlic or oregano can arrest the growth of anthrax. Nor is there any scientific proof, just unproven federal dogma, that cipro is better than garlic and oregano for pulmonary anthrax. Nobody knows until they are clinically compared (Jim Duke, Tai Sophia Institute; February, 2002).

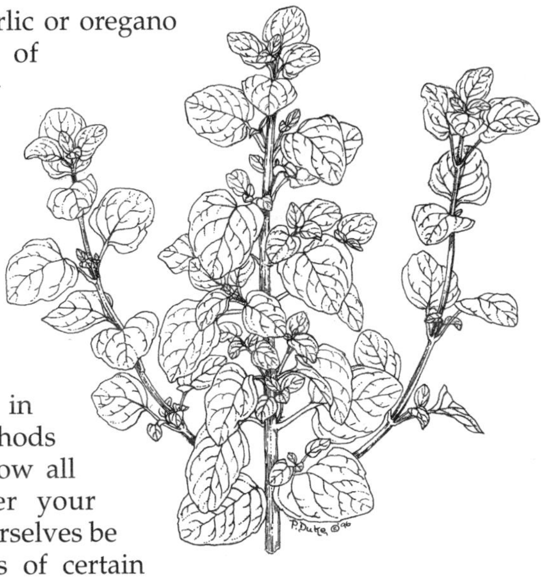

"Young men have faith in those powerful and safe methods of which we do not yet know all the secrets. And, whatever your career may be, do not let yourselves be discouraged by the sadness of certain hours which pass over nations" (Louis Pasteur, lecturing Sorbonne students, on his 70th birthday, Dec. 27, 1892).

Recently, I saw almost too much hype on the Internet claiming that oregano could help with anthrax. I'll agree it's better than nothing. For all I (and the CDC and FDA) really know, with proof, it may be better, may be worse, than Cipro. And if I had nothing, and knew I had been dusted with anthrax, I'd take bay leaf, garlic, and oregano, all of which Biblical herbs I have growing here at the **Green Farmacy Garden**. I really get mad when I hear the hard line put out by the CDC, FDA, even the herbal organizations like AHPA. They tell us there's no proof that garlic can help anthrax. Certainly there's no proof. There's little profit to be made in proving garlic. Then they tell us, and the FDA approves, that Cipro can help with pulmonary anthrax. Where, please is the proof? Go to the PubMed web site: http://www.pubmedcentral.nih.gov and you will find no clinical proof of Cipro against pulmonary anthrax in humans. Ditto for bay leaf, discussed earlier, and ditto for oregano. I think the FDA and CDC, if pressed in a scientific forum, would, certainly should, admit that oregano is less likely to breed anthrax-resistance than Cipro. They should agree that a human with a healthy immune system is less likely to get anthrax than a human with a depressed immune system. I think they would agree that at reasonable doses, several vitamins and some other phytochemicals in oregano are more likely to boost the immune system than Cipro. Why won't they agree that oregano, like bay leaf and garlic, should be compared clinically with Cipro? Why doesn't the alternative medicine program do such a clinical comparison? Both the allopathic and alternative physicians might be surprised. Oregano for example, according to the phytochemical database at the USDA, contains more than a dozen general antiseptic compounds and nearly three dozen antibacterial compounds, as of Groundhog Day, 2002.

And remember that Elgayyar et al. (2001) compared antiseptic activity of several essential oils against selected pathogenic and saprophytic microbes (anise, angelica, basil, carrot, celery, cardamom, coriander, dill weed, fennel, oregano, parsley, and rosemary). Oregano was strongest, inhibiting all test strains (*Listeria monocytogenes, Staphylococcus aureus, Escherichia coli, Yersinia enterocolitica, Pseudomonas aeruginosa, Lactobacillus plantarum, Aspergillus niger, Geotrichum*, and *Rhodotorula*) at an MLC ca 8 ppm. Inhibition was complete for oregano, completely nil with carrot oil (X11456186), (*J Food Prot* 2001 Jul; 64(7):1019-24).

But oregano has a lot more going for it than just bactericidal, if not antibacillary, or antianthrax activity. I'll wager a 365-dollar-book of mine, that covers 365 herbs, that at some concentration, oil of oregano will kill the anthrax bacteria in vitro. Just like garlic. Just like Cipro. Nobody knows until they are clinically compared. Why are not the natural antibacterials compared scientifically with the pharmaceuticals like Cipro? Herbophobic pharmacophilic ignorance generated by the press unwittingly aiding the profit-centered pharmaceutical firms, and our ACS, CDC, FDA, and NCI. None can tell you that Cipro has been proven better than garlic or garlic is better than Cipro. But let's not get polemic and forget some of the other promises of this green farmaceutical called oregano.

Some of the internet hype on oregano's "antianthrax" activity is speculative, as is much pharmaceutical off-label hype. Internet hype suggests that carvacrol, the main phytochemical in oil of oregano, is effective against spore-forming bacteria, "possibly similar to *Bacillus anthracis* (anthrax)." I doubt that carvacrol has been tested against anthrax, but it certainly has quite an array of antiseptic activities.

The USDA database suggests that horse balm, *Monarda fistulosa*, is a much better source of carvacrol, attaining up to nearly 2% carvacrol (to 19,900 ppms); thyme has up to 18,700, winter savory to 17,250, mother of thyme to 10,500, oregano to 8,000, summer savory to 6,000. Even the frost flower (*Cunila origanoides*) contains as much as 500 ppms carvacrol, pennyroyal 400, and cornsilk, surprisingly, may contain 200 ppms. I'd wash with a concentrated tea of any or all if I thought I had acquired dermal anthrax, especially if I could not get to stronger medicines. Remember, I want the best for myself and family in crisis, be it natural or be it synthetic. But we, and ABC, AHPA, APA, CDC, FDA, NCCI, NIH, and the PMA don't know for sure what's best unless they have been clinically compared.

So far, in spite of the efforts of luminary families like the Reagan's, modern science has done little to improve the lot of the Alzheimeran patient. But even the super scientists seem to agree that preserving acetyl-choline and preventing cerebral plaque, inflammation and oxidative damage to the brain are good things, possibly preventive. Summarily, a recent book by Newmark and Schulick shows how inhibition of cyclooxygenase 2 (COX-2) may help prevent Alzheimer's. They single out certain wholesome plants and providers of COX-2 inhibitors, among them oregano. The pizza herb, oregano, shares some of rosemary's antialzheimeran potential, being rich in antioxidant and antiacetylcholinesterase activities, and antiCOX-2 activity.

Natural COX-2 inhibitors include apigenin, baicalein, berberine, boswellic-acid, capsaicin, (+)-catechin, curcumin, kaempferol, melatonin, oleanolic acid, parthenolide, resveratrol and ursolic acid. COX-2-inhibiting herbs, like oregano, are probably cheaper and safer and may be as miraculous as Nonsteroidal Antiinflammatory Drugs (NSAID's) and pharmacy's so-called miracle aspirin, Celebrex and Vioxx.

Newmark and Schulick have been careful to document their conclusions. Re Alzheimer's, they quote a University of British Columbia study reporting 20 epidemiological studies indicating that those who take more anti-inflammatories have a slower mental decline or reduced incidence of Alzheimer's. The Louisiana State University Medical Center reiterated, "Long-term treatment by nonsteroidal antiinflammatory drugs has been shown to decrease the incidence of Alzheimer's disease." Oregano contains a number of NSAID's. They also suggested that too much COX-2 activity might lead to greater incidence of Alzheimer's. Newmark and Schulick say our brains are inflamed, literally on fire, with overheated COX-2 processes. COX-2 is 'overexpressed' in Alzheimeran neurons, causing oxidative damage in the brain. NSAIDs and COX-2 inhibitors taken over time reduce the cerebral inflammation. Overexpressed COX 2 leads to toxic levels in the brain and neuronal death following inflammation.

Apigenin, eugenol, kaempferol, oleanolic acid, quercetin and ursolic acid are COX-2 inhibitors reported in oregano. As so often happens, scientists seeking patent protection abandon the safer natural compounds. tweak the molecule a bit, create a non-natural molecule your genes have never known, making it much more easy to protect by patent, than the natural compounds they tweaked. Dartmouth scientists are seeking patentable COX-2 inhibitors among 80 so-called novel compounds derived from oleanolic and ursolic acid. Newmark and Schulick challenge their silver bullet mentality. Too many medical establishmentarians are in a linear rut (one gene – one peptide – one enzyme – one neurotransmitter – one receptor – one animal behaviour – one clinical drug – one clinical rating scale) (and many side effects, JAD). Remember that there are more than 50 transmitters, thousands of cell types, complex electromagnetic phenomena, continuous instability, and each herb contains thousands of biologically active compounds. The brain is not a chemical on-off switchboard. It is geometrically more complex than the simplistic models the scientists too often exploit. The whole herb is geometrically complex with thousands of biologically active compounds involved in thousands of homeostatic reactions, trying to keep the herb alive and well and reproducing.

And we borrow many of these, many needed in our own complex homeostatic reactions, all trying to keep us alive and well as well. While I do not praise COX-1 inhibitors, there are several compounds in my database cited simply as cyclooxygenase-inhibitors, which probably influence COX-1 more than COX-2: carvacrol, galangin, gallic-acid, quercetin, and thymol. These, too, could be classified as herbal NSAIDs, balancing out homeostatically with the COX-2 inhibitors, apgenin, kaempferol, oleanolic acid and ursolic acid.

Where there is Alzheimer's Disease, there is usually "Abeta" plaque. But all people with Abeta brain plaque do not necessarily develop Alzheimer's Disease. Newmark & Schulick conclude that Abeta plaque does not per se cause dementia, but triggers cerebral inflammation. This inflammation can be curtailed or reduced by antiinflammatory agents (e.g., COX-2 inhibitors). Parenthetically the authors remind us that cerebral gotu kola's asiatic acid inhibits the formation of Abeta plaque. So when I nibble on my gotu kola and oregano as I wander through my **Green Farmacy Garden**, I'm ingesting several chemicals that might help prevent Alzheimer's. And then there's my turmeric, whose curcumin can "abolish Abeta-induced apoptotic cell death."

Scientists only learned of COX-2 early in the last decade. But our genes have known it for millions of years; especially apigenin, kaempferol, oleanolic acid and ursolic acid in so many species. Oregano has many antiinflammatory and antioxidant compounds to work in concert (synergy) with the COX-2 inhibitors. COX-2 inflammation "is clearly the primary condition that gives rise to Alzheimer's Disease." Taking an herbal COX-2 inhibitor for arthritis "has the supremely wonderful side effect of also protecting tissues from cancer metastasis and the brain from neuronal death."

Lamaison et al. (1991) showed that oregano may be even better than rosemary as an antioxidant. Screening nearly 100 mints for their antioxidant activity, Lamaison found that my oregano, *Origanum vulgare* ssp. *vulgare*, had the greatest total antioxidant activity. They noted that the antioxidant activity of medicinal mints is due partially to rosmarinic-acid (which has antibacterial, anticomplementary, antiinflammatory, antioxidant, and antiviral activities), to flavonoids, and to other hydroxy-cinnamic-acid derivatives. Oregano was fairly high in rosmarinic-acid (55,000 part per million (ppm) compared to rosemary itself (25,000 ppm rosmarinic-acid), but oregano was 2.5 times more potent in total antioxidant activity. The ED50 of oregano was roughly 16 ppm, that of rosemary 40. Thus, it took 2.5 times as much rosemary in the "tea" to accomplish the same amount of antioxidant activity as the oregano tea.

Late in 1998, *CBS News* (November 11, 1998) praised the antiinflammatory COX-2 inhibitors, so-called miracle aspirin, as the next generation of medicines for arthritis. COX-2 inhibitors, unlike COX-1 inhibitors, scarcely damage the stomach. The same day, I read that the plantain, which herbalists from here to Connecticut to Chile use for various inflammations, contains not one, but two, COX-2 inhibitors, ursolic acid and oleanolic acid. But both these are also in our oregano.

Unlike *JAMA*, praising COX-2 inhibitors as the wave of the future, I consider them as the wave of the past. We are going back to our roots, the gentler herbal shotguns. The herbal alternative will remain cheaper and safer. I'm pleased that Newmark and Schulick saw fit to consult my USDA Phytochemical database, still online at the USDA, more than six years since my retirement. "Oregano, with 31 known antiinflammatories, twenty-eight antioxidants and four known potent COX-2 inhibitors, is one of the best foods" to fight inflammatory prostaglandins, leukotrienes, and the COX-2 enzyme.

But Newmark and Schulick single out rosmarinic acid from the 31 antiinflammatories because it also prevents the blood's platelets from getting sticky. The main reason some people take stomach disturbing aspirin is to reduce sticky platelets, preventing thromboses, like heart and brain attacks. (Synthetic Celebrex and Vioxx lack this antiaggregant activity.) But in addition to rosmarinic acid, oregano contains several other anti-aggregants: alpha-linolenic-acid, apigenin, caffeic-acid, estragole, eugenol, kaempferol, naringenin, quercetin, and thymol. The University of Cincinnati Medical Center researchers classified rosmarinic acid as a natural NSAID. In animal studies, rosmarinic acid was detected in the blood, bone, muscle tissues and skin, 4.5 hours after topical application. But remember that most of the antiacetylcholinesterase compounds are also absorbed transdermally. Oregano and rosemary in the bath, in food, in herb teas, in massage, in shampoo, even in the window flower box, just may contribute significantly or perhaps just trivially to the prevention of Alzheimer's, arthritis, cancer, and cardiopathy. But every trivial bit helps. And both are almost weeds in my **Green Farmacy Garden**. They may be better than the evidence based pharmaceuticals. If Steve Connor has quoted Allen Roses (2003), a Glaxo official, correctly, "most prescription medicines do not work on most people who take them." For example, he says that pharmaceuticals for alzheimer's work only ca 30% of the time, for asthma ca 60%, for cancer ca 25%; for cardiac arrhythmia ca 60%, for depression ca 62% (SSRI"s); for diabetes ca 57%; for hepatitis ca 47%; for incontinence ca 40%; for acute migraine ca 40%; for migraine prevention ca 50%; for rheumatoid arthritis ca 50%; for schizophrenia ca 60% (S. Connor. 2003. "Glaxo Chief: Our Drugs Do Not Work on Most Patients." *Independent Digital* [UK] Ltd).

Like the Feds, I have no proof that oregano would help with anthrax or Alzheimer's, or even that lingering bacterial or viral (or both) infection plaguing me in January. But I do have bibliographic proof below that oregano contains a lot of phytochemicals that have antibacterial, anti-inflammatory and antiviral activities.

# Raspberry (*Rubus idaeus*)

*The Wild Foods Forum* 11(4):8-9, July/August, 2000

What am I to think? I open my trusty Facciola (1991) and find he calls the *Rubus idaeus*, the European Red Raspberry. And my trusty Moerman (1998) calls it the American Red Raspberry. He even says it was the 6th most cited food plant in his *Native American Ethnobotany*. But when I turned to the USDA nomenclature database, I see that they are going with the European handle.

My red raspberry, American or Unamerican, is doing very well in the dysmenorrhea plot of my **Green Farmacy Garden**. Matter of fact, it did better there than it ever did in my small fruits plots. I rather doubt that *Rubus idaeus* was here before 1492, but I know that Native Americans are quick to learn from their caucasian friends. I have heard my healer in Peru, Antonio Montero Pisco, parrot things this year that I said for the first time last year. Medicinal plant information flows both ways, via "ethnobotanical drift." And Antonio recognizes the similarity between the tropical pokeweed and my pokeweed. So native North Americans would be quick to recognize the European raspberry as being kin to their own raspberries and blackberries. And they are quick to move new plant introductions into their folk farmacopoeias. But before we go into "modern" medicine, let's see what Moerman has to say about his "American" red raspberry and its folklore.

Algonquins used the roots for diarrhea and for hematuria. Cherokee use the leaf tea for bowel complaints and parturitional pain, and to wash boils, cuts, infections and wounds. They chewed the roots for cough and toothache. In an acupuncture-like approach, they scratched rheumatic pain with the thorny branches. Cree (like me), recommended the anthocyanin-rich fruits for cardiopathy (I frankly think the darker, purple-black raspberry would be better for that indication, and for the eyes). Iroquois used the leaf tea for bilious and kidney problems and painful urination (perhaps gonorrhea). They used the roots to "purify the blood" as when boils break out on the neck. They used it in birthing, both for humans and cattle (also introduced with the European). And shades of bidirectionality, like the ginseng, the root was recommended for low or high blood pressure (I don't really know how they diagnosed this in the early days; after measuring my own blood pressure for a couple years with a home monitor. I, in 2006, can usually predict, from that uptight feeling, that my blood pressure is up.) Ojibwa used root bark tea for sore eyes, the decoction for stomachache. Okanagan took the leaf decoction for heartburn. Potawatomi used roots in eyewashes.

For food uses, Moerman cites the expected: eaten fresh, in jams and jellies. And a surprise or two. Chippewa, Dakota, Omaha, Pawnee, and Ponca make a tea beverage from the branches. More surprising, the Woodland Cree eat the fruits with dried fish flesh and fish oil (that would be even better for the heart, me thinks). Additionally they peel and eat the centers of the young shoots. Upper Tanana fry the berries in grease with sugar or dried fish eggs. For winter use, they freeze the berries alone or in grease. European and Caucasian uses are even more diverse. Facciola mentions brandies, compotes, jams, jellies, liqueurs, pastries, syrups, vinegars and wines. In colonial times, there was raspberry rob (raspberries, sugar, vinegar and water). In Belgium, "framboise lambic" is a popular fruit-flavored beer. Raspberry juice is often added to make the red colored version of "Berliner weisse," a wheat beer in Germany. While I don't endorse kombucha, I mention that Facciola states that brewing kombucha with raspberry leaves imparts an apple flavor.

According to Robbers and Tyler (1999), tannins from several berry bushes (esp. *Rubus* and *Vaccinium*) tend to arrest diarrhea by their astringency which reduces intestinal inflammation by binding to the surface protein layer of the inflamed mucous membranes, causing it to thicken, thereby hindering resorption of toxic materials and restricting secretions. The most widely used astringent herbs include several edible berry plants. Because of similarities, blueberry, blackberry, bilberry, and raspberry leaves are used similarly. The leaves contain tannin and are consumed as teas, prepared by pouring boiling water over one to two teaspoons of the finely cut leaves. Then they are steeped for 10 to 15 minutes. Material may be mashed in cold water for about two hours and then strained. A cup of tea, up to six a day, may be necessary to effectively control diarrhea. Teas from bilberry leaves may "be used effectively as a mouthwash or gargle for sore mouth and inflammation of the mucous membranes of the throat."

Robbers and Tyler (1999) are more skeptical of one widespread use, even here in the U.S., among midwives and backwoods mothers, not to mention a few modern urban mothers seeking alternatives. This is use of the leaves in tea for metrorrhagia and parturition, i.e. during bad monthly periods and deliveries. The scientific evidence supporting the effects of raspberry leaf on the uterus is scanty, and clinical evidence is non-existent." They cite conflicting studies of the leaf which contains many active constituents, "the actions of which are mutually antagonistic" – (1) smooth muscle stimulant (2) anticholinesterase (maybe they should try it for alzheimer's, or at least add it to the rosemary shampoo, the tannin also being useful for dandruff) and (3) spasmolytic (the latter of course possibly useful for menstrual and parturitional cramps). I doubt that Robbers and Tyler (1999) believe, as do I, that when given a whole menu of biologically active compounds, the human body, smarter than the doctor, knows and recognizes and "grabs" those that it needs. On human uterine strips, the herb had no effect on non-pregnant tissue but was myocontractant in tissues 10-16 weeks pregnant. They mention the folkloric use for morning sickness, and then use the negative approach (absence of long term toxicity data, including teratogenicity) as a basis for contra-indicating it in pregnancy. If a medicine was needed by a pregnant friend of mine, I might prefer she believe in the long used folkloric medicine, that has stood the empirical tests of millennia, to the centennial synthetic, 50% of which will probably be recalled and relabeled due to unexpected toxicities.

Here is where I would argue with these pharmacognoscists and with Dr. Bernadine Healey, who must, of course, be conservative and cautious against using unproven drugs. (Are there any herbs that they would say are proven? Robbers and Tyler might say that Commission E approval approaches that; but no, there are almost no herbs approved by the U.S. FDA that are proven efficacious without a doubt.) Robbers and Tyler say a bit dogmatically about raspberry leaf: "the consumption of any herbal product of unproven safety and efficacy is especially unwise during pregnancy. Deviation from this rule will certainly produce more harm than good." I am not nearly as certain as they are. Drop the word herbal and I am more comfortable with the dogma. I say in contrast: if a pregnant woman needs medication, she and her health practitioner should carefully consider both the herbal and pharmaceutical alternatives. Safety might, in such cases, be more important than total efficacy. Her genes in general will know and tolerate, indeed require many of the millennial herbal phyto-chemicals. Her genes will not know many of the centennial synthetics, especially the big new ones they push so hard, long before their possible long-term effects are knowable. On average a millennial herbal is less likely to have serious side effects than a new synthetic. I would even go further – I suspect that blackberry, dewberry and maybe even strawberry leaves, all of the rose family, might share many of the proven and yet-to-be-proven folklore about raspberry leaves. And by extension, based on Robbers and Tyler's comment, the leaves of bilberry, blackberry, blueberry and raspberry may be considered as a group (JAD).

Even in December I can find a few leaves hanging on the plant, grown organically, dried by nature, and waiting for the picking. And yes, I can get my astringent polyphenols for free, making a hot tea in winter with the leaves. But like too many southerners, I have to sweeten and lemon my tea. The astringent, the sweet and the tart all adding to the pleasure of the tea, be it green tea (*Camellia sinensis*) or raspberry leaf tea (*Rubus idaeus*).

If I were having a baby, or just had a baby, or were suffering the problems of an uncomfortable monthly episode, I'd probably or possibly crave, as do many American women, a raspberry leaf tea. In Great Britain "raspberry leaf tea is widely recommended to be taken during pregnancy to help facilitate easier parturition." After saying that, the authors discourage its use during pregnancy, the very time when the folks are recommending it. And they discourage its conventional folk usage for pink eye (which is often bacterial or viral, and tannin is antiviral and antibacterial). Then the authors say in *Herbal Medicine – a Guide for Health Care Professionals*: the documented presence of tannin constituents supports some of the reputed folk uses. For example, the antiviral activity of raspberry has been attributed to its phenolic constituents, particularly tannic acid. No, raspberry tea is not approved by Commission E, although they do acknowledge several string folk usages (see KOM in HDR). The brand new herbal PDR (*Physicians Desk Reference*, Gruenwald et al, 1998) notes that "Raspberry Leaf is used for disorders of the gastrointestinal tract, the respiratory tract, the cardiovascular system, and the mouth and throat... No health hazards or side effects are known in conjunction with the proper administration of designated therapeutic dosages... To prepare an infusion, scald 1.5. gm finely cut drug, steep for 5 minutes and then strain (1 teaspoonful = 0.8 gm drug)."

Fortunately I'm not pregnant nor do I have conjunctivitis, so I can just enjoy my raspberry tea. I often add it to my antivirali-teas around the house, specifically for the astringent tannins. I am comfortable that I get many of the benefits of the OPC's and tannins when I vary my tea routine with raspberry leaf. See below if you want to see what has been said about these OPC's and tannins, which occur in the green tea and in the red raspberry teas.

In an article by Schwitters, author of *OPC* (Oligomeric Procyanidins) *in Practice*, we find a quote that supports what I have been saying for years – "OPC is not only found together with the red pigments. It is found in all plants, vegetables and fruits, such as oranges and lemons." Since data on OPC's have rarely been tabulated, I cannot quantify who's the best among them. Since they often co-occur with water-soluble tannins (polymers) and catechins (monomers), one might search for good sources of these and presume that, under certain circumstances, these same sources might be good sources of OPC's. I currently prefer the peanut testae (red membranaceous tissue immediately outside the seed) hulls and the red wines and grape juices to pine bark. A single flavan-3-ol molecule (monomer) is catechin; the pairs and triples (dimers and trimers) are OPC; quadruples (tetramers) and higher polymeric procyanidins are tannin. The whole group is identified as bioflavanols or flavanols.

## References

Schwitters, B. 1995. "OPC in Practice." Special Advertising Section. *NFM NSN*, October, 1995.

Robbers, J. E. and Tyler, V. E. 1999. *Tyler's Herbs of Choice*. "The therapeutic use of phytomedicinals." The Hawthorn Herbal Press, Binghamton, NY. 287 pp.

# St. Johnswort (*Hypericum perforatum*)

*The Wild Foods Forum* 15(1):8-9, Winter 2004

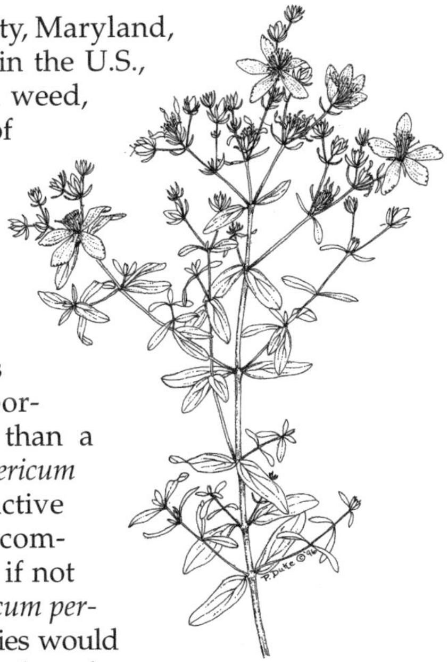

Along Highway 29, Howard County, Maryland, and probably along most highways in the U.S., in full sun, you'll find the introduced weed, *Hypericum perforatum.* But drop out of the heat of the highway into the cool shade of the eastern deciduous forest, and you'll find the shade-tolerant native American medicinal plant, also known as St. Johnswort, *Hypericum punctatum,* with bigger leaves and smaller flowers than the European weed. More importantly, analysis provided me more than a decade ago showed me that my *Hypericum punctatum* contained more of the active ingredient, hypericin and related compounds, than the weed. This tells me, if not the FDA, and the merchants of *Hypericum perforatum,* that our native American species would be more medicinal for those activities based on hypericin than the better studied weed.

From a commercial view, *Hypericum punctatum* might be a poor man's generic equivalent, cheaper and more potent, than the processed standardized *Hypericum perforatum* extract. But yes, I also believe that those who can afford the processed standardized St. Johnswort are more likely to get a specified dosage of hypericin. Remember these secondary metabolites like hypericin often vary 10-fold, sometimes more than 100-fold. So without analyzing my *Hypericum perforatum* anew I don't know how much hypericin it contains. Nor would I know how much the weedy species along Highway 29 contained, without analysis.

The FDA was correct when they recently announced that St. Johnswort was a detoxifier, as herbalists have long maintained. And they were right when they said grapefruit juice could potentiate many medicines.

But St. Johnswort reportedly detoxifies the same drugs that grapefruit potentiates. So if you are taking some pharmaceutical poisons, you may not wish to use St. Johnswort, either the weedy species or the woodland species. (Or as Herbal Ed Smith quipped, when he heard about the depotentiation of potent pharmaceutical poisons, he was going to give up the poisonous pharmaceuticals instead of the St. Johnswort.) It may detoxify that medicine, nullifying or reducing the intended medical effect.

Here are some things I published a decade ago relating to the same subject, but long before it was proven that *Hypericum* was a detoxifier:

## From the Archives – ... (A decade ago)

With Gordon Cragg, National Cancer Institute (NCI), and his associates, I collected several vouchered specimens of *Hypericum*, including *Hypericum hypericoides*, St. Andrew's Cross. Evenly divided samples were submitted independently to Drs. Neil Towers and Leon Zalkow for analysis. Their analysis, while varying quantitatively, show reasonably good qualitative agreement, with *H. punctatum* being highest and *H. hypericoides* being lowest by both analysis.

Strangely and unexpectedly, Gordon Cragg (personal communication) wrote that only the *H. hypericoides* showed any activity in the NCI AIDS screen. Dr. Cragg even reported that synthetic hypericin showed no activity. This goes against what we had expected from the *National Academy of Science* (85:5230/4, 1988):

> "Hypericin and pseudohypericin display an extremely effective antiviral activity when administered to mice after retroviral infection."

Around St. John's Day, June 24, I obtained flowering material of *Hypericum perforatum* for analysis. Parallel flowering material of *H. hypericoides* will perforce come later since it is phenologically different.

*H. perforatum*, supposed to peak flowering around the summer solstice and St. John's Day, is reported to possess more biological activity and antiretroviral hypericin at flowering time. *H. punctatum*, at least at **Herbal Vineyard**, starts flowering a bit later than *H. perforatum*, but well before *H. hypericoides*. St. Andrew's Cross flowers later. St. Andrew's Day is much later than St. John's Day, too, falling on November 30, well past the flowering time of *H. hypericoides*, mostly July and August here in Maryland. While pondering phenology of various *Hypericums*, it is appropriate to quote from Chris Hobbs' excellent review of the St. Johnswort, "Some early Christian authors claimed that red spots, symbolic of the blood of St. John, appeared on leaves of *Hypericum* spp. on August 29, the anniversary of the saint's beheading, while others considered that the best day to pick the plant was on June 24, the day of St. John's feast" (*HerbalGram* No. 18/19).

In Hartwell's *Plants Used Against Cancer*, St. Andrew's Cross, under the name Peter's Wort, is mentioned as a South Carolina "remedy" for tumors. According to Moerman (*Medicinal Plants of Native America*, 1986) the Alabama Indians used the whole plant infusion as a collyrium (eye medication) and for dysentery, the decoction for children who were too weak to walk. Choctaw took the root decoction for colic, also using the infusion as a collyrium. Houma packed the bark into aching caries, using the scraped root decoction for fever and for pain. Other references suggest folk astringent, hemostat, lithontriptic (dissolving deposits such as gallstones and kidney stones), purgative, resolvent and tonic activities.

It's clear that phytochemical profiles and bioactivities of plants and people vary phenologically, ecologically, and even show diurnal (day to night) and possibly lunar variations. Certainly, photoactive compounds like hypericin must show diurnal variations as well. Is it possible that photoactive plants collected at midnight might have different activities than the same plant collected at noon?

## Hushpuppy

I remember that sad day
In the year 2002
When I heard the TV say
St. John ain't good for you
I reckon they forgot
What you really oughta know
2 billion bucks of zoloft
Placed second to placebo

I reckon they forgot
The good Doctor Cott
The first one to outline
The study design
But after Cott was gone
The design it was redrawn
With no redeeming graces
They took on basket cases.

They forgot the good St. John
Was the German's number one
With better deutsch direction
They take John for their depression
What's the story we were fed
By our U.S. Institute
They misled us instead
Saying herbs they ain't "sehr gut"
Maybe Institutes of Health
Misleads us local yuppies
They rob health to pay off wealth
Their studies are hushpuppies
And the press in all its wisdom
Said what *JAMA* didn't score
St. John reduced orgasm
But zoloft reduced it more
Hushpuppy
A most depressing tune
Hushpuppy
Keep howling at the Moon
St John
Ain't you groaning in your grave
Pray John
Make the NIH behave
They muted the real news
The placebo beat the pill
But the news gave me the blues
Like liars always will
They forgot to tip us off
What I think that all should know
2-billion-bucks zoloft
Was poorer than placebo
That's what really is the news
Hope that everybody knows
Zoloft did really lose
Outdone by mere placebos.

So I'm plowing up my herbs
They're much too hard to grow
Gonna move to the suburbs
And grow me some placebo

Hushpuppy
A most depressing tune
Hushpuppy
Keep howling at the Moon
Hushpuppy
Did you want the herb to lose?
Your study
Was really just a ruse
St. John
Ain't you groaning in your grave
Pray John
Make the NIH behave.

– *Jim Duke*

# Water Mint (*Mentha aquatica*)

(Unpublished)

**CremeDementia**

> *Smell is a potent wizard that transports us across a thousand miles and all the years we have lived.* Helen Keller

I've been so busy this week, trying to stay ahead of students, and the spring greenery, already tinting the **Green Farmacy Garden**. Whoops, here it is time for another, hopefully new, newsletter. This one is brand new, but it is a redraft of a fantasy I had this weekend, contemplating the very likely possibility that mints can slow dementia. And I will present it to some eager young bright students at the exciting new Tai Sophia Institute, in their Master's Program for Botanical Healing. So this letter may be a bit tougher sledding than some of my earlier newsletters. But mental exercises, like mints, have the capacity to slow dementia.

Can a creme de menthe prevent dementia? Yes, say I, at least to a degree. (But too much alcohol can speed dementia; careful; mint teas are more salubrious in quantities than mint liqueurs). The mint family contains dozens of pleasantly aromatic herbs containing a beta-blocking, antiacetylcholinesterase, anticomplementary, antiinflammatory, antioxidant, and cyclooygenase-2-inhibiting (COX-2-I) phytochemicals. All such activities (if not the phytochemicals possessing them) are being explored, some being exploited (and sometimes even overpromoted off label) by the pharmaceutical industry in their failing attempt to come up with a good drug for Alzheimer's. They are in fact exploiting certain of the more dangerous isolated phytochemicals like galanthamine (approved just last year), huperzine A (probably not yet approved by the FDA), and physostigmine (approved decades ago), in their quest for successful prevention, deceleration or alleviation of Alzheimer's.

Once I tried to convince California friends to send a potted rosemary to President Reagan, knowing that the GRAS herb rosemary contained several acetylcholinesterase inhibitors (AChE-I's), some active even if just inhaled. Today I count 13 AChE-I's in the watermint (*Mentha aquatica*). If I were targeted for Alzheimer's, there'd be rosemary or watermint or some other AChE-I containing herb in my window, in my tea, in my shampoo, my body lotions, and on my chicken. One AChE-I, cineole, common to both rosemary and watermint, e.g. improves a rat's ability to master a maze, whether offered inhalationally, intragastrically, or topically.

Young folks in the first TAI SOPHIA course in Botanical Healing don't yet have to worry about Alzheimer's, unless it is in their circle of family or friends. Recent reports hint that even working crossword puzzles and the like can slow the onset or progress of dementia. If mental exercise will hinder Alzheimer's (or conversely stated, idle minds lead to dementia), I have a big puzzle that could prevent Alzheimer's. Go to my USDA database <http://www.ars-grin.gov/duke and find out which plants are best endowed with AChE-I's, those compounds that prevent the breakdown of acetylcholine.

Manually, this might drive you batty even though it prevented the onset of dementia. Many plants contain half a dozen or more of these phytochemicals. Spend a few long boring hours calculating to see which herb has the greatest quantities of these phytochemicals. That's the easy part of this mind-boggler. Then contemplate their IC50's, inhibitory concentration at which 50% of the degradation is inhibited. Surprisingly, to the naive, the higher the IC50, the weaker the compound. For example in the list above, three of the stronger common inhibitors are viridiflorol (IC50=25 ug/ml), elemol (IC50=34 ug/ml) and cineole (IC50=41 ug/ml), listed in order of descending potency. I assume that all our genes know these three compounds and do not worry about them in dietary dosages. And I assume that if deceleration of dementia is dose-dependent, every little bit could conceivably help. Thus ingesting a tea or tincture containing 25 milligrams or a tea containing 34 mg elemol or 41 milligrams cineole could conceivably help, one as much as the other, and a tea containing all three at these levels could help even more, three times as much if additive, more than 3 times as much if synergistic. (Since these compounds are also natural pesticides, I assume they are more likely to be synergic than additive and more likely to be additive than antagonistic. But we have a big enough puzzle if we assume that there is no synergy for calculating purposes.) So for purposes of nonchaotic simplicity, let's just assume mathematical additivity.

Further complicating the issue, some of the phytochemical activities are reported in other units, like one of my favorite phytochemicals, limonene at IC25, i.e the percentage at which only 25% inhibition is achieved. Naively assume, other things being equal, that a chemical with an IC25 of 100 ug/ml is equipotent with a chemical with an IC50 of 200 ug/ml (probably an incorrect assumption, but ballpark). Your challenge, line up the phytochemicals tabulated above from most to least potent, ignoring for the time being those that lack an IC dosage figure. That mental exercise will help your brain resist Alzheimeran dementia. Thus assuming no synergies, and no interactions, and all test procedures comparable, one can rank the potencies of the phytochemicals at preventing the breakdown of acetylcholine in vitro. You could even assign a computerized ranking for each compound, and an assumed low figure for those with no dosage data. That puzzle might keep you busy for a day or two.

But there's yet another mental challenge. Go through Duke's online database and line up all the plants that contain one or more of these AChE-I's. I'll wager there are nearly a thousand species in the database that contain one or more of these. Pull them out, even if there are no quantitative data, for further mental exercise. Your species, like watermint, may contain as many as 13 AChE-I's, each with a "dosage score." Now we are to merge that dosage score with a quantity score, the quantity of that phytochemical (in parts per million, {ppm}). Clearly if we have 100 ppms of a compound X that has an IC50 of only 25ug/ml, that would have to be weighted heavier than a second compound Y present at levels of 500 ppm, but with an IC50 of 500 ug/ml (relatively low activity). I'd suggest that the overall contribution of compound X to AChE-I activity should be weighted much more potent than the overall contribution of compound Y. But remember there may be as many as 13 AChE-I's today (more after the next study). There are several ways that this could be calculated, assigning a total score for AChE-I activity.

In the sample that follows, I've rounded off figures on just five of the AChE-I's reported from water mint, which I have growing in the filter pond feeder of the **Green Farmacy Garden**. But remember, like the students at TAI-SOPHIA, the herbs in the TAI SOPHIA garden each contain thousands of biochemicals, not just five. Complex??? Chaotically complex?????

AChE-I LEVEL – IC 50
CARVONE – 500-1,800 PPMS 1,800
CINEOLE – 50-2,000 PPMS 41
LIMONENE – 100-700 PPMS 3,200
MENTHOL – 0-3,500 PPMS 2,000
VIRIDIFLOROL – 50-1,000 PPMS 25

Should we use the low, high, average or mean quantity? Or some other figure? Cineole and viridiflorol are clearly most important as AChE-I's. The others, being orders of magnitude weaker, are making minor contributions at best.

If you had nothing else to do in your spare time for a year, you could indulge in mathematical assumptions like this and, making several untenable assumptions, come up with a reductionistic estimate, based on the phytochemicals present, of the relative AChE-I activity of all the herbs in my database, and of course, decide which herb was most promising for AChE inhibition. Then you could do another week, month or year calculating similarly on antioxidant phytochemicals. Another on anticomplementary; and another on COX-2-I activity! Then you could another week teaching the computer how to do your years of work in a few seconds. But garbage in, garbage out. All that figuring might prevent you from getting Alzheimer's, but you'd do better at preventing Alzheimer's if you put them into the hands of clinicians, practicing herbalists with dementia-prone patients, to compare with the more dangerous pharmaceuticals. Remember too that most of these aromatic compounds will add antiseptic, attractive aromas to an otherwise depressing environment. Many are also anti-depressant.

Miyazawa et al. (1998) actually compared the activity of the whole essential oil of several varieties and species of the genus *Mentha*, and found water mint richest in AChE-I activity. Similarly Perry and associates (1996, 1998, 1999, 2000, 2001) compared oils and alcoholic extracts of lemonbalm, sage and rosemary, etc., in one study at least with living human brain cells in tissue culture, and found AChE-I activities of the

Part Four

# Herb A Day...

# Far East

# Basil, Sweet (*Ocimum basilicum*)

*The Business of Herbs* 5(5):6-7, November/December, 1987

## Basil and the HERP Index

My Italian pesto-packing friends were alarmed, as was the American Spice Trade Association (ASTA), when they heard that Ames' HERP INDEX (*Science*, April 17, 1987) mentioned the carcinogenicity of basil. But I see no need for alarm. As I read the HERP index, the one gram of dry basil which Ames thinks might represent average per capita consumption per day (high for me, low for my Italian friends) is only one-fourth as carcinogenic for its estragole as two slices of bread are for their formaldehyde. Still, I enjoy my basil-tomato sandwiches.

I have rearranged and rounded the important numbers from Ames' index so that it will be easier for those of us who don't think well in fractions to understand. Ames would be the first to point out that he is extrapolating from crude reactions of experimental animals to humans. Many other caveats are included in his article.

Roughly, Ames uses one liter of chlorinated tap water as the standard unit of measure against which the others are measured. Chlorinated tap water has a certain carcinogenicity due to the chloroform resulting from the chlorination. Most of us drink more tap water than the daily liter Ames takes as a reference for the average person. But one cup of comfrey leaf tea* is rated 30 times more carcinogenic, along with peanut butter, 1 oz for its aflatoxin, and on these winter days as I edit these old columns, I am getting more peanut butter than that.

We heard about the nitrites in the hot dogs, but the 5 g mustard put on my hotdog is 70 times more carcinogenic than the tap water. One gram of basil was scored as 100 time more carcinogenic than the liter of tap water (close to the carcinogenicity of 15 g mushrooms). Sassafras tea, such as my 100-year-old grandmother consumed, having not read of its carcinogenicity, is 200 times more carcinogenic. That sounds bad until you see that two slices of bread is twice as bad as the sassafras.

This may appear to be bad for herbalists and natural food enthusiasts. But wait! Here's the good part (but bad for alcoholics and "colaholics" and the industries they support). Because of formaldehyde, Ames depicts a cola beverage as 2,700 times more carcinogenic. For the ethanol, a 12 ounce beer is rated as 2,800 times more, a fourth-liter wine 4,700 more carcinogenic than the liter of tap water. Ames goes on to blame 3% of American cancer deaths on alcohol, 30% on tobacco, leaving the herbal industry looking rather salubrious, compared with the food and spice industries. Perhaps you'd all feel better now.

Then Ames notes that we ingest 10,000 times more natural pesticides than synthetic pesticides, hinting that synthetic pesticide residues contribute less carcinogenicity than tap water. As to those natural pesticides, like the estragole, formaldehyde, ethanol, etc., of which we are supposed to consume more than 10,000 times more, I suggest the food processing industry, adept at removing fiber, vitamins, and minerals, take the natural pesticides out of our food and put them in the pesticide cans were they belong!! Could they compete with the $16 billion synthetic pesticide industry while lessening the carcinogenicity of our foods? While they have all that biomass in their pilot plants, they might as well convert the residues to other useful products like alcohol, leaf protein, animal feed, and/or mulch and manure. This could help balance our payments on the sixty billion dollar oil and fertilizer import kills. Utopian? Today, perhaps. But maybe not tomorrow when the petroleum is all floating on the Persian Gulf.

Thinking positive, let's consider basil as healthier than bread, cola, beer, and wine, rather than thinking of basil as 100 times more carcinogenic than chlorinated tap water. Almost [[if not]] all our spices and herb do contain medicinal and pesticidal properties as well as culinary properties. Basil oil inhibits bacteria and yeast, the synergies in the oil being more effective than the individual components. The book *Magic and Medicine of Plants* confirms that basil extracts inhibit the dysentery organism. The oil is larvicidal for the mosquito larvae, and, synergistic with a household insecticide. Essential oil [[of basil at 20 parts per million killed no larvae, while the Asian Indian insecticide Finit (not available in U.S. markets) produced 68% mortality. Both in combination (at dilute concentrations) produced 100% mortality.]] Petroleum ether extracts of basil seed attained 100% kill of *Bagarda cruciferarum* on turnips in the field after 72 hours. Holy basil oil at 100 ppm killed 16% of mosquito larvae, basil oil killed 8% at 20 ppm, and eucalyptus oil killed 15% at 20 ppm, but synergistically, they killed more!

What are some of the pesticidal compounds in basil? Israeli studies show that most of the fungicida1 activity is due to cineole, linalool methylchavicol and eugenol. Eugenol and methyleugenol were active against six fungi and four bacterial strains, while caryophyllene lacked such activity. If the basil in pesto doesn't help cure the yeast, maybe the garlic will.

What the HERP index suggests to my Italian friends is to cut back on the beer, bread and wine more than you cut back on the basil. I tend to agree. If Ames' data are correct, the quarter-liter wine is nearly 50 times as carcinogenic as the gram of basil.

# Celery (*Apium graveolens*)

(Unpublished)

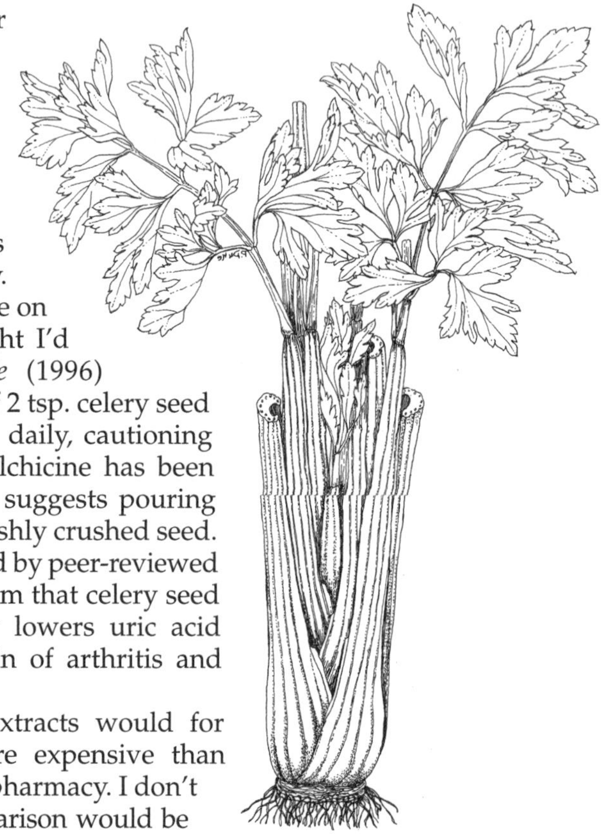

You'd think that after a week on the Amazon I'd be writing about an exotic Amazonian rain forest mystery. Instead, I'm all hyped up about celery and celery seed, yet another serious addition to food farmacy.

I'd seen so much hype on celery seed that I thought I'd give it a try. *Time-Life* (1996) suggests for gout a tea of 2 tsp. celery seed in a cup of water, thrice daily, cautioning against herbal teas if colchicine has been prescribed. Bisset (1994) suggests pouring boiling water over 1 g freshly crushed seed. Recent ads, not yet backed by peer-reviewed scientific publication, claim that celery seed extract (CSX) effectively lowers uric acid levels and alleviates pain of arthritis and rheumatism.

Unfortunately, the extracts would for me be three times more expensive than allopurinol at my HMO pharmacy. I don't yet know what the comparison would be between unsubsidized allopurinol and unsubsidized celery seed. My HMO gives me a discount rate on the allopurinol; an optimistic dealer is providing me with free CSX.

In lectures over the years, I have often been recorded as saying that if I did not take my allopurinol for a day or two and consumed a six-pack of beer, I could almost guarantee an attack of acute gout, known as the crisis, debilitatingly painful. So what better test was there than to substitute celery seed extract for allopurinol? For a week here at home, near my indomethacin (antiinflammatory) in case I failed, and a more dangerous week in Amazonian Peru, I quit taking my regular medication. That's after nearly 18 years of one allopurinol pill a day to keep the crisis away.

## Tempting Fate

Walking several miles a day over a cross-tie-like array of split-wood sections, I was tempting fate – but no gout attack. Amazing. Thanks to CSX? After a week, we all reconvened in the main Tahuampa Bar, a thatch-roof edifice, stilted over a tributary of the Amazon. It almost always happens this way; after a week in the rain forest people are ready to let their hair down. For the parting ceremonies, there is always over-vigorous dancing to a group of the guides who play great mariachi, ranchero and salsa music. Once before, my spirited dancing to their spirited music with spirituous Amazonian rum had precipitated an attack of gout, so I was fearful of participating. But I got with the flow. Barefooted, we were shaking the mahogany floor of the Tahuampa. After leaping higher and higher, I finally felt an agonizing pain as I landed on my left foot. It felt as if I had dislodged the hipbone from the pelvis ("antepierna" in Amazonian Spanish). In spite of the excruciation, I finished out the dance and absented myself quietly, barely able to walk.

I went to bed and slept until 5:00, when they got us up for: (1) breakfast, (2) two hours on the Amazon, and (3) a long wait at the International Airport at Iquitos, Peru. It was difficult and painful walking, but I tried not to show my pain, not wanting to dampen anyone else's fun. I took my CSX and packed my indomethacin where I could reach it, almost sure a gout crisis was in store. Traumatic injuries, like traumatic parties, can trigger a crisis. I also took a series of echinacea, hoping to prevent an internal infection near the damaged joint. I crashed when I got home, after taking some antiinflammatory turmeric and boswellin capsules I had at home. I was fully expecting a crisis that next day, in spite of the CSX. But no. Serendipity, perhaps. Perhaps not. But no attack of gout [[And now, 2006, I reiterate what too many of my audiences have heard, either celery seed, senility or serendipity have prevented the crsis all these years; surely it's time for the HHI to do a third arm trial: 1 – allopurinol vs. 2 – celery seed extract vs placebo]].

I got up and tried my usual back exercise. Possible, but not fun. Walked out into a beautiful Indian summer day at home at the **Herbal Village**. Took two of the CSX pills and two each of the boswellin, echinacea, and turmeric capsules. Did some more back-stretching exercise, trying not to overprotect the damaged area. It was improving fast; my limp was lessening. I had nearly decided that I wouldn't have to go to a chiropractor or osteopath.

## Adding an Herbal Alternative

For two weeks, during which I would have twice wagered big bucks on a gout crisis, were it not for the CSX, the crisis had not materialized. This so excited me that I updated my *Herbal Alternative* draft to include CSX as an herbal alternative, albeit more expensive than the pharmaceutical alternative, allopurinol. I'll discuss this with some of my holistic physician friends who are looking for some herbal alternatives to try clinically. At this point, I think that two CSX capsules are as good as one allopurinol – but, based solely upon my own anecdotal experience.

Just for kicks I went to my database. For our search, I typed in *Apium* for the genus, *graveolens* for the species, and antiinflammatory for the activity. When I told it to query, it responded in about 25 seconds with a list of 26 antiinflammatory chemicals: alpha-pinene, apigenin, ascorbic-acid, bergapten, butylidene-phthalide, caffeic-acid, chlorogenic-acid, cnidilide, copper, coumarin, eugenol, ferulic-acid, gentisic-acid, isopimpinellin, linoleic-acid, luteolin, magnesium, mannitol, myristicin, protocatechuic-acid, quercetin-3-galactoside, rutin, scopoletin, thymol, umbelliferone, and xanthotoxin. Is this combination of chemicals preventing my gout? Are there other plants in my database containing even more of these and other antiinflammatory chemicals?

I did another search: Chemical Constituents with Calcium-antagonist Activity in *Apium graveolens* L. (Apiaceae), revealing that celery contains at least four calcium antagonists which might make the plant useful in preventing heart disease. (Matter of fact, incipient cardiopaths might do well to add hawthorn to their celery juice.)

Back in 1981, when Kay Wain and I had compiled our database with 100,000 folkloric entries on plants, including celery, we had no info on celery for high blood pressure (hypertension). Today, I'd heartily recommend four sticks of celery, juiced with two cloves of garlic, half an onion, and half a tomato for people who are marginally hypertensive. Could a tomato-rice soup, salt-free, but seasoned with high fiber herbs like celery, lower high blood pressure, especially when accompanied by an increase in exercise and carbohydrate and a reduction in alcohol, animal fat, cholesterol, and tobacco? Four celery sticks alone have lowered hypertension in some subjects.

## Inventing a New Tonic

Might ANGELADE-juiced angelica, carrot, celery, fennel, parsley, or parsnip be as safe and efficacious and cheap as verapamil as a calcium blocker? (Apparently the hypotensive four stalks of celery will block the uric acid crisis; fiber itself is hypouricemic.) Might that partially explain the lower incidence of cardiopathy in vegetarians? So, celery contains hypotensive, hypocholesterolemic, and calcium-blocker phytochemicals. How about antiarrhythmic compounds? There's apigenin, apiin, magnesium, and potassium. Is heart of celery better for the heart than what your physician suggests? Would ANGELADE, with a wider variety of vegetables be better? Methinks yes! But I'll probably never know. I'd bet, however, it would do more good than verapamil.

Today, as I write this, Pascal Celery was on sale at my supermarket, two bunches for $0.98. I bought four bunches, weighing a total of 6.75 pounds, for $1.96, less than 30 cents per pound. Remember, that's 90 to 95% water. Campbell's "Cream of Celery Soup" – also 90 to 95% water, I'll estimate-was $1.62 per pound. Celery seed, with almost no water, was another matter, ranging from $39.41 per pound for whole seed, to $46.99 per pound for ground seed powder (but in those cute little $4.00 jars for the spice rack). So, you guessed it: I'm going the cheapskate food farmacy route, juicing the celery that was on sale and freezing the juice. That's the cheapest and probably the healthiest approach to food farmacy with celery. But this is just another of the tall tales of super foods in the spice rack at the supermarket, and one of the herbal alternatives.

I maintain that many herbal alternatives are better, safer, and cheaper than the pharmaceuticals we are getting (be it for cardiopathy, gout, or hypertension). But we'll never know, until we have clinically compared allopurinol, celery seed extract, and celery stalks, which is the better approach to hyperuricemia. And, even though I am inclined to believe that natural foods, like celery and celery seed, are safer than synthetics and semi-synthetics, like allopurinol, I do not know it. Taking CSX daily for 18 years, as I have taken allopurinol for 18 years, might lead to fewer or more side-effects. I'm not sure I have 18 more years left, so I'll go with my instincts, that the natural is less likely to do harm than the unnatural.

# Eclipta (*Eclipta prostrata*)

*The Business of Herbs* 13(3):12-13. July/August, 1995.

> *We shall begin with the worst of all evils, namely, the stroke of snakes.* Pliny the Elder, *Natural History*, Book XXV (77 AD)

With summer coming more people will be heading into fields and forests, some of which are said to teem with venomous snakes. How'd you like to learn an herb with the reputation of counteracting the effect of snake venom? More, it has been proven to counteract venom.

Maybe you don't worry as much about snakebites as did Pliny the Elder or a lot of the ecotourists who accompany me to the Amazon. Then how'd you like to learn an herb reported to make the hair grow better, even to turn it dark again (if you are old and gray like me)? Orientals widely use the sap of the pounded plant, heated or crushed in oil, to keep the hair black and stimulate its growth. The dye seems to have a particular affinity for scar tissue. Hence it is used in Africa to tattoo scars, turning them a bluish black.

This same herb is reportedly good for the complexion, the hair, the eyes (especially night blindness, one of the perils of old age), and the teeth. Too good to be true? I think I'll coin a new name for this herb. Shall I call it "Amazonian snakeroot," or "Amazonian snake-oil?" Surely you won't recognize it under the name "erva botoa," "herbe a l'encore" (ink plant), "huanguilla," "naparo cimarron," or "yerba de tajo" or more than 20 other even more obscure names tabulated in *Indian Medicinal Plants* (Asian Indian). For now I'll call it eclipta, much shorter than Amazonian snakeroot.

I see this plant in summer around Maryland where the snakes are out only in summer; and I see it year-round in the Amazon, where the snakes are out all year. I've never used it, but I was prompted to write this article, remembering that my right-hand man, Narcisco Bristan, was almost killed by a bushmaster snake in Panama more than 40 years ago. So I'll dedicate this little study in snakebite plants to him and Panama, my first ethnobotanical stomping ground, and to many people who have asked me what I would do if snakebitten in the jungle.

## Too much folklore

Eclipta is one of those plants with so much folklore you don't know what to believe. Chinese are reported to use it to protect their hands when they are working in the rice paddies. This may possibly be due to thiophenes, which are phototoxic to bacteria, fungi, nematodes, and yeasts. Thiophenes could explain the analgesic properties of the plant; as with several other asteraceous plants, the flower heads are used to alleviate toothache. Crushed plants are applied to bruises, burns, cuts, etc.; and the juice is effective against some fungal dermatoses. It is also used as an antidote to the stings of the scorpion fish. Extracts are even said to be estrogenic and muscle relaxant (Duke and Ayensu, 1985).

I suffer under the unflattering name of reductionist, i.e., I try to find a chemical rationale behind the folklore many people take for granted. Seems that aristolochic acid may explain the antivenom properties of the Virginia snakeroot (*Aristolochia serpentina*) and reserpine, the activities of the Indian snakeroot (*Rauwolfia serpentina*). But three, possibly four, compounds in the Amazonian snakeroot (*Eclipta alba* alias *E. prostrata*) can help inactivate snake venom.

## Anti-snakebite synergy

Test-tube experiments suggest that the muscle-poisoning effects of the South American rattlesnake are almost completely inhibited by an alcoholic extract of eclipta. There is even a prophylactic effect in living rodents. "The venom, dissolved in saline solution and preincubated with the plant extract, was injected in mice thighs… All the animals used in the experiment survived… Similar results were obtained both in vitro and in vivo with the venoms of three other South American Crotalidae: *Bothrops jararaca*, *B. jararacussu* and *Lachesis muta*…Assayed in mice…50 mg/g of crude extract or 5 mg/g wedelolactone reduced the hemorrhagic response to 4 mg/g *B. jararaca* venom to about one-fifth of its original value… Somewhat less intense inhibition was found with sitosterol and stigmasterol" (Mors, 1991).

Mors et al. earlier (1989) had given even more detail about the eclipta snakebite antidote. I see it as another example of synergy, where the whole plant's chemical mix (minus water) is more potent than an equivalent amount of any one of the magic-bullet compounds. "Samples of ethanolic extract corresponding to 1.8 mg dry extract per animal neutralized up to four lethal doses of the venom...Three substances isolated from the plant – wedelolactone (0.54 mg/animal), sitosterol (2.3 mg/animal) and stigmasterol (2.3 mg/ animal) – were able to neutralize three lethal doses of the venom… Individually, these substances are less active then the extracts."

We can translate that to mean that the whole plant extract was better than the magic bullet, wedelolactone. It would take 22.5 times more extract than venom to neutralize the venom four times. While it would take only seven times more wedelolactone, but nearly 30 times more sitosterol or stigmasterol to neutralize three bites. Or, reduced to common denominators, 5.6 times more extract, 2.25 times more wedelolactone, 9.5 times more sitosterol or stigmasterol to counteract the venom one time. Wedelolactone was about four times more potent than the ubiquitous compounds sitosterol and stigmasterol, and more than twice as potent as the dry extract. [[Even I don't fathom this now, jad 2006]]

Duke and Vasquez had summarized the activity of the most potent magic bullet: "Wedelolactone is antiinflammatory and inhibits hemorrhage and the liberation of creatinine kinase induced by snake venom." This means that the active ingredient reduces bleeding, inflammation, and intoxication.

## Add more ingredients

I'd add some other compounds to my snakebite mix, following my reading of Mors's interesting account. Perhaps persimmon juice would help. Extract of unripe persimmon fruit (in this case, *Diospyros kaki*), strongly detoxifies venoms of several species of snakes, both neurotoxic and hemorrhagic venoms, so much so that Asian scientists recommended the extract as a washing agent for emergency treatment of snakebite wounds. The active ingredient was characterized as a water-soluble tannin. Red wine or grape juice might make a reasonable substitute.

Turmeric extract has both proteolytic activity and neurotoxin-inhibiting activity, which might be due to direct inactivation of the toxin. Lacking turmeric as a source of proteolytic activities, might one resort to other jungle proteolytic enzymes such as bromelain from pineapple, dumbcain from dumbcane (not a food), ficin from figs, zingibain from ginger? But the possibility of anaphylactic reaction to these enzymes cannot be ruled out, if they are introduced into the bloodstream with the venom.

If the doctor were out, I might rub Amazonian snakeroot, turmeric, and astringent (tannin-bearing) fruits or barks, into the bite. Were I bitten by a snake in Amazonia, I'd probably go to a local shaman rather than some northern physicians who might have come along as ecotourists. Yes, I'd try what had been told me by my Amazonian "shaman," Antonio Montero Pisco. Very few people bitten by a snake take the head of the snake to their physicians, and very few physicians can identify tropical snakes. I am almost as afraid of the antivenoms as the venoms, after the experience of my associate, Narciso, in Panama.

I'd also apply heated tubers of the root of what I'll just call Amazonian jack-in-the-pulpit (*Dracontium loretanum*). The natives call it "jergon sacha," which is also their name for the dreaded fer-de-lance snake. I'd apply it topically, with or without the turmeric and/or cat's claw admixed.

Rather fearful of proteolytic enzymes introduced into the wound, I might drink fig, papaya, or pineapple juice. (It is well known that papaya enzymes can sometimes cause anaphylactic shock if injected.) We can assume that some of the birthworts (*Aristolochia*) around Explorama, like Virginia snakeroot back home, contain aristolochic acid which is said to inactivate snake venom. [[But it is definitely a compound with which not to toy.]]

As Mors (1991) notes, antiinflammatory activity seems to be a property common to many, if not all, anti-snakebite plants. Like probably all Araceae (jack-in-the-pulpit), the "jergon sacha" probably contains the antiinflammatory salicylic acid. Poulticed onto the punctured area, the "jergon sacha" would be providing both internal and transdermal compounds. These three in a mixture are being clinically studied for anti-AIDS activity. The mix might be better studied for snakebite. I'd add onions to that mix as well.

Mors mentions that protocatechuic acid can inactivate snake venoms.

You guessed it: The best source of protocatechuic acid is a folkloric snakebite remedy. It can contain up to 1.7 percent protocatechuic acid. It is said to contain 0.078 percent nicotine, much less than tobacco, which is also used elsewhere in snakebite. Containing so much nicotine, it is expectedly bactericidal. The root is applied as an antiseptic to wounds, if not snakebite, in cattle.

# Geranium, Nepalese (*Geranium nepalense*)

(Unpublished)

Though there had been one frost, there were still a few straggling specimens of what I have long called *Geranium nepalense*. This species looms big, in my view, in the Nepalese and Tibetan pharmacopoeia. As I long correctly challenged soy (it's not the best source of estrogenic isoflavones), I may now challenge green tea (is it really a leading source of polyphenol?). Those are among the compounds that get green tea a lot of press, to prevent everything from cancer to cardiopathy (and tea's fluorine might even prevent caries or cavities). Is green tea better than average quantitatively in the polyphenols or is it just better studied, than other green leaves we ingest for various reasons. If we analyzed 100 woody species for polyphenols in the leaves; would *Camellia sinensis* be average, above average or below average? I'd really like to know. I don't know, nor do I know anyone else who knows for sure.

But I still had a few sprawling specimens of *Geranium nepalense* or *G. thunbergii* in my yard. In spite of its white flowers, it best keys out in Brown and Brown's *Herbaceous Plants of Maryland* as *Geranium nepalense* var. *thunbergii*. The USDA nomenclature database however cites that as a synonym of *G. thunbergii.*, a species native to northern China, Taiwan and Japan. In contrast to *G. nepalense*, *G. thunbergii* is not so slender, has larger leaves, slightly larger flowers and is covered with glandular hairs. I see no glandular hairs on my weed, so am tentatively still calling it *G. nepalense*.

Except for the white flowers, it matches *Geranium nepalense*, as described in *Plants and People of Nepal* (NPM). Nepalese chew the fresh fruits as food, but the roots contain 25-32% tannins. The plant is folklorically used in Nepal for renal ailments.

The coarse, glandular *Geranium thunbergii*, the "genoshokko" or "Furoso" of Japan, or "Chuisoni-phul" or "Kosip chho" of Korea, was very popular as a medicine for loose bowels. "Young leaves are edible. Old leaves were used as a tea substitute." As of today, the Nepalese cranesbill is the richest source of geraniin [ca 1.2%, ZMB] in the USDA phytochemical database [http://www.ars-grin.gov/duke].

Reductionistically, I suspect that many of the activities of geraniin might accrue also to the geranium tea I served my garden volunteers on Oct. 16, 2003. I also had the GFG volunteers dissect the flowers and follow through the keys with me so they'll know more about the botanical workings of this weedy wildflower, adventive in my garden, source of the tea they were drinking. Then I force fed them some of the info one can readily derive from the NIH PubMed database: [[http://www.ncbi.nlm.nih.gov/entrez/query.fcgi]].

This is the sort of thing I dredge up at the last minute for an impromptu lecture about some item in flower in the lovely **Green Farmacy Garden**. The PMID serial number is all you need to type in to the database and you can see the abstract that I saw in compiling information on this herb, only recently entering my personal pharmcopoeia.

## Polyphenolic Summary

Starting with isolation of a crystalline tannin (geraniin) from popular herbs (*Geranii herba*), various polyphenolic compounds including those belonging to new classes of tannins (oligomeric hydrolyzable tannins, complex tannins, and other metabolites and condensates) have been isolated from various medicinal plants. Noticeable biological and pharmacological activities (inhibition of carcinogenesis, host-mediated antitumor activity, antiviral activity, and inhibition of active oxygen, such as inhibition of lipid peroxidation and lipoxygenase, xanthine oxidase, and monoamine oxidase) have been found for several of these polyphenolic compounds (PMID 1417694).

## Cancer

Geraniin and corilagin, both found in *Geranium thunbergi*, are effective tumor necrosis factor-alpha (TNF-alpha) inhibitors. IC50 values were 43 uM for geraniin and 76 microM for corilagin, cf (-)-epigallocatechin gallate (26 uM). Treatment with geraniin inhibited okadaic acid tumor promotion in a two-stage carcinogenesis experiment on mouse skin. Geraniin has potential as a new cancer preventive agent (X12628509). Geraniin exhibited moderate selective cytotoxicity against PRMI-7951 melanoma cells with ED50 values in the range of 0.1-0.8 microgram/ml. was inactive (> 10 ug/ml) against lung carcinoma (A-549), ileocecal adenocarcinoma (HCT-8), epidermoid carcinoma of nasopharnyx (KB), and medulloblastoma (TE-671) tumor cells (PMID 1431932).

## Hypertension

A single intravenous bolus injection of geraniin into anaesthetized hypertensive rats lowered the arterial mean blood pressure in a dose-dependent manner without affecting the heart rate. A similar action was also observed in normotensive rats at a higher dose. Geraniin did not modify the baroflex sensitivity in the phenylephrine-challenged. The authors suggest that geraniin possesses the ability to lower systemic blood pressure through the reduction of noradrenaline release or by direct vasorelaxation (PMID 7911162). Further, geraniin, is an angiotensin-converting enzyme inhibitor (PMID 3379417).

## Immunomodulation

Geraniin, a tannin in *Geranium nepalense* and *G. thunbergii* Sieb. et Zucc. caused a marked retardation of the recovery from fully spread surface membranes and a highly reorganized cytoskeleton of macrophages, whereas endocytotic activity, phagocytosis and pinocytosis in the cells were significantly inhibited (PMID 1804795).

## Ophthalmology

Geraniin (tannin from *Geranium thunbergii*) reduces oxidative damage to the mouse ocular lens. Oxidative damage in the lens was induced by diamide, diazene dicarboxylic acid bis (N, N-dimethylamide); diamide oxidized the sulfhydryl groups in both the membrane and cytoplasm but did not increase lipid peroxide. Geraniin showed protective effects on the changes in the Na+/K+ ratio, GSH level, Na,K-ATPase activity, GSH reductase activity and the sulfhydryl level of the membranous protein in the diamide-treated lens, but such protective effects of geraniin were not observed in the cell-free system of the lens. In addition, geraniin itself was unable to reduce GSSG to GSH and also unable to inhibit the oxidative reaction of the sulfhydryl group to diamide. These results suggest that in the intact lens geraniin would act primarily on the lens cell membrane surface to inhibit an influx of diamide into the inner part of the plasma membrane and the cytoplasm, and consequently that geraniin may protect sulfhydryl groups in the cell membrane and cytoplasm from their oxidation by diamide and keep the redox system of the lens in a normal state (PMID 3184550).

## Pain

Ellagitannins, and our geraniin, at 3 to 30 mg/kg, ipr, given 30 min before testing, exhibited significant and dose-related antinociceptive properties against acetic acid-induced abdominal constrictions in mice. Geraniin was about six to seven times more potent at the ID50 level than aspirin and acetaminophen (PMID 8657748).

## Sepsis

Gallic acid, corilagin and geraniin, all found in geranium, have demonstrated antimicrobial activity (PMID X10925407).

## Ulcers

Geraniin (10-100 mg/kg), given 30 min prior to EtOH perfusion, produced potent inhibitory effects on those ulcerogenic parameters provoked by EtOH in a dose-dependent manner. Cytoprotective effects of geraniin can protect gastric mucosa against acidified EtOH-induced damage, at least partly through the inhibition in acid back-diffusion and the elevation of gastric mucus production (PMID 8925673).

## Virus

Purified gallotannins (geraniin and corilagin) were active at 0.24 ug/ml at blocking HIV-1 replication. The authors demonstrated 70-75% inhibition of virus uptake at concentrations of 2.5 ug/ml geraniin. In addition, a concentration-dependent inhibition of HIV-1 reverse transcriptase (RT) could be demonstrated in-vitro. (IC(50) values varied from 1.8 to 14.6 ug/ml, suggesting potentiating the chemotherapy of HIV infections (X2742578). Geraniin at the non-cytotoxic concentration of 50 micro m, suppresses hepatitis B expression effectively (PR17:449).

# Hot Tuna (*Houttuynia* spp.)

(Unpublished)

That's the standardized name given by Art Tucker in the *Big Book of Herbs*, and I like it better as a common name than the standardized common name, Houttuynia (also the scientific name), offered us by the American Herbal Products Association in their book, *Herbs of Commerce*. It's another love-hate herb. Ask 12 people what it smells like and you'll get ten answers. And they may all be right, it is so variable. Tucker and DeBaggio (2000) remind us that it exists in several chemotypes: one scented of lemons or oranges, another suggesting "raw meat, fish and fresh cilantro" (the latter itself a love-hate smell, sometimes compared to bedbugs). Japanese plants are rich in dodecanoic-acid, 2-undecanone and methyl dodecanoate, reminiscent of cilantro.

Leaves are frequently eaten in salads, sauces, soups and stews, fruits and roots also reportedly edible. Chinese add the leaves to salads; Vietnamese chop the leaves in fish sauces, and require the heart shaped leaves as a garnish for fish stews and boiled fertile duck eggs, three days from hatching (FAC; TAD). But, according to Tucker and DeBaggio, the Japanese eschew the flavor in food and instead "plant it around their outhouses." Japanese Tanaka (1976) says leaves and roots are used as a vegetable, though "they are rather stinky" (TAN).

It took us minutes to establish this invasive alien in the **Green Farmacy Garden**. It took days to get rid of it (if we did). Always keep it contained, or be prepared to have more of a marginally edible weed than you want. Though killed back by frost, it is hardy to zone 5. Tucker and DeBaggio note how easy it is to grow, how difficult to control, taking over by underground rhizomes.

American scientists studied aqueous extracts of forsythia, honeysuckle, hot tuna, licorice, all antiinflammatory and antiviral properties. The hot tuna extract inhibited NO production in a dose-dependent manner, but minimally (approximately 30%) inhibited TNF-a secretion at 0.0625 and 0.125 mg/ml (X16047559). Other oriental Americans, comparing hot tuna with *Bidens* found that hot tuna was more promsiing for Herpes Simplex 2 (IC33% = 250 ug/ml) (X12943167).

Chinese scientists showed that including 2% hot tuna in the diet led to better regulation of the xenobiotic-metabolizing enzyme system. Aqueous extracts look useful in managing mast cell-mediated anaphylactic responses (X16204936). I'm not into herbal injections but rats showed antiedemic effect (IC50= 4 ul /g) when treated with hot tuna. Working during the SARS epidemic, the scientists demonstrated antiinflammatory activity (X16213118). Hot water extract had modest activity aginst 5 leukemic cell lines ( IC50 = 478-662 ug/ml and 662 microg/ml. *Bidens pilosa* var. *minor* was more effective (11527072). German scientists note inhibition of prostaglandin synthesis, suggesting antiinflammatory and immunomodualtory activities. Japanese showed that the steam distillate inhibited several viruses, herpes, HIV, and influenza. Three major components, methyl n-nonyl ketone, lauryl aldehyde, and capryl aldehyde, also inactivated these viruses, working against enveloped viruses by interfering with the function of virus envelope (X7617766). Koreans found the leaves stimulate immune responses in mice (TAD). Other Koreans demonstrated that aqueous extracts benefited mast cell-mediated anaphylactic responses (PMID: 16204936).

Many of these sentence summaries, mostly from PubMed abstracts, might suggest a possible help in avian flu. But those fertile duck eggs somehow remind me of duck flu. Some TCM practitioners include garlic, *Smilax* and *Houttuynia* herb for Lyme disease. And that's why I drafted this, fearing I am suffering from post-Lyme sequelae. If the hot tuna works as a medicine for Lyme Disease, I will suffer no shortage of medicine.

# Hyena Vine (*Gymnema sylvestre*)

*The Business of Herbs* 7(2):6-7, May/June, 1989

You've probably never heard of the Hyena Vine, *Gymnema sylvestre*. I first heard of it only recently but predict you'll be hearing more about it in the future. For example, here is a "sanitized" quote from the March 6, 1989, *Chemical Marketing Reporter* (CMR): "...an Indian herb [is] available that suppresses sugar cravings, metabolizes fat and promotes weight loss. The herb, *Gymnema sylvestre*, ...has been successfully marketed in Japan."

Since I, like many obese Americans, need an herb that suppresses sugar cravings, metabolizes fat, and promotes weight loss, I immediately turned to my copy of *The Wealth of India* (WOI), my favorite economic botany encyclopedia. There I read that this vine, relative of our comparatively dangerous milkweeds, is "stomachic, stimulant, laxative and diuretic...useful in cough, biliousness and sore eyes." Chewing the leaves, more importantly, paralyzes the sense of taste for sweet and bitter substances. Hence the leaves have been used by diabetics who have a sweet tooth but must avoid sugar.

According to WOI, hyena vine "has been used for parageusia, furunculosis and as an errhine," which translates to mean the herb has been used for bad tastes in the mouth, boils and to make the nose run. Dave and Paula get after me for using big words, with good reason; but you might enjoy adding parageusia to your vocabulary, especially if you want to tell someone they leave a bad taste in your mouth.

The leaves have been shown to lower blood sugar in diabetic experimental animals. At doses of 100 milligrams (mg) per kilogram (kg) of body weight (equivalent to 10 grams or about ⅓ ounce in a 212 pound or 100 kg man like me) the leaf preparation (alcoholic extract) significantly lowered blood sugar in experimental animals with high blood sugar but not in those with normal blood sugar levels. So there is experimental evidence that the plant might be useful in regulating sugar levels in diabetics.

The CMR clipping said that the plant promotes weight loss. Too good to be true? Perhaps so! Another good Indian source book, *Medicinal Plants of India*, Vol. 1 (1976), says that animals receiving the hyena vine weighed more, though fed less, than control animals not receiving the herb. Yet another Indian study, by T. Chakrabortty, suggested weight gains rather than losses. So my cursory scans of the Indian literature available here at **Herbal Vineyard** give no hint of using hyena vine for weight loss, on the contrary, suggesting that it might cause weight gain!

Chakrabortty's studies with 61 diabetic humans, males and females ages 23-60 years, showed a blood sugar stabilization in 70% of the cases, with beneficial effects apparent in two to four weeks. No cases of low blood sugar were induced. These patients received only 120-360 mg Gymnema in 60 mg capsules. Such dosage rates are 100 times smaller than the rates that proved toxic to experimental animals. Scientists often speak of the therapeutic to toxic dose ratio, which here seems to be close to

1:100, the toxic dose being approximately 100 times the therapeutic dose. In the much more dangerous digitalis, the ratio is closer to 1:2, the toxic dose only about twice as high as the therapeutic dose.

While there is abundant evidence that hyena vine can reduce blood sugar in diabetics, I so far find no evidence, except the uncorroborated CMR clipping, that hyena vine can help metabolize fat or promote weight loss. (A catabolic herb like ginger or hot pepper may do so.) Without more convincing evidence, I suppose I'll forego the hyena vine and stay fat and happy. But I'll try to get some seed for further experimentation, in case the CMR report is right. In big words, that is proactive germplasm procurement.

[[Seventeen years since publication of this not-too-flattering article; the seventeen-year itch induced me to see if more evidence had been forthcoming. I'm not going to bore you with all the formatted data in my CRC *Handbook of Medicinal Herbs* (ed. 2). Translating that ponderous tabulation of "Indications," I see animal or phytochemcial rationale for glycosuria, high cholesterol, obesity, snakebite, stomachache, syndrome X, and water retention, with clinicial support for diabetes. But under "Activities," I see it can be lipolytic or lipogenic. I would cetainly try it if I had diabetes or syndrome X (metabolic syndrome) especially if I had it growing here at GFG [CR2].]]

# Mung Bean (*Vigna radiata*)

(Unpublished ca. 1998 -9)

## The Mung Dynasty

Ever since my friend, the great botanist and physician, Andy Weil, had some alarming things to say about legume sprouts, I have wanted to come to the sprout's defense, at least defending cooked mung bean sprouts, which I enjoy often in chow mein. Andy's newsletter late in 1998 implied but did not exactly say that all legume spouts contain toxins, and readers interpreted his newsletter to mean that they all contained the toxin canavanine. I do not think the latter conclusion is correct. I do agree that all legumes and legume sprouts, indeed all plants and sprouts, contain toxins but usually at manageable levels. Alfalfa sprouts, as well known, may contain dangerous levels of canavanine. Here's the letter that prompts this defense of mung bean sprouts. Having trouble getting through to Dr. Weil, one of his readers addressed the following query to me.

> "I recently read in Dr. Weil's *Self Healing* newsletter, that alfalfa and other leguminous sprouts contain canavanine, a toxin that can harm the immune system. This toxin is inactivated by cooking. I have not been able to verify this. Do you have any information to verify or debunk?"

Ironically soy, which Andy praised, is reported to contain canavanine. So far I find reports of canavanine only from uncommon legumes, a few vetches, clover, indigo, lespedeza, locust, wisteria and other more obscure legumes, rarely consumed as foods and as indicated, the widely consumed and praised soy genus, *Glycine*. Specifically, I have heard of canavanine in the legume genera *Astragalus, Bossaiaea, Canavalia, Coursetia, Cracca, Dilwynia, Genistidium, Gliricidia, Glottidium, Glycine* (including the overpromoted soy), *Gompholobium, Hardenbergia, Hedysarum, Hippocrepis, Hypocalyptus, Indigofera, Lennia, Lespedeza, Medicago, Millettia, Mirbellia, Mundulea, Neocracca, Olneya, Oxylobium, Peteria, Poissonaea, Pultenaea, Robinia, Sabinea, Sesbania, Sphincto-spermum, Trifolium, Uraria, Vicia,* and *Wisteria*. I have not yet heard of it in the genera *Phaseolus*, to which my favorite beans belong, and the genus *Vigna*, to which belong other favorite foods, black eyed pea, mung bean, and yardlong bean. So while canavanine is rather widely distributed, it has not been reported, yet at least, for my favorite leguminous foods (soy is not my favorite). Nor has it yet been reported in edible kudzu roots, or sprouts, the roots at least shown to be much richer in estrogenic isoflavones than soy.

So despite the inference in Andy's great newsletter, I find no evidence that the widely consumed mung bean sprouts contain canavanine. If the evidence is there I hope Andy will point it out in his newsletter, and compare the levels of canavanine in soy with mung beans, sprouted and unsprouted. With that data quantified, and an idea of what level of canavanine it takes to do damage, we could approach the potential toxicity of legume sprouts with level heads on a level playing field (maybe a mine field).

I do find evidence that mung bean contains the same estrogenic compounds for which soy has long claimed to be the best, or a unique source of, genistein and daidzein. And if the sprouts contain more isoflavones than the soybean seed (I'll wager they do), all the glamour and glitter (and caveats on the flip side, like estrogenization) attributed to them in soy might as well or better be attributed to mung bean sprouts.

Natives of Asia (eating more beansprouts, kudzu, mung bean and soy than we normally do) have lower rates of breast and prostate cancers and cardiovascular disease than do we. All the beans above soy in my table below are better (and to my palate tastier) sources of genistein, and might be cheaper and more palatable than soybean, without its subsidies. Granted the mung beans, unsprouted, are only about ⅓ as rich in the two estrogenic isoflavones, genistein and daidzein, as soy. But I'll wager that the sprouts, especially if fungally infected, will have more isoflavones than unsprouted soy. My colleagues, Dr. Kaufmann et al, cited below, could verify this, should such an inquiry be financially supported.

Sawa et al. (1999) in their title suggest that it is vegetables in general they are talking about, but in fact, their data strengthen an old hot-headed hyperbolic paracelsan hypothesis of mine, that mung beans may explain the differential cancer rates between Americans and orientals in hormone-dependent cancer rates, specifically breast and prostate cancer. Heretofore, soy has gotten all the press. But orientals also eat a lot more mung bean sprouts than soy sprouts and more mung bean and soy than Americans eat. Sprouting legumes often have 10-100 times more estrogenic isoflavones than unsprouted seeds. While Sawa et al do not list daidzein for their mung bean soup they add it to the list of antiradicular anti-tumor-promoters. Reviewing Weil's newsletter and the Sawa et al. study, I still recommend all those edible beans, especialy for me, genetically targeted for colon cancer, that are not yet reported to contain canavanine.

Sawa et al. (1999) found that water soluble extracts of various vegetables inhibit free radicals which cause major DNA damage – a major event in carcinogenesis. Water extracts of several vegetables, and specifically cold and hot water extracts of mungbeans, scavenge these ROO radicals. These extracts have a strong anti-tumor-promoter effect in transforming B-lymphocytes carrying Epstein-Barr virus (Raji cells). The authors used quercetin as a milepost with a minimal effective dose of 82.1 uM. Rutin was nearly 9 times more potent than quercetin (they share many biological activities and usually hang together anyhow, compensatorily, i.e. cooccurring in the same plant parts, a lowering in one often compensated for by an increase in the other). Rutin and chlorogenic acid activities were much greater than those of water soluble antioxidants, e.g. 8 times greater than l-cysteine, 17 times greater than reduced glutathione, and 33 times ascorbic acid, on a molar basis.

Sawa et al. (1999) note detectable quantities of the antioxidants isoquercitrin, kaempferol, kaempferol-7-o-rhamnoside, quercetin, robinin, and rutin are found in aqueous extracts of mung bean sprouts. With the exception of isoquercitrin, all increase from 2.5 to 10 fold in sprouting. Hot water extracts (I'd call that a sprout tea or decoction) will contain 2-4 times more of these flavonoids than do cold water extracts. Scavenging capacity of cold water extracts increased daily, peaking at 6-8 days after germination. Hot water extracts harvested on day 6-8, the time to eat them, had 4-5 times the scavenging capacity as cold water extracts.

Caffeic acid increases plasma and lipoprotein levels of a-tocopherol in rats. Perhaps phenolics indirectly increase ROO-scavenging capacity in vivo by augmenting levels of alpha-tocopherol.

The authors conclude conservatively that certain flavonoids and phenolic acids, effective scavengers for alkylperoxyl radicals, may have the potential for reducing long-lived alkylperoxyl radicals and radical mediated pathogenesis such as carcinogenesis. Their data expanded the list of cancer-preventing phytochemicals in my database. Those marked below with an asterisk have been reported from the mung bean.

The Sawa et al. data add several cancer-preventing compounds to the USDA database, most of them also in mungbean and probably other more mundane beans, even the soy. (But the soy might contain that canavanine Andy was warning about, especially in the sprouts.) Mungbeans contain chemopreventives: caffeic-acid, chlorogenic-acid, daidzein, gallic acid, isoquercitrin, kaempferol and its rhamnoside, naringenin, rhamnetin, robinin, rutin, shikimic-acid (used as one started material for TamiFlu), tannin, vanillic acid and vanillin. Frankly I think dietary mungbean is more responsible than soy for the low incidence of hormone related cancers in orientals. And I enjoy mungbean sprouts (true confession, with soy sauce) and a side dish of miso soup. I don't think the soybusters would recommend too much of that. So far, it looks better than tofu to me.

| Seed Sample | Genistein (ppms) | Daidzein (ppms) | Grams to Provide 70 mg Isoflavonoids |
|---|---|---|---|
| *Psoralea corylifolia* | 1528.0 | 539.7 | 30 |
| Kudzu Root | 316.9 | 949.8 | 55 |
| Yellow split pea | 45.8 | 0.4 | 1,550 |
| Black turtle beans | 45.1 | 0.4 | 1,540 |
| Baby lima beans | 40.1 | 0.4 | 1,730 |
| Large lima beans | 34.4 | 0.3 | 2,015 |
| Anasazi beans | 29.8 | 6.5 | 1,930 |
| Red kidney beans | 29.3 | 2.7 | 2,190 |
| Red lentils | 25.0 | 5.2 | 2,320 |
| SOYBEANS | 24.1 | 37.6 | 1,135 |
| Black eyed peas | 23.3 | 0.3 | 2,965 |
| Pinto beans | 22.3 | 23.2 | 1,540 |
| Mung beans | 21.8 | 0.3 | 3,165 |
| Azuki beans | 21.2 | 4.6 | 2,715 |
| Faba beans | 19.9 | 5.0 | 2,810 |
| Great northern beans | 17.7 | 7.2 | 2,810 |

Kaufman, PB, Duke, JA Brielmann, H, Boik, J and Hoyt JE. 1997. "A Comparative Survey of Leguminous Plants as Sources of the Isoflavones Genistein and Daidzein: Implications For Human Nutrition and Health." *Journal of Alternative & Complementary Medicine* 3(1): 7-12.

# Perilla, Beefsteak Plant (*Perilla frutescens*)

*The Business of Herbs* 10(1):10-11. March/April, 1992

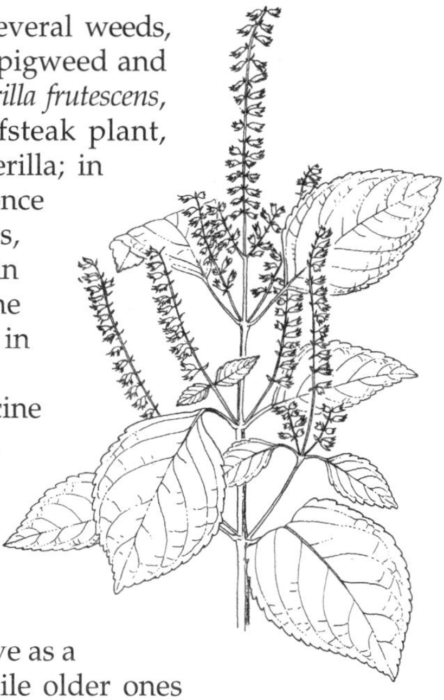

As a forager, I've enjoyed eating several weeds, e.g., burdock, dandelion, lamb's quarters, pigweed and purslane. I've enjoyed teas made of *Perilla frutescens*, known variously in English as the beefsteak plant, purple mint, wild coleus or simply perilla; in Japanese as shisho, shiso or chiso. But once it was one of my worst pasture weeds, reportedly causing respiratory problems in horses. Ironically, the Koreans use the leaves to treat respiratory problems in humans.

I thought of Perilla more as medicine than food. Stephen Facciola in *Cornucopia* makes Perilla sound more like a food: "Leaves are salted and used as a condiment for tofu and as a garnish for tempura. The young seedlings are eaten raw with sashimi (raw fish). Immature flower clusters serve as a garnish for soups and chilled tofu, while older ones are fried. The seeds are preserved in salt or used as a spice in pickles, tempura and miso. Source of an essential oil used to flavor candy sauces. The seed oil is occasionally used for culinary purposes."

Common in Asia. According to *Science* (August 5, 1977), Perilla seeds are available as bird feed at pet shops in Japan and are used to flavor various foods, including pickled ginger. The seed oil, containing antioxidant and antiseptic compounds, is used as a preservative in soy sauce. While the FDA may not view it as GRAS (Generally Recognized As Safe), it is what I call "GRAF" (Generally Recognized As Food), at least in the Orient. It is, like so many Oriental foods, also well endowed with medicinal virtues. Perry, in her *Medicinal Plants of East and Southeast Asia*, notes that the stems are prescribed for pregnant women with morning sickness and that the seeds are recommended in folk treatments of rheumatism and many other ailments. My earlier researches of Perilla suggest its use also for asthma, bronchitis, cholera, colds, cough, cramps, fish-poisoning, sunstroke and uterine problems.

But that's not what triggered this column. It was a cryptic note in Rudin's *The Omega-3 Phenomenon* (1987). If Rudin's conclusions are valid, we'll be hearing much more about Perilla.

## Major ALA source

Rudin says of his magic bullet, alpha-linolenic acid (ALA, an omega-3 fatty acid, as opposed to evening primrose's gamma-linolenic acid, GLA, an omega-6 fatty acid): "The plant food that has the highest production of alpha-linolenic acid is linseed oil." Rudin's table shows that linseed oil has 45% ALA; but Perilla is scored as having 67%! In scanning Rudin's book, I find no other mention of Perilla, nor is it indexed. I don't know why Rudin did not push the Perilla seed, eaten widely in Korea, Japan and China and by Asians in the United States, instead of flaxseed.

In a new book, charmingly entitled *Why George Should Eat Broccoli* (Dougherty Co. Milwaukee, WI), author and researcher Paul Stitt, calling the ALA the more melodious ALENA, champions it as a cancer preventive and as the vegetarian equivalent of fish oils. He says: "ALENA has been shown to improve learning ability in rats and monkeys, prevent agglutination of platelets in humans, remove cholesterol from arteries and prevent dry scaly skin...heal nerve damage and other skin disorders." Like me, you have probably heard, without really understanding, the health claims for so-called omega-3 and omega-6 fatty acids. Dr. Rudin says that the ratio of omega-threes to omega-sixes is important, suggesting an omega-6: omega-3 ratio of 4:1 to 6:1. Since he states that 2,000 mg of omega-3 might be a minimum daily requirement, that implies that 8,000 to 12,000 mg omega-6 might be a reasonable RDA, in his opinion, at least. Other writers (Neusinger and Connor, *Nut. Rev*. 44:285, 1986) suggest, at least for retinopathy, that the human diet provide an adequate amount of omega-3 fatty acids and an omega-3: omega-6 ratio of 1:4 to 1:10, particularly during pregnancy, lactation and infancy. High ratios are typical of evening primrose, chestnut, butternut and walnut oils, with a 1:4 ratio in Perilla, 1:3 in flaxseed oil.

## Commercial potential?

Since ALA is apparently more plentiful in Perilla than in flax, and in a more favorable omega-3: omega-6 ratio, we might think of it as a source of these curative qualities ascribed to flax and/or ALA. Unfortunately, though, poorly processed Perilla seed oil may contain the toxins 1-perillaldehyde and/or perillaketone, which may cause dermatitis. No doubt the FDA would challenge Perilla oil, if not the ALA in Perilla oil. I quote from ..., "use of this plant in human foods in Oriental countries should be questioned because of the obvious potential hazards to health."

Even common omega-6 oils like corn, safflower and sunflower aren't getting a completely clean bill of health. According to Dr. W. Mertz, head of the USDA's Human Nutrition Research Center, omega-threes seem to protect against certain types of cancer while the omega-sixes may actually promote certain types. Does this mean we should shift from corn oil to flax or Perilla oil? Let's wait for more data before doing anything drastic. But I wonder. So does the world. I'm sure we'll experience several flip-flops before we can really tack on an '!' instead of a '?'.

## Other benefits

The rather toxic perillaketone has been shown to promote rapid passage of materials through mice intestines by stimulating the circular muscles of the intestine. Mucilage and fiber in Perilla seeds might possibly benefit the body in the same fashion as psyllium, the recently controversial fiber source in OTC drugs like Metamucil™.

A remarkable table published by Suzuki et al. (1982) showed that an exhaustively extracted and concentrated 150-gram cup of Perilla leaf tea would contain 4,000 mg of potassium (more than the standard RDA), 615 mg calcium (<RDA), 642 mg magnesium (>RDA), 60 mg iron (>RDA), 10.5 mg manganese (>RDA), 1.8 mg zinc (<RDA) and 0.55 mg copper (<RDA), indicating that the leaves are very rich in nutrients. Additionally, Perilla, like so many other mints, contains the antioxidant rosmarinic acid in its leaves, and several others with the more mundane antioxidants beta-carotene and ascorbic acid. As I write this, I drink a diluted cup of Perilla tea with leaves and flowers but no ripe seed. Unsweetened, it tastes medicinally herbal; with lemon and sugar, it compares favorably with any hot tea.

Recent Japanese studies attribute the sedative activity of the leaf tea to perillaldehyde and stigmasterol. Activity against dermatitis-causing fungi was attributed to synergisms between perillaldehyde and citral. Chinese studies show that the leaves have hemostatic (blood-clotting) potential.

Perilla has great economic potential as an oilseed and medicinal plant. Caution, however, is indicated before indiscriminate consumption of the seeds and leaf teas, both of which are loaded with nutrients, but, like all plants, also contain toxins. Perilla seed reportedly contains more omega-threes than the widely heralded flax seed. Clearly Perilla contains some valuable compounds and nutrients. If we could just get those, avoiding the questionable compounds, Perilla might become a need and not a weed. Tomorrow, when oil and tempers sublimate in the middle east, we here in the west can tranquilly extract these useful chemicals and convert the residues into useful power alcohol. For that matter we could constructively extract the ALA from the seed oil and divert the other fatty acids into biodiesel to mix with our alcohol.

# Skullcap, Chinese (*Scutellaria baicalensis*)

(Unpublished)

I had planned to talk about spices all year but sometimes expediency and serendipity, both in this case, led me in other directions. Expedience because I had to prepare a lecture on flavonoids for my Tai Sophia class and the Chinese skullcap, *Scutellaria baicalensis*, is loaded with some interesting flavonoids. Serendipity because someone pleaded with me for info on herbal alternatives to sarcoidosis. When the sarcoid patient called, I knew none. I didn't even know what sarcoidosis was. But two days later I knew that skullcap and yarrow might be among the best of herbal alternatives for this elusive ailment.

Acording to Nakajima et al. (2001) some skullcap compounds can inhibit eotaxin, a chemokine associated with the recruitment of eosinophils to sites of allergic inflammation. Baicalein from skullcap root can inhibit eotaxin production by human dermal fibroblasts. Traditionally used as a kampo medicine for bronchial asthma in Japan, skullcap contains several potentially useful compounds. Four of its flavonoids inhibited eotaxin production at 10 ug/ml. Baicalein was more effective than oroxylin-A which was more effective than baicalin which was more effective than skullcapflavon-II. The baicalein was expressed dose-dependently, with ca 50% inhibition at 1.8 ug/ml. [Baicalein also prevented human eotaxin mRNA expression in IL-4 plus TNF-alpha -stimulated human fibroblasts.] Such data suggest the possibility of skullcap in pulmonary sarcoidosis as well as bronchial asthma. The flavonoids would, perhaps additively, perhaps synergicly, suppress eotaxin associated recruitment of eosinophils.

Newmark and Schulick (2000) showed how inhibition of cyclooxygenase 2 (COX-2) may alleviate and prevent arthritis, and other inflammatory diseases, e.g. alzheimer's and cancer. They mentioned baikal skullcap. I attributed my long-stated rosemary's antialzheimeran potential more to its antioxidant and antiacetylcholinesterase activity (terpinen-4-ol), and more lately added the AntiCOX-2 rationale, which figures heavily in Newmark and Schulick's new book (2000). The COX-2 Inhibitors they mention for baikal skullcap are apigenin; baicalein; and melatonin. (The latter also useful for sarcoidosis.) They make very convincing arguments for the strengths (balancing homeostasis, diminished side effects, economy, safety, synergy) of the herbal COX-2 Inhibitors, as opposed to the synthetic silver bullets celebrex and vioxx.

Noting that apigenin, baicalein and melatonin are the known COX-2 inhibitors in baikal skullcap, Newmark and Schulick challenge the silver bullet mentality. They chaotically remind American pharmaceuticalists that they are in a linear rut (one gene- one peptide- one enzyme – one neurotransmitter – one receptor – one animal behaviour – one clinical drug – one clinical rating scale (and, says Jim Duke, many side effects). There are more than 50 transmitters, thousands of cell types, complex electromagnetic phenomenology, and continuous instability based on autonomous activity at all levels, from proteins to the electroencephalogram. I remind readers that each individual herb, like each individual human, consists of thousands of chemicals, in thousands of homeostatic reactions.

More recent abstracts suggest that there are two more. Chen et al.'s (2001) title suggested that wogonin and baicalin and baicalein all inhibit COX-2, but the abstract says that only wogonin. Wonder what the article says. (I have ordered the article.) At any rate there are at least 5 Cox-2-I's reported from baical skullcap.

Spanish researchers showed that baicalein inhibited COX-2. Additionally the skullcap has several antiinflammatory and antioxidant compounds to work in concert (synergy) with the COX-2 inhibitors. Antioxidant compounds in the skullcap include apigenin, baicalin, baicalein, eugenol, isoeugenol, maltol, melatonin, phenol, vanillin, and wogonin. Baicalin was much stronger than bacelein and wogonin. Antiinflammatories include apigenin, baicalein, baicalin, butylidene-phthalide, cnidilide, eugenol, paeonol, wogonin.

Japanese scientists demonstrated that *Scutellaria* suppresses colon cancer, as would be expected from a COX-2 inhibiting herb. Baikal skullcap stimulates production of quinone reductase, an enzyme important in cancer detoxification. There's an association between peaks of nitric acid production and cancer. Baicalein and more so wogonin inhibit the generation of nitric acid. Baicalein induces apopptosis in four pancreatic cell types, and destroys pancreatic cancer cells by taking away their high-octane food source. U. Guelph researchers note that some *Scutellarias* are rich in melatonin, with important anticancer implications.

It has taken me several years to move the buzz-cliche word acetyl-cholinesterase-inhibition from the pharmaceutical antialzheimeran shelf to the herbal shelf. I suspect it will take that long to move the buzz cliche word COX-2-inhibition into the herbal pharmacopoeia as well. I launched that new effort in 1997, when I saw full page ads in *JAMA* promoting COX-inhibition as the wave of the future in arthritis medication. I quickly reported that two Ayurvedic herbs were well endowed, with COX inhibitors. And these herbs, ginger and turmeric, have a millennial folk history as antiinflammatory and antiarthritic. Clinical trials in Europe support these antiarthritic traditional credences. So instead of talking of COX inhibitors as the wave of the future, I refer to them as the wave of the past. And the silver bullet COX-inhibitors, whether an isolated phyto-chemical, never consumed pure by human beings, or brand new synthetic, never consumed, pure or impure by humans, will have more side effects. Small wonder that more than half of the newly-FDA-approved drugs have to be recalled or relabelled, because of side effects not uncovered in the 10-15 year (30 years with taxol) drug development period that costs, according to the Wall Street Journal, $500 million dollars [[1.7 billion by 2003]]. Few herb companies in the U.S. have annual sales much higher than $500 million, to the best of my knowledge. Newmark and Schulick will speed up public recognition of the value of COX-2 Inhibitors, especially the natural ones like baikal skullcap.

[[I'd be cheating, if I sneaked this comment in as though I had written it back when I started my harangue on COX-2's. But in my first Tai lectures, I predicted that celebrex or vioxx would be recalled or relabeled within a decade of their approval. I was just betting the odds; 1 of 2 newly approved drugs will be recalled within a decade. Both have been relabelled and one has been permanently recalled. On his radio show, Gary Null says it killed 100,000 people. I haven't been able to find a published citation of that fatality figure. Those afraid of synthetic COX-2-I's might try the herbal COX-2-I's like Chinese skullcap. In my **Green Farmacy Garden**, I have the beautiful baical skullcap, flanked by American *S. galericulata* and *S. lateriflora*. Our American skullcaps contain many of the same biochemicals but have not been so well proven out in clinical studies.]]

# Soybean (*Glycine max*)

(Unpublished)

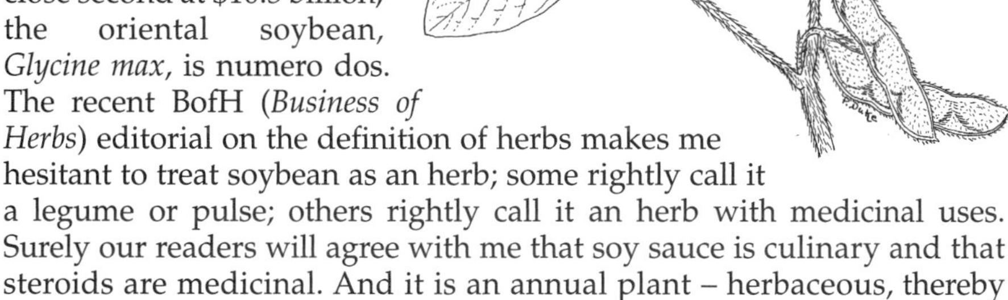

Some people raised their eyebrows when I treated corn as one of my *Herb a Day* subjects. From an economic point of view, corn is numero uno in the U.S., contributing $12.1 billion annually to the economy. But running a close second at $10.3 billion, the oriental soybean, *Glycine max*, is numero dos. The recent BofH (*Business of Herbs*) editorial on the definition of herbs makes me hesitant to treat soybean as an herb; some rightly call it a legume or pulse; others rightly call it an herb with medicinal uses. Surely our readers will agree with me that soy sauce is culinary and that steroids are medicinal. And it is an annual plant – herbaceous, thereby qualifying in all respects as an herb.

The oriental soybean was once a new crop in the U.S., introduced from China into Savannah, Georgia, in 1765. After 200 years the U.S. was producing 56% of the world's soybeans. During that time, many scientists have worked on America's number two money crop; many have even devoted their entire careers to soy.

Dr. Samuel Sun, University of Hawaii, Honolulu, is attempting to incorporate a high-methionine gene from the Amazonian brazilnut into the Chinese soybean. Soybean is not well endowed with the sulfur-rich proteins, methionine and cysteine. Methionine supplementation costs the American poultry industry some $100 million dollars a year, much of which could be saved if a new breed of soybeans already contained that methionine. I suggested to Dr. Sun that he might try incorporating the gene into *Apios americana*, a native American perennial legume that produces both edible tubers and seeds and is tolerant of acid, high-aluminum, waterlogged soils.

## Healthy Legumes

Many legumes, such as guar, peanut and soybean are assuming more importance to the health food industry because of their high soluble fiber content, high protein levels and goodly quantities of choline, lecithin and tocopherols, not to mention Bowman-Birk inhibitors, galactomannans and sitosterol. Many of today's sterols, made from natural soybean sterols, come as a byproduct of the soy meal industry.

Some people swear by peanuts to keep their blood sugar down. Soybeans also have marked hypoglycemic [lowering the blood sugar] and hypocholesterolemic [lowering cholesterol] effects (*Medicinal Plants of India*). Popular literature at least suggests that beans (in general or specifically *Phaseolus*) have some antidiabetic, cancer-preventive, cholesterol-lowering, flatugenic, insulin-sparing and laxative properties.

## Designer Food Program

On my 61st birthday I was negotiating with scientists representing the National Cancer Institute to work with them on the Designer Food Program. Instead of looking for medicinal herbs to cure cancer as I did from 1977-1982, I'd be helping them look for the best active plant ingredients to help prevent cancer and I'd be looking for the best varieties of the best species of plants bearing the greatest quantities of these cancer-preventive compounds. In addition to the cabbage, flax, mint and onion families of herbs, the program would also be looking at some legumes, the family that includes *Apios, Astragalus* (huang-chi and gum tragacanth), beans, carob, fenugreek, guar, lentils, licorice, peas and soybeans, to name just a few.

Soybeans made new headlines in March, 1990, because of the cancer research of Dr. Stephen Barnes, University of Alabama at Birminghan. Soybeans contain several compounds called phytoestrogens, with mildly positive and negative estrogenic activities. Researchers believe many breast tumors need the hormone estrogen to grow. For that reason doctors often treat breast cancer patients with an anti-estrogenic drug known as tamoxifen. Barnes speculates that phytoestrogens may behave like tamoxifen, similarly, but more weakly, inhibiting tumor development. Rats fed a soybean diet developed up to 70% fewer tumors when injected with a carcinogen than rats not fed the soybeans. Asian women who eat soybean-rich diets are up to eight times less likely to develop breast cancer as American women. Daughters of Asian immigrants who eat an American diet, however, lose this advantage and have the same breast cancer incidence as Americans. Barnes asks: "Do you switch over to a diet dominated by soybeans? People shouldn't be encouraged to rush into this. But I don't think there is any harm in it."

Perhaps we should be more assertive in BofH. I suggest that women who smoke a pack a day give up the cigarettes and snack instead on carrots and soybeans [[and today 2006 other beans of their choosing; variety helps!]]. They could reduce odds for breast cancer more than twofold, especially if their total food consumption does not increase (as so often happens when one quits smoking). That's good news for women, curators of most American money today. Conversely, it's bad news for tobacco, which contributes almost $2 billion to the American economy. If tobacco takes nearly 500,000 American lives a year, as some people claim, that figures out at only $4,000 a life. Pretty grim statistic! I might not even see my family physician before switching from cancer sticks to beans and carrot sticks. I'd rather have gas than cancer! Note that cooking carrots or epazote with your beans is folklorically reported to reduce flatus.

# Turmeric (*Curcuma longa*)

(Unpublished)

## Patenting Paleolithic Phytochemicals; Patently Blatant

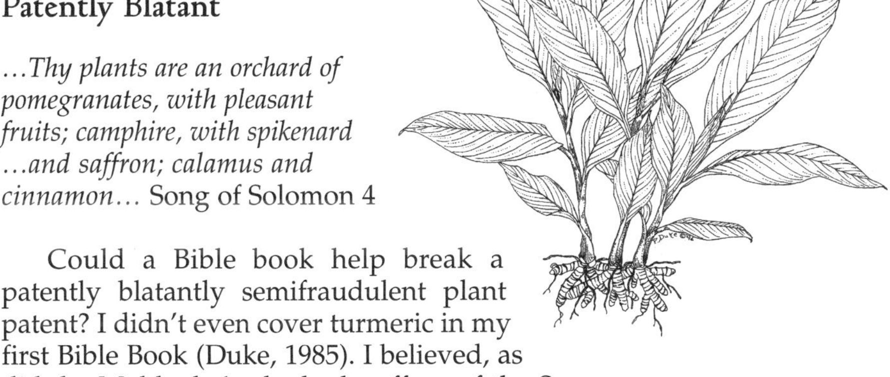

*...Thy plants are an orchard of pomegranates, with pleasant fruits; camphire, with spikenard ...and saffron; calamus and cinnamon...* Song of Solomon 4

Could a Bible book help break a patently blatantly semifraudulent plant patent? I didn't even cover turmeric in my first Bible Book (Duke, 1985). I believed, as did the Moldenke's, the herb saffron of the Song of Solomon, was the spice we today call saffron rather than the spice we today call turmeric. Either could have grown in any garden bearing also cinnamon and pomegranate. Cinnamon is subtropical, pomegranate more Mediterranean; but both can survive frost-free parts of the African/European landbridge occupied by modern Israel and Palestine.

Israeli authors like Zohary, more familiar with the Isareli flora and the Bible than am I, should be better equipped to speculate as to which herbs were really meant in some elusive passages. I'm both pleased and displeased to note that Zohary, too, leaves a few problems unresolved, including one involving these two major medicinal plants and spices, saffron and turmeric, and one minor medicinal, safflower, all sources of yellow dyes. All three can be grown in warmer regions of Israel, but the turmeric would be difficult. Alternating the garden and the greenhouse, I can even harvest a little turmeric here at the Green Farmacy Garden. Saffron and safflower would both be easy. Here are points which Zohary makes! "Saffron (in Hebrew, 'karkom') is mentioned only once in the Bible." Some commentators identify it with turmeric which "was never grown" in this country, others with saffron, which was probably grown only in post-biblical times. There is linguistic support for both possibilities. "There is no doubt that the sown "karkom" fields mentioned in the Mishnah (of the Talmud) refer to *Crocus sativus*." More data he presents point "to the identification of biblical "karkom" as turmeric and not as crocus... But doubt arises when one considers another widely cultivated annual yielding numerous heads of orange flowers" (safflower, *Carthamus tinctorius*). Where does this leave me? Should I include just one or all three of the candidates for the one mention of saffron in the Bible? From the medicinal point of view, turmeric seems even more important than saffron, which appears even more important than safflower. Ditto from the likelihood point of view, based on the views of Zohary.

With doubts like that clouding the issue, I included both *Crocus* and *Curcuma* in the new version, *Herbs of the Bible,* 2000 years of plant medicine (Duke, 1999). My opening sentences under Turmeric in that book: "Okay, I confess. I want turmeric to be the saffron mentioned in the Bible. It's such a good herb that it deserves to be in the Bible." And I concluded, "I am sure that humans have used saffron and turmeric for thousands of years. And I believe that turmeric as a pain reliever has preceeded aspirin (but not willow) by 2000 years. And like the new miracle aspirins of 1999 (Celebrex and Vioxx)...turmeric is easier on the tummy as it relieves biblical aches and pains." But in 2001 we read that the gentleness of the new pharmaceutical COX-2-I's may have been overblown, and they may be bad on the heart, if not the pocketbook. More strongly than ever, I now consider turmeric the herbal alternative to those pharmaceutical miracle aspirin, deserving of comparative clinical trials.

I started proposing curried celery with "karkom" as an herbal alternative to celebrex and vioxx, predicting that one or the other would be recalled or relabeled within the decade.

But wait! Some recent entrepreneur has patented our turmeric. One use that may have never been anticipated for my database is to challenge a patent, at least as that patent was so ably described by Karen Dean in *Herbalgram* No. 37, p. 18. My database said that antiprostaglandin, if not antileukotriene, activity was attributed to curcumin as early as 1986. So it angers me a bit that U.S. patent 5,401,777, issued Mar 28, 1995, reportedly "covers the use of the turmeric plant, *Curcuma longa,* or other curcumin-containing plants, or curcumin, or curcumin derivatives, to prevent or treat diseases associated with excessive formations of leukotrienes or prostaglandins. Conventional treatment of these conditions has generally relied on glucocorticoids to inhibit such prostaglandin mediators as leukotrienes. Glucocorticoid hormones carry risks as long-term therapeutics and often have serious side effects" (Dean, 1996). By covering or curbing the use of turmeric or its major bioactive compound for any inflammatory disease, does this 1995 patent make it illegal for me to make my gobo gumbo (heavy with turmeric and gobo) for my advancing arthritis, or bronchitis, or colitis, or dermatitis, or enteritis, or prostatitis? Or any -itis for that matter? The suffix -itis means inflammation! Do Ammon et al. have the right to curb my 20-year curcumin habit? Has the patent bureau been using the library that the FDA uses? Curcumin and/or turmeric (and other Jamu relatives that contain curcumin), have long been touted for most of the diseases mentioned in the patent, alphabetically: chronical bronchial asthma, chronic hepatitis, Crohn's disease, inflammatory bowel disease, psoriasis, and ulcerative colitis. As early as 1981, Duke and Wain (now housed in the database http://www.ars-grin.gov/duke) cited folkuse of turmeric for arthritis, asthma, bronchitis, colic, dermatitis, hepatitis, inflammation. And on that same database you can find dozens of published activities of curcumin, one of turmeric's major constituents.

The inventors claim to have found that at levels as low as 1 uM, curcumin interferes with the inflammatory process. Even my 1985 CRC *Handbook of Medicinal Plants* listed curcumin as antiinflammatory. Ammon et al. also mention that curcumin inhibits cyclooxygenase, and 5- and 12-lipoxygenase products. Two of these three were mentioned in my 1992 *Handbook of Biologically Active Phytochemicals and Their Activities*. Still identifying curcumin as a totally new type of antiinflammatory, the authors suggest its use in topical creams, emulsions or ointments for psoriasis or in inhalants or sprays for chronic bronchial asthma, or in capsules, solutions, suppositories or tablets for chronically inflammatory hepatatis and irritable bowel syndrome. Inhabitants of the Global Herbal Village, unite. Continue to use the folklore you inherited and knew about. Perhaps we should have a tumultuous turmeric revolution and spread the word to all village sufferers of all these diseases to take their turmeric in spite of Ammon's attempt to control via patent the consumption of curcumin. Curcumin and turmeric belong to the Global Herbal Village, not to Ammon et al., nor Steigerwald Arnzmittelwerk nor Germany where it cannot even be grown except under glass (Dean, K. 1996. "Plant Patents." *Herbalgram* 37: p. 18), (Ammon, H. P. T., et al., Tubingen, Germany. "Use of preparations of curcuma plant." U.S. patent 5,401,777, issued Mar 28, 1995. Assigned to Steigerwald Arnzmittelwerk, GmbH, Darmstadt, Germany).

So sickened by such an attempt to have our folk medicines tied up in patents, I devote this chapter to turmeric and arthritis and all those inflammatory diseases which terminate in -itis. I share Ammon et al.'s belief that turmeric and its curcumin is good medicine for inflammatory disease and reiterate my belief that, since there is nothing new (except maybe Crohn's disease, colitis, and 12-lipoxygenase inhibition) in their patent, I hereby proclaim myself free to infringe on that patent using turmeric as herbal and food "farmacy" for any and all my -itises. I could comb various databases and find hundreds of other cyclooxygenase a/o leukotriene a/o lipoxygenase a/o prostaglandin inhibitors. But I don't think I could or should apply for a patent to cover each of their uses for the -itises! I do sincerely thank the patent pirates for calling attention to the value of this great Biblical herb. Here at the **Green Farmacy Garden**, we can still safely enjoy turmeric and curcumin in our foods and farmaceuticals, ignoring pirating patents. (Incidentally the patent was rescinded, I'm told.)

Here's what the draft of *Green Pharmacy* said about turmeric before I was so inspired to take up my poison pen to the Ammon patent. This indicates what I thought about turmeric without consulting Ammon: "Curcumin is used widely in India and Indonesia for inflammation. A pleiotropic cytokine, Tumor Necrosis Factor-alpha (TNF), induces production of beta-Interleukin-1 (Il-1). Together these bad guys cause both acute and chronic inflammation, and have been implicated in atherogenesis, HIV and other autoimmune disorders as well as intracellular parasitic infections. At 5 uM, curcumin inhibits lipopolysaccharide-induced production of TNF and Il-1. Could that be good for arthritics yet bad for oncophobes? (Chan, 1995). Turmeric is close kin to ginger which also shows promise. Turmeric's curcumin inhibits prostaglandin synthesis (but weaker than ibuprofen). At high doses, it stimulates the adrenals leading to the release of endogenous cortisone (Srivastava and Srimal, 1985). Curcumin, a relatively non-toxic neutraceutical, is as antiinflammatory as cortisone or phenylbutazone in acute models, but only half as effective in chronic models (Srimal and Dhawan, 1973). Patacchini et al. (1990) say that both curcumin and capsaicin deplete nerve endings of the neurotransmitter of pain, substance P. In one study, the activity of 1,200 mg/day curcumin was comparable to 300 mg phenylbutazone. But some compounds, perhaps synergic with curcumin, are more potent. In a survey of antiinflammatory phytochemicals, Handa, Chawla, and Sharma (1992) ranked them this way for experimental antiedemic activity: sodium curcuminate > tetrahydrocurcumin > curcumin > phenylbutazone > triethylcurcumin. Still the triethylecurcumin was best at inhibiting granulomatous tissue formation. Two other natural analogues, feruloyl-4-hydroxycinnamoylmethane and bis-(4-hydroxycinnamoyl)-methane were actively antiinflammatory while diacetylcurcumin and ferulic-acid were inactive. (WARNING: Though it has a lower ulcerogenic index than phenylbutazone, curcumin at 2 x ED50, administered for 6 days, can produce ulceration in rats.) (Handa, Chawla, and Sharma, 1992). I now assume that beta-sitosterol occurs in all plants. Handa et al. say that beta-sitosterol from nutsedge has potent antiinflammatory activity against carrageenan and cotton pellet induced edema in rats (comparable to hydrocortisone and phenylbutazone ipr). It showed a wide safety margin with the ipr LD 50 ca 3,000 mg/kg in mice and the minimum ulcerogenic dose 500 mg/kg.

This herb, in concert with *rosemary*, *turmeric*, ginger, holy basil, green tea, *hu zhang*, goldthread, barberry, *oregano*, *skullcap*. The italicized ones are covered in the book, hu zhang as Japanese knotweed, is found in the renowned herbal COX-2-Inhibitor combo called Zyflamend, which I take daily to alleviate Lyme arthralgia, and prevent gout arthralgia. (see inside back cover [hindispeice] for a song about Zyflamend.)

## *Gobo Gumbo*

I don't know but I'll bet you can,
Cancel more than cancer with one
lignan
Turmeric and burdock roots,
Genistein from young bean shoots
Onion, garlic, chile, too,
All of them are good for you.

Guess gobo gumbo's worth a try;
Yes! I'd rather eat than dye
(freudian slip).

## *Curried Gobo Gumbo*

*Tune of Gotta Quit Kickin my Doggie Around*

One querulous quandry was begun
Saffron In Song of Solomon
Still today, this question provokes us
Was it Curcuma, was it Crocus
Or was it suggested a later hour
Saffron was merely the safflower
While one scholar disagrees
Turmeric is the best of these

Curry has much more than taste,
Controlling cyclooxygenase
I've been told, twxit me and you,
It'll inhibit Cox I and II
Sure it's not the Indian soma,
But 'twill inhibit some lymphoma.

Main ingredient in turmeric,
Sure curcumin does the trick.
It's what makes most curry yellow,
Not too hot and not too mellow.
Saffron is yet another yellow spice,
But bears a brazen bigger price.
I prefer the Indian spice,
When I start to steam my rice.

Antileukemic mumbo jumbo,
Added to my gobo gumbo.
If you're gettin' lean and scrawny
Better try my mulligatwany
I'm sure that it will help you some, tho
Not as much as gobo gumbo

Got a lot more going than aroma
It can lead to less lymphoma
Could curried cole slaw be one answer
Help prevent that colon cancer
You might need curcumin's helper
A nice long dose of long black pepper.

Part Five

# Herb A Day...

# Latin America

## Amazon Paradise Lost

(*Can be sung to the tune of John Prine's Paradise*)
Parody by Jim Duke

I praise you John Prine, and I hope you don't mind,
If I mimic your song, to help the forest along.
Even while I am singing, the axeman is swinging,
Choppin' down all that green, to plant corn, rice and bean

Daddy won't you take me to the Primary Forest
By the Amazon River where Paradise lies?
I'm sorry my son, but the forest is gone!
I'll show you some slides, that'll have to suffice!

If you'll not name me, there's something I'll mention
And so folks won't blame me, I'll quote Peter Jenson.
There may be stronger reasons, but I can't think of any,
We're losing the forest "because we're too many"!

Oh axeman unkind, you are blowing my mind!
Camu-camu and brazilnut, they can help fill your gut.
But year after year, once the forest is clear,
You'll have less and less food, and you'll run out of wood.

Never thought ecotours, could be one of the cures;
Taking "green" bucks from gringoes, getting mud on their toes.
If the ecotours thrive, Indian cultures survive,
And the children will strive, to keep tradition alive.

The Jason TV, caught the shaman and me;
The kids could all see, we taught medicinal trees.
Must of been quite a scare, for the Mahuna there;
For them the TV's, like a spaceship to me

So the great spaceship Jason, put down at ACEER
A whole TV station, with mountains of gear
And with crepidation, the natives came near
Fotos , captured spirits, no wonder their fear

No place I'd rather go, than to cruise on the Napo;
Hoping some of my pleas, kinda' help save the trees.
I'd rather you'd find me, sunnin' with the tree huggers
Than back in DC, a runnin' from muggers!

It's quite element'ry, our praise for Al Gentry,
Whose conserving career really helped at ACEER.
The best botany brain, went down with Al's plane,
And although he is gone, we must still carry on

Paud'arco, Sangredrago, Cacao, Uña Gato,
The forest's the best, for your medicine chest.
Aware of these goods, you still chop down the woods.
You'd best spare that tree, cause it might help spare thee.

Momma won't you take me to the Primary Forest
On the Amazon River where Paradise lies?
I'm sorry my daughter, but I don't think I oughta'
We've waited too long, now the forest is gone!

!!! If enough people sing this song, to enough people, maybe the forest will survive…!!!

jim duke, 2007

# Bauhinia (*Bauhinia* spp.)

(Unpublished)

## A Tale of Two Tales

The genus Bauhinia commemorates two early European botanists named Bauhin, not twins, but kin. In mid-July of 1994, I had a revelation as I lay in a hammock up at the ACEER (Amazonian Center for Environmental Education and Research) camp near the Napo River in Amazonian Peru. The ACEER has the longest canopy walkway in the world. Tuesday, my Indian guide, Antonio Montero, had disclosed something that he had never before disclosed to me, even though we had walked by this canopy vine a dozen times before.

It was a striking jungle liana, twisted and contorted as it had successfully extended its canopy of leaves into the canopy of a maze of lianas, trees and epiphytes up above, in one of the most diverse forests in the world (average 300 woody species per hectare). On earlier trips, Antonio referred to it as "escalero del diablo," or devil's ladder or, as other ACEER guides called it, "escalero del mono," or monkey's ladder. Its trunk was used in handicraft, but neither Antonio nor the other guides had mentioned medicinal uses. The fact that they had not included it in their guided tour brochure would suggest that they attributed little utility to the plant.

The late Dr. Alwyn Gentry estimated that 30% of the canopy biomass in the forest was composed of lianas like the Bauhinia. Many such lianas are visible from this canopy walkway, the ninth wonder of the world. With some 13 suspension bridge spans, covering about 1,560 linear feet (480 m), some of the tree towers between the spans are more than 100 feet above the forest floor. At times it is difficult to say which is epiphyte, which is liana, which is strangler, and which is anchor tree, the interwoven canopy being so complex. Some of the vines attain more than 12 inches in diameter down below. I have seen the Bauhinias attain more than 6 inches down in the forest, trailing on up, ladder-like, to the canopy. The beauty of the unique canopy walk is that you see the trees and vines from above, that you have already seen from below on the Medicinal Plant Trail. And you get to see the tops of some of the forest giants that you saw only as columns down below on the trail. On these trees, many leguminous (including one unknown to science before the ACEER was founded), may depend your lives.

But it is the beauty, not the fear, of the canopy, that makes your visit there very much a spiritual experience. So said my daughter, Celia Larsen, when the recording of the Peruvian nightjar, a bird known there as the "potoo," was summoned to the canopy one night by a recording of another "potoo." So say I after looking at the new red leaves of a giant *Inga*, one of the 14 anchor trees, also a legume, in the red sunrise, perforated by the call of the scarlet macaw.

This day, we were accompanied by twelve young ladies here for an educator's workshop in Amazonia. By some quirk of fate (or hormonally stimulated by a recent nick with a machete), one leaf had come out from the usually leafless trunk. The leaf resembled a redbud leaf back home, except divided into two halves, nearly to the base. That results in the twinned leaf, which historically led to its generic name *Bauhinia*. The genus contains some 300 species, mostly tropical and subtropical lianas (woody vines), but including some ornamental trees as well.

When Antonio saw the characteristic leaf, he changed his tune. He said, in Spanish, which I loosely translate here: Ah, Mr. Duke, this is the "icoja" vine, which has a secret use among some of the Amazonian Indians, like the Huitoto Indians. If the woman takes a tea of the trunk at the beginning of her period, and drinks it three times a day throughout her period, it will prevent conception. Further, if she does the same thing for 6 periods, she will be rendered permanently sterile. He added that it was a dangerous and cruel medicine, especially if given to a woman who had never had child.

In Amazonia, a young woman may start her menstrual cycles at around age 10, many women having a child a year thereafter, many of whom die. Such population growth is one of the main enemies of the rainforest, since hungry people with no jobs hack down the forest and barely eke out a living planting corn, rice and beans. But first world consumption is as great an enemy of the rainforest as third world over-population. Some scientists maintain that a North American child will consume 10-30 times as many consumables as an equivalent Amazonian child. If those scientists are correct, that means my two children will consume as much as 20-60 Latin American children, making their own dent in the rainforests which provide some of the money crops of the third world.

The young women in my class, especially one lovely lady just surfacing from her three week honeymoon, asked many questions of Antonio. Was it dangerous? (Yes!) Was it reversible? (No! Not if taken through six periods.) How had he learned this? (From other Indian groups with whom he had worked.) Had he used it in his own family planning? (No!) When I told the class that Antonio had never told me this before, the unanimous question was, why not? Because, without that twinned leaf, he hadn't recognized it as the famous contraceptive that it was. Furthermore, he added it's a dangerous secret you don't share with dangerous people. Although he was turning 50, and I had turned 65, Antonio further, and I fear, astutely speculated that I might out-survive him, and he wanted to share it with someone, apprentice-wise, who might use it wisely. So I really had a deja-vu "Shaman's Apprentice" feeling, about a year after reading Mark Plotkin's new book. I was Antonio's apprentice, a "Shaman's Apprentice." It's clear Antonio was hoping the other guides were not listening carefully, afraid the more educated guides might resent him for telling this tale, true or false. My "ecotourists," in general, are much more intrigued by medicinal plants, especially contraceptives, aphrodisiacs and hallucinogens than they are about edible, dye, firewood, and timber species, to mention just a few of the dozens of categories of useful ethnobotanical plants important in Amazonian lives. The guides have been quick to learn the tales that ecotourists like to hear, and like their North American counterparts (in this case me), sometimes take poetic license to exaggerate. Even though Antonio and I have evolved a mutual trust and friendship in the last three years, I didn't believe this story; I rather believed it was a tall tale he had picked up from others and recited as fact rather than mythical fable. Yes, I doubted my source.

I had Wednesday morning off. Antonio and I first went up to the canopy walk, a series of suspensions bridges (also "escaleros del diablo") through the Amazonian treetops, making labels, and then walked down to take a swim in the Napo, still teeming with dolphins and piranhas. Then he went about his assigned task of trying to boil up some wax from the jungle "waxpaper" (*Calathea* spp.) for a Swiss ski manufacturer to examine. Relaxed, I curled up in my hammock with a new book, *Rainforest Remedies – One Hundred Healing Herbs of Belize* (Arvigo and Balick, 1993 Lotus Press. Twin Lakes, WI). I almost fell out of my hammock when I read what they had to say about another species, from Central American, *Bauhinia herrerae*. I quote the authors:

> "This is an old remedy for birth control among Maya women, now apparently almost forgotten. Prepared from a handful of vine that has been boiled in 3 cups of water for 10 minutes, a cup is consumed before each meal all during the menstrual cycle. It is said that this dose is effective for up to 6 months. Drinking this decoction during 9 menstrual cycles is said to produce irreversible infertility in women."

So unrelated Indians with unrelated languages, almost two thousand miles apart, had evolved, perhaps empirically, pretty much the same sterility story about twin species in the genus *Bauhinia*. I was so excited with the parallelism that I took the new book with me with subsequent classes and read the excerpt above after Antonio recited his story, as we stood there beside the eerie Bauhinia trunk in the shade of the majestic rain forest canopy.

I couldn't wait to get back to my files at the office to see if I had other accounts like this about the Bauhinia. Here are the key medicinal words associated with the many species of Bauhinia in the Duke and Wain database of 1981: alterative, amenorrhea, anasarca, anodyne, antidote, aperitif, asthma, astringent, cataplasm, cholera, colds, convulsions, delirium, depurative, dermatosis, diarrhea, diuretic, dropsy, dysentery, eczema, epilepsy, eyes, fever, flu, headache, hemorrhage, hypertension, intoxication, jaundice, leukemia, liver, lymphoma, obesity, palpitations, piscicide, purgative, rheumatism, rinderpest, scorpions, scrofula, septicemia, skin, snakebite, sore, spasms, splenomegaly, stomach, stomachache, stupefaction, sudorific, swelling, syphilis, tigerbite, toothache, tumors, ulcer, venereal, vermifuge, vulnerary, wasp-stings, wounds, and yaws. Almost everything but sterility or contraceptive. The Duke and Vasquez *Amazonian Ethnobotanical Dictionary* mentions only that the stem of *Bauhinia glabra* was used for pulmonary ailments, that of *Bauhinia guianensis* for kidney diseases, the root as an amebicide and piscicide. Schultes and Raffauf's *The Healing Forest*, an excellent book, also mentions no sterilant activity for the Bauhinia species they cover.

So we have two tales of the twin Bauhinias commemorating the Bauhin boys. Could these two tales save the rainforest? Are there safe sterilants in the rainforest, like those that could conceivably be developed from plants like Bauhinia? Could they not only be taken by the natives to prevent more hungry mouths around the shrinking dinner pot, and at the same time to return, as money crops for the northern pharmaceutical firms, money to better feed those mouths already lining the dinner table? Even Antonio had stated strongly that sterility was a terrible thing to impose upon a young woman, who might change her mind. And the very words abortifacient, contraceptive and sterilant stir up controversy all too readily. I think that a benevolent God would rather see a reasonable number of reasonably well-fed people than too many starving people. That reasonable number of better-fed people, however it be attained, is more liable to appreciate the aesthetics of the tropical rainforests and less likely to destroy the source of tomorrow's medicines for today's and tomorrow's diseases. They are more likely to save today's forest for tomorrow's children to enjoy.

We don't just need dollar signs to magnify the green of the rainforest. Come join me in the rainforest canopy at the ACEER camp someday. You may agree that the aesthetic beauty of this forest is reason enough to save it. Visits to the ACEER forest provides more dollars to protect and expand this forest and to educate the local children to the value of the standing forest. Brazil nuts and rubber alone, over a period of ten years are said to return more dollars to the natives than the same area of forest, irreversibly destroyed and converted to farmland, for a temporary crop of soybeans or beef. If we add forest dyes, handicrafts, housing, medicines, musical instruments, renewable thatch roofs, vitamins, waxes, etc., to the equation, the standing forest becomes more attractive economically, as well as aesthetically.

# Brazil Nut (*Bertholletia excelsa*)

(Unpublished)

## Boosting Brazilnuts: Starting the Third Millennium with Selenium

I changed the millennium at a very inspirational point, the ruins around Machu Picchu, with my wife and fewer than 250 other humans from many continents. How well I remember flying off to the Amazon for a full-lunar solstice, flying over the clouds from Maryland to Peru. Amazon Bolivia, Brazil and Peru are the primary sources of the Brazilnut, *Bertholettia excelsa*, our best dietary source of selenium. And I really think many of us would be better off with a brazilnut a day, maybe even three a day for big 100-kg dudes like me.

I've been an ardent supporter of brazil nut for years. But in 1996 I really started saluting selenium, but not for skin cancers. Patients (n=1312; 18-80 yrs old, mean age 63, with a history of basal and squamous cell carcinomas) were treated with 200 ug oral selenium, the amount found in 2-4 average brazilnuts. Selenium treatment had no significant effect on the rate of skin carcinomas; there were more in the selenium treatment than in the placebo (377 vs 350). BUT the patients treated with selenium had a significant reduction in total cancer mortality (108 vs 119) and in incidence of colorectal, lung and prostate cancer. The authors recommend new studies before making public health recommendations. A ten year advocate of brazil nuts as a health food, good for you and good for the rainforest, I recommend a study giving 2-4- brazil nuts (of average selenium concentration) a day to patients genetically targeted for colorectal (genetically, that's me), lung (environmentally, that's me; heavy smoker for three decades; 90 pack years), and prostate cancer (probability, that's me, if I live 10-20 more years) (Clark et al., 1996).

Lycopene is better absorbed when consumed with fat; may I suggest a late snack of sundried tomatoes and/or tomato juice and three brazil nuts, the latter providing not only the fat but that 210 ug selenium hinted to prevent prostate cancer.

Nutritional Reporter Jack Challem (1999) summarized some of the potential benefits of selenium, once considered toxic, now clearly and correctly considered essential. In so doing, Jack introduced me to a new syndrome, acronym SIRS (Systemic Inflammatory Response Syndrome) so I'll cover that first. (It sounds suggestive of septic shock syndrome to me.) This systemic septic syndrome is a common cause of death in patients who are critically ill with blood infections. SIRS generates an uncommon amount of free radicals, some of which are battling the germs but others may damage body organs. Munich scientists, Angswurm et al. (1999) treated 21 SIRS patients with megadoses (535 ug selenium selenite daily), decreasing dosage daily over more than two weeks, another 21 with 35 ug. Both groups, entering with low levels of glutathione peroxidase, were monitored for clinical symptoms – kidney problems, respiratory problems, even death. Those on high dose experienced rapid return of glutathione peroxidase (within 3 days). Only one third of the megadose patients died, two thirds improving clinically compared to half of those (8 average brazilnuts would provide 535 ug selenium, ½ of an average brazilnut provides 35 ug).

Fifteen to twenty percent of Taiwanese carry the hepatitis B virus. Some 80% of liver cancers there are attributed to chronic hepatitis B and C infections. Yu et al. (1999) found that high levels of selenium in the blood were associated with lower risk for liver cancer (~ 40-80% reduction). Onions and garlic are also good sources of selenium, and brazil nuts are rare in Taiwan. But maybe they should import more brazil nuts, throwing some economic support behind the rainforest and its conservation.

Since overpopulation contributes to the dimunition of the rainforest, I'm less eager to report this one, but, selenium deficiency can contribute to male infertility, acording to a German Italian team (Ursini et al., 1999). Glutathione peroxidase is again involved. A seleniferous protein, phospholipid hydroperoxide glutathione peroxidase (PHGPx), produced profusely in developing sperm, seems to protect against free radical damage to DNA. Selenium is actually an essential building material for human sperm, the PHGPx maintaining the physical integrity of the sperm.

That's a capsular look at what Challem summarized in his excellent paper. There are other news nuggets though that make the brazilnut look like the nut of the millennium.

According to Finley and Penland (1998) selenium can apparently boost the mood and mental clarity. Subjects taking high selenium diets reported higher levels of composure, confidence, and mental clarity. That's in a study of 20 male volunteers taking high or low selenium diets for 105 days (Finley and Penland, 1998).

# Cacao (*Theobroma cacao*)

*The Business of Herbs* 12(6):12-13, January/February, 1995

## Cacao - My funky valentine

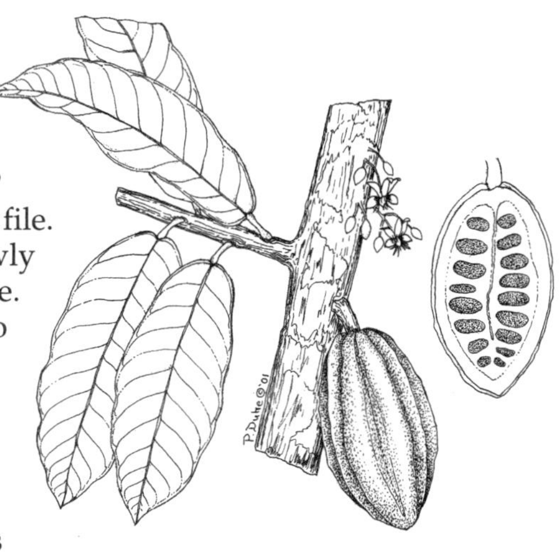


Charles Osgood (*The Osgood File*, Oct. 22, 1993) stated it best, speaking of it as belonging to his BOOAP (blown out of all proportion) file. He was responding to the newly breaking story on aminophylline. In studies of a cream applied to one thigh of each of several women fearing obesity, scientists found (and patented) a lipolytic activity that took 0.5-1.5 inches off the experimental cellulytic thigh (after five weeks), as compared to the control thigh.

I had received a fax the day before from a Louisiana associate, under the title "Discovery Offers Dieters a Leg Up" (*Baton Rouge Advocate*, Oct. 21, 1993). My associate had written onto the fax: "Jim, think how many suggestion-prone women would attend a seminar or workshop on this one!" But I do have reason to believe that if aminophylline rubbed onto the thighs will cause fat to disappear, so would my caffeinated cocoa butter with theobromine and theophylline. [I'd bet they'd lose more weight if the women had their thighs massaged by their "significant other" with cocoa butter. Yes, sometimes massage is good foreplay leading to thermogenic sex.}

Aminophylline is not exactly a natural product. According to my Merck Index, 11th Ed., aminophylline is a semi-natural product, containing one ingredient obtainable from the American rainforest, theophylline (three molecules), compounded with two molecules of synthetic ethylene-diamine. Described as a bronchodilator, it is used for asthma in humans. In veterinary medicine, it is described as a smooth-muscle relaxant, used as a diuretic "in dogs with congestive heart failure" and for "heaves in horses." (LD50 = 540 mg/kg orally in mice, making it about one third as toxic, orally, as caffeine, to which it is related.)

Thus aminophylline is a semisynthetic compound composed of the natural compound theophylline and the synthetic solvent diethylene-amine (LD50 = 1,160 orally in rats, even less toxic than the natural component). Drs. George Bray and Frank Greenway, holders of the patent on the anti-fat cream, say that aminophylline is the active ingredient.

Looking in my *CRC Handbook of Biologically Active Compounds and Their Activities* (CRC, 1992), I see several uses reported for aminophylline: anorexic (appetite suppressing), antianginal (reducing pain spasms), anti-apneic (asphyxia- or sleep-apnea-preventing), antiasthmatic, antibronchitic, anti-emphysemic, antihistaminic, antispasmodic, bronchodilator (opening the windpipe), bronchorelaxant, deliriant, diuretic, myocardiostimulant (stimulating the heart muscle), and myorelaxant (muscle relaxing). Its use in asthma and bronchitis seems to be by intravenous injection.

Looking to the natural theophylline, from our Amazonian cacao tree (*Theobroma cacao*), source of the chocolate we consume so avidly, I see that theophylline is used orally for asthma, at levels of 5 milligrams per kilogram body weight. That means for me, at 100 kg, I would need some 500 mg theophylline for a therapeutic antiasthmatic dose. Incidentally, its LD50 in mice is 600 mg/kg. It shares many of the activities with the aminophylline. Then there's the more toxic compound, theobromine, LD50 = 200 mg/kg orally in cats, almost as toxic as caffeine. It is also found in our cacao, along with the anorexic caffeine (LD50 = 192 mg/kg orally in rats).

Some of these xanthines (as caffeine, theobromine, and theophylline are called) are orally anorexic. This suggests that they can curb the appetite, but that's not going to take the fat off the thighs. There's even speculation that some xanthines speed up catabolism, if taken orally, which could also lead to weight loss, but not by topical application to the thighs. If the appetite-curbing potential of the xanthines is real, and if it were put there to protect the chocolate beans from insectivorous predators, it stands to reason that the various xanthines are more likely to be synergic than antagonistic in their properties.

## Synergic activities?

If my speculation is correct, a mixture or cream containing all three xanthines might be expected to be synergically more active than an equivalent amount of any one of the xanthines. Martindale's *Extra Pharamacopoeia*, 29th Ed., 1989, leads us to believe that their activities are at least additive, if not synergic: "The bronchodilator and toxic effects of theophylline or aminophylline and sympathomimetics or other xanthines are additive… Theophylline crosses the placenta; it also enters breast milk… Theophylline was significantly more effective than placebo in relieving headache."

There are good reasons for working with theophylline instead of aminophylline. "In the past 20 years, 31% of adverse reactions to aminophylline reported to the Committee on Safety of Medicines were of cutaneous or allergic origin compared with 12% with theophylline." (Lancet as quoted in Martindale, 1989). "Aminophylline…applied topically produces both immediate and hypersensitivity reactions."

Flat-chested males, if not females, may be interested in another report quoted in Martindale: "Gynaecomastia occurred in a 61-year-old man after one to two months of oral theophylline therapy." **BUT NOTE:** Martindale also reports many deaths due to aminophylline and/or theophylline, taken improperly. Oral treatment with theophylline can raise the blood sugar. "Theophylline or aminophylline should be given with caution to patients with peptic ulceration, hyperthyroidism, hypertension, cardiac arrhythmias, or other cardiovascular disease."

Also from Martindale: "It was reported that theobromine passed into the breast milk of 6 nursing mothers who had eaten 4 ounces of chocolate containing about 240 mg of theobromine." A cup of cocoa may contain 200 mg. But for asthma it takes oral doses of 10 mg/kg theobromine, 5 mg/kg theophylline, which translates to about 16 ounces of chocolate or five cups of cocoa to get the 1,000 mg needed by a 100-kg person.

I'm hinting that our rain-forest chocolate contains at least three xanthine alkaloids: caffeine, theobromine, and theophylline. Chocolate "beans" can contain 1,800-7,700 parts per million (ppm) caffeine, 13,000-20,000 ppm theobromine, and 3,250-4,750 ppm theophylline, on a dry-weight basis. I know all this because of some research I did at the instance of a man who wanted me to help him develop a low-fat chocolate. I told him that chocolate purchasers usually paid a premium for high-fat chocolate, and that the fat from that chocolate was squeezed out to make cocoa butter, much of which is made into suppositories, since cocoa butter melts very close to the normal human body temperature. How's that for an intimate connection with the rain forest?

I suspect, but cannot prove, that vigorous massage with cocoa butter, suffused with caffeine, theobromine, and theophylline, all natural Amazonian products from the cacao tree, *Theobroma* (which means "food [[or beverage]] of the gods"), of one obese thigh might do as well as the BOOAP cream. I will propose to my low-fat sponsor that he provide test materials and we round up 20-30 Amazonian ecotourists who voluntarily wish to massage one of their thighs with food-grade cocoa butter thrice daily, measuring each day to see if there is any significant loss of fat.

[[There may be yet another chemical rationale! PEA, or phenylethylamine, is yet another CNS-stimulant. It may release endorphins while potentiating dopamine, which is known to be involved with sexual arousal, and may even induce priapism as a side effect. Sex is one of the best of thermogenic exercises, I'm told. Chocolate eaters, like couples in love, may have more PEA on their mind and in their brain, especially during orgasm. Happy Valentine.]]

Bicycle instead? Couch potatoes might find that bicycle riding improves their thighs, as did I. In Washington, D.C., there are two and a half hours of TV news on a weekday evening. For fun I decided to ride my stationary bike, only during the commercials. But during just one half-hour segment, and only during commercials, I rode 5.5 miles, according to my odometer. (Which also tells me I ride about a mile during a two minute commercial, which tells me my evening news is somewhere between 15 and 20 percent commercials.)

Not quite so recently, Dan Mowrey, *The Scientific Validation of Herbal Medicine* (Cormorant Books, 1986), notes that psyllium or plantain has been used to treat obesity. Scientists in Italy, Russia, and elsewhere showed that they reduce the intestinal absorption of lipids. "Plantain before meals causes a definite decrease in triglycerides and beta cholesterol (the bad guys) with a proportional increase of serum levels of alpha cholesterol (the good guy)." Mowrey suggests that plantain protects against obesity, type II diabetes, and atherosclerosis. Three grams administered a half hour before meals, twice daily, with water, to dieting Italian females averaging 60 percent overweight, reduced their weight more than diet alone. (Throwing in exercise and catabolic herbs, such as capsicum and ginger, could have helped even more.) Russians have found that the lowering of body weight and cholesterol levels relates not only to the seed's mucilage but also to polyphenols in the leaves. As Mowrey summarizes: "It appears that plantain produces weight loss by limiting calorific intake, due to its appetite-satiating effect, and by reduced intestinal absorption of lipids."

[[Can't you see a couch potatoess riding her stationary bike, eating her caffeinated Metamucil™, or eating her plantain bran flakes, eating her chocolate with its CNS-stimulants, with her thighs coated with cocoa butter? I'll bet her thighs will improve better on this regime than on just aminophylline! Up with synergy! Down with cottage-cheese cellulite!!]]

One LD50 is a measure of how toxic a substance is. Specifically, it is the dosage per kilogram of body weight required to kill 50 percent of a group of experimental animals. In humans, it is useful to the extent that a substance with a higher LD50 is probably less toxic than one with a lower number, in about that proportion.

# Camu Camu (*Myrciaria dubia*)

*The Business of Herbs* 10(3):12-13. July/August, 1992

Starting out on a rainy, cold May morning, nibbling on my second carrot as I drove to work in the predawn quiet, I was pleased to hear (on *WTOP News*) more good vitamin-C news. The conclusions from the California story: 300 to 400 mg vitamin C a day could add six years to a man's life, one year to a woman's. Sexist? No. Women already have a life span of seven more years than the male of the species. Could camu-camu equalize life expectancies?

Camu-camu is a fascinating small tree I encountered on my eco-tours to Amazonian Peru-one of more than 200 Amazonian species of trees with edible fruits! Without getting into the old argument about the many definitions of herbs, I'll confess to stretching the definition, or using one of the broader definitions: (1) a plant of culinary or medicinal importance; (2) a useful plant.

Clearly it is a shrub or small tree of the largely tropical myrtle family (Myrtaceae). More familiar to us among the tropical fruits of the myrtle family would be the guava, less familiar: feijoa, grumichama, jaboticaba, jambolan, java "apple," malay "apple," rose "apple," rumberry, surinam "cherry" and water "apple," all delightfully covered in Julia Morton's *Fruits of Warm Climates* (Creative Resources Systems, Inc., Box 890, Winterville, NC 28590). I put the words apple and cherry in quotes because true apples and cherries belong to the rose family (Rosaceae), not the myrtle family.

## Juice power?

Just last month, a controversial new book, *The Juiceman's Power of Juicing* (Kordich, J., William Morrow and Company, New York) made the *New York Times* best-seller list. My phone rang off the hook, calls from reviewers wanting to criticize the book scientifically, writers from the *New York Times*, *Washington Times* and *Consumer Reports* and *20:20*, the TV program. They couldn't believe the juiceman's report that juices contained 95% of the nutrients in the whole fruit. I can't either!

Still, after searching the files, I didn't find much hard evidence to support or refute his claim. In *Ag Handbook* 8-9 I did find data on 15 fruits and juices (not necessarily fresh juices; vitamins do tend to deteriorate rapidly, especially without antioxidants). Nowhere did I find comparisons of freshly squeezed juice and the mash (dregs, residue) left after juice expression. The average fruit juices reported in the *Ag Handbook* were lower in all nutrients. Juices were higher in water and about equal in salt (perhaps due to fortification). The whole fruits averaged a little richer in vitamin C, about twice as rich in beta-carotene and nearly 10 times as rich in tocopherol (vitamin E).

## Juice studies to be done

Wanting to give the juiceman the benefit of the doubt, I have arranged for studies of freshly expressed juice and the mash, for these important antioxidant vitamins. Stay tuned. The herb purslane will be one of the items we juice and analyze.

Meanwhile, back in camu-camu country, they are selling the camu-camu as a delicious health beverage. I enjoyed it at the Iquitos airport. Especially tasty after a five-hour boat ride on the Amazonian, waiting for the flight back to Miami. This isn't news. Julia Morton reported in her book:

> "Half-ripe fruits have been found to contain 1,950 to 2,700 mg of ascorbic acid per 100 g edible portions, values comparable to the high ranges of the Barbados cherry ...These findings led to a certain amount of exploitation of the fruit, which must be harvested by boat. There is a trial plot at Manaus, Brazil, and some experimental plantings in Peru and the juice is frozen or bottled and exported to the United States for the production of `vitamin C' tablets for the `health food' market. In plantations, in non-flooded land a single plant may bear 400 to 500 fruits. On flooded lands, the per plant harvest has been 1,000 fruits."

[[Thus, the camu-camu has 10 to 20 times more vitamin C than the average fruit. Let's take a conservative 2,200 mg vitamin C per hundred grams edible portion and estimate 2,000 mg remains per 100 g (half cup) juice. Back to the California study. If 400 mg vitamin C will lengthen my life by six years and if my camu-camu or its juice contains 2,000 mg vitamin C [[In 2006, I think that's high, but I still think of camu camu as the leading edible source of vitamin C]]. It wouldn't take many camu camu fruits to give me the 400 mg to give me that extra six years. At age 76, and having seen my mother and grandmother in their last 10 years, often in pain and near blindness, I'm not sure how many more years I want. But the camu camu can help ease pain and prevent maculitis]].

## Sensationalists say...

Sensationalists, and I won't call the juiceman a sensationalist, because he didn't cover the camu-camu, might leave out a point or two and translate the above to: "Peruvian camu-camu can extend life by six years, according to California studies!" In these days of green consumerism (buying rain-forest products to help preserve the rain forest), I expect there could be a big market for camu-camu products. I don't think either the FDA or the USDA would condone marketing camu-camu as a life extender, though.

In "Mint Teas and the Antioxidant Index" (Duke, J. A. *Trends in Food Science and Technology*, May 1992), I suggested the importance of antioxidants (stressing vitamins A, C and E and selenium) in preventing all sorts of diseases. I failed to mention one important antioxidant, glutathione, in that paper. Hence I refer here to a connection between glutathione and vitamin C, and I quote the USDA who don't encourage their scientists to make health claims for various vitamins and nutrients. According to USDA's *ARS Quarterly Report* (Jan-Mar, 1992, p. 15), "glutathione fell 50 percent when the men consumed less than one-third the RDA (Vitamin C RDA is 60 mg.). Glutathione helps guard against heart disease, cancer and inflammatory diseases such as arthritis...low intake of vitamin C weakens the body's disease defenses...lowering glutathione is another path by which a low-C regimen impairs defenses."

That report tells me that (under these experimental conditions) 40 mg vitamin C might double levels of glutathione. A 100-g serving of camu-camu would contain 2,000 mg vitamin C. Would our FDA object if we sold camu-camu juice claiming that it contains 50 times more ascorbic acid than the amount the USDA says doubles levels of glutathione, which "may help guard against heart disease, cancer and inflammatory diseases such as arthritis." It could take less than an ounce of good camu camu to provide the RDA for vitamin C.

Ironically, I suppose, our federal authorities today would probably confiscate camu-camu if someone here were marketing it, claiming that it would prevent scurvy. Clearly it would. But it has not been proven. It has only been proven that ascorbic acid (vitamin C) will prevent scurvy. It would be "sensationalism" to say that camu-camu could do any of the dozens of things ascorbic acid has been proven to do. Not all North Americans, much less Latin Americans, can afford a doctor or a prescription drug, but many can afford a homegrown camu-camu. Take a camu-camu and thank the rain forest in the morning!

# Capsicum (*Capsicum* spp.)

*The Business of Herbs* 9(6):10-11, January/February, 1992

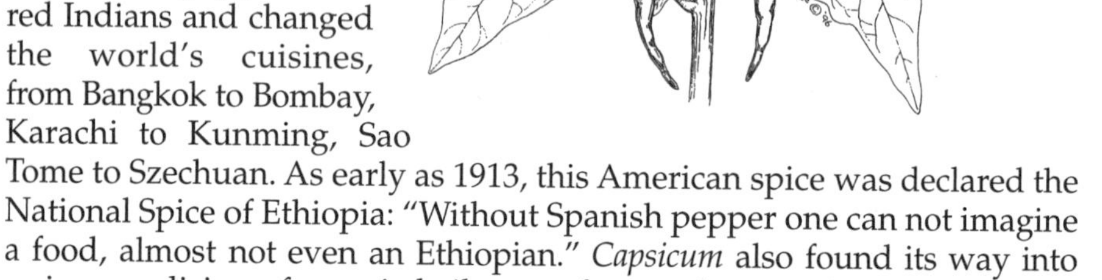

It seems more than appropriate for *The Business of Herbs* to celebrate the New Year, 1992, covering capsicum, one of Columbus' more valuable discoveries. *Capsicum* is the genus to which belong such valuable foods and spices as bell pepper, cayenne, chili, hot pepper, paprika and tabasco. When he set sail, Columbus was seeking black peppers and black Indians. Instead he found red peppers and red Indians and changed the world's cuisines, from Bangkok to Bombay, Karachi to Kunming, Sao Tome to Szechuan. As early as 1913, this American spice was declared the National Spice of Ethiopia: "Without Spanish pepper one can not imagine a food, almost not even an Ethiopian." *Capsicum* also found its way into serious medicines, for varied ailments, from arthritis to herpes.

If capsicum is really good for cataracts and colds and for the hangover and the heart, as many people claim, the old "Bloody Mary" or better yet the nonalcoholic "Virgin Mary" might be a great way to usher in the New Year. Richer in vitamin C (and storing better) than citrus, hot peppers, like limes, could have prevented scurvy among early limeys on long voyages away from fresh food.

## What's your CAI?

Capsicum is a good source not only of vitamin C but vitamin A (hot peppers may contain two to 16 times more vitamin A or its precursor, beta-carotene, than cool peppers) and vitamin E (alpha-tocopherol). Now these are the big actors in the new Cumulative Antioxidant Index (CAI) proposed by Dr. Duthie of the Rowett Research Institute in Scotland:

Eat a brazil nut (a good source of selenium) or two with your Virgin Mary, and you will dramatically improve your CAI. And if Duthie is right, the higher your CAI, the lower your chances of succumbing to America's most lethal disease, heart disease. And I hope that Bruce Ames, and the health food magazines for the last decade or so, are right, that high CAI will also help protect from the number-two killer, cancer. Bruce Ames specifically named the items on the top half of the CAI "formula"

Beta-carotene + Vitamin C + Vitamin E + Selenium

$$CAI = \frac{A+C = E+Se}{\text{Cholesterol}}$$

as cancer preventers.

You've probably heard of the NCI's new 20.5-million-dollar Designer Food Program, a cancer-preventive program headed by [[the late]] Dr. "Herb" Pierson. At last, the National Cancer Institute is taking a preventive stance against cancer. The Designer Food Program is looking at many herbs I advocated for cancer prevention in "Quack Salad" (*Natural Healing*, 1976). Capsicum was suggested for both quack salad and quack salad dressing with garlic and lemon juice (with their own cancer-preventive compounds).

## Anti-ulcer activity

Ironically, hot compounds, once thought to cause ulcers, have more recently shown anti-ulcer activity. These hot compounds, capsaicin in hot peppers, sulfides in garlic, gingerols in ginger, isothiocyanates in mustards and onions, may offer some cancer-preventive activities as well.

Due to low incidence of stomach cancer in Latin America where "aji" (*Capsicum* spp.) has long been the most important spice, some speculate that capsicum might prevent stomach cancer. "Ajo" or *Allium sativum* (garlic) may be the second most important spice in Latin cuisine. Witness the Latin saying: "Sin ajo, no hay cocina," without garlic there is no kitchen. That pepper-eating West Indians and Africans have low incidences of anorexia, piles, varicose veins, liver and blood-vessel ailments also suggests that pepper might help prevent such ailments.

There are many cancer-preventive or anti-tumor compounds in peppers, most of which are rather ubiquitous. We are most concerned with the principal active ingredient, capsaicin, the major hot constituent as well.

P. Gannet's work at the Eppley Institute shows that capsaicin helps to neutralize the mutagenic effects of dimethylnitrosamine. If you enjoy smoky sausages or barbecue, remember that the hotter it is with capsaicins, the less likely are the nitrosamines to induce cancer. Capsaicin also acts as an antioxidant, capable of neutralizing free radicals: "Spices in general have been recognized to have antioxidant activity... Hot red pepper fruits also show some antioxidant activity. However, in comparison to the antioxidant activity of rosemary and sage, the activity of Capsicum fruit is low..." (Suzuki and Iwai, 1984).

## Pain killer

Used in South America as an anodyne or painkiller for centuries, ground peppers have yielded forth their capsaicin to therapeutic preparations like

Axsaine and Zostrix. Twenty percent of people who have shingles later suffer from post-herpetic neuralgia. Seventy-five percent of those report pain reduction using capsaicin-containing creams. Capsaicin is being studied for its potential to deplete substance P, a normal body chemical that transmits pain messages from the skin. Capsaicin inhibits substance P production where it is applied.

Sufferers of cluster headaches (about 1% of the population) experienced dramatic relief when diluted capsaicin was applied to the nostril on the side where the cluster headache occurred. Further, capsaicin ointment prevented cluster headache when applied to the temples.

## Diet and mood enhancer

Obese Americans can speed up the burning of calories by spicing up their foods with hot pepper. One study reported in Woman's Day (1989) showed that volunteers who ate pepper-laden foods burned up to 76 more calories in a three-hour period than controls. *Capsicum* might be classified as a catabolic herb, speeding the metabolism.

Rats fed capsaicin at levels equivalent to Thai pepper consumption had fewer fat droplets in epithelial absorption cells, indicating that capsaicin reduces fat absorption (Suzuki and Iwai, 1984). Hot pepper on the "good ole" North Carolina barbecue might decrease the amount of that fat you'll absorb, if we can translate data on Thai rats to North Carolina humans.

Woman's Day also reported that peppers may be a "feel-good" food. They're believed to trigger the production of a natural morphine in the body that makes you feel good all over, sort of like the runner's high, triggered by the release of endorphins, or the pain relief of acupuncture which also triggers the release of endorphins.

How about hot peppers for the hot foot? About 20% of diabetics suffer from burning sensations in the hands and feet, a condition falling under the umbrella, diabetic neuropathy. Two thirds of such patients with burning feet are relieved with capsaicin.

## Support preventive medicine

As you can see, much of the research on capsaicin, like so many other herbal medicines, focuses on prevention rather than cure of diseases. More than half the people in the world, including increasingly more Americans, cannot afford conventional prescription drugs. Should the world not embrace the holistic trend towards preventive medicines? Investments in preventive medicine should pay much greater dividends for the world's poor than investments in prescription cures. Unfortunately, pharmaceutical firms are more interested in treating than preventing disease. Therefore more research dollars will go into those expensive prescription "cures" (which in many cases add a few miserable days to a miserable life without really curing anything) than into disease prevention.

We really must urge our National Institutes of Health to support preventive research, since it's counterproductive to the pharmaceutical industry's aims to support it. Write your congressperson. Ask if preventive medicine wouldn't produce better returns for the increasing tax dollars from the shrinking American paycheck than the illusive quest for cures? Ask her or him to document the answer. Ask her or him to support legislation to insure that as much taxpayer money goes into preventive as into curative research. If the congressperson concludes that preventive research is one, two, 10 or even 100 times more useful to lower- and middle-class Americans (by far the majority), half of whom cannot afford the expensive cures, insist that she or he pledges that ratio of support to preventive medicines.

If you believe as do I that more dollars should go to preventive than to curative research, let this be your New Year's pledge: "I pledge to write to my congressperson this year urging that more dollars go to preventive than to curative research and urging that pharmaceutical firms be required to compare any new synthetic or semisynthetic drug, not only with a placebo but also with a "third arm," one of the better of the herbal or food farmacy alternatives." [[I even addressed Capitol Hill on this third arm proposition last year.]]

HAPPY NEW YEAR!!!!

## Cat's Claw, "Uña de Gato" (*Uncaria tomentosa*)

(Unpublished)

Back in 1992 I told you about my problems with the nomenclature of some of the Peruvian medicinals and how I mask my ignorance by using the abbreviation "spp." *Uncaria*, a genus of thorn-bearing lianas, is very confusing as to species identification. Many, if not most, woody genera in the tropics are taxonomically confusing. Being lazy, I too often hide behind the "spp." concept, which means I don't know exactly what species is involved.

Species of *Uncaria* are called "uña de gato" (which translates as "cat's claw") in Spanish America. Like feverfew, which we all know, but which travels under as many as five scientific names, most rural Amazonians know what "uña de gato" is, but probably never heard of its generic name *Uncaria*. I'll mention a few specific names below, but we can't be positive that the authors of the popular books, not even the botanists, knew which species they were dealing with. The Peruvian cat's claw is probably more than one species. And each salesperson will say his or hers is the only authentic material that really works.

But let's take a trip through the "uña de gato" info in the books I take with me to Amazonian Peru. Working Amazonian Peru is Rodolfo Vasquez Martinez, assistant curator at the Missouri Botanical Garden (a position I held back in ~ 1963), and long an understudy to the late Dr. Al Gentry, Missouri Botanical Garden's powerhouse Latin-American taxonomist. Between tears at the memorial services for Gentry, we heard him eulogized and praised for having taught so many Latin-America botanists and inspired them to generate internal conservation movements to save their rain forests. I even dedicted our *Amazonian Ethnobotanical Dictionary* to him and remember him in my rainforest parody.

Rodolfo is living testimony of the great teaching abilities of Al Gentry and has contributed and will continue to contribute to conservation efforts in Amazonian Peru. He and I published it in 1994, our *Amazonian Ethnobotanical Dictionary*. All royalties from its sales were contracted to revert to the Amazonian Center for Environmental Education and Research (ACEER). This book, like its authors, Rodolfo and yours truly, is dedicated to the conservation a 250,000-acre ACEER Forest Preserve, where a hectare of land has 300 woody species, one of them being the woody vine *Uncaria guianensis*, the trunk of which can be a foot in diameter. You don't find many, if any, grapevines that big!

Here I translate what Rodolfo has to say about what he lists as "uña de gato," "uña de gavilan," "garabato," and "paraguayo" under the scientific name *Uncaria guianensis* (Aubl.) Gmel.: "Considered a remedy for cancer of the female urinary tract; also used for gastritis, rheumatism, and cirrhosis. The `Boras' use it for gonorrhea."

## Amazing attributes

In her latest edition, Nicole Maxwell (1990) has added a lot of fascinating information which I think reflects the exciting potential of the cat's claw. She informs us that Sidney McDaniel had submitted samples of "uña de gato" to the NIH cancer screen. (So did I.) "Dr. Monroe Wall, working on the 'uña de gato,' reported that they were finding some very encouraging tumor-inhibiting properties in it when the Reagan administration came into office and canceled the program." (That's when my five-year formal alliance with the NCI program terminated.) Nicole even makes some phytogeographic observations. "*Uncaria tomentosa* is a woody vine which grows in the foothills, chiefly at altitudes between 700 or 800 and 2,500 meters. A very similar lowland species, known by the same set of local names, is *Uncaria guianensis*; it is abundant in lower altitudes of the Peruvian Amazon. It was *U. tomentosa* that cured Mario Arguellas, but *U. guianensis* that Dr. Wall studied. It appears that the two species are as nearly identical in medicinal properties as they are in appearance. Some time later I learned that a man whose lung cancer was cured by "uña de gato" had, after continuing dosage, found that he could walk normally and even climb stairs, even though he had been badly crippled by arthritis. Then I got good evidence of its working wonders for diabetics. Could it be that this plant might perhaps be giving a tremendous boost to the immune system? I couldn't think of any other way of examining the diversity of its effects, its ability to eliminate so many problems that, as far as my limited knowledge let me guess, appeared to have only one thing in common: they were all degenerative diseases...Peter Rachau, who has been with the Urarina tribe...has more accounts of uña de gato's curing tumors, which may or may not have been malignant, in members of that tribe... An Italian doctor, Giaccarino Paolo Francesco, gave a long list of ailments for which it is used... One mechanism of its working is that it activates T-lymphocytes and macrophages...it normalizes the immunoglobins... Another report stated that no toxicity had been found, even with such massive doses as one gram of evaporated essence of the active principle per kilo of body weight... Uña de gato sometimes turns gray hair back to its original color."

If it was a cat, it would have scratched us: [[After writing this cat's claw HAD, the ACEER group, the Explorama Lodges of Peru, and indigenous Antonio Montero and I, "gringo brujo descalzo" alias "huacrapona," established the ReNuPeRu Garden near the ExplorNapo Lodge off the Sucusari, a tributary of the Napo, above the confluence of the Napo and the Amazon, in Loreto Peru. We labelled or transplanted specimens of nearly 300 medicinal species into the garden to teach the ecotourists who joined us on our Amercian Botanical Council ecotours into the ReNuPeRu Garden. We didn't have to transplant the *Uncaria guianensis,* it was abundant right there, with its strongly recurved spines. Eagle-eyed Rodolfo on a revisit to the garden spotted also *Uncaria tomentosa,* with its barely arcuate thorns. To both our surprise, we realized that both species had coexisted right there in our ReNuPeRu garden.

## Chemical components

I too will take the generic approach and list just a few chemicals already reported from one or another species of *Uncaria.* I report here only those for which I found published biological activities, many more of which are reported and more fully explained in Duke, 1992, CRC *Handbook of Biologically Active Phytochemicals and Their Bioactivities* and Duke, 1992, CRC *Handbook of Phytochemical Constituents in GRAS Herbs.*

All the above was written before I heard from one of four American importers. He, too, had gotten drawn into the confusion over the various species of "uña de gato" and *Uncaria.* He was kind enough to send me a generous sample, the label of which asserts that the contents are *Uncaria tomentosa,* and concludes with the following words: "En la lucha contra el SIDA, se la obtenido sorprendentes beneficios en Europa." (In the AIDS war, this has shown surprising benefits in Europe.) Apparently it was *U. tomentosa* that Wagner et al. studied, finding four phagocytotic enhancers.

Last year green tea (*Camellia*) got a lot of favorable press for the prevention of cancer. "Uña de gato" may have many of the same compounds for which the tea received all the praise. Ellagic acid from strawberries got a lot of similar good press. There is frenetic activity among optimists looking for alternative crops to "coca," source of cocaine. "Uña de gato" could be one agroforestry alternative, appealing to green consumerism. It should be investigated carefully. If it will turn grey hair black, or turn back the ravages of cancer and/or AIDS, for that matter, any of our degenerative diseases, it is worth a few million dollars, if carefully marketed to the North Americans. Lamentably, it will take more than a few million dollars to alleviate the cocaine problem. [[Native Americans have no problem with chewing the coca leaves, nor do gringoes. But when the "magic silver bullet" mentality prevails, isolating the much more active of several alkaloids, cocaine, the gringo can easily get hooked. Some people nearly worship isolation of phytochemicals or synthesis of analogues is the ultimate achievement of the pharmaceutical industry. Even now at age 76, I think the best things in life are all but free. And I refer to herbal medicines, many of which I have discussed in my herb a day columns. "Magic silver bullets" can be lethal and pharmaceuticals do kill more than 100,000 North Americans a year, taken as prescribed. The herbal shotgun is not so dangerous, ask Vice Presdient Cheney, not "VP Quail." Loaded with hundreds of gentle biologically active, often synergic phytochemicals, long known to your genes, the "herbal shotgun" presents an array of genetically familiar chemicals in a gentle medicinal mix, leaving your body to select those medicines it needs most. Your body has coevolved with natural chemicals for millennia (if you are of the creationist's cloth) or millions of years (if you are of evolutionary beliefs). Your homeostatic body, trying to attain normality, knows better than your acupuncturist, allopath, botanical healer, chiropractor, guru, gynecologist, herbalist, homeopath, nutritionist, orthopedist, osteopath, pharmacist, physician, podiatrist, psychiatrist, shaman, etc. what chemicals you need. Present your body their herbal menu called the herbal shotgun. Let it select the entrees' it needs.]]

# Chiriq sanango (*Brunfelsia grandiflora*)

(Unpublished)

## Brunfelsia: the Bad Trip

It's morning again, Monday morning, three days after I took my shaman's suggested dose of *Brunfelsia*, the powerful herb that he calls "chiriq sanango." Last night was bad-diarrhea, cold sweats, bad dreams – but I did sleep off and on. Why had I taken this draught?

I had just finished my 27th one-week ecotour to Peru, accompanied by my healer, sometimes called shaman, Antonio Montero Pisco. He had, for the first time, introduced a numerical classification of the energy of his herbs. For example, he said the chiriq sanango was the most potent of the herbs, with 50% energy. That, in his energetic classification, makes it 10 times more powerful (energetic) than the famous hallucinogen, ayahuasca, which he estimated to have an energy of only 5%. Other adjuvants used in his ayahuasca brew were closer to ayahuasca in power: 5 to 20%.

Remember that he also sees spirits in the plants, which spirits I tend to liken to the elusive molecular models I see as the energy of the plant. I was surprised that the chiriq sanango was viewed as the most powerful, but did remember from earlier descriptions he had given me that it would make you cold (give you chills) and that you needed to bathe periodically. But Friday morning he brought me his jug of chiriq sanango, asked me my weight, and poured me one-third of a drinking glass of the hydro-alcoholic extract, possibly because he had heard me lamenting my degenerative osteoarthritis – or possibly just to convince me of the power of the plant. I told him to be careful because I still had another class to teach and had to make a short speech at the closing ceremonies. He smiled and said what roughly translates to "don't worry, you're in good hands." He did make the interesting observation that I would feel some old bone aches I hadn't felt in a while. In other words, this would bring out some dormant bone problems.

So, a half hour before breakfast, I drank the equivalent of three shots of the extract. Some of the workers smiled knowingly as I took this big dose, claiming that it was an excellent regenerative tonic. Antonio told me I'd feel the energy soon. He was right. Within 15 minutes I had an impressive anesthetic tingling in my mouth. Even Antonio was impressed with the rapidity of the onset of the anesthesia, and said I should take a bath. So I took my first shower before breakfast. By then the anesthetic tingling had moved all the way to my feet. It was impressive but not alarming. There was a mild, aloof, other-worldly high as though I were in a fishbowl seeing and hearing everyone, but distinctly set off from them. After breakfast, I continued to feel an increased tingling, most noticeable in cervical vertebrae 5-7, where slipped disk problems had surfaced in 1991. Tingling was most pronounced in the two fingers of the left hand farthest from the thumb, which had been asleep since the slipped disk, giving this poor guitar player an excuse for some of my sour notes.

Occasionally I felt a sialogogue (saliva-generating) effect welling up in my throat, a feeling I have also experienced before. By noon, I had a touch of diarrhea, and asked Antonio if the drug were purgative. Only in overdose, he said.

In discussing my apprehension, Antonio reminded me that one naturopathic doctor had consumed a whole glassful of the stuff given him by an Amazonian physician. Antonio had helped him through this experience. I suppose he felt prepared to take me through my trip, should I take any turn for the worse.

## Feeling the Effects

After lunch and a couple trips to the latrine I began my afternoon workshop, still woozy from the chiriq sanango. Things went fairly well. Antonio talked to the class, through me, about the various jungle medicines he had assembled in his herb garden. Then we took a break during which I went to the john again. When I'd stand up, I'd feel frighteningly dizzy, as though I were about to pass out. My legs felt large and heavy. Antonio had predicted that as well.

After the break we walked down to the molasses/rum factory on the banks of the Amazon, where the class was to rendezvous with the film crew from "Newtons Apple," a popular children's TV show. We were to film my song "Paradise Lost" about the Rain Forest, with the Amazon flowing powerfully past. At this point, my condition had worsened, so we played sitting on a bench on the river bank.

I was fearful of my worsening instability, and now, the onset of chills to magnify the tingling. After dinner, I had to weave through the crowd to the stage with my guitar. The audience seemed satisfied. I was amazed that I made it to the stand and back. I decided not to participate in the vigorous mariachi dancing that usually occurs at the bar on our last night in the Amazon, taking the seat closest to the door, fearing diarrhea and now nausea as well. Antonio did not seem alarmed, more pleased that I was realizing the power of the herb, that the power of the herb was telling me that Antonio knew what he was talking about.

The night was unpleasant, and the chills made me appreciate the blanket for the first time that week. Dawn found me on the john, cold and weak, not hallucinating but having endured many wild dreams during the night.

On the boat back up the Amazon, I sat beside my coauthor Rodolfo Vasquez confessing that I was still on a bad trip from the chiriq sanango. If he had experienced what I was experiencing, he was not kind enough to tell me so. That morning, 24 hours into my ordeal, I felt less dizzy but more nauseated and weak. And I'd be on the river, the road, the planes, and the taxi for the next 15 grueling hours, on the long journey from the Amazon River to **Herbal Vineyard**.

Getting home at 11:30 p.m., I was too weak and tired to go outdoors and share Peggy's enthusiasm for the comet. The next day was equally bad. But it was good to be back home and see how spring had progressed among the wildflowers and vegetables. I was colder than anyone else, as Antonio had predicted. My stools were still completely liquid, a striking greenish-black and sulfurous. I feared that perhaps the chiriq sanango and the rum had done a double whammy on my liver and GI tract.

## Just as in the literature

To this point, I have written all this without consulting my books. I wanted to summarize my feelings without letting science sway my unbiased record of my reactions to, and feelings about chiriq sanango. Now to the book learning.

Ethnobotanist R. E. Schultes and his chemical partner Robert Raffauf say of the plant that the hallucinations have serious side-effects, among them: chills(!), cold sweats(!), heavy tongue(?), itchiness(?), nausea(!), stomachache(!), temporary insanity(?), tingling(!), and vomiting(?). Certainly I experienced those followed by (!). But there's not much mention of the diarrhea that still plagues me to date. Maybe I picked up a bug. Then again, the Indians expect and respect violent purging as part of their ayahuasca rituals. And chiriq sanango is an intimate adjuvant to many of the ayahuasca concoctions. *Chiriq sanango* is reportedly aphrodisiac; I detected no evidence of this side-effect. I reported purgative activity for the related manaca (*Brunfelsia unifloria*) in my CRC *Handbook of Medicinal Herbs*. Here I also said: "Excessive doses are poisonous, causing excessive salivation(!), vertigo(!), general anesthesia(!), partial paralysis of the face(?), swollen tongue(!), and turbid vision(!). Even in small doses, manacine induces strong muscular tremors and epileptiform cramps, lowered temperature, and death due to paralysis in experimental animals."

Many tribes use the chiriq sanango, leaves or roots, for arthritis, chills, fever, rheumatism, snakebite, venereal diseases, and yellow fever. Antonio was promoting it as a powerful antiarthritic.

There are several antiinflammatory compounds among those reported for the genus: aesculetin, chlorogenic acid, hopeanine, and scopoletin. I have experienced dizzy and faint symptoms such as the chiriq sanango induced when taking indomethacin on top of coffee and its caffeine on an otherwise empty stomach.

Two hours ago, I took the plug-it-up medicine, Imodium® (Loperamide HCl), 72 hours into my bad trip with chiriq sanango. I feel better already, and have been to the john only once in the intervening two hours.

This is a rather negative anecdotal report of my interaction with one of many potent medicines in the rain forest. Like almost all drugs, natural drugs, too, have side-effects, sometimes dangerous. Antonio taught me, his willing patient, that the chiriq sanango is a powerful medicine. Perhaps it might be useful to arthritics, but, like most NSAIDS, it has serious side-effects. If I had crippling and debilitating arthritis, I'd give it a try; but its side-effects are so strong that I'd be afraid to recommend it.

In a few days I'll be lecturing at the Rheumatology Division of the National Institute of Health. This little anecdote will embellish my lecture, as will other antiarthritic suggestions I have picked up in the field. Turns out that 18.5% of their patients are taking herbs, extracurricularly. Can't much say I blame them. Modern medicine, too, has little to offer arthritics that doesn't have a lot of side-effects.

# Chuchuhuasi (*Maytenus* spp.)

*The Business of Herbs* 10(4):12-13. September/October, 1992

Soon to be returning to Amazonian Peru, I have enjoyed reading and rereading some of the books that relate to that area. Many of you may not know how much disagreement there is among the anthropologists, botanists, curanderos and the ethnobotanists about the reliability of their data. Travel through your own country and inquire of 10 rural folks about the names and uses of 10 common plants. You'll end up with a hundred different answers.

There is a lot of ignorance hidden in the abbreviation spp. in my title above. Spp. is the plural of sp. which is the common abbreviation for species, a now-English word whose singular and plural are identical. Ask 10 botanists about 10 oak trees you have collected, and you might get 100 answers. Oaks are difficult to identify to species, often because of hybridization. Hence many of the botanists might call your oak *Quercus* sp. instead of *Quercus alba* or *Quercus nigra* or *Quercus rubra.* By calling it *Quercus* sp. the botanist avoids the difficult job of positive identification.

And so have I disguised my ignorance in the title, by not telling you which of several species of *Maytenus* are called chuchuhuasi in Spanish in Amazonian America. Like feverfew, which we all know, but which travels under as many as five different scientific names, most rural Amazonians know what chuchuhuasi is, but never heard of its generic name *Maytenus.* I'll mention a few specific names below, but we can't be positive that the authors of the popular books, not even the botanists, knew which species they were dealing with.

## Arthritis cure?

Let's take a trip through the chuchuhuasi info in the books I'll be taking with me to Amazonian Peru. Let's look first at Schultes' and Raffauf's *The Healing Forest* (Dioscorides Press, 1990). They heard "chuchuhuasi" differently than I, reporting "chuchuhuasca," "chuchuguache" and "chuchuguaza" as the Spanish names in Colombia and Peru for *Maytenus laevis.* Soaked overnight in the rural rum they call aguardiente in Latin America, the bark tincture is drunk by urban Peruvians as a pain killer "almost always in connection with rheumatism" and as a stimulant. They note that Colombian Siona Indians boil a two-inch piece of the trunk in two quarts of water, reducing it to one quart. Siona take a small cupful of this three times daily over a week to treat arthritis and rheumatism.

Schultes and Raffauf note that backwoods Indians don't consider this an important medicine, indicating that it may be a johnny-come-lately Caucasian concept. But if this plant is really effective against the cause and not the symptoms of arthritis, an unlikely possibility since no modern medicine yet has accomplished this, it is worth billions of gringo greenbacks.

In *Rio Tigre and Beyond, the Amazon Jungle Medicine* (North Atlantic Books 1985), Bruce Lamb spells it differently, at least in his index, as "chuchuhuasha" and says the bark is boiled in water, or steeped in alcohol or in cold water. His formulae also may include the leaves. The first uses he mentions are for leukorrhea and complications of childbirth. External jungle sores are washed with the extract. He recommends the root bark as a purgative for people with long-standing stomach disorders. But he tentatively identifies it as a completely unrelated genus and species, *Heisteria pallida*, in a different plant family, Olacaceae, to which the famed aphrodisiac "muira puama" belongs. Is he talking about *Maytenus* or not? I doubt it. I don't know.

## Peruvian work translated

Now let me introduce you to Rodolfo Vazquez Martinez, a Peruvian who has worked Amazonian Peru for years under the auspices of Al Gentry, Missouri Botanical Garden's powerhouse Latin American taxonomist. Rodolfo has compiled, in Spanish, a book whose title translates as *Useful Plants of Amazonian Peru*.

Following my recommendation, the USDA purchased from Rodolfo the rights to translate, edit, expand and publish his book. The USDA translated it into English. I added ethno-botanical data from regions of Latin America, and we published it as Duke and Vazquez' *Amazonian Ethnobotanical Dictionary*. All royalties were to (and do) revert to the rain forest via the Amazon Center for Amazonian Education and Research. Of course, the rain forest and I will remain much indebted to Rodolfo for his pioneer efforts. Under the name *Maytenus krukovii* Rodolfo has covered most of the uses reported in the previous paragraphs, but suggests it is used for diarrhea and dysentery rather than as a purgative.

Learning that Nicole Maxwell was languishing in a rest home in Florida, I rapidly read her *Witch-Doctor's Apprentice, Hunting for Medicinal Plants in the Amazonian*, 3rd ed. (Citadel Press 1990), another fascinating and readable account of Amazonia. Nicole mentions it under yet another spelling "chuchuwasi," pronounced just as I have spelled in in the title. She notes that many of the better bars in the boom-and-bust town of Iquitos were beginning to serve some jungle drinks, notably chuchuwasi.

"I can...vouch for its efficiency as an insect repellent – applied externally, of course." One of her Indian friends rubbed chuchuwasi on her at a wedding when she was being tormented by stinging gnats and mosquitoes. The insects abandoned her.

Leonard Clark in *The Rivers Ran East* (Funk & Wagnalls 1953) throws "chuchuhuasha" into the genus *Erythroxylum*, the genus from which so much cocaine is extracted in Latin America. However, his "medicinal data" would indicate that he is in fact talking about *Maytenus*: "The tree bark is pulverized and mixed in alcohol. Taken orally it is used by brujos to cure cancer." He elaborates that the bark is mixed with alcohol brewed from the aguaje palm and taken orally for skin cancer. Dr. Cragg of the National Cancer Institute tells me he will run it through the new cancer screen.

## Anti-cancer activity?

Years ago, the USDA collected an African species of *Maytenus* by the ton, and several anti-tumor alkaloids were found, with maytansine prominent among them. While I cannot guarantee that chuchuhuasi contains maytansine, I'll wager that it contains some alkaloids with anti-cancer activity.

As you have seen, each of my sources presents different interpretations of the name and uses of what I am calling chuchuhuasi. Unpacking the boxes after my office got relocated while I was in Kuwait, I found a book I had not consulted. Saving grace! Jaroslav Soukup's book, whose title translates *Vocabulary of the Common Names of the Peruvian Flora* and *Catalog of the Genera* (Editorial Salesiana, Lima), uses the same spelling I have used as the common name for *Maytenus guaianensis* while using "chuchuhuasca" and "chuchuhuasha" for *Maytenus krukovii*.

## Plant of many names

Thus there are about 10 common names, five scientific names (in three different botanical families) and 10 uses reported herein for the "best known of all jungle remedies." That's the way it is with folk medicine among rural people everywhere. Empirically, the natives have often discovered the most active medicinal species in their environment. And like modern medicines, such as aspirin and ascorbic acid, these too may have dozens of biological activities. I've come to believe that all drugs, natural and synthetic, have side effects, some desirable, some undesirable. Aspirin is not the only medicine for which new uses are being discovered.

# Clavo Huasca (*Tynnanthus panurensis*)

*The Business of Herbs* 11(2):12-13, May/June, 1993

## Amazonian Toothache Remedy

As the year 1992 drew to a close, I celebrated and contemplated Columbus' discovery of the Amerindians who discovered America. We still have a lot to learn from the Indians, if we but listen and they but talk. I enjoyed three week-long trips to Amazonian Peru in 1992, studying the ethnobotany of Amazonian America. My first impression of the word "ecotour" was negative. But since my first Amazonian ecotour, I am cautiously promoting ecotourism, as a means to learn more about the most diverse forest in the world (300 woody species per hectare (less than 30 here in Maryland). On all my trips, people (as many as 140) had a comfortable, healthy, safe, well-fed week on the Amazon and its tributaries. There were more than 20 well-qualified, well-seasoned instructors to teach the participants everything from anthropology to bats to birds to botany to bugs to butterflies, from fish and frogs to snakes, even how to catch and eat a grub or a piranha. Many of the most important medicines in the world can be extracted from this forest. Today I'll concentrate on a toothache medicine called clavo huasca, after diversions about my long-standing interests in toothache medicines of the tropics (largely because of poor dental health on my part). They have plants that yield dental floss, plants that can color the teeth black, in the process possibly preventing caries, and, if the caries come, they have a plant, the "insira," used for extracting the aching tooth. Meanwhile, there are plants to alleviate the pains of toothache.

## From Panama to Peru

As early as 1960, my Choco confidants, in Panama, not Amazonia, told me about a plant, *Piper* spp., kin to black pepper, as a remedy for toothache. When I bit, it numbed my mouth, much as roots of coneflower, *Echinacea angustifolia*, or leaves of coca, *Erythroxylum coca*, anesthetize the mouth and/or more importantly aching teeth. On my first ecotour to Amazonian Explorama Lodge below Iquitos, Peru, March, 1991, the first thing my Indian guide, Segundo, showed me was the same or a very similar *Piper*, also to alleviate toothache. He pulled up the root, scraped off the dirt, and invited me to bite into the inner root bark, which did anesthetize the mouth. So, yes, the "savages" of the jungles do have toothache remedies in Nature's Pharmacopoeia.

## And the USA...

Back in the asphalt jungles of urban America, it's another tropical "herb" to which I would resort if I had a toothache. It's clove ("clavo" in Spanish, "cravo" in Portuguese), flower buds of the tropical clove tree, *Syzygium aromaticum*. Oil of cloves or its main ingredient, eugenol, is used by many modern dentists as an anesthetic and analgesic. And, like so many jungle medicines, it works. In 1992, we celebrated Columbus' discovery of the red pepper by cautiously experimenting with the hot pepper for toothache. Topically applied, the hot ingredient, capsaicin, burns for a while, but depletes the activities of substance P, the pain transmitter. I bring this up only to hint that capsicum, an old folk remedy for toothache just might have a lot of fact behind the fancy.

## Active ingredients

In most cases, essential oils or related compounds, used singly or in combination, "are the chief active ingredients of toothache preparations. Of these, oil of clove and eugenol are undoubtedly most important, at least in my book, but thymol also finds wide use. Creosote, usually beechwood creosote, is another widely used material...Phenol, a frequent component of toothache preparations, especially the older types, is a potent local anesthetic and powerful antiseptic. It is, however, a dangerous drug..." (Lesser, 1946). "Clavo huasca" to the rescue. Getting farther back in the forest, at ACEER's Napo Camp, I first met the vine they call "clavo huasca." "Huasca" means vine and "clavo" means clove. That shows a phytochemical awareness on the part of the Yagua Indians. The "clavo huasca" is not at all related to cloves in the botanists "taxonomic frame of things"; it is closer to our crossvine in the U.S. The smell is overpowering, just like the oil of cloves my mother used to tamp into an aching cavity. Eugenol is the active ingredient in oil of cloves; the aroma of the *clavo huasca* tells me and the Yagua Indians that it is rich in eugenol. And it is used, like cloves, for toothache. One of my ecotouring students at Napo and I used the grated stem effectively for toothache. But my toothache led to a dental bridge collapsing, exposing foundations that were rotten beyond repair. Following extraction I started chewing at different angles, and a bridge on the other side collapsed, domino like, shortly thereafter. Lost in the jungle, as I have been on occasion, I'd have been up Piranha Creek without a paddle, with serious dental problems like this and no medicine. But the "clavo huasca," with its eugenol, can clearly alleviate the pain, enabling one to make it back from the paradise of "primitive aboriginal America" to the modern asphalt jungle with its high-priced dentists, building new bridges or prosthetics. [[More recently, 2004, I spent three months teaching salary in 3 visits to my Laurel dentist, totalling less than 3 hours.]] I owe the Amerindians and the "clavo huasca" great thanks for making my week pain-free in spite of the dental problems. Reading up on the "clavo huasca" back home, I see that it is also recommended for rheumatism, taken in spirits (alcohol). Taken in booze, "clavo huasca" does improve one's spirits, and added to Peruvian aguardiente, "clavo huasco" improves it immensely. And eugenol, the active ingredient in "clavo huasca," does have antiinflammatory and anesthetic properties, reportedly desirable for those suffering osteoarthritis or rheumatoid arthritis.

## Herbal homebrew

I began 1993 with another tour to Peru, including some of the subscribers of *The Business of Herbs*. It was a fabulous trip. Even my daughter joined us. And she now shares my contagious love for the rain forest. Since this group was devoted to ethnobotany, we discussed and consumed the famous tonic "chuchuhuasi." Bark of *Maytenus* was steeped in cane alcohol for several hours, I might add, turning the clear, foul-tasting, corn-liquor-like beverage to a reddish liqueur. This was supposedly a male aphrodisiac. Not wanting to be sexist, since we had more females than males on the trip, I asked my guides if they had a female aphrodisiac. They recommended the "clavo huasca," also steeped in the cane alcohol. One curious herbalist took both of these tonics home, and insists that both he and his wife were appropriately stimulated by the tonics. He and his lovely wife had been separated more than a week before his uncontrolled experiments, though, and "absence makes the heart grow fonder" or is it "absence makes the fondler grow hearter."

I can only say that the tinctures were more pleasant to drink than the raw cane alcohol, and surely contained some interesting phytochemicals. Matter of fact, I think almost any herb would improve that "moonshine" they call "aguardiente." But "clavo huasca" is a superior adjuvant. There is now a circular balsa wood sign hanging from the beams of the thatched roof at the Napo Camp. It's signed by all the participants in my tour, as the "clavohuasceros," meaning those who imbibed in "clavo huasca." A good time was had by all.

# Corn (*Zea mays*)

*The Business of Herbs* 5(1):6-7, March/April, 1987

## Mystery Herb (Shh! It's Corn)

I used the following "mystery" herb as an important herb at the Virginia Growers Conference in Syria, Virginia, held in January 1987. I wanted to bring home the point that what is said about an herb (PR) can sell it. My method was perhaps a bit unusual. Not telling them what herb I was talking about I dribbled out clues to see how many it took to identify the herb. I used the technical words knowing that the more common words would give me away.

**Clues:**

1. Health faddists should be interested in an herb whose seed oil, recommended for atherosclerosis and high cholesterol, contains about 1,000 ppm of the antioxidant tocopherol. [[I had fallen victim to the hypocholesterolemic corn oil hype back then; I'm finally liberated and back on butter.]]
2. Herbalists will be interested to hear that the styles and stigmas, much cheaper than the stigmata of saffron, are used on nearly every continent in diuretic teas with proven diuretic activity. Glycolic acid in the leaves and potassium in the core of the female inflorescence are also diuretic.
3. Cancer students' curiosity might be piqued to learn that the mystery herb, which has an anticancer folklore in, e.g., Illinois, Kentucky, Virginia, Peru, Spain, Venezuela, contains an antitumor compound, perhaps a polysaccharide.
4. Hippies might be expected to purchase more of the mystery herb if given a translation of *Hager's Handbook*, which intimates that the alkaloids in the styles and stigmata cause psychic excitation or delirium when inhaled.
5. Following New Year's resolutions to forego caffeine, some readers will be interested to learn that the scorched seeds have served as a substitute for coffee, the stem for sugar, and a tea of the bracts for condensed milk.
6. Those suffering indolent ulcers might be intrigued to learn that, like comfrey, the seeds contain the cell-proliferant vulnerary compound known as allantoin.
7. Mint lovers, will be curious about the fact that the stigmata and styles containing menthol and thymol, are used in Europe for sugar diabetes.
8. Those needing a wholesome diuretic might be fascinated to learn that (unlike digitalis where a lethal dose may be only twice as high as the medicinally effective dose) the methanolic extract of the style/stigmata

is diuretic at doses less than 1/100 the lethal dose in experimental animals.

9. Stigmata yield 1 - 2.5% oil, containing such hormone-like materials as stigmasterol, sitosterol, and ergosterol.
10. *Hager's Handbook*, in German, reports that the styles are used in cystitis, gonorrhea, gout, and rheumatism.
11. Zein, derived from our mystery plant was used to replace shellac in making phonograph records In World War II.
12. Extracts, available for both the food and pharmaceutical industries, are GRAS (generally recognized as safe §182.20).

Properly packaged, any one of the above claims might sell for more than the going $10 per pound, but also might attract the raised eyebrows of the FDA. Still, we are bombarded with TV soup ads extolling the anti-cancer activities of vitamins A and C and with fish-oil ads extolling their antiatherosclerotic and antithrombotic virtues.

The mystery herb has proven diuretic, hypoglycemic and hypotensive activities in experimental animals. How many billions of dollars are Americans spending on diuretic synthetics, hypoglycemic synthetics, and hypotensive synthetics, which are more or less safe and effective than the mystery herb. Frankly, I'd ask my doctor to let me try the mystery tea before I resorted to the more conventional pill-a-day.

How corny, Dr. Duke, you are talking about corn and corn silk nearly twenty years ago. What have you new to say about the mystery herb.

[[The mystery herb is CORN. 1. Corn silks, 2. corn silks, 3. corncob, 4. I used to smoke cornsilk when I was a kid. Though I found it cooler than my other herbal alternatives to tobacco, I experienced no psychic excitation or delirium. 6. corn husks.]]

[[Since then I have learned that the allantoin in corn silk, like maggots, could save a lot of people from diabetic ulcers. There are more than 75 phytochemicals reported from cornsilk in my updated USDA phyto-chemical database, and more than 6 are diuretic (adenine, betaine, caffeic-acid, chlorogenic-acid, friedelin, glycolic-acid, isoquercitrin, oleanolic-acid). And Latin scientists learned that purple corn is a better antioxidant even than blueberry.]]

# Jaborandi (*Pilocarpus* spp.)

*The Business of Herbs* 4(4):7, September/October, 1986

Jaborandi is the Brazilian name for several species of the genus *Pilocarpus*, another tropical member of the citrus family. According to scholars, jaborandi is an old Tupi Indian word which means "what causes slobbering." More discreetly we speak of herbs, or in this case, shrubs, which cause slobbering as sialagogues. It is the sialagogue properties of jaborandi that has caused a few recent headlines about it.

For years, pilocarpine has been one of the major drugs for glaucoma, reducing intraocular pressure. Of course, the Indians were not aware of this property at all. But they were aware it would stimulate slobbering and sweating. Steambaths were part of the health routines of many Indian groups, which do not tend to sweat as much as Caucasians. The Tupi Indians belonged to one group which did not use sweatbaths, apparently because, with the jaborandi, which induces copious sweating, they did not need the steambath.

In the folklore, jaborandi has many other uses, few, if any of which, have been scientifically investigated. Several Brazilians believe the decoction can stimulate the growth of hair, a property that could be worth billions if true. Other ailments for which it has been suggested include anemia, asthma, Bright's disease, calculus, catarrah, coronary, deafness, diabetes, dropsy, epilepsy, erysipelas, gonorrhea, intestinal atony, jaundice, malaria, mushroom poisoning, nausea, nephritis, opthalmitis, pleurisy, prurigo, psoriasis, rheumatism, spasms, syphilis, tonsilitis, and uremia. Detailed studies might show that the drug is as effective at these as it is at making one sweat (diaphoretic) or slobber (sialagogue). Most biologically active compounds [[natural and synthetic]] apparently have several activities, not just one or two.

The effective compound, an alkaloid called pilocarpine, is restricted to the genus *Pilocarpus*, which is restricted to Latin America. The alkaloid may run about 1% of the weight of the dry leaves. Currently, leaves sell for about a dollar a pound or less in Brazil. We can't grow *Pilocarpus* above the frost line in the U.S. I hope to graft it onto the frost-hardy roots of trifoliate orange (*Poncirus*). Then when frost comes, one could merely rake up the leaves, assuming that they manufacture pilocarpine under such peculiar circumstances. But the graft might not take, or the graft might not manufacture pilocarpine, or the graft might be killed by frost, not to return the following spring.

The "new" use for this old folk remedy, *Pilocarpus*, is in the treatment of xerostomia, or dry mouth syndrome. According to *American Health* (April 1986), as many as 2,000,000 Americans have difficulty swallowing because of a malfunction with their salivary glands. Xerostomia may also be a side effect of more than 400 common drugs. And an estimated 2% of Americans over age 60 suffer from dry mouth. Low doses of pilocarpine boost the salivary juices 2 to 10 times in double blind controlled studies, indicating that the drug is effective, as the Tupi Indian name suggested.

In spite of pilocarpine's long-established usage as safe and effective for glaucoma, its sialagogue use is still experimental, "and FDA approval is at least two years off." (AH, '86) But perhaps then, with FDA approval, we can use the pilocarpine as did the Tupi, "to make one slobber.."

# Jackass Bitters (*Neurolaena lobata*)

(Unpublished)

Everybody loves the name jackass bitters, and it is used for almost everything except diabetes in Belize. According to Arvigo and Balick, who acknowledge that at 250 mg/kg, the 100% ethanolic extract has anti-hyperglycemic activity (preventing a raising of blood sugar) and at 500 mg/kg it had hypoglycemic activity (lowering blood sugar) in experimental mice. Mind you that would be 25 and 50 g, close to 1 or 2 ounces respectively for me, if I am down to my target of 100 kilograms.

My friend Leigh Broadhurst called me shortly after my last trip to Belize. She asked me what antidiabetic herbs haven't hit the mainstream yet. "Here's one of my other favorite emerging cures, or remedies from emerging countries. Central American herbal expert Dr. Rosita Arvigo and I have listed a whole host of ailments treatable with what Belizeans call jackass bitters (*Neurolaena lobata*) (In Panama, I had known it three decades earlier as contragavlina): amebas, beef worm, candida, other fungi, giardia, headlice, intestinal parasites, ringworm, and screw worm. As a matter of fact, Rosita peddles jackassbitters as the primary ingredient of her "Traveler's Tonic" for tourists suffering Montezuma's revenge or malaria. Surrounded by a group of local female healers, some Mayan, some African-American, Rosita stressed the power of jackass bitters for vaginal yeast infections at the first "Rain Forest Pharmacy Workshop" held in Belize (May 20-28, 1995). "Boiled leaves are used as a fungicide or insecticide on diseased house or garden plants." I just got a letter last week asking what to do for the so-called beefworm or screwworm, the burrowing fly maggot that the Panamanians called "torsalo." Looks like jackass bitters should be tried.

My Panama experience did not suggest antidiabetic activity either. Here's what I say in my *Isthmian Etnobotanical Garden*, published way back in the early '60's.

*Neurolaena lobata* (L.) R.Br.: Tchëkili (BR); Gavilana (CR); Contragavilan (P); Gavilana (CR); Inaciabi (Cu); Mano de tigre (C); Gúye árani (GF) (Fig. 214).

"Around La Nueva, a favorite malaria remedy consists of the leaves mixed with honey and "vendejuana." A tea of the leaves is used in Darien as a febrifuge and to treat malaria. It is also applied to itching areas (!). The juice is rubbed on the skin as a reputed tick repellent. Some people consider it germicidal. It is taken internally as a bitter tea by the Ailigandi Cuna for stomachache (!). Some Colombians believe it is good for gonorrhea. Leaf decoction used orally or topically for childbirth and pregnancy, fever, hypertension, and as a diuretic by Garifuna Nicaraguans."

Now in Peru and elsewhere in the tropics, they diagnose diabetes by watching the ants attracted to the urine of the diabetic, full of sugar. My shaman in Peru recommends cocona, a local fruit in Peru, but grapefruit for those who can't come up with the cocona. So far *Neurolaena* has not been reported from Peru. But Rosita's aides suggested what may be a new test for diabetes. They say that the jackass bitters do not taste bitter to diabetics. If true, that could be a more attractive test than drawing blood, tasting urine, floating dip sticks, or watching to see if piss ants come to your piss.

But none of the Belizean folklore anticipates what may be the more promising activity of the jackass bitters, its antidiabetic activity. In my files at the USDA is a copy of a 1989 letter from a Florida physician to the then-director of the USDA Beltsville Human Nutrition Research Center, Dr. Walter Mertz: "Enclosed is a sample of 'weed' provided to me by a diabetic patient. This is a rather interesting adult-onset diabetic who had been insulin-requiring until beginning this 'weed.' The patient brought back this 'weed' from the Island of Trinidad. I am hoping you will be able to identify the plant and to determine its effective ingredient."

The patient reports that she mixes a small portion of the "weed" with vermouth and takes small sips of this about twice a day. This has resulted in normalization of her blood sugar over the past approximately six months. Knowing of my interest in folk medicine, Dr. Mertz sent me the letter and specimen, which I tentatively identified as *Neurolaena lobata*, having found a report that the leaf tea of *Neurolaena*, under the creole name "zeb a pic," was taken for diabetes; and in vermouth, for biliousness, colds, dysmenorrhea, fever, and malaria. I responded to the physician for Dr. Mertz, tentatively identifying the plant (only leaves had been submitted). "Research has confirmed the antidiabetic activity of jackass bitters. A 100% ethanol extract (a bit stronger than vermouth!) is antihyperglycemic (prevents high blood sugar) in mice orally at doses of 250 mg per kilogram. If I were a 100 kilogram mouse, that would mean I'd have to drink 25 grams of nearly 200 proof jackass vermouth. For those of you who don't think metrically, that's less than a single ounce shot. At a double-shot dose (500 mg/kg orally in the mouse) it certainly lowers blood sugar. I could probably even handle a double shot with a little lemonade for chaser. (But I would prefer that my lemonade be sweetened with the sweet leaf of Paraguay, *Stevia rebaudiana* [stevia], rather than demon sugar!) Personally I'd feel a bit safer with the jackassbitters than with the rosy or madagascar periwinkle, known to Belizeans as "ram goat" (*Catharanthus*) or the bitter gourd, known to Belizeans as "sorosi" (*Momordica*). I'm convinced that all three of these can lower blood sugar, though. Clearly the Jamaican "sorosi," or *Momordica*, is the most promising, at least as backed by scientific evidence, of the tropical answers to diabetes overall."

Good diet and exercise can usually prevent adult onset diabetes (NIDDM). But if our paleolithic diet has failed us, and we already have NIDDM, what next. We need to control both the diabetes and the complications. When Leigh was preparing her book, I sent her my fat files on diabetes, listing dozens at length, that I thought would be useful for treating NIDDM. Not too many of them survived in her book, and

I'll discuss the survivors first. But I like her food farmacy comment (p. 178): "The higher the consumption of fruits and vegetables...the lower the risk for...diabetes."

First she went for the exotics, bitter melon and jackass bitters, and I'll just quote the unedited inset I sent her. It lost a bit from the publisher's axe.

> *I asked Dr. Duke to tell me about some of the herbs that he has seen used successfully for diabetes while out in the field around the world. Jim replies*: "Few herbs have attracted as much interest as the food plant known as balsam pear or bitter melon (*Momordica charantia*). Research on the hypoglycemic properties of *Momordica* was first published in India in the 1960s, and in a recent trial a fall of 54% in blood sugar was achieved. Bitter melon juice, dried fruits, and seeds have proven oral hypoglycemic activity, due to several identified compounds. Authors recommend 2 oz. fresh juice or 100 ml decoction. (Chop 100 grams fresh fruit and boil in 200 ml water down to 100 ml.) In another study, consumption of 50 ml extract of bitter gourd reduced hyperglycemia by some 20%. Bitter melon was shown to delay the development of cataracts and other diabetic complications in rats. Dr. H. F. Dankmeijer of Bilthoven uses bitter melon as an insulin substitute in insulin-dependent diabetics. In NIDDM, where insulin resistance is the problem, treatment uses liver-cleansing agents such as *Carduus* (thistle), *Chelidonium* (celadine), and *Taraxacum* (dandelion), all of which have been cited as food plants elsewhere. I'd be reluctant to eat much *Chelidonium*. Better yet, just eat it as a side dish like the Asians and Indians do."

Dandelion is a bitter itself, some even speculate the Biblical bitter. Jackass Bitters might remind a wandering mind of a manger scene with donkeys and straw. Jackass bitters could be America's answer to the Biblical bitters, like chicory and dandelion.

# Jatropha, Bubblebush (*Jatropha curcas*)

(Unpublished)

## The Bubble Plant

## (ALIAS: The Great Spaceship Jason)

Two weeks in the rainforest, photographing live video to beam back live to the United States live, I blew my first bubble with the bubble plant, two weeks shy of my 70th birthday. The Great Jason Spaceship has come and gone, and the artificially noisy forest is now back to normal with those beautiful subdued sounds we associate with the rain forest. [[You never heard of the Jason Project? Amazing! It funded travel of many U.S. middle school students to my favorite spot in Peru; to see how the natives lived. I was delighted that they filmed, among many other interesting sites, in the ReNuPeru Garden that Antonio Montero and I had a hand in establishing]] Gone. Whew! The chronic diesel roar is gone. The birds are back where they belong, the diesel gone back where it belongs. What quiet bliss, once again!! Where there were two floating air-conditioned studios and two tug boats yesterday, there are just a few broken branches, scars that will heal quickly. Where last night you could only hear the buzzing of the air-conditioners for the studios, tonight it will be the laughing frog, pootoo, tinamou and whipoorwill. The latter alone is enough to call me back to the Amazon rain forest, not to mention homegrown tomatoes in winter. It will almost be spring when I get home, between Peggy's birthday and mine. What a great way to miss those snow storms we keep hearing about back home.

I call it the Great Spaceship Jason because I feel that's how it must have felt to the "big-ear" Indians (Orejones or Mahuna) who, until just recently, stretched their ears with big rings of balsa wood. Antonio Montero, the Napo "Shaman," was teaching the Orejones to grow their own medicinal plants on a two-hectare plot they are setting up at the edge of their village, Sucusari, on the Rio Sucusari. They were to raise enough medicine for the village, possibly showing it to some of the ecotourists who joined us on our Amazon ecotours. The Jason kids and the Orejon Indians visited the ReNuPeRu Garden, while being filmed from the garden. There were about twenty of them, women and children, and a few men, including Flores (flowers) who appropriately will be in charge of their garden.

Part of our live video was Antonio with a student and me, demonstrating some of the medicinal plants in the ReNuPeRu Garden (there were 182 at the latest count). But towards the end of the segment, Antonio's son, Gilmer, was to walk in with the bubble plant, and to try to teach the student how to blow a bubble in the bush with the bubble plant. I never called it that before. But the bubble plant is a well-known medicinal plant, *Jatropha,* which they call piñon, a very important medicinal plant.

We had labeled two species in the ReNuPeRu Garden for our Jason visitors to see on their quick visit to our garden here. Here's what Rodolfo Vasquez and I had to say about it in our *Amazonian Ethnobotanical Dictionary*:

"*Jatropha curcas* L. Euphorbiaceae. 'Piñón,' 'Piñón blanco,' 'Physic nut.' Cultivated ornamental, with multiple uses among rural people. Leaf decoction piscicidal; roasted leaves poulticed on swollen infections; 1-4 raw seeds are used as a laxative, 5-10 seeds mixed with food for constipation. Some people warn that they are too POISONOUS for internal consumption (TRA). Keeping leaves in rooms is said to be healthy. Leaf decoction used to protect the color of stained wood (SOU). 'Palikur' use the latex as a dental analgesic (GMJ). 'Tikuna' use crushed leaves in febrifugal baths (SAR). Crushed leaves with those of Petiveria used to bathe aching heads (SAR). Juice from the petioles applied in pediatric gingivitis (SAR). Chopped leaves applied externally in rheumatism; latex used for earache (FEO). Brazilians take the leaf juice, mix sulfur in, and apply to streptococcus-infected wounds (erysipelas) (BDS). Seeds yield an excellent industrial oil. (Fig. 132).

"*Jatropha gossypifolia* L. Euphorbiaceae. 'Piñón negro,' 'Black physic nut.' Cultivated. Latex used as a cicatrizant for infected wounds and erysipelas (BDS). Seeds contain oil and have purgative and emetic properties. The leaf decoction is used for venereal diseases as blood purifier, and as an emetic for stomachache. The roots are used as antidote to *Hippomane mancinella* and *Guarea guara*. The latex is used for hemorrhoids and burns. The leaves are poulticed onto swellings (PEA, SOU). Leaf tea used in baths for flu in Brazil (BDS). Mashed leaves poulticed onto headache (RAR). 'Créoles' use seed oil and leaf decoction as a purge; 'Palikur' and 'Wayãpi' use against witchcraft (GMJ). Another example of a reputedly POISONOUS folk cancer remedy containing compounds with antitumor activity, e.g. jatrophone (CRC)."

Like many plants containing soapy "saponins," this one, too, is used as a fish and mollusk intoxicant. But with all that information from so many informants quoted above, there's nothing about what Antonio told me. Back in the old days (ca 30 years ago) they used it to wash clothes, because of its sudsing saponins. If you break the leaf stalk (petiole) partially, making a 45E angle with the semi-detached parts of the stalk, you can retain a triangular wedge of a film, and if you blow on that just right, you can get a dozen small bubbles ("burbujas" in Spanish). How's that for a weird picture for 600,000 kids back in the United States? A 70-year-old barefoot bearded gringo in the rainforest blowing bubbles. Takes all kinds! On Gilmer's last day, I did even better than he did.

The day before, some of the film crew lured him to the jungle looking for the forbidden ayahuasca vine, purportedly only for "photographic purposes." Tugging on a vine that reached the canopy 100 to 150 feet above him, Gilmer was hit in the mouth by a falling piece of a rotten limb.

He was infected and couldn't pucker very well. But with many "doctors" of many disciplines, he recovered (later). Oral sores are hard to heal down here.

After our Jason show, which the Orejones viewed in the filming process, Roger Mustalish, president of ACEER, arranged for the Orejones to go inside and see the air-conditioned video studio. There they met face to face for the first time, dozens of live TV screens, all on at once, thousands of control buttons, huge air ducts for the air-conditioning. Remember that these people may have heard a radio or two, but probably never saw television, much less a full TV studio. Surely that must have been as alien to them as a real Star Quest spaceship would seem to me, capturing the spirits of all who walked in front of that strange gun (the camera).

I visited the Orejones in their garden the following week, after the Jason Spaceship had returned to inner space. I took a small ecotour group from the U.S. to see how their medicinal garden was developing. Will the Orejones remember this as vividly as I do the New York World's Fair when I was less than 12 years old? Trying to overcome the language barrier, I'll someday try to learn if they are as relieved as the laughing frogs and the whipoorwill are (and I am), now that the monstrous Jason spaceship has been pushed down the Sucusari River to the Napo and then up the Amazon, perhaps and perhaps hopefully never to return. But filled with spirits (photographic images) of many of the native Americans and the visitors from outer space. The Great Spaceship Jason is gone. And peace returned to the Amazon retreat and the ReNuPeRu Garden. And the naked kids will have to resort back to the bubble bush for entertainment. No TV couch potatoes here, yet. I shall return again in May, October, and December, hoping to inquire again what they thought about all this invasion of their turf. It would have scared me, too, had they invaded the Umstead State Park, where I worked as a junior park ranger as a teenager. more than 60 years ago. I'd like to hear what the Orejones say about the Great Spaceship Jason fifty years from now.

## Great Spaceship Jason

What a crazy safari, to the Rio Sucusari, what a school
The Amazon amazing,
to the great spaceship JASON, real cool
On the banks of the Napo,
study scorpion or sapo, what fun
And the student observes,
all Antonio's herbs, one by one

Hyacinth floating down,
from old Iquitos town, there she goes
How long will it be,
'til it reaches the sea, no one knows
The rainforest grows,
as the big river flows, there she blows
And the pink dolphin knows,
everywhere it all goes, I suppose
It'll take quite awhile, for the 2000 miles
When the rain comes and goes,
like the Andean snows
The scorpions and ants, and the curare plants,
kinda funky
With a twink of the eyes, the poison dart flies,
to a monkey
And though no sound is heard,
they can knock down a bird, on the wing

Empty stomachs, emaciation, decry conservation,
as I sing.
The rainforest conceives, the air everyone breathes
And the big timber trees, and the cures for disease
But the rainforest sighs, if it dies all else dies,
mark my word

Save it, it's true, then it might save you, have you heard?
Amazon rolling on, as I sing this last song, tearfully
If we just don't give in, then the forest can win, cheerfully.
Did my song all go wrong, are the jaguars all gone
Was the forest all sheared, to make plywood veneer

Not so bad as it seems, it was only a dream
JASON can help preserve, the ACEER reserve,
If the forest survives, it can help save OUR lives
Thank you, JASON and all, who heed the rainforest call.

# Papaya (*Carica papaya*)

*The Business of Herbs* 9(3):10-11, July/August, 1991

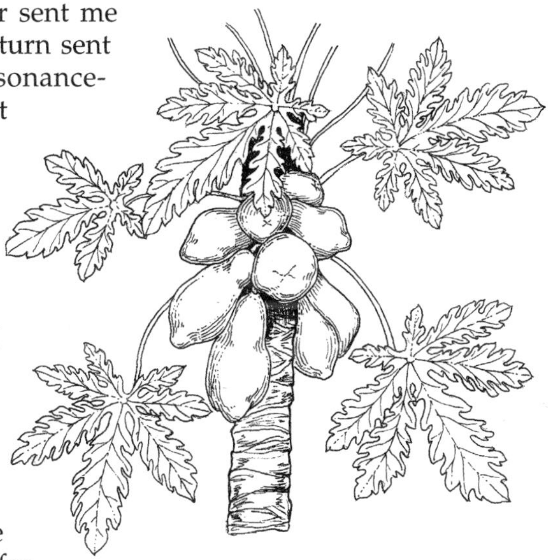

When my chiropractor sent me to an orthopedist who in turn sent me to a magnetic-resonance-imagery (MRI) specialist who then sent me to a neurosurgeon who then sent me for a CAT scan and cervical myelogram, I figured I had something more than a crick in the neck. Yes! I had a herniated (ruptured) disk between the fifth and sixth vertebrae in my neck.

Then came the hour of decision. I took the afternoon off and went for my scheduled appointment with the neurosurgeon. Finally after a half-nude half hour perched uncomfortably on the edge of his disposable-tissue-covered examining table, I was greeted by the neurosurgeon who said we were both wasting our time. The MRIs were lost! They'd order a new print, and we could reschedule. Terribly disappointed, I wrote International Expeditions and told them that I would be unable to teach about economic rainforest products in the rainforest at their Amazonian Explorama camp, four hours downstream from Iquitos, Peru.

Peggy, my wife, who is more aggressive than I and was tired of my moaning and groaning about the numbness, pain and postural peculiarities associated with my disk problem, called the receptionist to speed up the new appointment, once the MRIs were again available. She learned though that my neurosurgeon had gone overseas for several weeks. Meanwhile my physical therapist suggested I wear a polyester neck collar to keep my chin from drooping onto my chest as I read or typed and said I should go to South America anyhow. Feeling better, I agreed, thinking that if my neurosurgeon was out of the country, I might as well be also. So I called Dick Mills of International Expeditions, who was just about to open my letter of regretful decline, and told him to throw the letter away, that I'd be joining them in Peru.

## Disk dissolver

That's a rather long-winded introduction seemingly not relevant to that overgrown tropical American herb we and Latinos call papaya, the British call pawpaw, and Latin scholars and botanists call *Carica papaya*. Who would have guessed that the leaves used by primitive tribes in America to tenderize tough meats wrapped therein would be used in modern America to "tenderize" or dissolve herniated disks. It may be quite pertinent to my disk problem. You see, only in 1982 was the compound chymopapain, derived from the latex (milky juice) of papaya, approved for a process laboriously labeled chemonucleolysis. In this process, physicians inject the compound near the problem spot in the disk, trying to dissolve the disk away from the nerve it is irritating.

Some medicines are short-lived, though. Just approved in 1982, chymopapain was being questioned in *JAMA* (*Journal of the American Medical Association*) by August, 1989. Even this natural medicine takes a few lives. About one percent of those taking chymopapain injections will suffer anaphylactic reaction and one in 4,000 will die from shock (not bad, really; JAMA figures show that medicine kills one of every thousand hospitalized patients). Incidentally, women are up to ten times more likely than men to suffer anaphylaxis.

Once used, chymopapain should never again be given to the same patient. There's a high probability that the second course will be fatal. That's probably because so many Americans have been exposed to another natural products from papaya, this one another protein-dissolving enzyme called papain. The biggest end use of papain is in chill-proofing beer, but a lot shows up in fruit juices, meat tenderizers and tenderized meats (even pet foods), toothpastes, rennets, chewing gums, in processing (degumming) silk, removing hair from leather before tanning and cleansing solutions for soft contact lenses. And a lot of Americans consume the fruits fresh or mixed in juices. Some even consume herb teas containing the leaves. That might not be a bad idea; leaves contain vitamin C, vitamin E and beta-carotene.

## Beer clarifier

According to a report from the International Trade Center (ITC, 1987), the brewing industry takes 75% of the world's papain, so most beer drinkers consume a bit of papain whenever they consume beer. At one time the U.S. imported more than a million dollar's worth of papain a year. Should we call this a peculiar brand of green consumerism? As beer is cooled, cloudy hazes appear as proteinaceous precipitates form, unless the proteins are predigested by papain or some other protein-dissolving enzyme of which Father Nature has provided aplenty. Draught beer, which moves quickly, requires less papain than canned or bottled beer with a shelf life of three to six months. Export beer requires even more, its shelf life stretching to as long as two years.

## Meat tenderizer

Many meat-tenderizing processes and compounds are also based on papain, sometimes in combination with ficin, from fig, and bromelain, from pineapple. Some of the meat tenderizers are incorporated into spices shaken onto meats as they are cooked. Some such tenderizers have proven popular with scuba divers, not for tenderizing tough fish, but as an antidote to the stings of jellyfish or sea nettles. I'd rather use a meat tenderizer than urine, another suggested remedy. Seeing me stung by the earth nettle, *Laportea* sp., one of my Explorama students suggested I try papaya latex. Actually, it made the sting even more acute, and strangely, I manifested histaminic (allergic) reactions up the arm more than a foot from where I applied the papaya. So, I discourage the use of papaya latex for the earth nettle.

## Wart wizener

Stranger things yet happened when I tested the old folk wisdom about papaya latex dissolving warts. I had a perfect triangle on my right forearm formed by three nearly identical warts which had been there at least six months. On the first day of class at Explorama, and every day thereafter, I milked a papaya fruit and applied fresh latex to the worst of the warts, not treating the other two, the experimental "controls." By day three all had shrunk, but perversely, the controls shrunk the most, while the treated wart was irritated and red. One week later all had almost disappeared. [[BUT the triangle is still on my forearm as I draft this in February of 2006.]]

In retrospect, perhaps I should not have dedicated to papaya my introductory remarks and experiments at Explorama. Anaphylaxis it was not! Reaction it was!! But this compilation and my experiments rather dramatically showed how this tropical plant enters the lives of many North Americans unexpectedly. My neurosurgeon may suggest chymopapain as one option for my herniated disk, contrasted to diskectomy or physical therapy. My experiments have doubtlessly increased the chances that I will be allergic to chymopapain, perhaps eliminating one of the more promising options. Stay tuned.

# Pepperbark (*Drimys winteri*)

*The Business of Herbs* 3(6):8,11, January/February, 1986

I wanted to start the New Year with a new herb. Instead of dredging back into the past, I was going to expound on the exciting news about feverfew which travels under four or five aliases: *Chrysanthemum parthenium*, *Matricaria parthenium*, *Pyrethrum parthenium*, and *Tanacetum parthnenium*, even *Parthenium*. Thank goodness for the common name feverfew! The exciting thing is that British studies are proving this plant out for migraine. It is exciting, but it's not news: I've read about it in at least six other places in the last couple months.

Even more exciting is a new development about another old American herb, the pepperbark, alias "Canelo" or Winter's Bark, *Drimys winteri*. But first a little Herbal History! *Drimys* is called Winter's Bark after Captain Winter, captain of one of the three ships in Sir Francis Drake's expedition of 1577.

Stormswept they were driven to the Straits of Magellan where they spent several weeks trying to improve the health of the crews. Winter used the bark (he might have done better with the leaves) to treat scurvy. Following his success the bark was much in demand in Europe for sometime thereafter. It has a folk reputation for much more than scurvy; it has been suggested for such diverse ailments as cancer, dysentery, gastritis, and toothache.

My friend Patty Stern spent much time with the Indians of Chile and says that they used the "Canelo" for stomach problems and perhaps specifically for the bladder. Heated leaves were also poulticed onto wounds. You have probably already heard too much about the Inca "cancer cure," *Tabebuia* alias "pau d'arco," "taheebo," "lapacho," etc. Pepperbark is the Araucan "cancer cure." And the leaves have proven active in experimental leukemias!

Recently there have been rumors that the bark might be effective against yeast in humans (candidiasis), an increasingly perplexing problem here in the U.S. The bark has been reported to contain the compound, polygodial, which has shown antifungal activity against yeast, in vitro at least. Learning of that I wrote to my Chilean friend, Fernando Sanchez, who has introduced ginseng into Chile. I asked for a sample of the bark, and he came through, as always.

It's an amazing bark. I put one piece in my perennial tea cup at the office. And I left that piece of bark in the unwashed cup for two weeks having steeped at least 40 cups of melissa tea with the pepperbark. After more than two weeks, that one sliver of bark still added a bite to the supernatant melissa tea.

Pepperbark is yet another example of an Amerindian folk remedy which, on analysis, proves to contain biologically active compounds: the antitumor compound, taxifolin, and the candidicidal compound, polygodial. Wouldn't it be nice if we could get Mr. Claude Pepper to stimulate research on the Araucan pepperbark to see if it might help two scourges of our senior citizens (and sometimes young folks as well), cancer and yeast? To the best of my knowledge there have never been tests of the aqueous infusions (herb teas) of the pepperbark, taken orally in either mice or man, for cancer or yeast. If it works, it will certainly give senior citizens an interesting and cheaper alternative to current therapies.

I fear Mr. Pepper won't encourage the scientific analysis of the pepperbark. Our government has elected to leave such research to the pharmaceutical companies. And it costs them $100 million [[1,700 million in 2005]] to prove a drug both safe and efficacious. Since they can't easily patent either the pepperbark, the taxifolin, or the polygodial, they could not protect their patent if they proved any of these effective against cancer or yeast. Clearly no drug company wants to spend big bucks on something they cannot protect by patent. Few if any herb companies can afford this investment. The government is, by and large, not investigating medicinal plants (with the very noteworthy exception of *Artemisia annua* – (see *Business of Herbs*, Jan/Feb '84). So I start the New Year on a sour note. We will never know whether this Amerindian discovery is, or is not, safe and/or efficacious for cancer and yeast. But we will be offered new synthetic drugs for these ailments, drugs to which our genes have never been exposed before.

[[Always looking for proof of synergy, I was delighted to see a new paper by Kubo, who keeps turning up exciting examples of synergy. He describes synergy between polygodial as a fungicide against yeast. Polygodial was found to exhibit a fungicidal activity against a food spoilage. The fungicidal activity of polygodial was increased 128-fold by combining with anethole. Also activity of sorbic acid was enhanced 512-fold if combined with polygodial. Fungicidal activity of polygodial was enhanced 128-fold when combined with sorbic acid (X15969495).]]

# Picho Huayo (*Siparuna guianensis*)

(Unpublished)

I won't even translate the Peruvian name because it has sexual connotations. The leaves of *Siparuna guianensis* are believed by some of the Peruvian natives to be aphrodisiac. And there is no real English name for it, as so often happens with our Amazonian perennials. Even the family, Monimiaceae, doesn't have any U.S. members; hence, no good English family name.

We read in *Amazonian Ethnobotanical Dictionary* (Duke and Vasquez, 1994) that the aroma, applied to the skin of a hunter, prevents his quarry from smelling him (by masking his body odor, hence of some possible cosmetic application as a deodorant). The guides claim that this is not effective; in fact, they claim instead that it renders the hunter very attractive to the female of the hunter's species. An aroma like this, attracting the opposite sex there in Amazonia, is called a "pusanga(o)," I'm not sure which. Frequently around our camps you may hear someone singing: "yo no soy pusangero!" Thus men who don't hunt anything but women might make themselves more successful by rubbing their bodies with the fruit before the dance. One excellent Amazonian taxonomist swore that he had tried this with remarkable success, slyly saying only, "I have good empirical evidence."

Another day, another country, three of us, reminiscing about the good old days, discussed the story, when one remembered he had gotten almost the same story about *Siparuna* and sexuality in Mexico. And truffles, truffle pigs, and sex pheromones pervaded that ethanolic conversation, suggesting a possible link between truffles and "picho huayo" and human sex pheromones that might attract the female human to the male. Light bulbs went off in our female colleague's head, and she said she was going to look into it for one of the cosmetics' firms.

That was before I saw a strange article, "Underarmed and Dangerous," which went into the chemistry of armpits (Roach, 1992). That article leads off with a photo of a cadre of scientific armpit sniffers evaluating the aromas. Much of the body odor is due to emanations from the apocrine sweat gland. Around puberty, these start secreting a milky ooze that has no aroma until invaded by bacteria. After about six hours, the bacterial breakdown products stink. Wherever there are hairs there are apocrine glands. Some post-Neanderthals speculate that the apocrines evolved here because the hairs retained and broadcast the sexual scent. Men have more androgens and bigger apocrine glands than females. Orientals have few apocrine glands (military exemptions were even granted Japanese with B.O.). Much of the smell is due to androstenone (which some people can't even smell, much less spell).

Wild boars also produce androstenone, which causes the female to "present." So in the '70s and '80s everybody was spraying androstenone around, or wearing it, hoping to attract their females. Some claim it worked!

## The truffle connection

More recently, Maciarello and Tucker (1994) say, "Pigs, usually females, have traditionally been used for this task because of their natural affinity for truffles, probably induced by a pheromone-like response for 5-alpha-androst-16-en-3-alph-ol, a steroid component of the truffle odor also synthesized by boars during pre-mating behavior; this may also partially explain the weird, sometimes intense human lust for truffles as the same odorous steroid is secreted by men in their underarm sweat. Pigs with a propensity for finding truffles are termed...`searchers'." They also have an 1825 quote of a French gastronomist: "Truffle is a word...which awakens memories of eroticism and gourmandise within the sex which wears skirts, and memories of gourmandise and eroticism within the sex which wears beards."

If you are having trouble with these chemical names, welcome aboard! Neither androstenone nor 5-alpha-androst-16-en-3-alph-ol are in my Merck Index, which lists androst-16-en-3-ol, which has a pronounced musk-like odor, as a constituent of boar pheromone (isolated from swine testes). But all of them are talking about the malodorous boar pheromone with its musky odor that seems to attract some pigs. So far, none of them has been identified from *Siparuna,* but that might be a good place to look. Several compounds are shared by *Siparuna* and truffles, most of which are fairly widespread and have no aphrodisiac properties.

## Folklore

The plant has a wide-ranging folk repertoire. In a computerized index I put together several years ago (Duke and Wain, 1981), the species was described as having fever-reducing, insecticidal, pain-killing, and stimulant properties, but not aphrodisiac. It was used for colds, cramps, dermatoses, fever, gastritis, headache, mange, rheumatism, snakebite, and wounds. Duke and Vasquez also mention the leaf decoction as a treatment for fungus infections (it contains at least three antifungal compounds). Schultes and Raffauf (1990) note that Tikuna Indians eat the fruits for dyspepsia. Wayapi Indians use the leaves and bark for fevers; Creoles of Guyana believe the leaf tea can cause abortion. Still, they use it for fever (contains two hypothermic compounds). With salt it is believed to help lower the blood pressure. The leaf tincture is highly regarded to reduce bruises and swelling (contains two antiedemic compounds). Palikur use the leaves as an antiinflammatory poultice (contains two antiinflammatory compounds).

Kubeo Indians use leaves of *Siparuna ternata* Perkins for snake bite, making a tea of the fruits to alleviate nasal congestion of colds. Tikuna apply crushed fruits to sore gums. Waorani crush the leaves and fruits of the species they call "non-an-gong-ca" to treat fever and headache. From Brazil, *Siparuna cujabana* has been reported to induce abortion and sweating. *Siparuna nicaraguensis* reportedly helps colds, headaches, and rheumatism. *Siparuna pauciflora* is used for chills, fevers, influenza, and malaria. One

Ecuadorian species is said to alleviate sterility in females.

When different ethnic groups as far apart as Mexico and Peru have the same folklore for *Siparuna*, as an attractant to the human female, I'm reminded of the celestine connection between the Aztecs and the Incas. It warrants scientific investigation. I might even give it a try myself, if the androgens hold out.

# Prickly Pear, Nopal, Nopalito (*Opuntia ficus-indica*)

*The Wild Foods Forum* 17(4):8-9, Fall, 2006

This desert plant joins several other food plants in the paleolithic food-farmacy-alternative approaches to type II diabetes. But it is used for just about everything but diabetes in Belize according to Arvigo and Balick (arthritis, bladder problems, childbirth, fever, headache, high blood pressure, malaise). On my last trip to Israel, with the late Dan Palevitch, I learned that Russian immigrants in Israel were seeking out this once-American cactus, not for diabetes, as it is widely used in America, but for prostate. My data-base shows that prickly pear contains at least three anti-prostatic phytochemicals, beta-sitosterol, linoleic-acid and zinc. Since those phytochemicals probably occur in all plants, I'd add pumpkin seed and saw-palmetto to my cactus in my Food Farmaceutical for prostatitis. Might even make a vegetarian tuna salad, nopalitoes with pumpkin seed, brazil nuts and salsa (for the tomatoes with lycopene).

As noted by Steven Foster (*Business of Herbs*, 1990), interest in the nopal was triggered by a Mexican study showing that after fasting for 12 hours, non-insulin-dependent diabetics had lower blood glucose and insulin levels after taking nopalito. Controls were unchanged. The scientists speculated that the nopalito "pads" might help to improve the efficacy of available insulin, thus stimulating glucose to move from the blood stream to body cells to be used as energy or stored as fat. More recently, Broadhust (1999) notes that 8 diabetic Mexican patients were given 500 grams (that's more than a pound, mind you) on an empty stomach. After 180 minutes, fasting glucoise was lowered 22-25% by the cactus fruits, very rich in pectin. And in rabbits it improved tolerance of injected glucose 33%. After her research, Leigh recommends eating a daily cup of cactus, raw or cooked (watch out for minute, almost invisible spines).

Facciola notes the food use of the pads: "Young pads, called nopalitos, are boiled and used like snapbeans in salads, soups, omelettes or pickles. Even South Africans have a farming bulletin which in 1987 put out a bulletin – "A Novel Use of a Declared Weed - YOUNG PRICKLY PEAR LEAVES FOR HUMAN CONSUMPTION." Thus, the pad belongs in the Food Farmacy, especially for diabetes, which is ravishing some Amerindian tribes, e.g., the Pima, who may have as much as half their adult males diabetic. Much of this could have been prevented had they stuck with their tepary beans instead of going with the "trading store varieties." As reported in the *American Horticulturist* (Nov. 91, p. 8), ingestion of broiled pads before meals significantly reduces serum total cholesterol, beta-cholesterol, and triglycerides for obese and diabetic patients (and those adjectives apply to many Pima). More importantly perhaps, blood glucose levels are also decreased. There are at least 5 reportedly antidiabetic compounds in *Opuntia*, fiber and pectin, if you count those two instead of one, rutin, tocopherol, and xylose (Duke, 1992). Replacing shots of booze and/or scoops of ice cream with as many nopalitos would help mild diabetics, I think. But let me confess, I suspect that all fruits contain at least four of those phytochemicals. Diabetics should not "juice" their fruits, because that way they would lose most of the fiber and pectin, in effect concentrating the simple sugars at the expense of the more desirable (for diabetics, at least) complex sugars.

Foster mentions the edible fruits and flowers "as attractive as any rose." Amerindians also used the fruits and pads, even the milky juice, in folk medicine. He mentions that Chinese, post Columbus I presume, have learned many medicinal uses, often paralleling the Aztec usage. Cooked alone or with pork, the broth of the pads was given to strengthen weak patients. Pads were dried, pounded into pieces and mixed with oil for curing a scalded head. Pads were fried with eggs to treat numbness. Inner flesh of the pads is used to treat abscesses. In India, the syrup made from the fruits are used for asthma, cough and pertussis, viewed as antibilious, antiinflammatory and expectorant. I think of it as more important for diabetes. And my USDA phytochemical database enumerates some of the phytochemcials that might contribute to this activity.

# Prickly Poppy (*Argemone mexicana*)

(Unpublished)

Just returned from South Africa where I did indulge in an ostrich steak, just as I had enjoyed kangaroo steak when in the outback last year, and alpaca steaks at Machu Picchu. And I was not surprised to see a lot of our subtropical American species becoming weeds in South Africa, and that includes the prickly poppy, *Argemone mexicana*. Would you believe it. When an area gets infested with the weedy prickly poppy, they often move in a natural herbicide, in this case, the ostrich. You see, there have been poisonings in South Africa as in India, when grain gets contaminated with seeds of the prickly poppy. Here's a quote from *Medicinal and Poisonous Plants of Southern and Eastern Africa*: the prickly poppy "is browsed in times of drought by the sheep and the goat in the Bloemhof district...It has been a favorite food of the ostrich (to the extent of 'camping' ostriches on land infested with the plant in order to eradicate the weed...It had proved toxic to the horse...The seed is toxic to domestic poultry...Serious effects have been reported from the feeding of wheat contaminated with argemone seed to hens. The seed is narcotic...During 1946 and 1947 there were two epidemics of poisoning due to contamination of grain by the seed of *Argemone mexicana*. In one there were three deaths out of five case and in the second one death out of seven cases" (WBB). Small wonder that TRAMIL recommended it be abandoned as a folk medicine, even for gastralgia (TRA), the Caribbean equivalent of Commission E, and even more conservative, in my opinion, than Commission E, so much so that I call it Commission T for TRAMIL.

Though a dangerous plant, it is widely used medicinally. Some good medicines are quite dangerous, unless used most cautiously and skillfully. Still phytochemicals in this plant might contribute to some of South Africa's most pressing ails, other than AIDs, like MDR-tuberculosis and malaria. Berberine reportedly liberates the malaria organism into the periphertal circulation from internal organs, making it more susceptible to quinine. Extracts of the plant, without quinine, are ineffective in malaria. Teas made from berberine-containing barberries have been useful in decubitis, stomatitis, tonsilitis, and varicose veins. I have more than fifty medicinal uses for berberine in my database, including some that might suggest its potential utility for AIDs, the real scourge of South Africa. At the AIDs South Africa conference (which I did not attend), allopaths stressed the importance of synthetic reverse transcriptase inhibitors (RTI), protease inhibitors, and integrase inhibitors. Berberine is one such RTI. Other herbal RTI's include arctigenin in many compositae like burdock (IC69= 0.27 uM JNP 61:1447); baicalein in my baical skullcap (IC50=<1 ug/ml JNP 53(5):1239; 2 ug/ml EMP 5:225); chelidonine in celandine; columbamine ellagic acid (in strawberry guava bark then fruit, chebula, arjuna, clove); kaempferol (IC50=50-150 ug/ml JNP 54:142), also a COX-2 Inhibitor found in green tea (along with many other RTI polyphenols), cabbage and chives; punicacortein (ID50=5uM) and punicalin (ID50=8uM) from the Biblical pomegranate, quercetin (IC50=<1 ug/ml JNP 53(5):1239) from evening primrose and onion, taspine from our Amazonian dragon's blood; and trachelogenin (IC57= 0.52 uM JNP 61:1447) from burdock.

Some of the herbal protease-inhibitors include carnosol and carnosolic-acid (IC90=0.08 ug/ml JNP 56:1426) from rosemary; curcumin (IC50=11-250 uM) from turmeric and ginger; maslinic-acid (IC100=18 ug/ml JNP 59:643), in chebulic-myrobalan, sage, loquat clove); and ursolic-acid (IC85=18 ug/ml JNP 59:643) in rosemary, sage, pygeum lavender, thyme, savory.

Chicory the Biblical weed, also found in South Africa, is the namesake of a breakthrough integrase inhibitor, cichoric acid, though echinacea is even richer. Cichoric acid was reported very promising at the Vancouver AIDs meet; see C&EN Jul 29, 1996, p.45). Also an immune boosting antiviral, it could conceivably be even better than immunosupressing synthetic antivirals. Other phytochemical integrase inhibitors include arctigenin (found in burdock), curcumin (40-150 uM BP 49:1165) (found in ginger and turmeric, the latter in an Amazonian AIDS cocktail); 3-O-demethylarctigenin (IC50=100 uM LAB85); rosmarinic-acid (in many mints including alehoof, cornmint, lemonbalm, marjoram, oregano, pennyroyal, rosemary, sage, selfheal, spearmint and thyme) and trachelogenin (in burdock).

If I were an AIDS patient in the developing world, unable to afford the pharmaceutical cocktail we'll be loaning South Africa a billion dollars to purchase from American pharmaceutical firms, I'd certainly consider upping my ingestions of the healthier of these RTI-, protease- and integrase-inhibiting herbs. I could afford them, especially the herbs and weeds. I could not afford the AIDS cocktail.

# Pumpkin (*Cucurbita* spp.)

*The Business of Herbs* 3(4):8-9, September/October, 1985

## A Halloween Herb

Had you ever thought of the pumpkin as an herb? I hadn't. Not until I faced an audience of 600 friends of herbs, all interested in medicinal herbs. I had to frame a definition with which I was comfortable. An herb is a useful plant, culinary or medicinal, which is not woody and dies back to the ground in winter. (Of course that definition would not work in the tropics where there is no real winter. Some of the tropical herbs take their cues from dry seasons much as our temperate herbs take theirs from the march of spring, summer, autumn and winter.) The pumpkin is a nonwoody herbaceous plant, useful and culinary and medicinal, which dies back forever when hit by the hard frost of winter.

With Halloween just around the corner, I thought it might be nice to look beyond the pumpkin pies and the fried or toasted pumpkin seeds, seasonal culinary treats out at the **Herbal Vineyard**. We let our acorn squash, pumpkins and gourds trail through the vineyard after the June mowings show us the last semblance of order in the vineyard. By July the unkempt disorder has taken over until frost. Weeds and grasses grow so tall that it is amazing that the pumpkins can find room to flesh out. My grapes are growing in rows separated by sod, with vigorous teasels, yarrows, burdocks, even a few more delicate monardas, doing battle with the perennial grasses. And here come the pumpkins and gourds to join in the vegetable fray. By almost all definitions, all the plants aforementioned, save the grape, qualify as herbs.

But what is there beyond pumpkin pie and pumpkin seeds to make an herb out of the vegetable? Or is it a fruit? Depends on who you talk to.

The seeds contain 35-50% oil, of a composition similar to corn oil. Nutritionally it's perhaps superior to palm oil, inferior to safflower oil, at least as far as unsaturated fatty acids are concerned. Such oils may possibly be better than palm oils to prevent such things as hypertension, hypercholersterolemia, atherosclerosis and associated heart problems. The seeds may contain up to 0.4% lecithin and the oil may contain 40-50% linolenic acid. The seeds were also one of many folk remedies for cancer mentioned in Jonathan Hartwell's *Plants Used Against Cancer*. A tea made from the seeds had been suggested for hypertrophy of the prostate gland. The seeds do contain sitosterol, which has some questionable reputation, along with zinc, as beneficial in prostate conditions. In the Orient, in America, and in Africa, and probably elsewhere the seeds have developed a reputation for expelling intestinal worms in the consumer, be it animal or human or ostrich. In *The Honest Herbal* Tyler (1981) states that they "are administered orally not for their estrogenic activity but to compete with cholesterol for absorption sites in the intestine in order to treat atherosclerosis." Julia Morton (Morris Arb. Bull. 26:24, 1975) notes that sitosterol does have aphrodisiac effects, at least in male mice, while Jonathan Hartwell lists sitosterol as an anticancer agent. Cucurbitin, an unusual amino acid is the active anthelmintic property that causes the expulsion of worms. The seeds are also reported to contain the pain killer salicylic acid, close kin to aspirin.

Gradually archeologists have pushed back the finds of pumpkin seeds in Mexican sites from 5 to 7 to nearly 9,000 years B.C. With useful fruit rinds, edible pulp, edible seeds, even edible flowers, and fruits that reach 300 pounds or more in weight, keeping for some time without refrigeration; small wonder that the pumpkin is of long standing interest. And if you have seen a pumpkin field in October, with enough fruits to fill the house and barn, not just the fruit and root cellar, you might want to extend a medal of honor to the man who thought up the jack-o-lantern, enabling the farmer to dispose of a few more of the superfluous pumpkins.

There are many folk remedies attributed either to the pumpkin, the squash, or the zucchini, just some of the many species of *Cucurbita*. I frankly don't think that even the plant taxonomists can tell the species apart without special training in Cucurbitaceae. Philippinos use the sap from the stem for earache. Although the hairy leaves can be irritating to the skin, they are plastered onto the back as a maltreatment for chills and fevers. Powdered seed has been used in snail fever (tropical schistosomiasis, improving about 75% of the cases). Indochinese administered the root, with pigweed and goosegrass to lower fever in smallpox. The pulp of the fruits has been applied to boils, burns and carbuncles. In the West Indies the flowers have been used for such diverse ailments as jaundice, measles and smallpox. Indochinese make a pumpkin soup, recommended for gastritis and food poisoning. I don't suppose the FDA will get after the pumpkin soup for gastritis any more than they will the chicken soup for colds, or the name brand vegetable soup for containing anticancer vitamins A and C. The pumpkins also contain a lot of fiber. And the leaves no doubt contain vitamin E and antioxidants.

Even though they are reported to lower blood pressure (in chickens), and eliminate worms and prostate problems, let's not eat immoderately of the seeds. Scientific treatises from South Africa seem a bit equivocal: Stock owners report suspected cases of "crasiness" and symptoms of paralysis in domestic stock, and poultry, even ostriches, believed due to the seed. Following reports that sheep ate a lot of pumpkin, one scientist fed large quantities of fresh pumpkin seed to a young sheep with no ill effect except transient diarrhea.

So far I've enjoyed my pumpkin seeds, except those of one dealer who chronically oversalts his, and have suffered no hypertrophy of the prostate, schistosomiasis, or tapeworm.

## Stevia (*Stevia rebaudiana*)

*The Business of Herbs* 4(5):4-5,17, November/December, 1986

There are more than 2,000 folders in my office, each with a collection of facts and fables about various medicinal plants. But in one of these folders there's an old wrinkled envelope dated 5/19/45. In it are old leaves of Paraguay's "caaehe," meaning "sweet herb," *Stevia rebaudiana*. More than 40 years old, one leaf of the Stevia will still sweeten a cup of coffee or tea enough to satisfy my sweet tooth. Yet that leaf contains very few calories. Stevia contains a compound, stevioside, 300 times sweeter than sucrose without the aftertaste that I've come to associate with saccharin or cyclamates, and with less than a calorie.

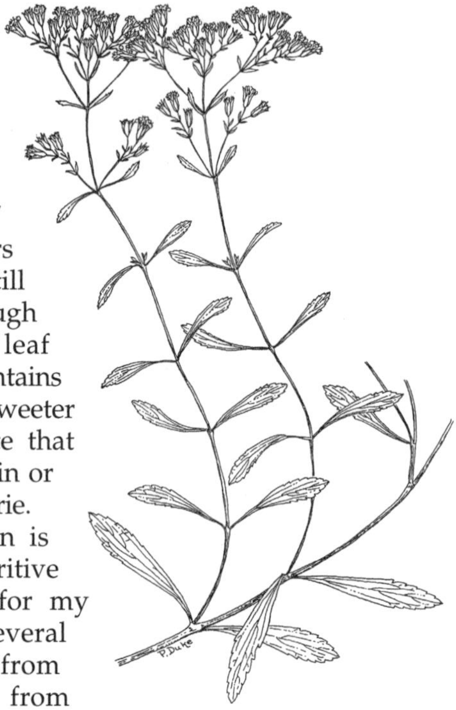

As far as this obese American is concerned, we still need a non-nutritive sweetener in this country. And for my money, this one's the best of several herbal candidates: monelin from *Dioscoreophyllum*, glycyrrhizin from *Glycyrrhiza*, phyllodulcin from *Hydrangea*, hernandulcin from *Lippia*, a glycoside from *Momordica*, osladin from *Polypodium grosvenori*, stevioside from *Stevia*, miraculin from *Synsepalum*, and thaumatin from *Thaumatococcus*.

Set out in spring, the herb Stevia, perennial in its native Paraguay and Brazil, grows to nearly two feet or more tall, flowering (and sometimes setting viable seed) here in Maryland, but killed by the frost. It overwinters well in the Caribbean islands and in the Mediterranean climate of California, e.g., around Davis. Around here it needs to be brought in to over-winter in the greenhouse. It does well in my greenhouse and can be stripped of its sweet leaves occasionally throughout the winter, though its recovery is much slower in the winter here.

A friend just returning from Paraguay was kind enough to send me three different samples of Stevia preparations from Paraguay. Showing just how newsworthy the herb is, he also copied for me a complete Brazilian symposium (1986) with over 20 chapters reporting research on Stevia. It's big in the herbal news here in America as well. In-Volume 1 of *Economic and Medicinal Plant Research*, the first chapter, by Kinghorn and Soejarto, concerns the status of stevioside as a sweetening agent for the human food chain. With an oral LD50 of 192mg/kg of one kilogram body weight, it takes only 192 mg caffeine to kill 50% of an experimental rat population. The LD5Os reported for Stevia and stevioside are more like 2,000 to 8,000 mg/kg, suggesting that the sweetener is less than one-tenth as toxic as caffeine. Hence people like me who drink too much coffee add little to their risks by using Stevia as a sweetener. The caffeine is more dangerous than the stevioside, at least as far as we can speculate based on LD50s.

Without reviewing the data in the 52 page-paper by Kinghorn and Soejarto, I summarize what I consider the most salient points: "Stevioside is considered to be appropriate for use as a sweetening agent for all foods, since it is highly stable to acids and heat; it has similar sweetness characteristics to sucrose; it can be regarded as noncaloric; it is non-fermentive, and it does not discolor when heated... Crude and purified *Stevia rebaudiana* extracts, as well as crystalline stevioside...are considered to be safe for human consumption." After such a nice clearance, they then toss in a few caveats which I won't detail here. They reiterate, "one might conclude, on the basis of these observations, that these materials offer no potential toxicity risk to humans." In spite of these cheering words, I predict rough sailing with our FDA for this non-nutritive sweetener. I hope it will make it.

In Paraguay, Stevia is recommended as an antiacid, cardiotonic and diuretic, for such diverse ailments as diabetes, gastroenteritis, hypertension, hyperuricemia and obesity. I'm not sure I'm ready to try it for any of these, except perhaps diabetes obesity, based on the publications I have seen thus far. I'm rather sure that replacing sugar with stevioside could alleviate some kinds of diabetes and obesity, if no compensatory carbohydrates were sneaked in to make up for the sugar replaced with the stevioside.

Although the Indians of Brazil and Paraguay have used Stevia to sweeten their maté for centuries, it was not discovered by modern science until this century. Stevia could be mixed with antioxidant GRAS lemongrass as a pre-sweetened tea, with no medicinal claims (BUT no naturally sweetened claims either, thanks to the perversity of FDA, perhaps with generous encouragement from the likes of Monsanto). As I read the rules, such a tea could be sold legally in the U.S. as a food. I think a lot of obese Americans with a sweet tooth would benefit therefrom. I'd buy it, were it available. I'd like to have a penny a teabag once someone starts marketing it here in the U.S. I'd suggest the quiet addition of some GRAS antiobesity herbs, as well, to make a non-nutritive, vitamin-rich "Dietea."

Part Six

# Herb A Day…

# Middle East

# Almond (*Prunus dulcis*)

(Unpublished)

Some people may object to my terming Biblical plants faith-based health foods or medicinals. Though baptized among southern Baptists at a tender and naive age, and though playing country music hymns for Holy Rollers, or whatever more respectful term they are called today, I don't classify myself as a religious or faith-based person. I am a devoutly curious spiritualist with a great respect for nature and natural medicines. Still I have heard that >90% of Americans pray so I was not at all surprised at the statistics I viewed for the first time on this Aug. 12, 2005.

Under the headline, "Religion Can Trump Medical Advice, Docs Say," *Reuters Health* says that many U.S. doctors believe religious convictions of the patient should outweigh their own professional advice re certain medical decisions. Surveying 794 physicians about religion and its effect on U.S. healthcare (23% said religion has a negative effect on healthcare, 30%, a negligible effect, and 47%, a positive). That tells me that twice as many physicians think religion has a positive effect on healthcare as think it has a negative effect. In such cases, both physicians and patients would probably both like to know about Biblical plants with positive health effects. Over half (57 percent) of the physicians surveyed said that a patient's religious reason for a medical course of action should trump a doctor's treatment advice. The other 43 percent said it should not (Reuters, 2005). I'd like to cap that off by saying that if the patient believes more in a faith-cased food like an almond, than he does in an expensive pharmaceutical, I, and some physicians and perhaps many more psychologists and placeboists think that patient is more likely to be cured by the Biblical food.

Dr. McNeilus, MD (2005) tells us of the physioloical and spiritual advantages of Christian meditation and prayer:

1. strong frontal lobe activity, with beta-waves predominating, even an altered state;
2. decreased stress hormones;
3. decreased susceptibility to mind control techniques; and
4. active communications with God (McNeilus, 2005).

Even skeptical Jim Duke can bring down his blood pressure significantly through deep breathing and meditation. And I know that high blood pressure, stress, loneliness, and non-communication are bad on the health. Proper exercise and diet can also lower stress and improve health and prevent cancer, cardiopathy, diabetes and iatrogenesis, the major killers here in the United States.

Having enlisted that modest bit or "religious support," I have consequently started looking into the active phytochemicals in Biblical food plants to see that, in fact, they do contain many biologically active compounds in useful quantities. Further we read that even the FDA admits that almonds, like many nuts, are heart friendly. Supportive research shows that eating "1.5 ounces per day of most nuts, such as walnuts, as part of a diet low in saturated fat and cholesterol may reduce the risk of heart disease" (FDA, as quoted by Hasler, 2003). The FDA disqualified brazil nuts, cashews, macadamias and even some varieties of Biblical pine nuts because they exceed the saturated fat levels specified for health claims. So with faith-based AND FDA support, let's look at some recent science.

Here are capsular summaries of some of the more recent studies showing medicinal potential of almonds. Chen et al. (2005), lead off saying that consumption of tree nuts such as almonds has been associated with lower coronary risks. Phytochemicals, sometimes concentrated in almonds skins (catechin, epicatechin, quercetin, kaempferol, and isorhamnetin) contribute to antioxidant activity. They are bioavailable and are synergic with vitamin C and E to protect LDL against oxidation In other words (mine), the almond, with husk, IS a multinutrient pill, competetive with store-bought multinutrient pills. Jambazian et al. (2005), fed three diets for 4 weeks each: a control diet, a low-almond diet, and a high-almond diet, in which almonds contributed 0%, 10%, and 20% of total energy, respectively. Almonds help meet the revised RDA of 15 mg/day alpha-tocopherol and increase plasma and red blood cell alpha-tocopherol concentrations. Jaceldo-Siegl et al. (2004) evaluated long-term almond supplementation in healthy men (n 43) and women (n 38) aged 25-70 years. During the first 6 months, subjects followed their habitual diets; in the second 6 months, subjects added almonds to their diets. On average, the almond supplement was 52 g/d (about forty-two nuts, ca 1.25 g per almond) containing 1286 kJ. When subjects changed from habitual to almond-supplemented diet, the intakes of MUFA, PUFA, fibre, vegetable protein, alpha-tocopherol, Cu and Mg significantly increased by 42, 24, 12, 19, 66, 15 and 23% respectively; the intakes of trans fatty acids, animal protein, Na, cholesterol and sugars significantly decreased by 14, 9, 21, 17 and 13% respectively. These spontaneous nutrient changes closely match the dietary recommendations to prevent cardiovascular and other chronic diseases.

An older study already had me, genetically targeted for colon cancer, already eating a handful of almonds a day, when I am lucky enough to have them on hand. Davis and Iwahashi (2001) showed that almonds and almond fractions reduce aberrant crypt foci in rat models of colon carcinogenesis. Their results suggest that almonds may reduce colon cancer risk via a lipid-associated component. And I certainly like them, whether or not they also contain significant quantities of laetrile-like compounds. Dicenta et al. (2002) found cyanogenic compounds (amygdalin and prunasin) in kernels, leaves, and roots of 5 sweet-, 5 slightly bitter-, and 5 bitter-kernelled almond trees. Prunasin was reported only in vegetative parts (roots and leaves). Amygdalin was detected only in the kernels, mainly in bitter genotypes (2050-4115 mg/kg, calculated from amygdalin content, slightly bitter types, 20-330, sweet types 0-105).

Prunasin seems to be present in most almond roots (with a variable concentration); only bitter-kernelled genotypes are able to transform it into amygdalin in the kernel. I think I am right in suggesting that the higher the amygdalin, or prunasin, the higher the cyanide AND the higher the laetrile equivalent. Certainly Dicenta et al. calculate their amygdalin and prunasin as cyanide. Figuring that a small almond weighs one gram, makes it easy to see how much cyanide it might contain, from 0 in the sweetest of the sweet through to 2-4 mg in the bitter.

Working with closely related peach pits, Fukuda et al. (2003) found four minor components, (with the major cyanogenic amygdalin and prunasin) and characterized them as mandelic acid glycosides (beta-gentiobioside and beta-D-glucoside) and benzyl alcohol glycosides (beta-gentiobioside and beta-D-glucoside). All significantly inhibited the Epstein-Barr virus early antigen activation induced by tumor promoter. They also delayed two-stage carcinogenesis on mouse skin comparable to (-)-epigallocatechin gallate.

Amygdalin has more than chemopreventive activities, it is probably one reason why different *Prunus* species show up in OTC and herbal cough medicines. It is antiinflammatory, antispasmodic, antitussive and expectorant (FNF). Here's a case where I think almonds should be seriously compared, as a third arm, with placebo and pharmaceutcial: (1) for coughs and cold, (2) for cardioprotection, and (3) for chemoprevention of cancer.

Almond is loaded with phytochemcials that can help with many ailments. Although it has been with us nearly a decade, I fear that the new "genomic medicine" may perhaps be an order of magnitude more expensive than current humdrum allopathic medicine, the latter treating us all as average. I'm not average! Are you? We vary in our responses to medicines 10-100-fold, sometimes more, and that's genomic. Even if it is the wave of the future, who can afford genomic medicine except the wealthiest?

Fearing the cost, I appreciate a possible side effect. Listening to the chants of the genomic doctors, humdrum humans will now realize they aren't average. They may finally realize their average HMO physician cannot figure them out in the average 6 minute visit. Ten years from now this will lead Americans to the herbal/food farmacy realization that, unlike the synthetic pharmaceutical cocktails (of 2-3 chemicals) they are dreaming up today, the herb is and has been for millennia a pharmaceutical cocktail of thousands of gentle natural chemicals with which we coevolved and from which our individual genomes instinctually and homeostatically mine those phytochemicals we need and reject those we don't need, trying to get our body back to norm via homeostasis.

# Chasteberry (*Vitex agnus-castus*)

*The Business of Herbs* 13(5):12-13. November/December, 1995

Though frequent as an ornamental in the United States, the chasteberry tree has only recently emerged as an important medicinal plant, following on the heels of an explosive emergence as a European phyto-medicinal. As important as it has become, it is significant to note where chasteberry has been overlooked: in Grieve's *Modern Herbal*, Varro Tyler's *Honest Herbals*, most pharmacopoeia and dispensatories, and all of my early books.

Apparently deriving its scientific name from virilium, which means plaiting, the wiry branches of *Vitex agnus-castus* were once used in constructing wattle fences and basketry. Another name, "hemp tree," is due to the young plant's resemblance to marijuana. [[Many is the time Peggy and I have seen vistors in our sunroom gape in disbelief as they look out our picture window. The well pruned chaste tree looks very much like marijuana, until it comes into flower; then it looks more like a nice butterfly bush]].

Alcohol and ether extracts of the leaves stem the growth of *Micrococcus pyogenes* but not *Escherichia coli*. Aqueous and alcoholic extracts have inhibited the fungus *Neurospora*. At 500 mg/ml the hydroethanolic extract killed *Fusarium oxysporum* but not *Aspergillus fumigatus* or *A. niger*. The seeds, prescribed for colic in horses, yield a dark oil which elicits progesterone-like activity in mature female rats. It's that reference that prompts me to write this column.

## A long history

Hippocrates, in the fourth century BC, suggested chasteberries for injuries, inflammation, and enlarged spleen. Leaves were steeped in wine for hemorrhage and passing of afterbirth, the latter perhaps portending its current hormonal use.

The idea of chasteberry to suppress libido also arose in antiquity, ca 55 AD. Dioscorides anticipated some of the chasteberry's modern usage: "It both brings down the milk and expels ye menstrua – being drank in wine... A decoction of the seed is for inflammation about the womb."

Dioscorides also mentioned mixing it with pennyroyal for headaches, perhaps accompanying dysmenorrhea. As a poultice it was suggested for bites, inflammations, and wounds. Dioscorides hinted that the anaphrodisiac (opposite of aphrodisiac, a turn-off instead of a turn-on) reputation stemmed from women placing the foul-smelling branches and leaves upon their beds to deter amorous men. The anaphrodisiac reputation may date back to the Greeks and Romans, maybe earlier.

It has been used as a diaphoretic, diuretic, emmenagogue, febrifuge, galactagogue, tonic, and vulnerary. Arabs have used it for epilepsy, hysteria, and insanity. A tea of the roots has been used in malaria and typhus.

Elsewhere (in Unani medicine) the plant is suggested to be abortifacient and emmenagogue; seeds are used for dropsy and inflammation and to purify the brain and liver. The hot seed decoction is reportedly used as a contraceptive. In Ayurvedic medicine, the seeds are considered abortifacient, alexiteric, diuretic, heating, and stomachic; they are used for burning sensations, itch, thirst, and to improve the taste. Indians may have used the plants for eye ailments and stomachache. Patients with colds may bathe in the leaf tea, and the plant is used for pains due to chills. Homeopathically, the plant is used for depression, neurasthenia, and impotence. Studies suggest that chasteberry can help control acne in teenagers.

The Catholic Church in Europe encouraged blossoms of the shrubs in the clothes of novice monks to suppress the libido. Owing to the aroma of the fruits, it was once known as "monk's pepper" and was reportedly used in seasoning their food – Asian herbal "saltpeter." The fruits, with 4,000 to 12,000 ppm of essential oil, are used as condiments and vegetable preservatives.

## Modern uses

Currently, European women use the fruits to regulate the menstrual period and to control or alleviate dysmenorrhea. Ancient Greeks and Romans noted that it increased a mother's milk. One recent study indicates that it can not only increase milk production but also the efficiency of production, and decrease mastopathic conditions. Such activity might be due to as yet unidentified hormones and/or stimulation of the master endocrine gland, the pituitary.

Chasteberry is said to have progesterone effects, decreasing the estrogen to progesterone ratio, thereby benefiting in premenstrual syndrome, which may result from excessive estrogen. The fruit extract seems to inhibit the release of follicle-stimulating hormone and increase the lutenizing hormone, thereby easing menstrual difficulties. Chasteberry is also believed to modulate prolactin secretion from the pituitary. Clinical studies have confirmed the lactagogue effect in lactating women with poor breast milk production. For my daughter, I would suggest chasteberry extracts orally, combined with topical wild yam, to improve estrogen-progesterone ratio.

John Lee, author of the 1993 book, *Natural Progesterone*, often referred to an over-the-counter skin moisturizer cream which was apparently based on wild-yam-derived progesterone. Seeking synergy and the mastogenic activity of fenugreek, I would combine chasteberry, fennel, fenugreek (containing up to 1.9 percent diosgenin, the "natural" progesterone precursor; so far, I find no reports of diosgenin from chasteberry), and wild yam extracts to make my mastogenic moisturizer cream with the delightful side effects of helping in such things as cyclic migraine, dysmenorrhea, frigidity, mastitis, osteoporosis, PMS, and the like.

Stephen Dentali (American Herb Association) noted that diosgenin can be the starter material for natural progesterone, which, topically applied, better than oral progesterone, may help in breast cancer, cervical dysplasia, dysmenorrhea, endometrial cancer, endometriosis, hot flashes, menopause, metrorrhagia, osteoporosis, ovarian cysts, PMS, and uterine fibroids (Lee, 1993). While we don't know that chasteberry contains diosgenin, we could combine it with fenugreek and/or wild yam to ensure the presence of diosgenin, starter material for natural progesterone.

## Some concerns...

There is no proof at all that our bodies convert diosgenin to progesterone. It is a rather complex reaction that may possibly happen with stomach acid, but remains to be proven. [[Most chemists with whom I speak say it does not happen. Some questionable reports mention natural testosterone and progesterone as natural components of the plant.]] After talking with responsible chemists, I suspect that the "natural progesterone" in the wild yam creams may, in fact, be synthesized from natural diosgenin. [For more discussion of the reported diosgenin-progesterone connection, complete with a healthy dose of scientific skepticism, see "Herb a Day," *The Business of Herbs*, May/June 1995.]

Naturopaths warn us that chasteberry should not be used during pregnancy. Itch or rash may occur as a side effect in one or two percent of patients. Menstrual flow may increase during treatment (often an indication of therapeutic efficacy). There may be early resumption of menstruation after childbirth.

# Chickpea (*Cicer arietinum*)

(Unpublished)

## Dhal, Gram, Hummus and Provender (Biblical)

*And the oxen and the asses that till the ground will eat salted provender, which has been winnowed with shovel and fork.* Isaiah 30

I could write a book on writing books. I can't even find a copy of my first real published book, *The Handbook of Legumes of World Economic Importance.* (Oh yes; I found it; my industrious illustrious illustrator, Mrs. Duke, had it. So maybe I should quote it.) I do have the Japanese translation however. Legumes is one common name for members of the bean family. Legumes are often also called pulses, and, in India, grams. The first medicinal entry under today's legume, the chickpea reads: "aphrodisiac"; that oughta sell a lot of hummus. "In the 16th century, chickpeas were believed to be aphrodisiac: Curiously enough, lentils were considered to have the opposite effect, and this was probably the reasons why the lentil was included in the diet in monasteries on meatless days." That's one thing I had to say about chickpea in that first Plenum book (Duke, 1981). H'mm. Maybe I should eat more Biblical chickpeas and forego some of those monastic Biblical lentils. Now with all the health hype on soy, maybe I could talk Plenum into a second edition. We could set the stage right. Soy is good, but it is not a unique nor even an unusually rich source of estrogenic isoflavones. And even though soy is approved as a heart healthy legume for lowering the cholesterol, it is probably, like the peanut, too oil rich, and not the most heart healthy of the common edible legumes. Soy contains ten times as much fat proportionate to its protein, than do many of those other legumes (except peanut). Of course when the soy industry processes the bean they take out that oil and sell that as another product and then do their research on the defatted soybean. The Asian Indians see thru the soy hype. Here's what they say about the venerable chickpea, *Cicer arietinum*, subject of this week's newsletter. "The nutritional value...is superior to soybean, cowpea, faba bean, mung bean, pea, lentil, pigeon pea and blackgram."

Most beans are rich in phytates or phytic acid. Remember that phytic acid is termed an antinutrient; but it is also termed a cancer preventive. It does reduce the nutritional potential but increases the anticancer potential of the bean that contains it. If you want the most nutrition, "soaking, cooking of soaked seeds, sprouting and autoclaving reduce the phytic acid content and increase the digestibility" (WO3). But do you really want to reduce antinutrient chemopreventives like phytic acid? If you are more afraid of cancer and/or obesity than starvation, maybe you ought to keep the antinutrients. Here's what my USDA database says about phytic acid and/or phytate, a cancer preventive compound:

**PHYTIC-ACID:**
Antiaggregant LAF; Antitumor JAF44:2663;
Antioxidant JAF44:2663; Cancer-Preventive 525/; Fungicide JAF44:2663;
Hypocalcemic (*Sodium phytate*) M11; Hypocholesterolemic JAF44:2663;
Hypolipidemic JAF44:2663;

Yes, there are other antinutrients, e.g. an alpha-amylase inhibitor. UV irradiation, pressure cooking and germinating can eliminate that problem. Though Andy Weil has cast aspersions on sprouted legumes, there is much good to be said for sprouting. I worry more about those few legumes, like alfalfa, that contain canavanine, which may induce lupus-like symptoms in susceptible people. Note above that sprouting diminishes two antinutrients. "Germination is found to increase in vitro digestibility." In germination, there is an increase in nutritional quality of the protein and significant increases in Vitamin C. "Germinating gram (their name for chickpea in this text) has provided maximum benefit for animal growth" (WO3). Germination followed by cooking reduces oligosaccharides by 60%; germination also improves mineral availability. Overnight soaking of chickpeas reduces polyphenolic compounds by 50%. [But those are some of the polyphenolics the health food and green tea people are promoting.] Roasting or parching also reduces some antinutrient levels.

Now if you are diabetic, you might prefer that your beans are less digestible, leading to delayed insulin spikes. Yes, the USDA and food processors brag about removing antinutrients from your food chain, but all these, even the estrogenic isoflavones, are anticancer compounds. They make the food more digestible, yet less medicinal. Should you even throw out the soaking water? Alas, you may pass more gas if you don't discard it, but you may perhaps increase your potential for cancer, cardiopathy and diabetes if you do. Those "antinutrients" are also cancer preventives.

Beans, beans, just might be the answer;
Both to diabetes and to cancer;
Beans, beans, good for the heart;
The more you eat, the less you infarct.

In Turkey and India, chickpea is even recommended for baby foods as well. In Indonesia it is made into tempeh, whose shelf life can be extended by the addition of lactobacillus. That lactobacillus, probiotic, with prebiotic oligofructans, might be very useful to patients recovering from a yeast overgrowth and antibiotic treatment. *The Wealth of India* praises chickpea as "preventive diet for atherosclerosis because of its rich phosphorus content" (WO3). Pangamic acid is respected as the "stamina-building [aphrodisiac?], antistress and antihyperlipidemic principle of gram."

The seed is a great source of folate, but not as great as reported in *The Wealth of India*. They said there was some 140 to 185 mg/100 gram serving (WO2). Too bad! They surely must have meant to say micrograms. I did not even enter their figure for folate in my database, fully discounting it.

But if they meant 1.4 to 1.8 mg per kilo on a fresh weight basis, that translates to 2 mg/kg ZMB, fairly rich in folate, to provide all those benefits associated with folate. The highest source of folic acid in my database is *Corchorus olitorius* with 32 mg/kg. A hundred grams of the latter would satisfy my RDA. What are the reported benefits of folic acid?

**FOLIC-ACID:**
Antianemic 5-20 mg/man/day; Antitumor (preventive) CRH7:61; Anticervicaldysplasic 8-30 mg/wmn/day/orl PAM; Anticheilitic DAS; Anticoronary 400 ug/man/day CRH7:61; Antidementia 10-20 mg/day WER; Antidepressant 800 ug/day DAS WER; Antigingivitic 2-5 mg/day/man PAM; Antiglossitic DAS; Antigout 10-40 mg/day MUR; Antiinfertility WER; Antimetaplastic 10 mg/day WER; Antimyelotoxic 5 mg/day/orl/man M29; Antineuropathic DAS; Antiperiodontal 1 mg day PAM WER; Antiplaque PAM; Antipolyp (preventive) CRH7:61; Antipsychotic M29; Anti-spina-bifida DAS; Hematopoietic M11; Immunostimulant CRH7:62; Xanthine-Oxidase-Inhibitor PAM; Uricosuric PAM; "RDA"=400-800 ug/day DAS; LD50=100 (ipr mus).

Yes; I really suspect that India's dhal or gram, like America's bean soup or bean, might be more heart-healthy than the soybean. Clearly chickpea has significant cholesterol lowering activity in rabbits and rats. In clinical studies, 80% of the patients lowered their cholesterol on a 67 week program. Chickpea also significantly lowered serum lipids in humans. Additionally gram was significantly antiatherogenic, at least in rabbits, lowering the cholesterol measurements in the aortic wall. The isoflavone biochanin-A, present in many legumes (Biochanin-C is reported for soy), prevents egg-yolk-induced hypercholesterolemia in rats. Every continent has its suite of edible legumes, all of which seem to be heart healthy. As they occur in the field, the soy and peanut are probably the least heart-healthy of the commonly consumed edible beans because of their much higher fat content. I like most of them better than soybean. I certainly prefer the lean, mean, American bean. And hummus, with its garlic and olive oil, seems to be a bit more heart healthy and flavorful than tofu.

Running around 0.2% choline, chickpeas are again one of the richer sources of this heart healthy compound, which might not only prevent Alzheimer's in the aging, but speed up learning, maybe even in utero, and certainly in young rat offspring. Matter of fact, I've convinced myself, if not anyone else, that the choline in the beans my mother ate while I was in the uterus, facilitated my learning and will retard dementia. And we didn't even have an RDA for choline until a couple years back in the 90's. Chickpea mixed with alu methi (fenugreek) would really rev up the choline content of an Indian dish. What does choline have to offer. Let's ask the USDA database.

**CHOLINE:**
Antialzheimeran 5-16 g/man/day; Antichoreic; Anticirrhotic (6,000 mg/man/day); Anticystinuric; Antidementic; Antidiabetic; Antidyskinetic 150-200 mg/kg/man/day; Antimanic 15-30 g/man/day/orl; Cholinergic; Hepatoprotective; Hypotensive; Ileorelaxant; Lipotropic; Parasympathomimetic (1/1000th acetylcholine).

Hmm; choline and often co-occurring lecithin both contribute liver-protective activities, making this a hepatoprotective food farmaceutical as well. Legumes, in general, are good sources of lecithin and/or choline, some of which can cross the blood/brain barrier. Lecithin itself has been shown to prevent cirrhosis in gorillas, if not Jim Duke. The soy people brag about their high lecithin content (1.5-2.5%), but they don't have as much to brag about as *The Wealth of India* (WO3), reporting 3-9% lecithin in the chickpea, second in my updated database only to the brazil nut. And here's what the database says about lecithin:

**LECITHIN:**
Antialzheimeran 40-100 g/man/day/orl; Antiataxic; Anticirrhotic; Antidementic; Antidyskinetic 40-80 g/man/day/orl; Antieczemic; Antilithic; Antimanic; Antimorphinistic; Antioxidant (Synergist); Antipsoriac; Antisclerodermic; Antiseborrheic; Antisprue; AntiTourette's 20-50 g/man/day/orl; Antitumor(Lung); Cholinergic; Hepatoprotective; Hypocholesterolemic (20-30 g/man/day); Lipotropic.

In my first *Medicinal Plants of the Bible,* I did not include the chickpea, as none of the scholars I had read seemed to stress that possibility. Since then though, I have read that the word "provender" of the Bible might better have been translated hummus, indeed may have been the chickpea. And yes, the leaves of the provender are eaten, more by animals than by humans. But humans do ingest cooked young leaves like spinach. According to Zohary, the Biblical hamitz, cognate with the Arabic humus, and the Aramaic himtza, means chickpea, and today himtza is modern Hebrew for chickpea. ("The RSV translation as 'provender' is mistaken.") Chickpea was apparently originally domesticated in Turkey and some neighboring countries. It has been found in prepottery Neolithic levels of some prehistoric sites, in Early Bronze Age deposits of Jericho, in Iraq as well as elsewhere. Earliest records are from Turkey "dating from 5000 BC." Today I believe that chickpea was one of several pulses already cultivated in the Biblical World in Biblical Times, more than 200 years ago.

Chickpea belongs in my diet and in my list of medicinal plants of the Bible. I just discussed four of the dozens of important reported phytochemicals in this powerhouse. There are no doubt thousands of lesser chemicals. Had I given you the biological activities for all of just those listed below, you might have limply concluded that chickpea, indeed all legumes, have some phytochemicals that may contribute to the alleviation of almost all diseases. That's the beauty of food farmacy. The foods, herbs and spices contain hundreds of biologically active compounds with which your genes have co-evolved for millions of years. And during the process, homeostasis evolved for many if not all these compounds, such that the deficient body grabs for them while homeostatically excluding those in access. So look at that long list below in a different light; look at it as a menu of biologically active phytochemicals. If man evolved in Africa and then spread out of Africa through the Biblical land bridge, consuming Biblical legumes along the way, your genes have a long aquaintance with Biblical phytochemicals. And, believe it or not, Jim Duke says your body is smart enough to grab those it needs and exclude those it does not need, to a point. That's the beauty of homeostasis. And even if you are a chemophobe, your body is nothing but a mountain of biochemicals continuously involved in thousands of reactions and continuously striving for homeostatic balance. A multiple menu food farmaceutical helps with that balance. A synthetic pharmaceutical is more likely to throw your body off its homeostatic balance. A long familiar food contains many phytochemicals your body needs. And that may be why Hippocrates said: "Let food be your pharmacy."

# Cumin, Black or Fitches (*Nigella sativa*)

(Unpublished)

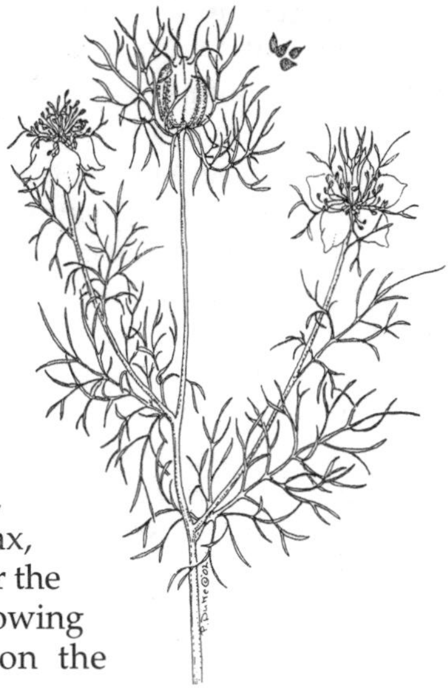

Usually at this festive time of year, I bring out my frankincense and myrrh, as subjects for some seasonal little article for various newsletters. Fitches were so important to the Christians, that they are mentioned in the Bible, along with a lot of other spices (almond, anise, bay, black cumin, caper, carob, cassia, cinnamon, coriander, cumin, dill, fenugreek, galbanum, garlic, juniper, leek, marjoram or Biblical hyssop, mint, mustard, myrtle, onion, poppy, rue, saffron, sage, spikenard, storax, and wormwood). Roughly 600 years after the birth of Christ, the world's fastest growing religion, Islam, was founded based on the revelations of the prophet Mohammad.

Oriental spices were important to Mohammad, founder of that great religion, as they were to Jesus, namesake of another great religion. Mohammad even married a spice merchant 15 years his senior. Yet I don't find many of the spices, not even Arabian frankincense and myrrh, listed on a very useful website hosting the writings of the Hadith. [The Hadith is a vast collection (ten volumes in one collection) of the sayings of the Prophet Muhammad.] I do find some mention of black cumin, garlic, hyssop, leek, mustard, onion, and saffron, but no cinnamon, cassia, caraway and coriander, e.g.

Among Muslims, no spice seems to attract higher praise than the black cumin, *Nigella sativa*. "I heard Allah's Apostle saying, 'There is healing in black cumin for all diseases except death'" (from MSA-USC Hadith Database: www.usc.edu/ dept/MSA/reference/searchhadith.htm).

I don't have a searchable Qu'ran on my computer like I have a searchable Bible. Unlike the Bible, the Qur'an was compiled over a very short period of time and is entirely orientated towards revelation and the word of Allah. The Qur'an does mention the benefits of consuming certain foods, e.g. honey, and abstinence from alcohol. But, like the Bible, contains few specifics on disease and health. Prophetic medicine was mostly prayer. The Hadith, however, details guidelines on diet and the treatment of simple ailments like sore throat, conjunctivitis and fever.

I published a CRC *Handbook of Medicinal Spices* in 2002, 510 years after Columbus, long after the Native Americans discovered the hot pepper, my favorite spice, unknown in the Old World until Columbus. Yes that most important of spices (to me) never left America until after Columbus opened up the New World to the Old World. Actually Columbus was seeking Indians and black peppers but instead found America, red Indians and red peppers. Still I find that all the spices in my spice book have medicinal uses. I had not at first considered the black cumin so important, until I started searching the PubMed database. And lo and behold, this Muslim favorite, as hinted by the Hadith, does seem to be the panacea of Muslims of the Middle East.

Its most common name, black cumin, is a misnomer, as it is a member of the buttercup family (Ranunculaceae), not the celery family (Apiaceae) to which true cumin, *Cuminum cyminum* belongs. It has other common names, e.g. in the USDA nomenclature database (equally misleading from the taxonomic point of view): Roman-coriander, fennel-flower, and nutmeg-flower. In the Bible, black cumin seed are known as "fitches." Black cumin is about as well known as a spice as a medicine. The aromatic seeds are used whole or ground as a flavoring, especially in oriental cookery. Known Biblically as "fitches," the seeds were used in Biblical breads, and still show up, e.g. in Russian rye bread and Turkish breads. Called *siyah daneh* or onion seed, they are spinkled on cakes, flatbreads and rolls. Arabs mix the seed with honey as a confectionary. The tiny seeds, hot to the palate, are sprinkled on food like pepper. In Europe they are sometimes mixed with real pepper, and were used like black pepper before the introduction of black pepper. French once used the black cumin in lieu of black pepper under the name "uatre epices" or "toute epices." In the Bible, Ezekiel recites a recipe I have seen nowhere else. "Take thou unto thee wheat, and barley, and beans, and lentiles, and millet, and fitches, and put them in one vessel, and make thee bread thereof…And thou shalt eat it as barley cakes…" Bean bread, good for the heart; the more you eat the less you infarct.

As the Hadith states, the black cumin is good for many if not all the maladies of man, and certainly can be recommended for many. Here in America, the big killers, after pharmaceuticals in the United States, are cardiopathy, cancer, diabetes, and respiratory problems. And yes the "kalanji," as it is called in Pakistan, offers something for each of these killers. [Even for the hard core killer pharmaceuticals, by acting synergistically with them, thereby reducing dosages required.] Though we are more concerned about cancer, because it is generally more painful, more of us are killed by the more merciful quick killer, cardiopathy. The essential oil of the black cumin seed lowers arterial blood pressure and slows the heart beat. Consequently this seed oil has been recommended as an antihypertensive agent. The seed oil improves serum lipid profile in rats. Oil administration significantly decreases serum total cholesterol, LDL, and triglycerides and significantly elevated serum HDL. The plant is loaded with antioxidants as well, and I feel that these too are useful at preventing heart disease. The seeds also seem to serve cardiopathically as reasonably safe calcium-channel blockers.

There's a bit more research on the anticancer attributes of the black cumin. Jordanian scientists, studying local folk remedies for cancer found that aqueous extracts of nigella augmented natural killer cells (NKC's) which fight cancer and showed cytotoxic activity against tumor targets. The seed extracts potentiated these NKC's – 62.3% of 52.6% for garlic, and 30.6% for onion extracts, all mentioned in the Bible and the Hadith. Two of the ingredients, thymoquinone and dithymoquinone, reduce several types of human tumor cells, even those which seem to have developed multidrug resistance (MDR). That's why I mention them in conjunction to some pharmaceutical anticancer drugs to which MDR has evolved.

I'm worried about colon cancer, and thymoquinone can inhibit "forestomach," if not "afterstomach" cancer, at least in mice. With a folk reputation for indurations and/or tumors of the abdomen, eyes and liver, the seeds are rich in sterols (5,100 ppm), of which >63% is the antitumor sterol, beta-sitosterol. Black cumin seems to kill certain cancer cells while leaving normal cells intact. It is being suggested as a supplement to anticancer drugs by preventing toxicity of such drugs in the human body, including protection of bone marrow against chemotherapy. Most important in my book, seed extracts enhance immune response, increasing activity of T-helper and natural killer cells, and interferon-like responses. Cisplatin, a widely used chemotherapeutic drug, can be toxic to the kidney. But taking the drug together with cysteine, vitamin E, black cumin and saffron can reduce its toxicity.

There's not nearly as much there for diabetes (so far) as there is for respiratory diseases. But there are reports of hypoglycemic phytochemicals in the seed, and a lot of antidiabetic folklore.

Algerians sometime take the roasted seeds with butter for cough. Nigellone in the seed oil protects guinea pigs against histamine induced bronchospasms, suggesting the rationale behind its use in asthma, bronchitis, and cough. Scientists report that the volatile seed oil dose-dependently stimulates respiratory rate and intratracheal pressure. Thymoquinone, one of the major ingredients, at 1.6-6.4 mg/kg increased intratracheal pressure but did not affect the respiratory rate. "Kalonji" seed are used traditionally for asthma, and do, in fact, exhibit broncho-dilator and spasmolytic activities mediated possibly through calcium channel blockade, proving their utility for asthma.

So that's a quick look at some of the quick killers in the United States. But that's just a beginning. For the LIVER: The seed oil protects against hepatotoxicity and improves serum lipid profile in rats. Oil administration significantly decreases serum total cholesterol, low density lipoprotein, triglycerides and significantly elevated serum HDL. Sounds even better for the heart. Thymoquinone has been shown to be hepatoprotective, at least against hepatotoxicity of carbon tetrachloride in mice.

Relative to GERM WARFARE and our current anthraciphobia, I did find one report that black cumin is active against one species of *Bacillus*, but not against *Bacillus anthrax*. Still if I had no cipro, I'd load up on garlic and black cumin, among other spices, because both kill certain species of *Bacillus*, the bacterial genus to which anthrax belongs, and both boost the immune system. Scientists screened 35 Indian spices for antimicrobial activity: black cumin, bishop's weed, camboge, celery, chili, clove, cinnamon, cumin, garlic, horseradish, nutmeg, onion, pomegranate, tamarind, and tejpat proved potently antimicrobial against *Bacillus subtilis, Escherichia coli* and *Saccharomyces cerevisiae*. Such results confirm traditional uses of spices as food preservatives, disinfectants and antiseptics, not necessarily effective at protecting one from GERM WARFARE.

For the FEMALE, seed extracts show lactagogue activity in rats, verifying its folk usage as a lactagogue (increasing the flow of mother's milk). Arabian women use the seeds for that purpose. Mixing curry (which contains fenugreek, another lactagogue) with black cumin, Indians have a double whammy lactagogue. BUT in large quantities the seed may possibly induce abortion. In Ayurvedic medicine, the herb is considered emmenagogue; in Unani, abortifacient.

For the arthritics suffering INFLAMMATION: The fixed oil (fatty oil as opposed to volatile oil ) of the seed and its pure thymoquinone inhibit the cyclooxygenase and 5-lipoxygenase. The thymoquinone was quite potent, with approximate IC50 values against 5-lipoxygenase and cyclooxygenase of < 1 microgram/ml and 3.5 micrograms/ml, respectively. Thymoquinone was sometimes ten-fold more potent. Still, since the inhibition of eicosanoid generation and lipid peroxidation by the fixed oil is greater than would be expected from its content of thymoquinone (ca. 2000 ppm), there must be synergy or other contributing phytochemicals, supporting the traditional use of the seed and derivatives for rheumatism and other related inflammatory diseases.

For the alcoholic ULCER: scientists report positive effects of the seed oil on gastric secretion and ethanol induced ulcers in rats. The oil led to significant increases in mucin and glutathione decreases in mucosal histamine. Ethanol administration produced 100% ulcers in rats; black cumin prevented many of these.

I was once confronted with a query about the use of black cumin for OBESITY. So I asked my computer what activities and nonubiquitous phytochemcials might help with obesity, and also probably with Syndrome X, which seems intimately tied to obesity and cofactors.

## *Nigella sativa* and Obesity

Antiedemic: beta-amyrin; damascenine; hederagenin; rutin Antifeedant: rutin CNS-Stimulant: carvone Catabolic: rutin Hypocholesterolemic: cycloartenol; d-limonene; rutin; thymoquinone Hypoglycemic: indole-3-acetic-acid

And last but not least, the lice: Over a hundred years ago, my Watt's *Dictionary of Economic Products of India* offered the following formula for eczema and head lice: 2 ounces bruised *Nigella* seed, two ounces bruised *Psoralea* seed, two ounces bdellium, two ounces *Coscini* root, one ounce sulfur in two bottles of coconut oil. But you'll have a tough time coming up with all those today in America. Finally, the seeds are sprinkled among woolens as a moth repellant.

Here's what I said in my *Medicinal Plants of the Bible* (Duke, 1983):

***Nigella sativa* L.; Black Cumin Fitch (Biblical)**

*...For the fitches are not thrashed with a threshing instrument.*
*...but the fitches are beaten out with a staff... .* Isaiah 28

"Black cumin is widely cultivated for its aromatic seeds, used whole or ground as a flavoring, especially in oriental cookery. Whole seeds used in Russian rye bread and for flavoring Turkish breads. Seeds may be used as a stabilizing agent for edible fats. A reddish-brown and semi-drying fatty oil is obtained from the seeds with benzene and subsequent steam distillation of the extract to remove about 31% of the volatile oil. Arabs mix the seed with honey as a confectionary. The tiny seeds are very hot to the palate, and are sprinkled on food like pepper; in fact, in Europe they are sometimes mixed with real pepper. Ethiopians add them to *Capsicum* pepper sauces. They are also added to bread and sprinkled on cakes. Ethiopians may add *Nigella*, *Aframomum*, *Piper*, and *Zingiber* to local alcoholic beverages. Seeds are sprinkled among woolens as a moth repellant."

According to an Arab proverb, "in the black seed is the medicine for every disease except death" (30). Regarded as carminative, digestive, diuretic, emmenagogue, excitant, lactagogue, purgative, resolvent, stimulant, stomachic, sudorific, tonic, and vermifuge, fitches have been suggested as folk remedies for asthma, bilious ailments, bronchitis, calluses, cancer, colic, corns, cough, eruptions, fever, flu, headache, jaundice, myrmecia, orchitis, puerperium, sclerosis, skin, snakebite, stomachache, swellings, tumors of the abdomen and eyes, and warts. Algerians take the roasted seeds with butter for cough, with honey for colic. Nigellone in the oil protects guinea pigs against histamine induced bronchospasms, suggesting the rationale behind its use in asthma, bronchitis, and cough. The lipid portion of the ether extract of the seeds has shown lactagogue activity in rats, verifying its folk usage as a lactagogue. In large quantities the seed are also used to induce abortion. The seeds contain ca 1.5% melanthine, a bad-smelling fish poison. Lebanese took the seed extract for liver ailments. In Indonesia, the seeds are added to astringent medicines for abdominal disorders. In Malaya the seeds are poulticed onto abscesses, headache, nasal ulcers, orchitis, and rheumatism. Ethiopians mix the seed, with melted butter, wrap it in a cloth, and sniff it for headache. Arabian women use the seeds as a galactagogue. With a folk reputation for indurations and/or tumors of the abdomen, eyes and liver, it is not surprising to find that 100 g seed contain 510 mg sterols, of which 63.1% is the antitumor sterol, beta-sitosterol. In Ayurvedic medicine, where used as a purgative adjunct, the herb is considered anthelmintic, apertif, aromatic, carminative, emmenagogue. In Unani, it is further con sidered abortifacient and diuretic, and used for ascites, coughs, eye-sores, hydrophobia, jaundice, paralysis, piles and tertian fever.

CRC Press is in the process of editing Edition 2 of my CRC *Handbook of Medicinal Herbs* (1985) in a big book that will have more than 400 illustrations (nearly 200 in color).

# Faba Bean (*Vicia faba*)

(Unpublished, May 27-June 3, 2001)

The last day of May, I was visited by an old musician friend, younger than me, but a friend of nearly three decades. We both used to play with a band called the "Appalachian Rain." His brother has Parkinson's disease and naturally, knowing of genetic tendencies towards Parkinsonianism, he was anxious to see the Biblical faba bean in the **Green Farmacy Garden**. I had told him about faba beans and Parkinson's disease on his visit a year before, both times with his very compromised brother. Sad. But the younger brother really loves his faba beans, especially with olive oil, though he eschews my favorite additives, hot pepper and garlic, but he can take a little raw diced onion. I like all these mixed in with my bowl of beans, "Cicero's Passion." And yes, I have reason to believe that might be a food farmaceutical answer to Viagra.

Then, just one day later, on June 1, faba beans once again surfaced, on the telephone. A pleasant feminine voice rang in and asked for Dr. Duke, author of *The Green Pharmacy*. It was the kind of phone call that almost always starts: " I have your book, and..." Usually they have a health problem and want free council, and often take much more than the 6 minutes the average physician gives the patient for a paid visit. This one was a bit more interesting and less demanding than too many of such calls are. When she said her husband had Parkinson's, I wilted, assuming she wanted to know the herbal approach. She had read the chapter in *The Green Pharmacy* and had been giving him faba beans once a day. But shyly she asked if aphrodisia might be experienced when on faba beans. She was afraid she might have to cut back on the faba beans, because the old man seemed to be getting randy again. I told her I would not be afraid to eat a cup of faba beans a day myself, having on three successive days consumed a 19 ounce can each day. And all I experienced was flatulence, no obvious increase in unrequited randiness. She was very impressed with this side effect of the faba beans. I assumed that it was bringing sunshine back into their lives, but no, she said it was getting him into trouble!

They had a female aid come by every day, as had been the case back in the pre-FABA days (then without problem). Problem now, in FABA days, he was attempting to seduce the aid. So yes, I reminded her that perhaps it was the Biblical faba bean that incited Cicero to passion. And yes, priapism (she had never heard of the word, and asked me to spell it) is an infrequent side effect of l-dopa. And yes, faba beans are one of the best food sources of l-dopa. I mentioned the old reference to the Italian Stallions, who purportedly consume a lot of faba beans. I mentioned a Parkinson's web site (http://www. parkinson.org) wherein faba beans had been discussed as an option in Parkinson's. And yes, I told her, I would not be afraid of the Biblical bean, which man has been consuming for millennia. Although some people may have a serious reaction.

Faba beans were probably domesticated in the Middle East, in Neolithic times, maybe almost 10,000 years ago, perhaps near or in what is now Israel. They may be one of our oldest cultivated crops. Reportedly faba beans reached the east coast of Spain by the end of the fifth millennium B.C. and were possibly introduced to China with the silk trade. Until *Phaseolus* beans were introduced into Europe in the 1500's with the Columbian exchange, faba beans were the only European bean. And when it says bean in the Bible, it usually means faba bean, although lentil may have sometimes been intended.

The more digestible faba bean sprouts may have 10 times as much l-dopa as the unsprouted beans. And they are more digestible. Greiner et al. (2001) showed that the sprouts have a phytate digesting enzyme. But like most phytochemicals, phytates have a bad and good side, badly chelating some minerals we need. Some novel useful effects more recently emerging for phytate and some of its degradation products are: amelioration of heart disease (by controlling hypercholesterolemia and atherosclerosis), prevention of kidney stones, and reduced risk of colon cancer. That makes a bean lover out of me, with guacamole as a side dish, having learned that avocado contains a COX-2-Inhibitor. And the genistein in faba beans might help my prostate and lower Mrs. Duke's chances for breast and other hormone-dependent cancers. The daidzein, and it is a very rich source of daidzein, might make it a prime candidate for those who are gentically or environmentally targeted for osteoporosis. I suspect the sprouts of faba beans will be richer even in daidzein than the unsprouted seed. Stems of faba bean may contain more than 0.1% daidzein, which has been demonstrated useful in alcoholism, if not cocainism, morphinism, and nicotinism.

So, that's what I have to say today about the Biblical bean. Here's what I said in *Medicinal Plants of the Bible*, closer to 25 years ago:

"So ancient is this vegetable that is recorded by Pliny. Even today, broadbeans are cultivated in Biblical countries, and their meal is made into bread today as in Biblical days. They are boiled and eaten also. Elsewhere they are cultivated as a vegetable and used green or dried, fresh or canned, and for stock feed. Broadbean has been considered as a meat extender or substitute and as a skim-milk substitute. Sometimes grown for green manure, but more generally for stock feed. Large-seeded cultivars are used as a vegetable, and frequently grown as a home-garden crop, and for canning. Roasted seeds are eaten like peanuts in India. Beans are fed to horses and the stalks are given to camels. In ancient days beans were used in collecting votes from the people; a white bean signifying approval of the measure proposed; a black one, condemnation. Magistrates were elected by casting beans.

"Said to be antidotal, aphrodisiac, cyanogenetic, diuretic, estrogenic, expectorant, stomachic, and tonic, faba bean is a folk remedy for chest, pneumonia, sclerosis, stomatitis, swellings, tumors, viscera, and warts. Inhalation of the pollen or ingestion of the seeds may cause favism, a severe hemolytic anemia, perhaps causing collapse. It is an inherited enzymatic deficiency occasional among Mediterranean people (Greeks, Italians, Semitics). Injected intravenously in rabbits, broadbean extracts have produced hemoglobinuria and death. An ethanol-ether extract of broadbeans has estrogenic activity, 50 mg stimulates the nonpregnant uterus at dioestrus. The LD50 of the bean extract in mice was 19,000 mg/kg body weight. L-Dopa and pinene have been reported from the seeds. L-Dopa is said to induce priapism in elderly males receiving it for Parkinsonianism. Hartwell cites faba bean as a folk remedy for such cancerous maladies as calluses, cancer of the breast, corns, felons, indurations of the breasts, heels, liver, spleen, and stomach; tumors of the bladder, breasts, eye, eyelids, genitals, glands, parotids, penis, and testicles; warts, and wens. In Iran, the shoots are said to be efficacious in rousing a drunkard from stupor. North Africans take two grilled beans in the morning for stomach distress; they also use them for hepatic and nephritic pain."

# Frankincense (*Boswellia sacra*)

(Unpublished)

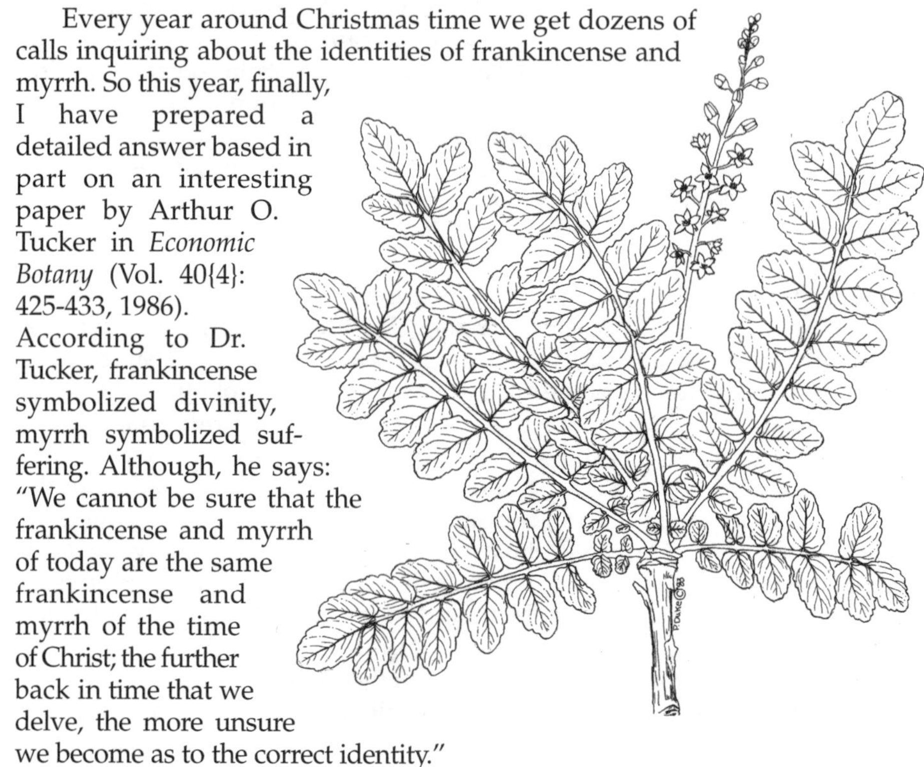

Every year around Christmas time we get dozens of calls inquiring about the identities of frankincense and myrrh. So this year, finally, I have prepared a detailed answer based in part on an interesting paper by Arthur O. Tucker in *Economic Botany* (Vol. 40{4}: 425-433, 1986). According to Dr. Tucker, frankincense symbolized divinity, myrrh symbolized suffering. Although, he says: "We cannot be sure that the frankincense and myrrh of today are the same frankincense and myrrh of the time of Christ; the further back in time that we delve, the more unsure we become as to the correct identity."

In the following account I treat several of the species that have been suspected of being the frankincense and myrrh, listing some of their uses. Data are taken from Dr. Tucker's excellent paper, a proposed revision of the CRC *Handbook of Medicinal Plants* [[which was published as edition 2 in 2002]] and my 1983 *Medicinal Plants of the Bible*.

*Boswellia carteri*, Birdwood, Frankincense, Olibanum, a small tree native to Iran, Iraq and Somalia, is the principal frankincense of today. *Boswellia sacra*, the classical Arabian species, or *Boswellia papyrifera* may be the source of the Biblical frankincense. Incisions, made by cutting into the bark, exude a milky juice that hardens into "tears" within a couple of weeks. The "tears" are favored in Lebanon, primarily as an incense, but secondarily as a medicine or cosmetic.

Frankincense was highly esteemed by the Egyptians for embalming and fumigating. It has been suggested to be a mosquito repellent. Oil of olibanum, once used as a depilatory, is still used in high-grade perfumes. Tucker lists several modern perfumes which contain frankincense including *Mennen Millionaire*, *Sculptura* by Jovan, *Volcan d'Amour* by Diane von Furstenburg.

Frankincense figures prominently in the Bible, mentioned 16 times as an item of worship, three times as a product of Solomon's garden, twice as a tribute of honor, only once as an item of merchandise. Today, it is still used as an incense in Roman Catholic churches.

Frankincense has quite a wide array of folk medicinal applications. Early on, Pliny mentioned the resin as an antidote for poison hemlock. In Tanganyika the resin is boiled in sesame oil and taken for bilharzia. Tanganyikans also decoct the resin with cinnamon and cardamom for stomachache. (Of course, cinnamon alone has a pretty good reputation for this.) Swahili use the resin as a diuretic. East Africans use it in treating syphilis; Asian Indians, for rheumatism and disorders of the nervous system.

## *Commiphora molmol*, Myrrh, Somali Myrrh

Cited as the Biblical myrrh (of Ester 2) and myrrh of commerce, this species is one of several that may be sources of the aromatic myrrh, so useful in incense, perfumery and medicine, even the embalming trade. Yes, ancient Egyptians burned myrrh in their temples and used it to embalm noteworthy people. Some scholars maintain that Biblical myrrh was a mixture of *Commiphora* and *Cistus* (rockrose).

The term "myrrophore" referred to women who bore myrrh, an ingredient of holy oil, to the sepulcher of Jesus, with aloes, cassia and cinnamon. Conversely, myrrh was burned at noon as incense for the sun god at Heliopolis. Legend says that Myrrha, daughter of the King of Cyprus, became Oedipally obsessed with her father, was exiled to the Arabian desert and transformed to the myrrh tree, to weep her perfumed tears of repentance, the tears of myrrh.

Today myrrh oil is used as an astringent in mouthwash and gargles and as a fixative or fragrance component in creams, detergents, lotions, perfumes and soaps. Approved by the FDA for food use, it is used in alcoholic beverages, baked goods and gelatins and puddings.

In China, myrrh is regarded as an antispasmodic and stomachic. Algerians dress suppurations with myrrh. Grieve lists a broad range of medicinal attributes while admitting that no one is really sure of the specific identities of myrrh. It is difficult to identify fruiting specimens of this family (Burseraceae). How then does one identify an exudate long removed from the mother tree, and perhaps mixed with exudates of other species of the same or different families?

## *Commiphora africana*, the African Bdellium or African Myrrh

Possibly the Biblical bdellium of Genesis 2, it is one source of an aromatic gum suggestive of gum arabic. Following incisions into the bark, the gum oozes out, gradually hardening and becoming waxlike, resembling pearl. Egyptian women carry the "pearls" in their handbags as a perfume. Kenyans chew the gum. Both roots and fruits are eaten in various places. Ethiopians, for example, eat the roots raw. Ugandans make a warming beverage by pounding the unripe seeds and adding to water. Foliage is readily browsed by cattle. West Africans use the resin as an insecticide to repel termites. Ghanans fumigate their clothing with the fragrant smoke of the burning wood. Africans also chew the stems to cleanse the teeth. Nigerians plant the spiny shrub as a fence hedge. Because it survives cutting so well, it is a Tuareg symbol of immortality. The wood has various uses, for starting fire by friction, for firewood, for tool handles and utensils. The wood, like the seeds, is used in necklaces. Bark is a good tannin source. Bark extracts are insecticidal. Nigerians take the root decoction for tapeworm; Tanganyikans, for diarrhea and stomachache and to speed up parturition. The bark decoction is used against male infertility in the Ivory Coast and for insanity in Nigeria.

## *Commiphora mukul*, the Gugul, Gum Gugul or Indian Bdellium, sometimes called Indian Myrrh

This small spiny tree, like several other members of the genus, yields a gum-resin when the bark is incised. This gum-resin is used as incense, medicine, in perfumery and as a substitute for, or adulterant of, African bdellium or myrrh. Where real medicine begins and folk medicine ends in the literature is not readily apparent. Various sources list too many medicinal uses to list here. *The Wealth of India* states that, like all oleoresins, gugul causes an increase of leucocytes in the blood, stimulating phagocytosis. Said to have no effect on unbroken skin, gugul is astringent and antiseptic to the abraded skin and mucous membranes. Crude gugul lowers cholesterol. Alcoholic extracts administered orally to rats and rabbits at 25-50 mg/kg reduce serum cholesterol levels. Several gugul fractions including steroids, tend to reduce total lipids, cholesterol, triglycerides and phospholipids, hinting that gugul might be helpful in combating atherosclerosis in humans.

## *Commiphora opobalsanum*, Balm, Judaean, Mecca or Palestinian Myrrh

Possibly the Biblical balm of Ezekiel 27, this is yet another gum-producing species that may have been mixed in with bdelliums and myrrhs over the years. Moldenke says the tree, native to Yemen, is believed to have been introduced to old Palestine by the Queen of Sheba at the time of her famous visit to King Solomon. It was still being cultivated around Jericho during the Roman conquest. Roman soldiers carried balm branches back to Rome as a symbol of their victory over the Hebrews. The balm of Ezekiel probably shares the usages reported for the other species of *Commiphora*. Believed astringent, carminative, demulcent, diaphoretic, digestive, diuretic, expectorant, stimulant, stomachic, sudorific and vulnerary, balm is an often-used folk remedy.

Whatever the Biblical frankincense and myrrh actually were, they were presented as gifts because of their great value to the people of that time. With all the uses of these plants today, they may be just as valuable in our time.

# Lentils (*Lens culinaris*)

(Unpublished, 2005)

## Lean Heart-Friendly Lentils

The 7-seed bread at my grocery store is now over $2.00 a loaf, and it sure beats what my mom used to call "lite bread" in her southern drawl. Of course I'm getting old now but can remember when that lite bread was more like a dime a loaf back when Mother did the shopping. The seeded and whole wheat breads today are much more tasty and nutritious, often, almost always, over $2.00 a loaf. But they aren't new. I wish I could go out today and purchase what I'll call the Biblical 6-grain bread. *Take thou also unto thee wheat, and barley, and beans, and lentiles, and millet and fitches, and put them in one vessel, and make thee bread thereof* ...Ezekiel 4. In the Ezekiel recipe we have three cereal seeds, barley, millet and wheat; two legumes, beans and lentils; and one little known spice, fitches, more often known today as back cumin. In the King James version it is fitches, in the Revised Standard Edition and the New World Translations, it is spelt, yet another cereal, rather than fitches. I could write a full column extolling the virtues of each (many or most such virtues lost in modern processing), and the potential health synergies therein, providing hundreds of useful phytochemicals, useful chemicals that your genes have known for thousands of years.

If you enjoy your Bible, perhaps you'll have more faith in the Biblical lentil and faba bean than you have in the oriental soybean as a natural alternative to HRT (Hormone Replacement Therapy). You've probably heard a whole heap of hype about the estrogenic isoflavone, genistein, in the soybean. Once upon a time, soy scientists said only soy had it. Wrong! The soy scientists and their reporters don't often tell you that the Biblical beans, chick pea, faba bean and lentil, contain that same estrogenic isoflavone and another, daidzein. In Kaufman et al. (1997) we read that lentils and soy both contain ca 25 ppm (parts per million) genistein, and faba beans contain about 20 ppm. So you don't have to go to tofu to get your estrogenic isoflavones. Instead make a heart friendly HRT Biblical Bread to go with your Biblical Lentil Soup (a/o chickpea a/o fababean soup) and spice it up with Biblical garlic, leeks and onions, and COX-2-Inhibitor turmeric. Some suggest the Biblical black cumin as an alternative to black pepper, which was not specifically named in the Bible. But add fresh black pepper, whether it is Biblical or not. That will significantly increase your uptake of the curcumin, active ingredient in the turmeric. Dipping your Biblical bread in Biblical olive oil, and sipping a Biblical grape juice, or eating stuffed grape leaves, will make an extremely heart healthy meal with some anticancer potential as well. The grape juice contains resveratrol, which made news just this month (May 2005). Though long championed as a heart friendly anticancer phytochemcial, resveratrol was this month suggested to be useful in warding off the flu. If the flu is going around put more Biblical garlic in your soup and on your bread with that olive oil

(I'm getting hungry just writing this). If HRT is on your mind, finish off your Biblical lunch with half a pomegranate, which is the best plant source of human identical estrone. That delicious meal is what I call FBFF, faith-based food farmacy, composed of plants (except the non-Biblical black pepper) and phytochemcials known to your genes for at least 2000 years.

Last month they reported on the failure of one of the herbal alternatives to HRT after a 4-week study. I find that hilarious, a study of the cycle that lasts no longer than one cycle. Still many American women (including Mrs. Duke) were, for decades, not four weeks, taking pharmaceutical HRT, falsely lured into non-evidence based propaganda for the prevention of heart disease and osteoporosis. Laxt year they formally debunked this lingering lie. But in that same year, several studies came out confirming that the phytoestrogens were heart friendly. I assume that most legumes, as well endowed with phytoestrogens as soy, would be as heartfriendly as soy. In the Bible, we find three bona-fide legumes, chickpea, faba beans, and lentils, and another member of the legume family, fenugreek, which will add further antidiabetic and hypocholesterolemic phytochemcials to your Biblical Bean Soup.

At age 76, I still believe that the beans my mother ate while I was in the womb are helping me remember my lines today. Beans are a good source of the memory compound choline, and dietary choline, especially with garlic (which contains chemicals believed to inhibit Alzheimeran plaque), may help delay the onset of Alzheimer's. So could Biblical mint teas with their many anticholinesterase chemicals, which can prevent the breakdown of choline, one problem in Alzheimer's. So the Biblical beans and lentils can provide the choline, and the Biblical mints can provide compouds to prevent premature breakdown of the choline. A decade ago, they deemed choline unnecessary for humans, but after learning that even in utero exposure to adequate levels of choline enables experimental animals to learn better and retain longer. So the choline can contribute to the deceleration of Alzheimer's.

**NOTES (LENTIL)**

> *...Then Jacob gave Esau bread and pottage of lentiles; and he did eat...* Genesis 25

Zohary points out that lentil was the first pulse mentioned in the Bible. I'd like to add that it is the first one to be done when you are cooking a seven pulse soup. Even dried lentiles can be rendered edible with a half hour of simmering. Small wonder that lentils were important staples during Biblical and post-Biblical eras. Maybe even earlier. Zohary reports carbonized lentil seeds dating to 6 or 7 millenia BC. Since the Bronze Age, lentils have been found in association with barley and wheat. (ZOH). My late friend, anthropologist Jane Philips said some "people think it was the food that made Daniel wise" or that it was the "mess of pottage for which Esau sold his birthright" (HJP). Lentils have been found in Syria prior to

5000 B.C., in Iran before 5000 B.C., and in Greece (with barley and wheat) earlier than 5000 B.C. (Zohary, D. 1972 *Econ. Bot*. 26:326). Seeds are a source of commercial starch for textile and printing industries. Green plants used as green manure (BIB).

This faith-based article was drafted by Jim Duke from his **Green Farmacy Garden**. Dr. Duke often leads Biblical tours of the garden, and suggest that if you are attending conventions in Washington D.C. or Baltimore Maryland, you might enjoy one of his tours (1-24 persons, 1 car to 4 vans; no buses). As part of the tour, visitors receive an autographed English copy of the best selling book *The Green Pharmacy* (over a million copies sold in six languages now). For a schedule, contact jimduke@comcast.net.

## *Biblical Bean Soup*

alias *Cerebral Choline Soup*

*(Possibly forestalls or prevents Alzheimer's and Cirrhosis)*

Mix to taste several varieties of legume seeds e.g. the Biblical chick-pea, faba-bean, fenugreek, lentil (and the non-Biblical azuki bean, black bean, blackeyed pea, field pea, groundnut, kidney bean, lima bean, mungbean, navy bean, pea, scarlet runner bean etc). Make it cheap on yourself; buy one each of each variety of dried beans and peas at your grocery, usually all below $1.00 per pound, compare with meat or fish, and consider replacing some red meats and fat meats with legumes.

Soak overnight and bring to boil the following morning. Slurry in blender with fennelseed (for its fenchone), rosemary, sage, savory and thyme, for several compounds with anticholinesterase activity, and hot pepper sauce and diced onions and/or garlic, the latter spices for taste more than anything. (Garlic has been reported useful in encephalitis.)

The curcumin in turmeric (perhaps the Biblical saffron) is a COX-2-Inhibitor and has been suggested to help prevent alzheimer's and epidemiologically correlated with lower incidence of Alzheimer's. Turmeric and fenugreek go well with "mulagtawnis" or curried bean soups, making them even heart friendlier.

Gather dandelion flowers and add, at the last minute of simmering, up to one cup for each two cups of beans. (Dandelion flowers are good sources of lecithin; and for each flower you pick, you may have prevented 100 seeds or more.) Tender young nettle leaves are optional (they contain both acetyl-choline and choline).

**NOTE:** Legumes are good sources of lecithin and/or choline, some of which dietary choline can cross the blood/brain barrier. Lecithin itself has been shown to prevent cirrhosis in gorillas.

# Onion (*Allium cepa*)

(Unpublished)

*Treat disease through diet, by preference, refraining from the use of drugs; and if you find what is required in a single herb, do not resort to a compound medicament...*

Baha'u'llah in a Tablet to a Physician ca.~1880

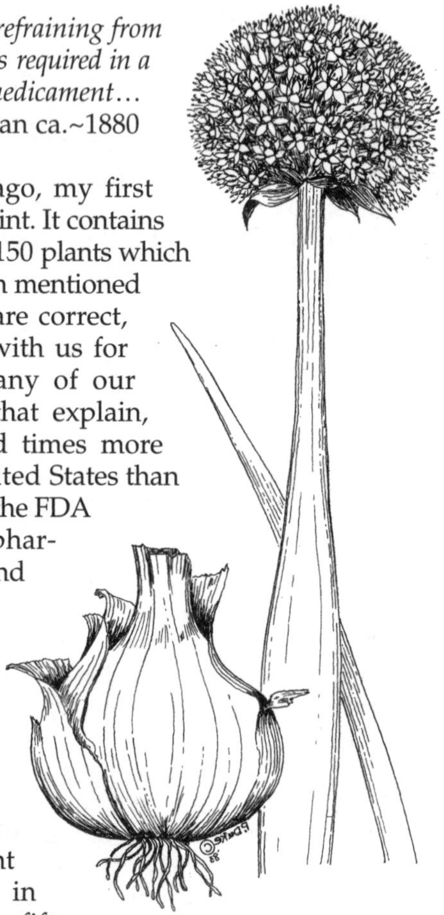

Published more than 20 years ago, my first *Medicinal Plants of the Bible* is out of print. It contains a lot of good information on nearly 150 plants which some scholars interpret as having been mentioned in the Bible. If those interpretations are correct, that means these herbs have been with us for more than 10 times longer than any of our synthetic pharmaceuticals. Could that explain, perhaps, why there are a thousand times more pharmaceutical fatalaties in the United States than herbal fatalities. Yes, methinks. Even the FDA warns against trying the newest pharmaceuticals, the ones most loudly and blatantly hyped.

You've probably heard herbs described as dilute drugs and I like that description. Containing a lot more water (ca 90%) than garlic (ca 60-65%), onions contain many of the same sulphur compounds that make garlic such a treasure house. But there are a few different chemicals. Onion is much richer in quercetin than garlic; for more than fifty biological activities of quercetin (see the phytochemical database: http://www.ars-grin.gov/duke).

Since there are slight chemical differences (each plant species is presumably chemically distinct from all other species, and individuals within the species, like individuals within the human species, vary widely in their chemistry). I add both onions and garlic to almost all my soups and most of my salads and veggie dishes, hoping to stave off cancer, cardiopathy, and diabetes, maybe even anthrax, bubonic plague, smallpox and west Nile virus. Regular use of 50 g/day onion reduces the insulin requirements of a diabetic from 40 to 20 units a day – Onion oil and dipropyldisulfide-oxide are significantly hypoglycemic (WO2). Allicin, a compound found in garlic and onion, is also hypoglycemic, as well as antiseptic, bactericidal, hypocholesterolemic, insecticidal, and larvicidal. The quercetin, with which onion is so richly endowed, has recently been identified as a COX-2- Inhibitor, so I'd like to propose "Curried Onion" (I never heard of it before either, but it's good, almost habit forming) as the food farmacy alternative to Celebrex. We'll never know which is the better until they have been clinically compared. But my "Curried Onion" contains a dozen COX-2-Inhibitors, none probably as strong (or as dangerous, at least at the levels they occur in food plants) which my genes have known for 2,000 years, if not 2 million years. And if the pharmaceutical COX-2-I's can be touted for alzheimer's, arthritis, asthma, and colon cancer, I suppose I could speculate that my natural COX-2-I's shared in those praiseworthy activities, at a lower price and with fewer side effects.

But I have to be honest. When I looked at the PubMed website re abstracts on >onion AND asthma< I got almost as many abstracts suggesting that onion caused allergies as I did abstracts relating to onion and/or its phytochemicals as alleviators of asthma. Unfortunately many people are allergic to onion and garlic and other wholesome members of the family (like chive, elephant garlic, leek, ramp, wild garlic (garlic grass), and wild onion. I've eaten all of those with more or less pleasure, but vidalia onion still is a culinary treasure in my book. If I were suffering asthma, hay fever, or sinusitis, I'd probably cook up a bunch of stinging nettle to go with my "Curried Onion" (the latter great over toast or rice).

As long ago as 1984, Dorsch et al. (1984) recounted the inhibitory effects of crude ethanolic onion extracts on allergic skin reactions in man as well as on allergen-induced bronchial asthma in man and guinea-pigs. Dorsch and associates were studying sulfur containing compounds. They concluded that the antiasthmatic effects of onions and – perhaps – other plants may be mediated at least in part by isothiocyanates. [Makes me think of my garlic mustard, with its allicin and isothiocyanates] (X6526069). In 1985, Johri et al. (1985) studied onion saponins and their relation to the cells in the mesentery and peritoneal fluid of rats subjected to anaphylaxis. They found that onion saponins, if not onions, stabilized the mast cell membranes (X3932203). Later Dorsch, alligned with Wagner et al., said that onion oils counteract bronchial obstruction due to PAF inhalation (X3570522). By 1990, Wagner et al. (59-62) had found nine different thiosulfinates and four "cepaenes," isolated from onions and/or synthesized in the lab, which showed dose dependent (0.25 to 100 uM) inhibitory effects on both cyclooxygenase and 5-lipoxygenase activity. The authors considered it very likely that these in vitro effects are responsible for anti-inflammatory and antiasthmatic properties of onion extracts observed in vivo, at least in part (X2111027). Swiss studies show that feeding a rat a gram of onion a day lowers the incidence of rats' equivalent of osteoporosis (*Alt. & Compl. Therapies* 5(6): p. 330-1). All the more reason for old Jim to enjoy his curried onion.

According to Quillin (1998), the United States has already invested $39 billion seeking a "magic bullet" for cancer at the National Cancer

Institute. Yet we see a net increase in the incidence and death rate due to cancer. [[Early in 2006, they finally reported a reduction for the first time in the incidence of cancer deaths. Let me here predict that too will be flip flop; they'll tell us it isn't true after another study or meta-analysis.]] Five-year survival rates still hang around 50%. Cancer caused 3% of American deaths in 1900, 35% in 1994. Cancer has exceeded cardiopathy as the number-one killer in Alaska and Massachusetts. Apparently the NCI, like the Pharmaceutical Industry, incorrectly assumes that human technology can improve on Nature. That very assumption has become a cause of modern disease. We dissect food, take out major bioactive compounds, try to recreate them in the lab, and label them as "active ingredients." But it is really synergy, "the symphony of nutrients working synergistically," that provides the great healing power of whole foods. Quillin notes an RDA for 13 vitamins, 12 minerals, two fatty acids, protein, and calories (and we added choline in 1998, JAD). Still, there are thousands of identified and many thousands of unidentified components in whole food stores that probably contribute to an individual's cancer-fighting capacity. Whole, fresh Biblical food can be an elegant combination of anti-cancer ingredients. Take for example, faba beans with onion and garlic. The NCI has slaved for years to discover "biological response modifiers" that would beat cancer. But Nature has offered us potent substances since man evolved, maybe 6 million years ago in Africa. Whole onion soup or Curried Onion might beat the magic bullet, without making your hair fall out. Yes, your genes have known the compounds in onion and garlic for thousands of years, but they can't have known tamoxifen more than four decades, raloxifene more than two. I'd rather take bean soup with onions and garlic (and non Biblical hot sauce), if I feared breast or colon cancer. Enjoy your medicine! In vitro, quercetin (onion is the best Biblical source) inhibits growth of such human cancer cells as breast, colon, GI, ovarian and leukemia. Working with rats on an artificial high cholesterol diet, Indian scientists (Sheela and Augusti, 1995) showed that 20 g of garlic and onion contain enough sulfur compounds to help prevent coronary heart disease and cancer of the breast and bowels.

Here's what I said about onion in 1983:

***Allium cepa* L. Onion**

> *...We remember the fish, which we did eat in Egypt...the leeks, and the onions...* Numbers 11

Onions are generally produced as green or dry onions. Green onions are eaten raw with meats, fish, cheese or as a vegetable, or chopped and added to cottage cheese, or cooked. Dry onions may be served as a vegetable dish, or to flavor meat, fish and poultry dishes. They are good raw, boiled, baked, creamed, broiled, fried, french-fried, roasted or pickled, and in soups, stews, dressings, or salads. Onion is used widely with other ingredients for innumerable dishes. Although widely used in Biblical times, and probably millennia before, the onion is only mentioned once, in

Numbers 11. Like garlic, the onion is highly regarded as an antiseptic, apertif, aphrodisiac, bactericide, carminative, diaphoretic, digestive, diuretic, expectorant, pectoral, sedative, soporific (yet stimulant), stomachic, suppurative, tonic, and vermifuge. Among other ailments, it is often recommended for abscesses, albuminuria, alopecia, anasarca, angina, arteriosclerosis, bilious ailments, bladder ailments, bleeding, breast cancer, Bright's disease, bronchitis, bubo, burns, cancer, cataracts, catarrh, chest, chilblains, cholera, cold, colic, consumption, corns, cough, diabetes, diarrhea, diptheria, dropsy, dysentery, earache, edema, epilepsy, erysipelas, eyes, felons, fever, flatulence, flu, fracture, freckles, gallbladder, gangrene, gout, gravel, hangover, headache, heart, heartburn, hepatitis, hoarseness, hydropsy, hyperglycemia, hypertension, impotency, indurations, inflammation, liver cancer, paralysis, piles, rabies, rectum cancer, rheumatism, scarlatina, sciatica, stones, syphilis, tuberculosis, tumor, urogenitary problems, uterine cancer, venereal disease, warts, whitlows, whooping cough, worms, and wounds. Allicin, a compound found in garlic and onion, is antiseptic, hyperglycemic, hypocholesterolemic, insecticidal, and larvicidal. Arresting putrefaction and fermentation processes in the gastrointestinal tract, onion might help prevent cancer of the lower gut. Widely distributed, beta-sitosterol has shown several types of antitumor activity. Rutin, isolated from onion, is said to be antiatherogenic, antiedemic, antiinflammatory, antispasmodic, antithrombogenic, hypotensive, and is said to prevent cancer as well as protect against x-radiation. Roasted onion has been applied to tumors. The seed, with honey, is a folk remedy for warts. The juice is said to help cancers of the breast and rectum. The bulb, prepared in various manners, is said to help indurated glands and tumors. Reputed to be hypotensive, onions have recently been shown to contain the antihypertensive agent prostaglandin A1, but only at ca 1 ppm. Lebanese believe that onions prevent typhoid, and alleviate or cure colds, dyspepsia, jaundice and nephritis. They apply onion juice to abscesses, boils, earache, eyeache, rhinitis, and sinusitis (30). Onion seeds are sold in Iran and Iraq as demulcent stimulants. Boiled with sugar and almond oil, they are given as a purgative during typhoid fever.

### *Curried Onions*

Cover 4 diced onions with water; simmer adding water as needed and 1 diced clove garlic,

1-2 diced celery stalks, 1 diced nib ginger, 1 diced nib turmeric (or two tbsp yellow mustard with curry), a dash of black cumin, holy basil, rosemary, sage, thyme, and to taste, ground black pepper [to increase uptake of curcumin] and capsaicin.

# Pomegranate (*Punica granatum*)

(Unpublished)

## Solomon's Song of Pomegranate

*...I would cause thee to drink of spiced wine of the juice of my pomegranate.*
Song of Solomon 8

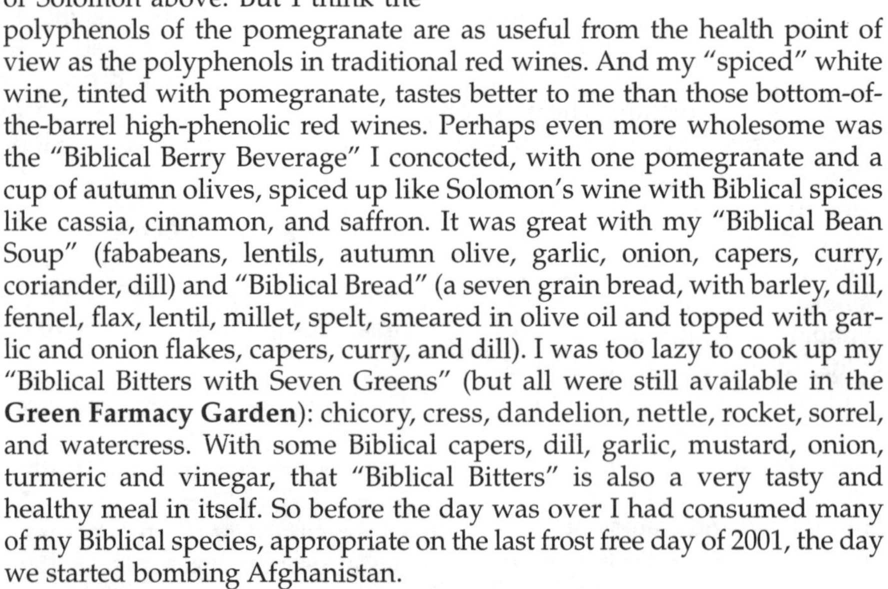


Preparing for the first Bible tour of my garden (I have over 50 plants growing here that are also reportedly mentioned in the Bible), I decided to add some of the purplish juice around the seeds of the pomegranate to a cheap white wine. Results, a rather different spiced wine that than that of Solomon above. But I think the polyphenols of the pomegranate are as useful from the health point of view as the polyphenols in traditional red wines. And my "spiced" white wine, tinted with pomegranate, tastes better to me than those bottom-of-the-barrel high-phenolic red wines. Perhaps even more wholesome was the "Biblical Berry Beverage" I concocted, with one pomegranate and a cup of autumn olives, spiced up like Solomon's wine with Biblical spices like cassia, cinnamon, and saffron. It was great with my "Biblical Bean Soup" (fababeans, lentils, autumn olive, garlic, onion, capers, curry, coriander, dill) and "Biblical Bread" (a seven grain bread, with barley, dill, fennel, flax, lentil, millet, spelt, smeared in olive oil and topped with garlic and onion flakes, capers, curry, and dill). I was too lazy to cook up my "Biblical Bitters with Seven Greens" (but all were still available in the **Green Farmacy Garden**): chicory, cress, dandelion, nettle, rocket, sorrel, and watercress. With some Biblical capers, dill, garlic, mustard, onion, turmeric and vinegar, that "Biblical Bitters" is also a very tasty and healthy meal in itself. So before the day was over I had consumed many of my Biblical species, appropriate on the last frost free day of 2001, the day we started bombing Afghanistan.

Pomegranate hence assumes importance in these unsettled days as a survival plant for the disturbed Middle East. Many parts of the plant serve as food. Witness the wise words of Stephen Facciola in his *Cornucopia II: A Source Book of Edible Plants*: "the refreshing fruit pulp is eaten out of hand, or in salads, cocktails and desserts. The juice, made into grenadine or as is, is used likewise in beverages, desserts, juices, and salads, even daiquiris. The dried seeds, known as the spice 'anardana,' are used in seasoning in 'dal,' 'chat masala,' 'samosa' (fried pastries), stuffings and chutneys. Boiled leaves are said to be eaten. Dried, soaked flowers are cooked with fish to reduce the odor." So, all told, the leaves, flowers fruits pulp and seeds are used as food. And that could come in handy if you found yourself lost in the Middle East. Don't eat the roots, stem bark or the rind of the fruits, though, unless you have cholera or worms. On the other hand if you think you have been subject to anthrax and have nothing better on hand, use that hard outer coating of the fruit, or the stem bark, or root bark to make a bactericidal tea, to drink and to wash yourself. With two related cases of anthrax in the Florida "tabloid" building, I think I'd be cautious before entering that building. The tannins in the woody parts of pomegranate, or in tea itself, might be somewhat better than nothing at arresting bacteria like anthrax.

## Oct. 11, 2001

An auspicious date, one month after the twin tower trouble, on the NBC morning show, Dr. Sue Bailey said what I translate to mean: "Something possibly effective against anthrax is clearly better than nothing against anthrax." Some of my suggestions may be better than nothing.

- Avoid crowds. Don't open suspect packages. Wash frequently.
- Boost your immune systems [[But not for avian flu, they say, 2006]] with such herbs as echinacea and antiseptic garlic. Both have immune-boosting and antiseptic phytochemicals.
- Drink plenty of tannin rich beverages, like tea itself, antiseptic mint teas, focusing on herbs with at least folkloric potential for antianthrax activity.

If you believe you have dermal anthrax, take a tannin rich bath, or wash with bark teas, drink tannin rich teas, and take more garlic and echinacea (but not mega-doses; action of echinacea may even be reversed at ten times recommended dose). Actually I recommended that New York give out echinacea and garlic capsules rather than spray for the west Nile Virus in years past. The insecticidal spray weakens the human immune system while ultimately leading to spray-resistant mosquitoes, ultimately worsening the likelihood of Nile fatalities. If I thought I might be the target of germ warfare, I might try antiseptic mints as a primitive germ-mask, stuffing the leaves into my nostrils, and breathing only through my nose. [[Late in 2005, Dr. Know (*Discovery*, New Zealand, was filmed in the **Green Farmacy Garden**, with leaves of *Glechoma hederacea* up his nose]]. I have done that in the past to treat sinusitis (it worked, but I don't know whether my sinusitis was bacterial or viral). Almost any mint could help (to identify mints, note aroma, opposite leaves, square four-sided stems, and the four tiny nutlets at the base inside the flowers).

If I knew it was anthrax, I might dine on some of the edibles among the folkloric antianthrax herbs listed in my Herbal Desk Reference; agrimony, ashwagandha, black nightshade, dogwood, lemonbush, marijuana, milk thistle, olive leaf, papaya, purslane, valerian, walnut, watercress, and most of all yellow dock. Here in Maryland, I'd make a tea of dogwood bark, walnut bark, and yellow dock root. And I'd eat the leaves of the yellow dock.

Controversially, I have speculated that pomegranate is more likely to be the apple of the Garden of Eden, than what you and I now call apple in the United States. But there are no voucher specimens for the medicinal plants of the Bible, and we can only speculate as to what they intended with their colloquial names. I think I can safely speculate that the pomegranate has existed longer in what we now call the Holy Land than has the apple. I even question the old expression – "As American as apple pie," believing the apple to be another alien, that did not originate in the continental United States, like 90% or more of our "food basket" plants here in the United States of America.

Clearly more Americans today eat apples than pomegranates. But the modern pomegranate might have more modern benefits than the modern apple a day. I fear that the plant breeders, almost in concert, make all of our fruits bigger and juicier, yet less nutritious, as science marches on, so often in the wrong direction. Here in the U.S., they haven't yet tampered too much with the pomegranate. If you overindulge in pomegranates, however, you could possibly experience some mild estrogenic effects. I always get excited about serendipitous coincidences. One of November 1996, was so great that I still remember it and now relive it with you. I thought it particularly auspicious for Mrs. Duke who was visiting her physician re osteoporosis. She took with her several *JAMA* (*Journal of the American Medical Association*) talking about estrogens and osteoporosis and a *Science News* one-pager that considered estrogens and osteoporosis. Then I read a new article by Nagle and Yeykal (*Prevention*) on pomegranate, under the legend "SUPERFOOD." They had missed the most important phytochemical. You see, pomegranate is the best-known plant source of estrone, an estrogenic hormone.

That same month, the editor of a respected alternative medicine periodical and I exchanged e-mails about a study of a pomegranate. (Purchased at supermarket for 3.00 per kilo or about 20¢ for each milligram of estrone that it is reported to contain. I'm curious to know how much the Upjohn estrogen, in their new product Ogen, costs per milligram.) I added that fruit to my blender with lemonade and made a great estrogenic beverage, noting no changes in my attitude or physiology or depth of voice, but enjoying the beverage immensely, especially when spiked and raised to the alcoholic levels suggested in the Song of Solomon. And remember, one alcoholic drink alone, without pomegranate, can increase circulating levels of estrogen significantly. (TWO IS CONTRAINDICATED HOWEVER.)

Nagle and Yeykal were addressing cuisine, not medicines and liqueurs, equally interesting to me. Correctly describing pomegranate as delightfully messy, they praise its potassium and dietary fiber contribution and acknowledge its help re vitamin C, most B vitamins, copper, pantothenic acid, magnesium, and phosphorus, with less than 1 gram fat and only 105 calories per pomegranate.

That prompted me to do a new query on my "Father Nature's Farmacy" (FNF) database, now expanded and presented in a newer, more flexible format. Now interactive, it can be consulted on the World Wide Web (http://www.ars-grin.gov/duke). This database represents an expanded and interactive advancement of the data published by Duke in 1992. I view the database as the ghost of Jim Duke, retired from the USDA in 1995.

In this so-called "High Concentration Chemicals Query," one can display a list of the chemicals in a particular plant with concentrations greater than a selected percentage deviation above the mean (for concentration among all plants in the database). Activities of these high-concentration chemicals can be listed subsequently. To enter the query, I typed the generic name, *Punica*; the species epithet, *granatum*; and plant part, various. Then I clicked on the "Submit" button. Seeking real superchemicals I first clicked on 2 standard deviations; nothing came out for fruit or seed. Clicking on 1 standard deviation I got only estrone for the seed. Relaxing my standards, I clicked on 0.5 standard deviations and got interesting details for the fruit, confirming very well what Nagle and Yeykal had suggested. Here's part of the printout:

High Concentration Chemicals in the Fruit of *Punica granatum* L. (Punicaceae) [Pomegranate] (chemical concentrations 0.5 standard deviation(s) above the mean):

BORIC-ACID 50 ppm
CARBOHYDRATES 162,000-927,000 ppm
ESTRONE 17 ppm
FIBER 2,000-232,000 ppm
PANTOTHENIC-ACID 6-31 ppm
PHOSPHORUS 80-3,182 ppm
POTASSIUM 1,330-18,950 ppm
WATER 780,000-823,220 ppm

On the back cover of the November 27 issue of *JAMA* was an Ogen ad. I'll paraphrase the ad. It talks about Ogen, a registered, named, natural plant-derived product, stated to prevent osteoporosis and to relieve moderate to severe "vasomotor symptoms." (Mrs. Duke translated that to "hot flashes.") The ad, copyright 1996 by Pharmacia & Upjohn Company, makes one claim that not all physicians will necessarily accept, "There is no evidence that natural estrogens are more or less hazardous than synthetic estrogens at equiestrogenic doses." The ad does not mention pomegranate. They cite as their evidence for antiosteoporotic activity Harris et al. (1991). They suggest 0.75 to 3 mg daily of their product for hypoestrogenism, osteoporosis prevention, vasomotor symptoms, and vulval-vaginal atrophy associated with menopause.

The December issue of *Consumer Reports on Health* also arrived. I had even served as herbal adviser for one article in this issue. There we read, "The preferred treatment for post-menopausal women with osteoporosis has long been estrogen therapy, which stops bone loss, increases bone density and cuts the risk of fracture roughly in half. Estrogen therapy is even more effective for preventing osteoporosis. It reduces risk of fracture by some 70% if started at the onset of menopause, some 60% when started as late as age 65. Estrogen also slashes the risk of coronary heart disease, eases menopausal symptoms, and may decrease the risk of colon cancer, tooth loss, and possibly osteoarthritis and Alzheimer's" (Leff, 1996).

[[Almost all of that has since been reversed in another of the frequent flip flops we experience in America. HRT is no longer generally recommended for preventing heart disease and osteoporosis, that's the only reason Mrs. Duke took HRT. Now it's mostly suggested for hot flashes. But I'll still suggest, in moderation, natural and weak phytoestrogens for staving off heart disease and osteoporosis.]]

For those who can't get or afford the prescription estrogens, food farmacy may help. A 100-gram serving of the Biblical pomegranate pulp and seeds, converted into grenadine, could contain 1.5 mg estrone. Added to kudzu-root macerate, also edible, one would obtain other widely-promoted phytoestrogens, at levels considerably higher than one would get in unfortified soy products. I propose my G-K "formula" (Grenadine/Kudzu) as the herbal alternative to Ogen, itself advertised as a "natural plant-derived product." Yes, I'll even bet my atrophied ovaries, if any, that grenadine/kudzu will do as well for female osteoporosis as Ogen (tyrademark) (Freudian slip).

High-boron leafy veggies are also suggested for osteoporosis-prone women; as little as 3 mg boron doubles blood levels of estrogen. Plums and prunes contain 3-255 ppm boron, the lower figure for the freshest of plums, which may be 90% water with a correspondingly low level of minerals, and the higher figure the driest of prunes, devoid of water, hence, much richer in minerals. A half cup of prunes containing 250 ppm boron could contain 25 mg boron, nearly 10 times the dose required to double estrogen levels. Pomegranates are reported to contain some 50 ppm boric acid (dry weight), meaning that a 100 g serving, fresh weight, would contain only 0.5 mg boron on a fresh basis, 5 mg boron on a dry basis (assuming that the fresh pomegranate is 90% water).

So pomegranate joined my long list of herbal alternatives. A pleasant and inexpensive grenadine liqueur, made from the Biblical pomegranate and containing 1.5 mg estrone might be as safe and efficacious as the semisynthetic estrogens used in Estrogen Replacement Therapy (ERT).

One neighbor has, under her physicians scrupulous scrutiny, used phytoestrogens like these in lieu of ERT, with such satisfactory results that she has written me long letters praising the results and encouraging me to share her experience with others. She has successfully achieved ERT via Food Pharmacy.

In the February issue (1997) of *Good Housekeeping*, Dr. Susan Love, MD, reflecting the soybean party line, suggests that soy can treat the symptoms of menopause and also lower the risk for heart disease, osteoporosis, and breast cancer. "That's because it contains isoflavones, a phytoestrogen (plant estrogen) that is turning out to be one of the best dietary alternatives to estrogen drugs. It's thought that one reason Japanese women have lower rates of breast cancer, heart disease, and osteoporosis and also seem not to have hot flashes, is that their diet is high in soy." For those who don't like soy, most legumes contain the calcium, estrogenic isoflavones, and high protein:fat ratios that Dr. Love applauds in soy. Sprouts and stems of the Biblical faba beans contain even more estrogenic isoflavones than soy. And I personally prefer the Biblical faba beans and the Amerindian black beans to the Oriental soybeans.

In the Holy Land you may encounter at least three estrogenic Biblical foods/medicines: the date, faba bean, and the pomegranate. I've focused on pomegranate today. I'll cover the others another day.

Here's what I said back in 1985:

**Pomegranate (*Punica granatum* L.)**

> *... I would cause thee to drink of spiced wine of the juice of my pomegranate...* Song of Solomon 8

"'Pomegranate' literally means 'apple with grains,' the reference being to the many clear ruby-colored seeds, covered with a thin skin and full of juice, found in each fruit. A syrup made from the seeds is known as grenadine. The first sherbet was a preparation of pomegranate juice mixed with snow. Apothecaries use the blossoms, known as balausts, in the preparation of an astringent medicine used in treating dysentery. The acid pulp surrounding the seeds is the edible portion of the fruit, used as a salad or table fruit, or made into beverages or jellies. In Syria and Iran fruit is cut open, seeded, strewn with sugar and sprinkled with rose water. Wine is made from fruits, and seeds are used in syrups, preserves, gelatin desserts, icings, puddings and sauces. As fruits ferment easily, they are used in Egypt to make a wine. Grenadine is a soft drink based on pomegranate, and grenadine syrup is used to flavor drinks. Rinds used for tanning Morocco leather, giving a yellow color. Flowers give a red dye. Plants made good ornamental hedges, especially in dry climates. Also useful as a greenhouse potted plant. Cut flowers are long lasting in arrangements. Pomegranate is the national flower emblem of Spain. Wood, though scanty, is hard and can be used for small objects and for walking sticks. Flowers are used by some women to give a red color to the teeth, and rind used in Polynesia to give shining black color to teeth. In some areas an unfading ink is made from the rind. Dried rind, called Malicorium, is sold in curved brittle fragments. In China, the pomegranate symbolizes fertility; women offer pomegranates to the goddess of mercy in the hope of being blessed with children. Boulos reports that the seed oil is estrogenic, perhaps providing a rationale for the Chinese beliefs (60).

Most important is the specificity of the rootbark for tapeworm. Considered anodyne, astringent, bactericide, cardiotonic, parasiticide, refrigerant, stimulant, stomachic, styptic, taenifuge, and vermifuge, the pomegranate appears in folk medicaments for amygdalitis, asthma, bilious afflictions, bronchitis, caked breasts, cancer, colic, conjunctivitis, cough, diarrhea, dysentery, dysmenorrhea, dyspepsia, epistaxis, fever, flux, gingivitis, halitosis, heart, hemorrhage, hemorrhoids, inflammation, leucorrhea, malaria, menorrhagia, metrorrhagia, night sweats, oxyuriasis, paralysis, pimples, prolapse, rectitis, rectocele, sore throat, snakebite, spienomegaly, stomatitis, tapeworm, thirst, throat, tumors, and urogenital ailments. Ayurvedics use the fruit rind, appropriately enough, for diarrhea, dysentery and worms; the root for worms, the flowers for epistaxis; the bark and seeds for bronchitis; the ripe fruit, considered astringent, aphrodisiac and tonic, for biliousness, burning sensations, fever, heart disease, sore throat and stomatitis. Unani use the astringent bark for anal prolapse, colic and piles, the flowers for biliousness, hydrocele, nausea, sore eyes and sore throat, the green fruit for inflammation and keratitis, the ripe fruit for brain disorders, bronchitis, chest ailments, earache, scabies, sore eyes, sore throat, splenitis, and thirst, the seeds for biliousness, bowel ailments, hepatitis, liver ailments, nausea, scabies and sore eyes. Leaf juices inhibit some viruses. The rind is a folk remedy for indurated tumors, excrescences of the fundament, corns, carcinoma of the mouth and anus, and wens. The leaf cataplasm is said to cure tumors. The juice, prepared in various manners, is said to remedy pterygia on the finger, nasal polyps, tumors of the fauces, etc. The fruit is said to cure various types of tumors. Small wonder, then, that it contains tannins, betulinic, gallic, and ursolic acids, all recognized experimental antitumor agents. Iranians use the flowers, powdered with *Nummulites* sp. and *Rhus coriaria* for painful gums. For oral ailments, Filipinos gargle with the leaf decoction.

# Rosemary (*Rosmarinus officinalis*)

*The Business of Herbs* 6(2):10, May/June, 1988

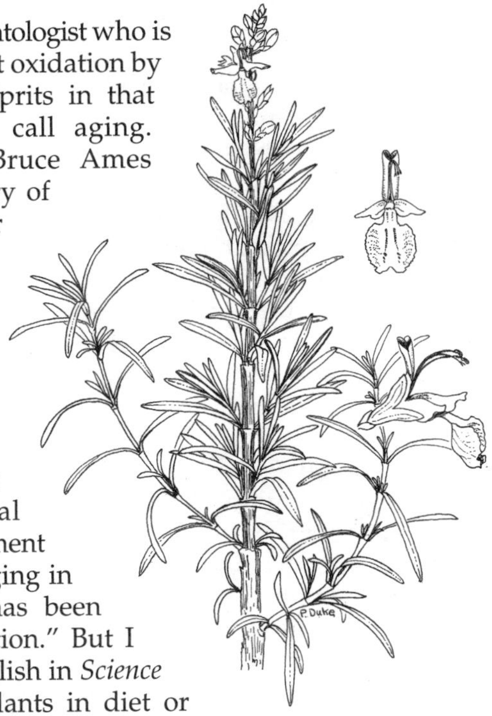

It's easy enough to find a gerontologist who is more than willing to suggest that oxidation by free radicals is one of the culprits in that unwelcome phenomenon we call aging. Once again, let me quote Bruce Ames (*Science*, 83): "A plausible theory of aging holds that the major cause is damage to DNA and other macromolecules and that a major source of this damage in oxygen radicals and lipid peroxidation. Cancer and other degenerative diseases, such as heart disease, are likely to be due in good part to this same fundamental destructive process. Age pigment (lipofuscin) accumulates with aging in all mammalian species and has been associated with lipid peroxidation." But I can't find anyone who will publish in *Science* and say the converse; antioxidants in diet or herb tea can retard those degenerative diseases, "liver" spots and deteriorating memory. Could rosemary, the so-called memory herb, actually help the memory or slow its rate of deterioration?

Old herbalists who had learned that rosemary could slow the rancidity and/or putrefaction of meats in the days before refrigeration are the same herbalists who generated the old spouse's tale that rosemary could, as Mrs. Leyel so boldly put it – "improve a bad memory." Modern scientists have found that compounds in rosemary, the antioxidants as they are called, can retard the onset of rancidity and rotting of meats. Some of them are even more effective than the synthetic antioxidants BHA (Butylated hydroxyanisole) and BHT (Butylated hydroxytoluence) that you can find on nearly every other food wrapper you pick up. Soon, some of the natural antioxidants from rosemary will be reaching your neighborhood grocery. I heard that sales of rosemary antioxidants already total more than 1 million dollars a year. And I would rather have a natural than a synthetic antioxidant.

Rosemary is loaded with antioxidants, more than a dozen. That's partly what led me to concoct that liqueur I termed "Alzheimaretto" (*Living Liqueurs*, 1987; available from Quarterman Publications, Inc., P.O. Box 156, Lincoln, MA 01730 $15.00). At age 58, I frequently find myself having trouble dredging up a plant or person's name from the cobwebs of my mind. Clearly, my memory is not what it used to be. And I'm not about to prescribe alcohol for a failing memory. Alcohol is more cause than cure!

But if you're going to take a nip, why not add a few rosemary antioxidants to your nip. Alzheimaretto is a thick tea of rosemary, and some of the other memory and/or antioxidant herbs, parsley, sage and thyme, and even more lemonbalm and lavender to which a little vodka is added. All six herbs contain vitamins A, C and E, or their precursors, and these are antioxidants. But rosemary contains more than I have found reported for the other herbs. Rosemary contains the following antioxidants: apigenin, caffeic acid, carnosic acid, epirosmanol, isorosmanol, labiatic acid, rosmanol, rosmaric acid, rosmarinic acid, rosmariquinone, and O-O-N-trimethylrosmaricine, not to mention ascorbic acid, carotene, and tocopherol. [[Just for kicks I went to the database Feb. 19, 2006 and see that there are more than 2 dozen.]]

So the old timers were right when they figured that rosemary could retard spoilage of unrefrigerated meats, both by its antioxidant and now -proven antiseptic (germ-killing) properties due to such antiseptic compounds as anethole, bornyl acetate, caffeic acid, camphor, carvone, carvacrol, chlorogenic acid, cineole, cymene, geraniol, linalool, methyl eugenol, myrcene, safrole (yes, the so-called carcinogen for which sassafras root was banned by the FDA), terpineol, thujone, and thymol. [[Rosemary is loaded with natural antioxidants and natural pesticides, many of them expected to be synergic at protecting the plant from the oxygen it generates in photosynthesis and the pathogens attacking the plant. And most of these natural compounds have already been experienced by our genes and immune systems during our coevolution, if our ancestors also ingested rosemary. My reasoning suggests that those natural compounds might also be synergic at protecting us from oxygen and pathogens. That's precisely why I prefer the natural antioxidants and antiseptics; my genes and immune system have not been exposed to tomorrow's synthetics.

## Rosemary (*Revisited*)

*The Business of Herbs* 12(5):12-13, November/December, 1994

The *Science News* article "Mossy Memory-booster for Alzheimer's" reached me the same day (September 9, 1993) that Dan Rather announced on CBS the FDA approval of Cognex (tacrine) for Alzheimer's. *Science News* (SN) said that Huperzine A (found in club moss) is more effective, more specific than THA (tacrine), the newly approved FDA drug. "Huperzine A is proving to be one of the most potent and selective acetylcholinesterase [[the enzyme which breaks down acetylcholine, a neurotransmitter]] inhibitors under study for the treatment of Alzheimer's disease, which damages memory and affects four million U.S. residents." Clubmosses also contain nicotine, which also inhibits cholinesterase (SN 143: p. 47).

Quite possibly nicotine and huperzine would be synergic as insecticides and as acetylcholinesterase inhibitors. Tacrine also inhibits the breakdown of acetylcholine. But are these chemicals safe? Like so many drugs, tacrine causes liver damage in about 25% of the Alzheimer's patients studied; helping, slightly, some 25% as well. And tacrine only helps about 25% of people, and those usually no more than 2 years. [[But that's about par! If Steve Connor has quoted Allen Roses (2003), a Glaxo official correctly, "most prescription medicines do not work on most people who take them." Roses says that pharmaceuticals for alzheimer's work only ca 30% of the time. (S. Connor, 2003). Glaxo Chief: "Our Drugs Do Not Work on Most Patients" Independent Digital (UK) Ltd.]].

## What causes Alzheimer's?

Alzheimer's has been blamed on oxidative and inflammatory processes and on the breakdown or deficiency of choline and acetylcholine in the brain. Last decade, researchers are concentrating on the acetylcholine, seeking especially compounds that might prevent the breakdown of choline and acetylcholine. Conversely some have sought ways to feed more acetylcholine or choline to the brain. Various beans, all good sources of choline, can contribute dietary choline, a small fraction of which can cross the blood-brain barrier. Some scientists, detecting a lower incidence of Alzheimer's in patients who have taken a lot of antiinflammatories for arthritis, speculate that anti-inflammatories, such as aspirin or willow's salicylates, might reduce the incidence of Alzheimer's. Many scientists note that part of the problem in Alzheimer's results from oxidative damage, some of which could be prevented by antioxidants, e.g., rosmarinic acid. Yes, rosemary contains more than two dozen antioxidants. "Indeed because oxidation can foster so many disabling changes in the elderly, many researchers now suspect that aging may merely constitute a lifetime's accumulation of oxidative damage" (*Science News*, Aug. 14, 1993). Still, scientists concentrate on preventing the breakdown of acetylcholine.

To further complicate the issue, *Science News* (Dec. 5, 1992; "Anatomy of Alzheimer's") notes that not only antiinflammatory compounds, but a special subset called anticomplementary compounds might also help. Stephen A. Johnson, neuroscientist at the University of Southern California in Los Angeles believes "the complement system somehow leads to brain cell death and dementia." The complement system is described as a particularly lethal group of about 25 proteins in the immune system that helps destroy disease-causing microbes. In an autoimmune malfunction, the system may target brain cells instead of microbes.

## What helps?

I load you up with these details because rosemary, the herb of remembrance, is the namesake of the only compound in my updated database (CRC *Handbook of Biologically Active Phytochemicals*, 1992) to have anticomplementary, antiinflammatory, and antioxidant activities. Rosemary contains more than two dozen antioxidants and a half-dozen compounds reported to prevent the breakdown of acetylcholine. And rosemary contains up to 3,500 ppm of rosmarinic acid [[can attain 25,000 ppm; jad, 2006]], with anticomplementary, antiinflammatory, and antioxidant activities. I'd bet my head of hair that rosemary shampoo, rosemary tea, or rosemary in the bath water would have activities parallel to tacrine or huperzine at retarding the progression of Alzheimer's.

Compounds in GRAS herbs in our food chain reported to prevent the breakdown of acetylcholine are carvacrol, carvone, cineole, fenchone, limonene and limonene oxide, pulegone and pulegone oxide, and thymol. Of the rosemary compounds that retard the breakdown of acetylcholine, several, if not all, are dermally absorbed and some can cross the blood-brain barrier. Thus rosemary shampoo could possess antiacetylcholinesterase activity comparable to tacrine.

It might be more effective, less effective, or ineffective. It could be safer. It surely would be cheaper. Rosemary is certainly better known, has a long history of human usage, and is already on the market as a shampoo. In the cosmetics market, the FDA regulations are not so rigid. But if herbalists started selling rosemary shampoo, claiming that it contained more than 12 antioxidants and a half-dozen compounds that slow the breakdown of acetylcholine, our regulatory agency would bar, confiscate, destroy, or harass such medicinal rosemary shampoo.

What they should do – in a society where 25% of us, and more than half of the elderly who are most likely to suffer Alzheimer's, are not covered by insurance to pay for Cognex and/or the doctor to prescribe it – is to determine which is safer and more effective, tacrine or rosemary shampoo. Incidentally, with herbs other than rosemary, I could design shampoos with twice as much of the compounds that prevent the breakdown of acetylcholine.

Nobody knows whether tacrine is better and safer than rosemary shampoo. Americans deserve to know, not to have the herbal alternative taken away from them by a regulatory agency disinclined to believe the empirical wisdom evolved over millennia. America deserves the best medicine for Alzheimer's. Could it be a Scarborough Shampoo – parsley, sage, rosemary, and thyme?

Having bet my hair that rosemary shampoo would do as well as the approved drug, what next? The price of proving a drug safe and efficacious has risen dramatically, $90 million, to 125, to 231, to 285-300, and finally in May of last year to $359 million [[to 1.7 billion in 2003]]. Who would invest that kind of money to prove that rosemary shampoo is better than Cognex? You and I could grow our own herbs, make our own shampoo, and self-medicate, and there'd be no way to recoup the investment. I suspect that, if herbalists started pushing rosemary shampoo, that our regulatory agency would declare rosemary a hazard to society (when it is probably less hazardous than what they have approved).

Passing age 65, I think it's time I propose a regime I'll call "Duke's

Balmy Mix for Alzheimer's," comprising only changes in diet. My mother, approaching 100 years of age like her mother before her, has the memory of an elephant. She remembers things about me I'd like to forget. So, genetically, I am not targeted for Alzheimer's. If there is any substance to the weakly reported association of aluminum beer cans with Alzheimer's, I may have invited Alzheimer's when I drank too many cans of beer. Certainly ethanol is famous for damaging the brain; and some people, rightly or wrongly, point Alzheimeran fingers at beer cans.

Here's what I would do, were I obsessed with the fear of Alzheimer's, and I truthfully believe it would do more for Alzheimer's than tacrine, the approved drug. I'm so impressed with the potential that I would unhesitatingly urge practitioners working with early Alzheimeran patients to try this regime on half their wards. Remember, these are foods, not drugs.

## Duke's Balmy Regime

- Replace one or two meat dishes a day with bean dishes, laced with oregano, rosemary, savory, and thyme, all of which contain rosmarinic acid.
- Replace two of your canned caffeinated beverages with mixed mint teas, also well-endowed with the stimulant yet anticholinesterase compound, 1,8-cineole, and rosmarinic acid.
- Pick (getting stung in the process-the stings are micro-injections of choline and acetylcholine) and cook stinging nettle greens, adding shredded walnut after cooking (both are good sources of serotonin).
- Eat a mess of heal-all (*Prunella vulgaris*) occasionally spiced up with oregano, savory, and rosemary.
- Make and use bath bags, shampoos, and massage oils containing the GRAS herbs: balm, eucalyptus, fennel seed, monarda, rosemary, and thymol.
- Plant (getting more exercise and fresh air in the process), nurture, and try to figure out why these herbs will help, stimulating your thinking capacities in the processes. All these plants can be grown, at least as annuals, just about everywhere, for almost free.
- Figure out how much tacrine will cost you and enumerate all its side effects. Write to Hillary saying the FDA should be directed to prove that tacrine is safer and more efficacious than rosemary shampoo, if it is. If it isn't, let America know, so they can self-medicate with safer, cheaper GRAS herbs.
- [[In the new millennium, beta-plaque fibrils seem to be alzheimer's whipping boy, even more contributory to alzheimer's than cholinesterase. Get plenty of dietary abeta-blockers (e.g. garlic, pomegranate).
- Sleep at night in a dark room; that generates more of the abeta-blocker melatonin.]]

# Sage (*Salvia officinalis*)

(Unpublished)

## SAGE, SAGACITY and SagaciTEA

*Sage is singularly good for the head and brain, it quickeneth the senses and memory, strengtheneth the sinews, restoreth health to those who have the palsy, and taketh away shakey trembling of the members* (Gerarde as quoted in Grieve's *Modern Herbal* [GMH]).

No, that quote from Gerarde is not an early description of Alzheimer's, nor Parkinson's. But it's not too far off target. Since Alzheimer's is a relatively newly named disease, we don't find much old folklore for Alzheimer's. The quote does suggest though that in Gerarde's day, some believed that sage stimulated sagacity, i.e. the senses and memory, hence my alliterative title. Folklore has long called rosemary as the herb of remembrance, and now rosemary proves to have more than 6 acetylcholine sparing compounds, as does sage, which I'll now term "the herb of sagacity." All this follows on the receipt of a copy of a sagacious clinical trial of sage, not real strong admittedly. But it does strengthen the rationale for the beverage I have been suggesting for a decade, "Alzheimaretto," and the more recently coined "SagiciTEA" for Alzheimer's Disease.

"SagaciTEA" is my name for sage infusion, which really needs lemon and stevia, for my taste, but not for my underarms. Sagacitol is my name for an ethanolic sage tincture, which is OK applied to my tough old armpit, probably more armpit-friendly than aluminum-based deodorants. But sage is not only an aromatic, it contains dozens of antiseptic compounds which might kill those critters responsible for underarm aroma. Even if ingested, sage dries up certain body secretions, like milk and sweat. I only have two chemicals in my database for anhydrotic, both dangerous: atropine, which we'll leave out of food farmacy discussions, and ethanol. Those of you who may have had too much to drink last night may recognize anhydrosis. But yes, sage is an antiperspirant. And I think sage prudently ingested in incipient Alzheimer's. But I'd add several other anticholinesterase herbs.

## ALZHEIMARETTO

This is a drink I make only for myself and cannot, for litigious reasons, recommend it to anyone else, except perhaps as a bath ingredient. Since the advent of tacrine (alias cognex; cerca 1994), my lectures have been suggesting rosemary, the herb of remembrance, sage and melissa teas or tinctures, flavored with amaretto-scented wild cherry bark (hence "AlzheiMARETTO"). The drink is made by steeping (in cheap vodka) herbs rich in compounds that prevent the breakdown of choline or acetylcholine, at least in test tubes. Mint compounds which are reported to prevent the breakdown of acetylcholine and/or choline include carvacrol, carvone, cineole, cymene, fenchone, isomenthol, isomenthone, isopulegol, limonene, limonene oxide, (+)-p-menth-1-ene, menthol, menthone, pulegone and puelgone-oxide, -terpinene, (-terpinene, terpinen-4-ol,and thymol). Rosemary, the herb of remembrance, contains many of these anticholinesterase compounds. Sage, the newly termed "herb of sagacity" contains more than half a dozen of these too. And so does *Melissa*. Many if not all of these compounds are dermally absorbed and some can cross the blood brain barrier. Thus rosemary/sage shampoo could spare acetylcholine, perhaps comparable to the FDA approved drug for Alzheimer's (cognex or tacrine). As mentioned in *Organic Gardening* (Duke, July/August 1995), horsebalm (*Monarda* spp.) is my best mint for carvacrol and thymol, spearmint (*Mentha*) is my best mint source of cineole, mountain mint (*Pycnanthemum*) my best mint source of limonene and pulegone (DANGEROUS). Add melissa, oregano, rosemary, sage, and self-heal for their marvelous antioxidant properties, and/or high contents of rosmarinic acid, which has different activities showing promise in Alzheimeran research. Caraway, dill and fennel , not mints themselves, could be used to top off this herbal imbibition. (Add wild cherry bark to impart the aroma of Amaretto.) Recent British research induced me to add lemonbalm and sage as major components. Easy with the sage; it is rather high in thujone (DANGEROUS in large quantities). Finally there is clinical evidence. I saw it for the first time coming back from an herbal conference in Beckley, West Virginia, where I had suggested all three – lemonbam, rosemary and sage, as a potential alzheimeran combo. An Iranian dbpc study showed the efficacy of sage extract (60 drops/day/4 months) [1:1 in alcohol 45%, i.e. 1 kg dried leaf to 1 liter alcohol] in managing mild to moderate Alzheimer's disease. [A total of 103 patients were screened for the study and 39 were randomized to trial medication. No significant differences were identified between patients randomly assigned to the group 1 or 2 conditions with regard to basic demographic data including age and gender (Table 1). Thirty patients completed the trial. In the *Salvia* extract and placebo group, the number of drop-outs were four and five, respectively.] X12605619 (Akhondzadeh et al., 2003).

This study raised my 1 score (for in vitro data) to 2 (clinical proof) for Alzheimer's and dementia in the updated profile of *Salvia*, heavily updated since originally published in my CRC *Handbook of Medicinal Plants* (Ed. 2, 2002).

# Walnuts (*Juglans regia*)

(Unpublished, 2001)

## An Herbal Alternative for Alzheimer's and even Anthrax???

Monday, September 24, 2001, 5:00 PM, and the garden looked better than it had ever looked. The lawn-mowing Latino crew had just left, having done a final pass, shortly after I edged the garden for the first time with my back-breaking weed whacker. Yes, I had the garden looking real good. Photographers from *Modern Maturity* (the AARP periodical) were due to take some pictures for their December issue, which is scheduled to include an herbal article by Michael Castleman. They were after pictures of black cohosh, bilberry, garlic, ginkgo, echinacea, hawthorn, horse chestnut, milk thistle, saw palmetto, and turmeric. True, there aren't many places in the world where you can find all those growing together, but I have representatives of all in the **Green Farmacy Garden** (GFG). So it was really peaceful, with all the workers and machinery gone for the day. I enjoyed my silence and solitude in the autumn afternoon. Then a drop or two of rain came, so I went inside to my typing terminal (since I don't use it to compute, seems strange to call it a computer). Grandkids came running in, with their parents, all excited after a successful crabbing trip in eastern Maryland. They came in like the tornado that was soon to follow. The local news was warning that they had spotted funnel clouds, and had most of us under a tornado warning. Eerie black and blue-green clouds were there as they often are preceding violent storms. The radio was right. We closed all windows and watched the TV. Cousins called to warn us in case we weren't watching the TV. And it came, heavy rains and heavy winds, dumping leaves all over the immaculate GFG, no longer immaculate. And three big tulip poplars, earlier damaged with herbicides and still showing herbicide damage, lost huge limbs, dumping them down, completely covering my floral clock, and my favorite fern beds on the lower end of the garden. And these big poplar branches, some more than a foot in diameter, brought down with them big branches off my maples and walnuts, which had not shown so much herbicide damage.

What a mess. This was the edge of the tornado that killed a pair of sisters in College Park, Maryland, and leveled many of the old trees at my USDA campus, 3 miles north of College Park in Beltsville, Maryland. (As a result, my USDA database was off line for three days, but is now alive and well; there was no electricity for two days; one of my former co-workers there was working late that Monday on the 4th floor of Building 003, when he saw a chain-link fence blowing by. Quick thinking, he cut off the computers that house the GRIN database, which houses my Father Nature's Farmacy database.)

All of us – kids, grandkids, and I, worked a couple of hours after things cleared up on Wednesday when my daughter-in-law, Sandy, brought my son John's chainsaw, just to liberate my floral clock. After taking the burden off the floral clock, we started on the more extensive damage to the fern garden, trying to clear all the aisles between the four terraces of the GFG. But dark came and we had barely started on the fern beds, my favorite part of the garden, which had been at peak. John used his chain saw to reduce the walnut and the poplar branches to 2-foot logs 8-15 inches in diameter. He'll use them as second class firewood this winter in his mountain home west of here. Sandy picked up the smaller branches and hauled them away manually to temporary dump piles, away from the garden. My grandson, John, loaded debris into the wheelbarrow and pushed it to another temporary dump site. (Which it will be illegal for me to burn; for so-called environmental reasons. Their "environmental" alternative: bag them up in individual plastic bags [not energy wise] to be hauled away to the local land fill, where they will slowly decay into pretty much the same gases that burning would have produced. So, instead of a single match to make all this debris disappear, I must use a hundred plastic bags and the energy it takes to bag them up, and burn the fuel to provide the energy the truck would use hauling it away to the landfill, losing the fertilizer of the ashes.) My usual garbage pickup only comes once a week, and hauls away three cans at the most, so I'll have to haul all those environmentally unsound plastic bags two blocks, uphill, to get them to my curb. Might even have to haul them to the dump. But, by Thursday, in spite of all this, we did have the garden aisles all clear, everything pretty clear except my fern beds, still languishing under all that biomass. John's back gets aggravated by the chain saw, like mine gets aggravated by the weed whacker. I raked by the pond with the break of dawn Thursday a.m., and the place looked all clear, uphill of the pond, following 12 accumulated working hours. And we're just half through. As I told the AARP (*Modern Maturity*) photographers when they got there at 9:00, I've been a senior citizen 22 years, but I am not very modern or mature yet. This week aged me beyond my years, my second experience like this. I'd been caught in a hurricane near Myrtle Beach, South Carolina, hitchhiking my way home following a musical gig. Ended up spending the night in a tobacco barn, when I saw that trees were uprooted in both directions and cars no longer passed at which to wave my thumb. Yes, Mother Nature can be destructive. Why do they always say Mother Nature and Father Time? Sexists!

But yes, nature can be naughty, and so can man. Still reeling from the events of September 11, 2001, when inhumane humans snuffed out hundreds of innocent lives and did billions of dollars of damage, the smoke still rising from the late World Trade Center Twin Towers, I find it amusing that the Biblical walnut, the nut of the garden of Solomon, belongs in an Afghan survival manual. Yes, the Biblical walnut is cultivated in Afghanistan, where it is called "Ughz" or "Waghz." I suppose there are few edible nuts remaining in a food deprived country like Afghanistan.

Walnuts are really a luxury, a health food, here in the United States, where proven beneficial in heart disease. Walnut's omega 3 fatty acid has many other proven uses, notably antidepressant and antimanic, according to my friend, Dr. Jerry Cott. And walnuts are easy to recognize. They belong in any area survival manual as a source of food and antiseptic. Matter of fact the oleuropein in olive leaves and something in walnut (not necessarily juglone), make that a useful thing to try should you be alerted to an anthrax attack. Clearly these plants or their extracts or phytochemicals can kill *Bacillus* in test tubes, if not in man. That's why I was pleasantly surprised to find maggots in the green husk of my walnut as I filmed the walnut for a Paleolithic Survival Manual and Biblical Herb Video. Those maggots have overcome the plant's biochemical defenses. The husk is supposed to be very rich in juglone, which reportedly has antifeedant, bactericidal, fungicidal, molluscicidal, and piscicidal if not insecticidal properties. The husk was riddled with maggots, one of which I ate (no taste at all) on camera. When you find an insect in a poisonous part of a plant like this, there's the possibility that it has learned to survive, maybe even concentrated the phytochemical. Could that phytochemical help thwart a bioterrorist's anthrax attack. I'm sending the maggots off to entomologist friends to look into that possibility. But it's not necessarily the juglone that kills anthrax. According to *The Wealth of India*, aqueous extracts of fresh walnut leaves, free of juglone, possess strong bactericidal activity against *Bacillus anthracis* and *Corynebacterium diptheriae*, weaker activity against *Bacillus subtilis, Escherichia coli, Micrococcus pyogens, Pneumococci, Proteus, Salmonella typhosa, S. typhimurium, S. dysenteriae, Streptcocci,* and *Vibrio*. If I knew I was being attacked with dermal anthrax you can bet a pair of walnuts I'd be washing in a decoction of walnut and olive leaves, both available in Afghanistan (and in my back yard).

But let's talk medicine instead of bioterrorism. It's difficult to open a black if not a Biblical walnut; it's a tough nut to crack. I was unable to open black walnuts with a nut-cracker. Had to revert to the stone age, and smash them between two stones. It worked quite well. Incredible. I had heard that only 5 of 100 of our local walnuts would have seed. But the first three I smashed had a generous stash of flavorful meat (walnut, not maggot, meat; the maggots were in the inedible pericarp). If you'll look at the whole seed of walnut, you'll see that it looks very much like a miniature brain. Around that cerebral edible meat is the filmy pellicle ( I assume it is the skin of the embryo), which turns out to be much richer in healthful compounds than the meat itself. Mine is not the Biblical walnut (*Juglans regia*), but the local black walnut (*Juglans nigra*). All walnuts are rich in serotonin and omega-3 fatty acids making them particularly useful as "brain food." While I'm not a devout believer in the so-called "brain foods," I find it interesting that the kernels of walnuts, corrugated and folded like the brain, contain high levels of serotonin, one of the "brain foods," sometimes implicated in migraine. Ironically, it is the outer seed coat, more suggestive of the brain, that contains most serotonin. Austrian scientists (Lembeck & Skofitsch; Zeits. *Pflanzenphys*. 114:349-53. 1984) found 3.5 ppms (parts per million) serotonin in the embryo, 800 ppm in the so-called endosperm of developing seed, but the withered seed coat in older seed contained ca 1,600 ppm serotonin. Even sprouts 2 months old contain nearly 1,000 ppm.

Martindale's *Extra Pharmacopeia* described serotonin as an antiaggregant, which might partially explain the walnut's role in preventing cardiac arrest and strokes. More importantly from the Alzheimeran point of view, Martindale also suggests that serotonin has anticholinesterase activity, an activity being investigated as potentially useful in Alzheimer's disease. Could the walnut seed help the ailing brains of demented Alzheimeran's? (I have corresponded with two men who have been to China seeking an anticholinesterase alkaloid, huperzine, for their Alzheimeran fathers. Huperzine, sometimes accompanied by another anticholinesterase alkaloid, nicotine, occurs in some clubmosses, reportedly used for food.) Should I suffer Alzheimer's, I'd rather my son stung my neck with stinging nettle (thereby injecting me with acetylcholine and choline, near the blood-brain barrier), and fed me choline-rich beans and lecithin-rich brazilnuts, and serotonin-rich walnuts. I don't know and nobody knows that it would be as effective as the synthetic tacrine (or Cognex), which also increases acetylcholine, a chemical that is low in the Alzheimeran brain, but I'll bet it would be a lot cheaper. Without head-on trials, we'll never know. Conceivably this multifaceted botanical alternative could be more effective, safer, and cheaper than tacrine. In my monotonous theme, the Botanical Alternative, I urge that new drugs be compared not only with placebo but with one of the more rational herbal alternatives.

The nettle/bean/brazilnut/walnut/regime, coupled with transdermal anticholinesterase nicotine patches, might comparatively outshine tacrine, which typically rolled back the course of the disease by about six months. The overall message, say tacrine proponents, is that: "(1) some Alzheimer's patients can be helped by medication alone, and (2) increasing acetylcholine appears to be right" (*Remedy*, Jan/Feb, 1993. p. 7). The nicotine and/or scopolamine patches possibly could, via their anticholinesterase activity, slow the breakdown of choline and acetylcholine in the brain, thereby effectively increasing acetylcholine in the brain. And in the deserts of Afghanistan we could use our jimson weed leaves as transdermal scopolamine patches.

"Nicotine... (administered through injections or tablets also) spurs improvements in attention and awareness of one's surroundings among Alzheimer's disease patients ... But these effects fall well short of sparking major progress in performing daily tasks or remembering routine information" (*Science News* 143, Jan. 16, 1993, p. 47).

"When a brain cell is damaged, growth factors – and estrogen – come to the rescue by spurring new neural connections and boosting enzymes that produce acetylcholine, a chemical that's key to memory – and is depleted in Alzheimer's patients. After menopause, women may lose their repair capacity, and damaged nerve cells may continue to deteriorate, leading to memory decline and – potentially – Alzheimer's." (Men may be spared this problem since testosterone, available into old age, is converted to estrogen in the brain.) (K. Dalton. 1992. "Estrogen Side

Effect Giving Brains a Memory Boost," *Longevity*, Aug., p. 10.)

"Nerve cells in the brains of people who develop Alzheimer's have lower levels of key membrane molecules called phospholipids than do nerve cells in healthy individuals. One of these phospholipids, phosphatidylcholine, is also a precursor of acetylcholine, a chemical messenger between nerve cells that is reduced in the brains of Alzheimer's patients. The researchers posit that nerve cells hungry for choline compounds raid their own cell membranes for phospohatidylcholine; this leaves holes on the underside of the membrane..." (*Science News*, Mar 7, 1992, p. 15.).

Today I'd also be sipping plenty of mint teas, and I'd even have lemon balm in my bathtub, were I genetically targeted for Alzheimer's. All contain compounds absorbed transdermally as well as in the gut that have anticholinesterase activity. Only in 1997 did I learn that lemon balm, rosemary and sage could prevent the break down of acetylcholine in human brain cells (in tissue culture).

Walnuts aren't just survival fare; they are health foods. Compared with the Mediterranean diet, a walnut diet produced mean changes of -4.1% in total cholesterol level, -5.9% in LDL cholesterol level, and -6.2% in lipoprotein(a) level. Substituting walnuts for part of the MUFA (monounsaturated fatty acid so prevalent in olive oil) in a cholesterol-lowering Mediterranean diet further reduced total and LDL cholesterol levels in men and women with high cholesterol. Chinese scientist, S. L. Liu (1990), showed that a combination of walnut oil, with the phytochemical borneol (common in cardamom, my top source, and mints like sage and rosemary) was more than 95% effective in purulent otitis media, compared to 85% effectiveness for neomycin.

Walnuts are a major source of dietary serotonin, quickly broken down in the gut (where there are serotonin receptors; Gershon, 1998). Serotonin reportedly has analgesic, antiaggregant, anticholinesterase, anticonvulsant, antiendotoxic, antigastrisecretogogic, antireserpinic, bronchoconstrictor, cardiovascular, coagulant, euphoriant, myorelaxant, myostimulant, neurotransmitter, oxytocic, teratogenic, ulcerogenic, and vasoactive activities.

Back when Prozac was extolling Prozac's virtues at signaling satiety via elevated cerebral serotonin signals (lookout serotonin syndrome), the editor of my book, *The Green Pharmacy* at Rodale Press, was turned on when I said that this story had suggested to me that serotonin, whether from prozac or the food chain, should give the same satiety signal. The editor said three half walnuts seemed to curb her appetite. And my database said members of the walnut family, like walnut, butternut, pecan, and hickory nuts were the richest sources of that brainfood, "satiety signalling," serotonin. Could dietary serotonin have this effect? One pharmacotherapist said no; that the serotonin would be broken down in the gut. The pharmacotherapist also said that dietary serotonin would not therefore cerebrally signal satiety. And he should know, because he treats bipolar patients, and praises omega-3's, if not serotonin, highly. And walnut is well endowed with both omega-3's and serotonin. But the dietary serotonin was ruled out before Gershon's revelation that there were serotonin receptors in the gut, the so-called "second brain." That's where dietary serotonin may be broken down, before and/or after sending a satiety signal to the other brain [Gershon, 1998].

Nice of walnut to combine dietary serotonin and omega-3's. Selective serotonin reuptake inhibitors (SSRI's) like Prozac are also important in depression. The use of omega-3 fatty acids in bipolarity and depression has also been noted at a National Institutes of Health (NIH, 1998) symposium. Walnuts are probably the tastiest if not the best source of omega-3s for vegetarians who don't care to consume animal (mostly cold water fish) omega-3's. Omega-3's also inhibit COX-2 and thus help prevent conversion of arachidonic acid (AA) to the bad prostaglandin 2's and other series 2 eicosanoids. Pharmaceutical COX-2- Inhibitors have been promoted for the prevention of Alzheimer's and the colon cancer to which I am genetically targeted. Of course COX-2's are more promoted for relief from arthritis. Omega-3's have been reported to reduce the incidence of breast cancer; probably by this mechanism.

Depressed people, wishing to bootstrap themselves out of depression, might consider extracting 10 grams (one-third ounce) of St. Johnswort (...) in 20 ml walnut oil for the omega-3's and serotonin. Jerry Cott, PhD, prefers high-carbon fish oil omega 3's, but adds that even the vegetable omega-3's, like walnut, can be useful in depression, including manic depression, which some of my relatives suffer. (Yes, my mother was manic depressive too). A little sunflower oil might be a useful additive, too, if it retained its antidepressant phenylalanine, and evening primrose oil, if it retained its tryptophan. All these might have great application as massage oils, even as sexual lubricants, in depressed and manics resisting pharmaceuticals. And as a massage oil and salad oil for depressed geriatrics, I'd also add about 7 saffron stigmata (30 mg), having learned that would be equivalent in activity to 100 mg imipramine as an anti-depressant. That could make the mix even more useful for moderate depression and Seasonal Affective Disorder (SAD), thinks geriatric Jim Duke. And that salad oil, sprinkled over purslane as a salad, would add the priapistic effects of l-dopa (for the depressed) and the anti-depressant activities of norepinephrine in the purslane (for the geriatric). Hmm. Maybe I need a massage. Or a dish of Biblical dopaminergic faba beans, loaded with arginine-rich garlic and Biblical walnut oil (walnuts are also rich in arginine, presumed aphrodisiac).

Walnut bark is used in some countries as a toothbrush. Its extract shows broad-spectrum antimicrobial activity in a dose-dependent manner, inhibiting growth of several species of pathogenic micro-organisms representing gram-positive bacteria (*Staphylococcus aureus* and *Streptococcus mutans*), gram-negative bacteria (*Escherichia coli* and *Pseudomonas aeruginosa*) and a pathogenic yeast (*Candida albicans*). The extract has either synergic or additive action when tested with a wide range of antibacterial drugs. It also increased the pH of saliva. Thus, brushing the teeth with this bark may improve oral hygiene, prevent plaque and caries formation, and reduce the incidence of gingival and periodontal infections (Alkhawajah, 1997).

Here's some of what I had to say in my *Medicinal Plants of the Bible* about the European walnut more than 2 decades ago:

**Juglans regia L.**
**Carpathian or Persian Walnut, English Walnut, Nuts (Biblical)**

> *...I went down into the garden of nuts to see the fruits of the valley, and to see whether the vine flourished, and the pomegranates budded...* Song of Solomon 6

"One of King Solomon's most valuable fruit trees was the walnut, a handsome tree with smooth gray bark and fresh green leaves. Walnuts were widely cultivated in Biblical times for the nuts and timber. Greeks and Romans regarded walnuts as symbols of fecundity, and scattered walnuts about at weddings. The heavy green rind encasing the nut is steeped in boiling water to produce a brown dye. In Jesus' time, walnut trees grew on the shores of the Sea of Galilee. His seamless coat was a rich brown, the dye said to have been made from walnut leaves and nuts. Walnuts are also used to tint gray hair black. In Algeria, the leaf decoction is used as a shampoo against fall of hair. Today the walnut is principally valued as an orchard tree for commercial nut production. Nuts consumed fresh, roasted, or salted, used in candies, pastries, and flavorings. Ground nut shells used as adulterant of spices. Crushed leaves or a decoction used as insect repellant and as a tea. Outer fleshy part of fruit very rich in vitamin C and produces a yellow dye. Fruits, when dry pressed, yield a valuable oil used in paints and soaps; when cold-pressed, yield a light yellow edible oil, used in foods as flavoring. Young fruits pickled. Decoction of leaves, bark and husks used with alum for staining wool brown. Wood hard, durable, close-grained, heavy, used for furniture and gun-stocks. Tree often grown as ornamental.

Orientals use the kernels for laryngeal and lung disorder, and mix them with almond and ginseng for chronic cough; the oil they used for skin ailments. Lebanese think the nut increases fertility. Leaves, bark, and hulls are alternative, astringent and laxative. Leaf infusion considered antidiabetic, antiscrofulous, astringent and tonic. The oil from old nuts, gone rancid, was applied to old ulcers. Husks of the nuts were used by the Lebanese as an anodyne. Algerians burned the shells in sugar for headache. Other North Africans inhaled the smoke of burning shells for coryza and influenza. The bark they use to cleanse and whiten the teeth, to redden the gums and lips, and to alleviate gingivitis, halitosis and pyorrhea. Regarded as alterative, anodyne, anthelmintic, astringent, bactericidal, cholagogue, depurative, detergent, digestive, diuretic, hemostat, insecticidal, laxative, lithontryptic, stimulant, tonic, and vermifuge, walnut is a folk remedy for anthrax, aphtha, backache, caligo, carbuncle, carcinomata, chancre, colic, condylomata, conjunctivitis, corns, cough, dysentery, eczema, egilops, favus, gangrene, heartburn, impotence, inflammation, legs, leucorrhea, lungs, rejuvenation, renitis, rheumatism, scrofula, skin, swellings, syphilis, toes, warts, whitlows, and worms. Walnut is a folk "remedy" for cancer of the intestine, lip and stomach; scleroses of the liver and uterus; tumors of the breast, fauces, gullet, kidney, stomach, and throat. With such an anticancer folk history, it is interesting to note that walnut contains the antitumor compound, juglone, a compound with some pesticidal and weedicidal attributes as well. According to Keys, the Chinese use the leaves and powdered hull as an astringent and as a depurative in syphilis. The decoction is used externally in phylctenular conjunctivitis. According to Kirtikar and Basu, Ayurvedics and Unani regard the therapeutic properties as the same as *Aleurites moluccana*, i.e., antibilious, apertif, aphrodisiac, constipating, and used for blood and heart disease and burning sensations. In Ayurvedic medicine, walnut is anodyne, aphrodisiac, cardiotonic, carminative, expectorant, and used for bronchitis, bruises, piles, rabies, ringworm and watery eye in Unani."

**Dosages:** FNFF = !!!

Nuts consumed fresh, roasted, or salted, used in candies, pastries, and flavorings. Ground nut shells used as adulterant of spices. Fruits, when dry pressed, yield a valuable oil used in paints and soaps; when cold pressed, yield a light yellow edible oil, rich in omega-3's; used in foods as flavoring. Young fruits pickled. French make a liqueur from the green nut; green nuts also pickled; leaves rarely consumed as tea (FAC, TAN; EB54:155); .5 tsp. chopped lf/cup water (externally only; APA); 2-3 g lf/100 ml water for compresses (KOM); 3-6 g (PHR); 4-8 ml liquid leaf extract (PNC).

- Algerians use leaf shampoo against alopecia (BOU), fresh leaves and bark as styptic (HJP), burning sugar with the shells for headache (HJP).
- Arabians believed in the famed antidote of Mithridates; two walnuts, two figs, and twenty leaves of rice, rubbed together with a grain of salt (DEP).
- Arabians inhale fumes from burning nut shells for coryza and flu (BOU); or to repel insects (GHA).
- Asian Indians suggest spirits distilled form leaves or fruits as antispasmodic and in 1-2 drachms used to check morning sickness (NAD).
- Asian Indians suggest the edible cold pressed oil for dimness of vision (NAD).
- Ayurvedics and/or Yunani regard the therapeutic properties as analgesic, antibilious, apertif, aphrodisiac, cardiotonic, carminative,

constipating, expectorant used for blood disorders, bronchosis, bruises, cardiopathy, hemorrhoids, rabies and ringworm (KAB).

- Chinese use leaves and powdered hull as astringent and depurative in syphilis (BIB).
- Greeks and Romans regarded walnuts as symbols of fecundity, and scattered walnuts about at weddings.
- Italians use the plant as an antiparasitic in cheeses (X15619562).
- Lebanese think the nut increases fertility, use rancid old oil to treat old ulcers (HJP).
- Malayans say the kernels fatten the body and strengthen the muscles, suggesting them for colic, dysentery and heartburn (KAB).
- Turks clothe nude patients in leaves for fever, rheumatic pain and sunstroke (EB49:406).
- Orientals use the kernels for laryngeal and lung disorder, and mix them with almond and ginseng for chronic cough; the oil they used for skin ailments (BIB).
- Saudis used bark ("bambar" in Saudi Arabia, "dandosa" in Pakistan) soaked in water and rubbed on gums and teeth, bot as cleanser and cosmetic imparting reddish color to gums, considered attractive (GHA).
- Turks take the fruit decoction taken internally for malaria (EB49:406).
- Yemeni eat the nuts for nervous tension (GHA).

## Downsides

Class 2d. Juglone is mutagenic. External carcinogenic effects noted after chronic external use. (AHPA, 1997). None known for the leaf at proper dosage (KOM; PHR; PH2); Commission E reports fruit-shell not permitted for therapeutic use; usefulness not documented adequately. Fresh shells contain the naphthoquinone constituent juglone, which is mutagenic and possibly carcinogenic. The juglone content of dried shells has not been studied adequately (AEHD).

## Extracts

Guarrera et al. (2005) mention walnuts antiparasitic use for cheeses (X15619562). Regular nut consumption can result in a 10% reduction in LDL-Cholesterol in a few weeks. Nuts often rich in arginine, vitamin E, folate, fibre, potassium, magnesium, tannins and polyphenols. Although nuts contain approximately 80% fat the nut feeding trials have not shown any associated weight gain in those ingesting nuts suggesting the addition of nuts in the diet may have a satiating effect. Daily ingestion of a small quantity is an acceptable lifestyle intervention to prevent coronary heart disease (X15294495). Gallic acid in the pellicle shows potential for inhibiting of aflatoxigenesis (X15053524). Colaric et al. (2005) list chlorogenic, caffeic, p-coumaric, ferulic, sinapic, ellagic, and syringic acid as well as syringaldehyde and juglone from ripe fruits of 10 walnut cultivars Not only in the kernel but also in the pellicle did syringic acid, juglone, and ellagic acid predominate (average values of 33.83, 11.75, and 5.90 mg/100 g of kernel; and 1003.24, 317.90, and 128.98 mg/100 g of pellicle, respectively), and the contents of ferulic and sinapic acid (average values of 0.06 and 0.05 mg/100 g of kernel and 2.93 and 2.17 mg/100 g of pellicle, respectively) were the lowest in all cultivars. It was found that the walnut pellicle is the most important source of walnut phenolics. The ratio between the contents in pellicle and kernel varied by at least 14.8-fold for caffeic acid (cv. Adams) and by up to 752.0-fold for p-coumaric acid (cv. Elit) (X16076123). One study indicates an absence of tocotrienol, another found it consistently but at levels below 2 ppm (X15941326; X15969535). Good source of dietary serotonin, quickly broken down in the gut (where there are serotonin receptors). Serotonin is reportedly analgesic, anti-aggregant, anticholinesterase, anticonvulsant, antiendotoxic, antigastrisecretogogic, antireserpinic, broncho-constrictor, cardiovascular, coagulant, euphoriant, myorelaxant, myostimulant, neurotransmitter, oxytocic, teratogenic, ulcerogenic, and vasoactive [LD50=117 ipr rat; LD50=160 ivn mus; LD50=868 ipr mus]. Juglone reortedly has allelochemic, allergenic, anticariogenic, antidermatophytic, antiEBV, antifeedant, antiherpetic. antiparasitic, antiseptic, antitumor, antitumor-promoter, antiviral, bactericide, chemopreventive, dermatitigenic, fungicide, keratolytic, molluscicide, sedative M11, sternutatory, and viricide [LD50=2.5ppm (orl mus)]. The combination of tannin with all its pesticidal activities and juglone may be pretty potent. Aqueous extracts of fresh walnut leaves, free of juglone, possess strong bactericidal activity against *Bacillus anthracis* and *Corynebacterium diptheriae*, weaker activity against *Bacillus subtilis*, *Escherichia coli*, *Micrococcus pyogens*, *Pneumococci*, *Proteus*, *Salmonella typhosa*, *S. typhimurium*, *S. dysenteriae*, *Streptcocci*, and *Vibrio*. (WOI)

## References

Alkhawajah A M. 1997. "Studies on the antimicrobial activity of Juglans regia." *American Journal of Chinese Medicine*, 25(2):175-180. 1997.

Gershon, M.D. (MD; Columbia University, NY). 1998. *The Second Brain*. Harper-Collins, NY. 314 pp.

Liu SL. 1990. "Therapeutic effects of borneol-walnut oil in the treatment of purulent otitis media." *Zhong Xi Yi Jie He Za Zhi*. 1990 Feb; 10(2):93-5, 69.

NIH, 1998. "Workshop on Omega-3 Essential Fatty Acids and Psychiatric Disorders," 1998.

Part Seven

# Herb A Day…

# North America – Native

# Bee Balm (*Monarda didyma*)

*The Business of Herbs* 6(4):6, September/October, 1988

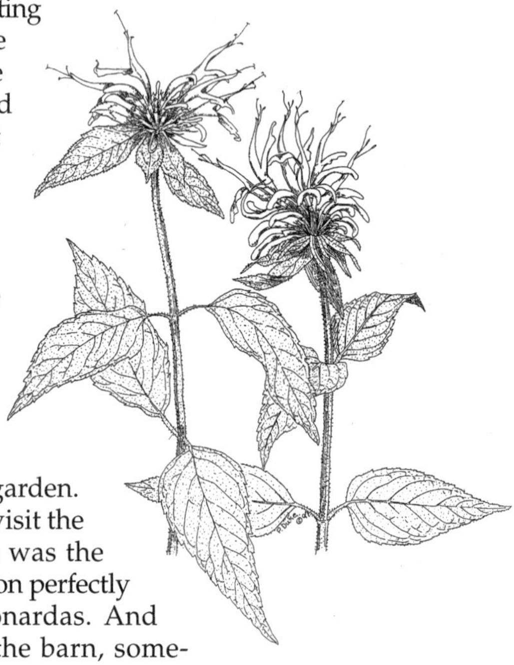

Independence Day. How fitting this year that I have *Monarda* (the horsemint, Oswego tea, or bee balm genus) in reds, whites, and blues. And marching to a different drummer this year, I'm celebrating the Fourth of July with a different kind of pyrotechnics, floral fireworks.

Instead of merging with the masses on the D.C. mall to see the fireworks, I've instead moved my chair and table out beside my brilliant red bee balm, *Monarda didyma,* eccentric to my medicine wheel garden. How fitting that the first bird to visit the bath at the center of the garden was the purple finch, whose head coloration perfectly matches one of my purple monardas. And following that a lizard fell off the barn, something I never witnessed before. Nor had I ever seen the bumblebees tumbling with fallen flowers of the "narcotic" linden tree under which I sit, but that bumblebee appears narcotized. But then came the expected ruby-throated hummingbird, to sip from my monarda, the real fireworks for me this year. With flowers too deep for honeybees, the flowers are more often foraged by bumblebees and hummingbirds.

And, of course, I'm drinking "pink lemonade" for the Fourth. You see, if you put the petals of *Monarda didyma* in plain water, the color doesn't come out. But when you add the lemon juice or "lemonade" powder, out comes the pinkish-orange color and the exquisite flavor. The extracted flavor of the bee balm does not taste like old-fashioned Gulfspray as the fresh flowers smell. The marvelous *Magic and Medicine of Plants* (Reader's Digest, 1986), says of the Owego tea, alias *Monarda didyma,* "an appropriate herb for consideration on Independence Day." The Oswego Indians of western New York made tea from the dried aromatic leaves of *Monarda didyma* and shared their fondness for it with Colonial settlers who went on to use it as a substitute when imported tea became scarce after the Boston Tea Party. The Shakers thought the tea effective in treating colds and sore throats, while other settlers steamed the plant and inhaled the fumes to clear sinuses. The Reader's Digest book adds that *Monarda didyma* is also known as scarlet bergamot because its scent is similar to that of the bergamot orange, a citrus fruit. From my *Living Liqueurs* (now out of print): "During the American Revolution, patriotic Americans used the tea used by the Oswego Indians while they boycotted the British tea at the Boston Tea Party. With all I read about caffeine, I think we should consider a Boston caffeine party and dump some of the the other caffeine-containing beverages. Teas made from bergamot leaves and flowers are soothing and sedative. Adding one part vodka with a spray of lemonbalm or lemon verbena adds zip to my "Balm Calmer." Leaves are used to flavor fruit cups, jellies, and salads. Fresh or dried leaves and/or flowers spike the flavors of wines and cocktails. Alone, but better in combination with rosemary, or thyme, this makes a good "Bergamot Liqueur" with sugared vodka. Boiled with catnip and sugar, it makes an interesting liqueur with gin.

In reviewing *Living Liquers* one critic warned that he was allergic to bergamot. I suspect he meant bergamot orange, rather than *Monarda*, but it's conceivable that someone could be allergic to *Monarda*, or any other plant for that matter.

I recommend a collection of red, white, and blue *Monardas* to any herbalist for their color, for their aroma, and in the case of Oswego tea, for its historical significance.

# Birch (*Betula* spp.)

(Unpublished)

Sure, some people don't like to call trees herbs. But I think of the birches as a classic source of "herb" beers and teas. I drank a few birch beers up in Maine one year. And I love the wintergreen aroma of the "cherry birch," due to the compound called methyl salicylate. That's the same aroma that used to grace Teaberry chewing gum-don't see that around much anymore. I got turned on to it again after reading in the *New York Times* that betulinic acid (we'll call it BA from here on out) worked better on melanomas in mice than the drug most commonly used to treat human melanoma.

Dr. John Pezzuto, University of Illinois, Chicago, reporting on that research, noted that it might take 50 pounds of paper birch (*Betula papyrifera*) bark to provide enough BA to treat 100 patients. Although I have written Dr. Pezzuto for further information, I don't yet know how much BA the birch bark contains. Fifty pounds of dry hogbean could provide 180 grams of BA, if my database is correct. My source, *Hager's Handbook*, suggests that hogbean roots contain 0.1-0.8% BA. I went to my database to look for the closely related compound betulin. It had only one quantified entry for betulin, which may well be ubiquitous in woody plants. Sage weighed in at a lowly 15 ppm betulin. But in *JAFC* 38(2) we read that *B. papyrifera* bark contains 120,000 ppm betulin and *B. verrucosa* up to 300,000 ppm on a dry-weight basis. So, even though I don't yet know how much BA birch bark contains, I can tell you it is one of the world's better sources of betulin: 12-35%, if we can believe the scientific literature.

Betulin occurs widely in trees and shrubs, often in high concentrations. The outer cortical layer of *Betula platyphylla* contains about 3.5% betulin. BA is also of widespread occurrence: in rhododendron bark, for example. Both betulin and BA possess antitumor activity against carcinomas. Data in my database (1992) suggest that BA is six to 12 times more active than betulin at killing certain types of cells, perhaps even cancer cells. We might infer that BA is six to 12 times more potent than betulin as an anti-cancer or antimelanoma agent. We might speculate that some natural mixtures of these two compounds might be even better than pure betulin, maybe even pure BA.

This is another case of a folkloric plant listed by Hartwell in his *Plants Used against Cancer,* later to prove promising against cancer. Hartwell listed it for cancer, citing sources using the French word *bouleau* for birch. Bark of the "hua-mu-p'i," *Betula mandschurica* or *B. latifolia*, was reportedly used for mammary carcinoma more than a thousand years ago, during the Sung Dynasty. Finns used the bark tea for cancer, especially abdominal cancer. Swedes, referring to it as "bjerk," used oil from the bark for warts (Hartwell, 1982).

This is also another example of a plant containing several anticancer compounds, some of which logic might suggest would be synergistic. I'll go out on a birch limb and predict that a mixture of betulinic acid, betulin, methyl salicylate, and squalene would have greater antifeedant, antiseptic, and/or antitumor activity than an equivalent amount of any of the individual constituents. All four occur in birches, and all four have anticancer reputations.

Among Amerindians, paper birch was used by the Algonquins for skin problems (but not, apparently, melanoma), even diaper rash. Cree used it for skin and lung ailments as well as for gonorrhea. The Creek used it for tuberculosis, and the Ojibwe for stomach cramps. Apparently, the betulin-rich bark was most frequently used.

Foodwise, Facciola mentioned even the very young leaves of the paper birch, eaten in salads or stir-fries, or made into teas. The sap, like that of maple, is made into a tea, beer, sugar, or vinegar. Whether the sap contains betulin or BA remains to be seen. Shoots and catkins are also consumed. Inner bark of some species, even the wintergreen-scented cherry birch, is made into flour as an emergency food.

Jones and Alli (1987) showed that the paper birch can yield 80 liters of sap (about 1% solids). Birch saps contains about 9 grams carbohydrate per liter, so total sugar yields could approach 750 grams per tree. Fructose and glucose are the main sugars, with minor or trace quantities of galactose and sucrose.

Many people regard antioxidant activity as useful in fighting or preventing cancer, cardiopathy, cataracts, melanoma, and several other ailments, especially degenerative ailments. Lamaison et al. (1988) studied birch oil's antioxidant activity. It was second only to clove oil in a study of 17 essential oils.

We can round this off and say that, under Lamaison's circumstances, birch oil, though inferior to clove oil, was about five times better than cinnamon; six times better than absinthe; eight times better than thyme; 10 times better than nutmeg; 12.5 times better than anise, cajeput, niaoli, and melissa; 16 times better than coriander, ginger, lavender, and rosemary; and 25 times better than cardamom oil as an antioxidant. I find a mix of clove oil and birch oil an attractive "farmaceutical" mix. But remember: any essential oil, natural or synthetic, organic or inorganic, can be lethally toxic if ingested in large quantities.

Visionary people prone to abdominal or breast cancers or melanoma, who also believe that an ounce of prevention is better than a pound of cure, might be foolish enough to enjoy "Bog Bitters," a mix of birch bark and hogbean bitters to which some other plants reported to contain BA (including dogwood, eucalyptus, forsythia, grape, henna, jackfruit, jujube, mulberry, rosemary, sage, and teatree) have been added. Some of these are better not ingested. Some may have more BA, some less. Very few quantitative data are available. I'd spice mine up with some clove oil for its flavor and antioxidant activity. Or, if I were down in Amazonia, I'd liven it up with their clove vine, an unrelated species loaded with eugenol. Lamaison et al. showed that pure eugenol was a tad more active than whole clove oil. Don't think that rules out synergy; that's comparing pure eugenol to 60-90% eugenol. For my food farmacy, I'd rather have the whole essential oil (in small quantities) than the pure eugenol.

# Black Cohosh (*Actaea racemosa*)

*The Wild Foods Forum* 9(3):8-9, May/June, 1998

## Coming Home from Europe

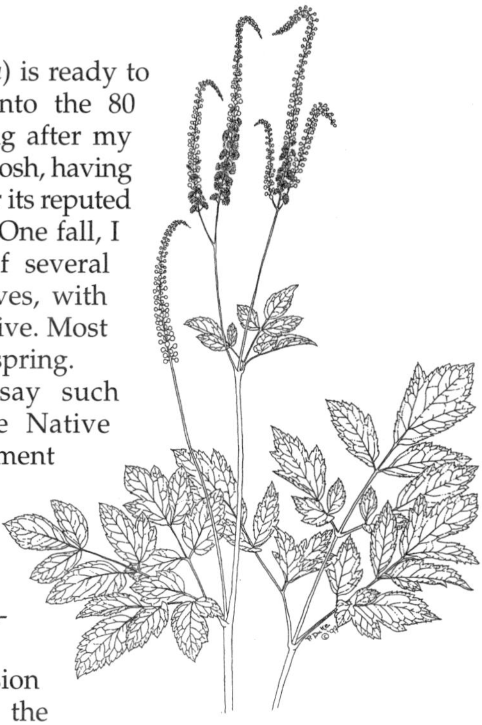

The black cohosh (*Actaea racemosa*) is ready to emerge from below the earth into the 80 degree end of March, early spring after my mildest winter ever. I've a lot of cohosh, having studied its renewable harvesting for its reputed (and real) bug-repelling capacity. One fall, I lopped off the bottom halves of several roots, and replanted the top halves, with the next year's bud ("eye") still alive. Most of them came back the following spring.

Dreamers rationalize and say such things as "It was used by the Native Americans primarily in the treatment of women's diseases." But that's not the impression you get reading Dan Moerman's *Medicinal Plants of Native America*, although there are a couple of female specific applications.

Cherokee took the root infusion "in spirits" for rheumatic pains; the plain infusion for colds, coughs, "consumptions" and constipation. Cherokee also used it as a tonic, diuretic, anodyne and to stimulate menstruation; plant given for fatigue, hives and to make babies sleep. Iroquois poulticed smahed leaves on babies sore backs, and used in soaks or steams for rheumatism; they used the root infusion as a lactagogue. Penobscot took the roots for kidney ailments.

I see little there to stress women's diseases, except lactagogue and emmenagogue activity, either of which might reflect estrogenic activities. Still black cohosh has travelled to Europe, been intensively studied there, and come back to us in advanced "estrogenic" herbal medicines, a bit more advanced than Lydia Pinkham's which Varro Tyler (1997) characterizes so well. It'll be a very short while, I predict, before we start hearing about herbal SERM's, as we are now hearing about herbal SSRI's and herbal COX-2-inhibitors. SERM is the abbreviation of the new pharmaceutical buzzword, selective estrogen-receptor modulators. And according to my non-binding interpretation, all the phytoestrogens that bind to estrogen receptors (and I think that's a lot if not all of them) will modulate selectively. Raloxifene (Evista), the second (after Tamoxiphen) in a predicted swarm of SERMs, recently approved by the FDA for preventing osteoporosis. I'll wager that the "estrogenic" isoflavone formononetin found in black cohosh is an herbal SERM that most of our genes have experienced over the course of our evolution. But in 2006, I have had my black cohosh analyzed and it contains no formonetin, so maybe it isn't a SERM. Stay tuned. SERMs, according to Andy Weil's *Self Healing* (April 1998), are intended to provide the cardiovascular and bone-protective properties of estrogen, without the concomitant risk of breast and uterine cancers. Dr. Weil is disturbed "by allegations that raloxifene's manufacturer, Eli Lilly and Company, failed to disclose evidence that the drug induced ovarian cancer in both mice and rats...Unlike estrogen, raloxiphene does not alleviate hot flashes and can actually make them worse" (Weil, 1998).

On the record I find that the word modulator is often used to mask our ignorance rather than refine the precision of our language. Modulate merely means to effect, positively or negatively, so the word immunomodulator is not as specific as immune-booster or immunosuppressant. All plants modulate the immune system. I'm not sure I completely agree with Andy Weil in the following somewhat equivocal quote "I believe that echinacea works not by stimulating immune function, but rather by modulating it – that is. the activity of some types of immune cells increases, while the activity of others decreases. As a result, I think it's safe for people with autoimmune disorders to use echinacea on a short-term basis to deflect a cold or the flu. I would not recommend it for long term use in cases of autoimmunity" (Weil, 1998).

Conservative Varro Tyler (1997) speaks highly of black cohosh. "Certain complex chemicals, especially triterpenes and flavonoids, are believed to be the active constituents. Some of them apparently act on the pituitary gland,...to suppress the secretion of luteinizing hormone (LH). High levels of LH in the blood are often associated with menopausal symptoms, including hot flashes, night sweats, headaches, heart palpitations and drying and thinning of the vagina. In contrast to stanbard hormonal therapy with estrogens and progestins, black cohosh does not seem to affect levels of two other pituitary hormones, follicle stimulating hormone (FSH) and prolactin. In other words the action is more selective (there you see it, that selective in the buzzword SERM) than with normal hormonal therapy. That's good because it tends to lessen side effects" (Tyler, 1997). Other constituents...bind to estrogen receptors, producing a weak estriol effect. Estriol, unlike its more potent estradiol, is not associated with increased risk of breast, ovarian or endometrial cancers (Tyler, 1998).

In Germany 6 preparations are commercially available. As early as 1940, black cohosh extracts were used as hormonal agents for disturbances of the hypophysis and also for premenstrually, dysmenorrheically and menopausally caused neurovegetative symptoms (Clay and Reichert, 1996). Dysfunction in young patients following hysterectomy improved significantly with a 6-month course of treatment with black cohosh. The extract "has shown itself to be superior to placebos and comparable to estrogens for treating neuro-vegetative menopausal symptoms" (Clay and Reichert, 1996). It makes sense to combine black cohosh and St. Johnswort for treatment of emotional and psychovegetative symptoms of menopause. In a multicenter trial (176 gynecologists) of the combo on 812 menopausal women for 12 weeks; 41% scored very good; 41% good; 11% modest or little, and 7% insufficient. Side effects were reported only in 2%.

# Blueberry (*Vaccinium* spp.)

*The Wild Foods Forum* 12(4):8-9, July/August, 2001

Since I really love blueberries, and think they might be saving my eyesight, my brain, etc. from the perils of free radicals, I am pleased to discuss them here in *The Wild Foods Forum*. Last year I updated my blueberry column for AllHerb.com, which lamentably, crashed in 2001. Then I started my own website which crashed even faster. My blueberries are in early fruit as I write this in June, 2001. And when I teach in Maine, one of the perks will be ripe Native American blueberries, in lieu of the European bilberries. Since my editors let me treat cranberry as an herb a while back, perhaps I can get away with the blueberry, even though it's bigger and woodier (and sweeter) than the cranberry. Being both culinary and medicinal, if not herbaceous, blueberries do fit the broader definition of herb, i.e. a useful plant. It's often difficult to find a plant that isn't useful, even in more than one way. As green plants, blueberries, bilberries and cranberries take carbon dioxide out of the air and turn it into carbohydrates (some of which we consume) and oxygen (some of which we breathe) and vitamins, some of which we take. You can say that about any green plant out there. But blueberries, like cranberries, are important Native American food species, with both food and medicinal uses to boot.

## Similar to the Bilberry?

Here we are talking about the American blueberry. Europeans influenced the Indians in their usage of native American plants, just as the Native Americans influenced newcomers with their foods and medicines. Authors heap deserved praise on the European bilberry as a medicinal plant, and I suspect that our blueberries share the bilberry's medicinal attributes, at least partially. Mowrey (*Guaranteed Potency Herbs*, 1988) doesn't share my opinion on this, saying, "Only *Vaccinium myrtillus* should be used. The North American blueberry, for example, is unsuitable for standardized medicinal preparation or use." (I have seen no data to support this quote.) A new article published in 1998 (Prior et al., 1998. *J. Ag. Food Chem.* 45) notes overwhelming evidence indicating that free radicals, and their oxidative damage, may underlie many diseases, cancer, heart, neurodegenerative and vascular diseases. Blueberries and bilberries are noteworthy for their antioxidant capacity. Hence these scientists compared in an unbiased fashion the quantity of anthocyanins and the antoxidant activity of several varieties of American blueberries and bilberry. With the exception of the bilberry, the antioxidant activities of the blueberries seemed to be concentrated in the skins. So the old wild blueberries, with a whole lot of skin and not much meat had proportionately more of the protective phytochemicals. But the bilberry outstripped them for anthocyanins. The authors concluded: "In general, blueberries are one of the richest sources of antioxidant phytonutrients of the fresh fruits and vegetables we have studied." Their data showed however, that bilberry was richest in anthocyanin (3,000 mg/kg fresh weight), with only one of the 30 other varieties of blueberry studied topping 2,000 mm. So if you're after anthocyanins and their antioxidant activity, you'll get almost twice as much in bilberries as you'll get in most blueberries. And that's why bilberry is among the top ten herbs I take, hoping to slow down the macular degeneration that many of us suffer. Blueberries will help too, But not as much as the bilberries, at least based on the interesting new data presented by Prior et al. (1998).

See Steven Foster's "Bureaucracy and the Bilberry" (*The Business of Herbs*, September/October 1990) for an interesting account of the bilberry's activities. Steven notes that the bilberry has been used since time immemorial as a food plant, emerging as a medicinal plant only in the 16th century. Apparently absent in the eastern U.S., bilberry is found in Pacific America, from British Columbia south to Arizona, New Mexico, and Utah. Mowrey states that the bilberry "is one of the best for mild diabetes, and may be especially beneficial for use in senile diabetes."

## Good for Allergies?

Just returned from the blueberry capital of Maine, Washington County, I found a letter from Jin Aye Lim soliciting medicinal info on *Vaccinium angustifolium* and related species. With the Prince Edward Island Food Technology Centre, Jin had been told that the dried leaves and twigs have been used by North American natives in one of their traditional herbal remedies for allergy treatment. The glucoquinone in bilberry leaves experimentally lowers blood sugar levels, and its quinic acid has been suggested to be useful in gout and rheumatism, according to Foster. Arbutin has been reported from the leaves of some species of *Vaccinium*. At 60-200 milligram dosages, arbutin is a urinary diuretic and antiseptic. The so-called anthocyanosides, pigments in the darker-fruited species like bilberry, reportedly have antiaggregant, antiinflammatory, antimenorrhagic, antisecretory, antispasmodic, myorelaxant, and vasodilator properties (Duke, 1992, CRC *Handbook of Biologically Active Phytochemicals*).

Blueberries may be used in lieu of bilberries as a food pharmaceutical. You might have to eat twice as many (what good luck) to get as many anthocyanins from the blueberries as the bilberries. New research at Tufts University suggest that blueberries might slow Alzheimer's as well (Joseph et al., 1999). One statistic has always puzzled me; there are more people living today than all those that lived before. (At least that was kicked around 10-20 years ago, and I didn't argue with it, considering the geometric growth of our population. Joseph et al. [1999] introduced another interesting one. "At present, the world population comprised of people over 65 years of age represents 50% of all those who have ever lived to attain this age.") Dr. Joseph equates his rat diet of 1.86% dry blueberry extract as close to a cup of blueberries in humans. I could live with that. Dr. Joseph is closely allied with Dr. Ronald Pryor who has helped develop the famous ORAC (Oxygen Radical Absorbance

Capacity) test. Among fresh fruits and vegetables, wild blueberry won their ORAC scores, due to their anthocyanins. It was followed by blackberry, garlic, kale, strawberry, spinach, brussels sprouts, plum, alfalfa sprouts, broccoli florets, [green tea steeped 5 minutes] beets, orange, red grape, red pepper, cherry, kiwi, pink grapefruit, white grape, onion, corn, eggplant, and cauliflower. Of course, all plants contain antioxidants.

Yes – Royal Airforce Pilots took their bilberries and I'd take my blueberries, if I had to make a night flight. The anthocyanosides tend to improve night vision. Come to Maine with me to get your antioxidants the best way, grazing on Native American food plants, as we study the ethnobotanical practices reported for the Abenaki, MicMac and Penobscot Indians. It's the cheapest and most pleasant and educational way to do Maine. Ask Vickie if you don't believe me.

## References

Duke, J.A. 1993. "An Herb a Day...Blueberry." *The Business of Herbs* 11(5):12-13, November /December.

Joseph JA, Shukitt-Hale B, Denisova NA, Bielinski D, Martin A, McEwen J, Bickford PC. 1999. "Reversals of age-related declines in neuronal signal transduction, cognitive, and motor behavioral deficits with blueberry, spinach, or strawberry dietary supplementation." *J. Neuroscience* 19(18):8114-8121.

# Buckbean, Bogbean (*Menyanthes trifoliata*)

*The Wild Foods Forum* 12(2):8-9. March/April, 2001

Never thought much about the bogbean. It shows up here and there, especially in northern peat bogs. I've not seen it often. I did see it in Maine last year, in a bog, where it was supposed to be. Come with me to Maine next summer and I'll introduce you to it. It's mentioned, usually not too excitedly, in most of the edible and medicinal plant field guides. I got excited when I found it was one good source of betulinic acid in my database (immediately after reading in the *New York Times* that betulinic acid worked better on murine melanomas than the drug most commonly used to treat melanoma). The research, reported by Dr. John Pezzuto, U. Ill (Chicago), noted that it might take 50 pounds of paper birch bark to provide enough betulinic acid for 100 patients. Fifty pounds of dry bogbean could provide 180 grams betulinic acid, if my database is correct. (My source, *Hager's Handbook*, suggests that the roots contains 0.1-0.8% betulinic acid.) This is another case of a folkloric plant listed by Hartwell in his *Plants Used Against Cancer*, later proving to have some promise against cancer. Hartwell listed it for skin cancer citing sources in Washington, D.C. and in France.

Foodwise, Facciola describes the bitter leaves of this plant, not too distant relative of the bitter gentian and perhaps even more bitter, as having been used as a hop substitute in making beer. He notes also that the roots have been used for making famine breads, or just chewed on. "In der likorindustrie zur Herstellung von Boonekamp unt Bitterschnapsen" (HHB). Its leaves are even GRAS (generally recognized as safe) in liqueurs in the U.S., at least in our unapproved HRF (Herb Research Foundation) listing. (FDA cannot be pinned down on this.) The leaves contain the bitters' ingredient, gentianine. Grieve's *Modern Herbal* suggests: "An infusion of 1 oz. of the dried leaves to 1 pint of boiling water is taken in wineglassful doses, frequently repeated." It is used in herbal teas for the gall bladder and liver.

Medicinally, Duke (1986) notes among Amerindians that the Illinois-Miami Indians used the roots for diarrhea and dysentery, while the Kwakiutl used them for bloody coughs and emesis. Moerman (1986) gives much more detail: "Aleuts use the roots for constipation, gas, and rheumatism, also using it as a potent tonic; Kwakiutl also took the root or leaf decoction to put on weight, especially when they had flu, and to treat stomachache." Menominee, Micmac, and Tlingit had more obscure, unspecified uses as well.

Europeans tend to have had more respect for the herbs than Americans. Some Caucasian uses have included ague, dermatitis, dropsy, dry throat, dyspepsia, eruptions, fever, gout, hepatoses, herpes, hypochondria, malaria, migraine, scurvy, trigeminal neuralgia, tuberculosis, etc. Boerhaave is said to have treated his gout by drinking bogbean juice with whey. Duke and Wain (1981) note that the plant is viewed folklorically as apertif, cathartic, cholagogue, deobstruent, depurative, diaphoretic, diuretic, emetic, hypnotic, intoxicant, laxative, narcotic, nervine, sedative, stomachic, tonic and vermifuge. Grieve adds the emmenagogue adjective. Nitpickologists skillfully warn that any herb with emmenagogue activity should be avoided by those wishing to carry a pregnancy to term. Echoing the alarmists and covering my frass, I must recite the warning.

Even in the days of Linnaeus (ca 1750), the bogbean was recommended for arthritis, nephritis, and rheumatism. More recently several cases of glomerulonephritis have been treated with bogbean rhizomes. This prompted Bohlin's group (1995) to check it out for glomerulonephritis. Buckbean decoctions showed dose-dependent antiedemic, antiinflammatory, antileukotriene B4, antiprostaglandin activity and inhibited PAF-induced exocytosis.

In my database (http://www.ars-grin.gov/duke), bogbean is by no means a major source of betulinic acid; still it is an edible source, moving it into the realm of what I call food farmacy. Winged bean roots, if my database is correct, could provide more than 6 times as much betulinic acid, making it an even more promising food farmaceutical. You too can search my database at the USDA.

This is one of many food plants with the compound, betulinic acid, that has shown activity against three of Gates' targeted ailments in Africa: HIV, malaria, tuberculosis. I'll bet big bucks, that if tried against Leishmania, it would help there too. Almost always I can dig in and find that there are related compounds, related, in this case, to betulinic acid, additive or synergic with the focus compound, betulinic acid. By the way, that is one of the most promising phytochemicals for melanoma and other pathologies, perhaps of more concern to Americans than Africans (today).

The curator of the USDA phytochemcial database, Mary Jo Bogenschutz-Godwin, has developed a query by which we can ask which plants (or just food plants) have been reported (in our limited database) to be useful for all 4 of the Gates targeted diseases. And another query tells us which phytochemicals in our database are reported useful for all 4. Very often, a plant or phytochemical useful against one septic organism is active against another septic organism.

Why go with food plants instead of pure synthetic pharmaceuticals. First off, cost!!!. Second, and more important, for your health rather than your pocketbook!!! Your genes have experienced many of the natural phytochemicals. On the other hand Leishmania, Mycobacterium, Plasmodium and maybe even the HIV virus, may or may not have experienced them. Well known to your body, phytochemicals are less likely to have side effects than newly developed synthetics that your genes have never experienced. Uncle Sam won't jump on you so readily if you suggest a food or immunomodulating foods in HIV, leishmanic, malarial or tubercular patients. Our database, with expansion, could select the best foods for exploration. And later, we could extract these natural phytochemicals, using all the residues (often much more than ninety percent of the biomass of the plant), to convert to energy alcohol, in energy-poor parts of Africa as in energy-poor America.

If the bog bean contains 0.1-0.8% betulinic acid, as recorded in my database, and we need that betulinic acid for one of the Gates' targets, that would leave 99% of the bogbean for conversion to energy alcohol. We could say that about the more readily cultivated sources of betulinic acid.

# Chokeberry, Black (*Aronia melanocarpa*)

*The Wild Foods Forum* 16(1):8-9, Winter, 2005

Our Paleolithic ancestors probably ate a greater variety of small fruits than we do today. In the process they may have gotten more phytochemicals than we do, like for example the red and purple anthocyanins in our berries. Believe it or not, these phytochemicals can help prevent the biggest killers of Americans today, cancer, cardiopathy, diabetes, strokes. A return to the paleolithic diet promises preventive phytopharmacy to combat these modern diseases with primitive fruits. Avoiding cigarettes and excess alcohol, and seeking the five fruits AND five veggies the NIH keeps pushing (I push for 7 and 7, coupled with adequate paleolithic exercise) are the most promising of preventive measures. Sell your pharmaceutical stocks before you indulge in these good habits, because if all Americans followed these guidelines, there'd be much less need for high-priced pharmaceuticals. Wonder why preventive medicine gets much less budget than poisonous pharmaceuticals which many of us cannot even afford. Preventive is much better than cure. But our NIH budget still does not reflect that. Could the pharmaceutical industry be running the NIH in absentia? Could berries be better at preventing flu than those shots we didn't get this year, or those relatively new pharmaceuticals (Relenza and Tamiflu)? January 14, four or five years ago, the FDA partially answered, saying that Relenza and Tamiflu do not prevent flu. Today I boast, without too much proof: "Boosting the immune system albeit with primitive berries, can prevent some types of flu." Even the allopaths and pundits, this year low on vaccine, may be unknowingly supporting the immune boosters to boost the immune system. They readily admit that people with depressed or suppressed immune systems are more liable to get flu or the terror of the year (anthrax, SARS, small pox, west nile and the like) than people with a healthy immune system. Still I have yet to hear an informed public official advise us to boost our immune system. Meanwhile in a country where 20% can hardly afford prescription medicines and/or the doctor to prescribe them and/or the insurance to cover them, the *AARP Magazine* (Nov. Dec., 2004) reports that Medicare beneficiaries, many on fixed incomes, are bracing for the heftiest dollar hike in the program's 40-year history (17.4% in 2005 Part B premiums).

I thought elderberry might be one of the best (and I might add most respected) folk remedies (and preventitive) for flu in the back woods of West Virginia. But there are many good tasting berries, more than elderberry, rich in antiviral anthocyanins, out east. The barely edible black chokeberry, *Aronia melanocarpa,* is one of them, second only to the inedible, maybe poisonous, mountain ash (*Sorbus americana*) in anthocyanin content, according to one comparative study reported later. (Many members of the rose family do contain cyanide, mountain ash for sure, chokeberry perhaps.) Authors of my favorite edible plant books (Facciola, 1991; Moerman, 1998, and Tanaka, 1976) apparently did not have the astringently bad first experience I had with the chokeberry, clearly explaining its name. I've learned to pucker up and enjoy them thinking they might be preventing cancer, cardiopathy, cataracts, and other cantankerous infirmities catering to us cagey old cosgers. I don't want to let one sour experience sour me for life!

Moerman says of the black chokeberry only that the Potawatomi used the berry infusion for colds. I'll bet the Potawatomi, like me, weren't always sure whether they had colds or flu. I'll bet a chokeberry rob, like an elderberry rob, would contain a whole lot of antiviral anthocyanins in a delicious medicine. Abenaki and Potawatomi both used this Maine species for food. Farther south in Maryland, I sometimes enjoy the puckery black fruits when wandering thru local peat bogs. One transplanted to the **Green Farmacy Garden**, on my dry south facing "yang" slope" is coppicing, even showing some weedy tendencies.

The black chokeberry is one of, if not the richest sources of anthocyanins. In reviews of anthocyanins, Mazza and Miniati (1993) and Takeoka et al. (1997) report 211-215 mg per 100 g serving of for black beans (with up to an incredible 2,370 mg in the seed coat or testae), 300-700 mg/100 g fresh fruit for bilberries, 80-325 for blackberries, 725-1050 in our black chokeberry, 160 in boysenberries, 250 in black currants, 7-495 for blueberries, 350-450 in cherries, 75-80 for cranberries, 300-420 in crowberries, 50-400 in hawthorn, 350 in huckleberries, 30-330 in lingonberry, 1,500 in mountain ash, 10-20 in red currants, 30 to 750 for red grapes, 20-60 in red raspberries, 25-180 in saskatoon berry (*Amalanchier alnifolia*), 140-380 in sea buckthorn, 115-256 in whortleberries. Boik (1995) notes that some anthocyanins, as anticoagulants, might prevent blood clots, even strokes. He reports also that they may protect collagen from degradation by inducing cross-linking of collagen fibers, by promoting collagen synthesis, and by preventing enzymatic cleavage of collagen. That makes them useful in arthritis. Anthocyanins inhibit collagenase. By inhibiting collagenase activity, anthocyanins may inhibit invasions by cancer cells. Boik suggests, for arthritis and capillary permeability, doses of 20 to 40 mg pure anthocyanins thrice daily, or 120 mg/day. Remember that the standard USDA 100 gram serving usually translates to about half a cup or ~3.5 ounces. That list above will show you where you can get your daily 120 mg anthocyanins, e.g. ca 1/6 to 1/12 cup bilberries. But it only takes about a twentieth of a cup black chokeberries to give you the 120 mg suggested for arthritis, one third cup to give you the 600 mg suggested for myopia and nyctalopia.

I'm pleased to say that my specimen in the **Green Farmacy Garden** flowered and fruited one year after it was planted in the "Heart Disease" plot. During its first fruiting year I enjoyed only 9 of the shiny black fruits. (1,050 mg anthocyanin per 100 g fruit) In 2004 there were hundreds of the astringent black fruits. So if you wanted to buy American, and if you attribute all bilberry activities to anthocyanins, you might be better off with black chokeberry than with the bilberries and blueberries which taste a bit better. If I am reading the literature correctly, 120 mg anthocyanins or that fraction of a cup of these berries could help alleviate or prevent worsening of arthritis, cancer, and capillary fragility (read preventing varicosities and vascular spiders). A half cup of a mix of these can help a lot of us, especially those who don't eat enough fruits. The more berries, fruits and veggies we eat, the longer we live, healthily. Still, the longer we live the more likely we are to get arthritis, cancers and capillary fragility. So let these fruits enhance your diet, your health, your longevity, and your future years.

Anyone can go to the USDA database http://www.ars-grin.gov/duke/ and find some of the many activities attributed to the anthocyanins. For eye problems a larger dose is indicated (600 mg anthocyanins a day for myopia and nyctalopia). But ⅓ cup of black chokeberries could provide that too. Black chokeberry might conceivably (and heretically) be better for bilberry and cranberry indications than bilberry and cranberry, if all the bilberry and cranberry indications accrue to their anthocyanins. and procyanidins respectively, and if chokecherry contains similar procyanidins (the ones responsible for urinary antisepsis in cranberry, bilberrry and blueberry).

Facciola notes that the good flavored fruits are astringent (puckery) like chokecherries (*Prunus virginiana*). Fruits are stewed in honey and/or sugar to make a fruit sauce. Pectin rich, like my hawthorns, they can be added to pectin-deficient fruits and make them jell (ditto with my hawthorn). Improved cultivars in Europe are made into a cranberry-like juice, that used to be available here in the United States. Facciola notes that this is available in U.S. stores catering to Polish and Russian ethnics.

But this berry, rich in anthocyanins and pectins, may combine the anticancer properties of both anthocyanins and pectin, maybe with homeopathic levels of laetrile. (I cannot yet prove this.) Dec, 3, 2004 – I sniffed the live green bark and the black mummified fruits and got no hint of benzaldehyde, the amaretto-like smell that suggests the presence of cyanide and laetrile.

# Chokecherry, Common (*Prunus virginiana*)

*The Wild Foods Forum* 11(5):8-9, September/October, 2000

Back in 1931, Yanovsky listed 1,112 food plants eaten by North American Indians; by 1998, Anthropologist Dan Moerman had raised the number to 1649. Today I'm going to talk about the one Moerman said had the most diverse food use citations. On top, with 163 food use citations is the common chokecherry (*Prunus virginiana* L), by no means not my favorite berry. (I prefer the wild cherry, *Prunus serotina*). I strongly believe that departure from our evolutionary paleolithic diets attributes to most modern death-dealing diseases, cancer, cardiopathy, diabetes and the like. And that's why the NIH is meekly and cheaply (low budget for cancer prevention, bigger budget for poisonous chemotherapies and high priced technological fixes we can't many afford) urging us to Strive for Five.

I'm not yet prepared to urge you to strive for the chokecherry, because I find them rather distasteful myself. However added to lemonades and compotes, or herb teas, they add that puckery tannin which may be as good as relenza at preventing flu. And it's those polyphenolics like tannins and oligomeric procyanidins that give China tea all its health hype. Chokecherries are, like most of our berries, rich in many important health-protecting phytochemicals our ancestors got more of.

I may offend some people here, but I disagree with them anyhow; I think going on a monotonous one-item diet, say a cabbage diet or grape diet is bad for you. Maybe for a one or two day cleansing period. I share that view as my candid feeling about longterm hi protein-hi fat diet, low in plants. Yes, many non-vegetarian paleolithic people would sometimes have hi fat-hi protein splurges after a kill, but in lean times, they were more liable to be eating and enjoying many roots and fruits, with weeds and seeds filling many of their needs. I do not recommend vegetarianism, but I advocate what I call jeffersonian vegetarianism, letting meat be a spice rather than the main course. My genes target me for colon cancer, and I believe too much red meat can contribute to colon cancer. Or too few berries and veggies can contribute to colon cancer. I do respect paleolithic variety with its high fiber and high phytochemicals, which modern Americans often sorely need.

Here in Maryland, I am more likely to encounter wild cherry (*Prunus serotina*, a welcome weed tree at my place) than the subject species, common chokecherry. As with strawberries, I have trouble telling the wild cherries and serviceberries apart. Yes it is often frustrating to learn that the species you have in hand doesn't conform to the descriptions in the books. My *Brown and Brown Woody Plants of Maryland* lists several species of the genus *Prunus* (which incidentally contains those tamer fruits like almond, apricot, cherry, peach and plum). So I turn to my college professors *Flora of the Carolinas*, and find that Radford Ahles and Bell (1968) suggest that *Prunus virginiana* has reddish to light purplish fruits 8-13 mm long and divergent teeth on the leaves while *Prunus serotina* has all but black fruits (and a little bit smaller, to 10 mm long) and incurved teeth on the leaves. At age 70, I'll nibble on any *Prunus* I see and finish it if I like it, spit it out if I don't. I suspect that's the way paleolithic predecessors foraged for fruit as well.

According to Dr. Moerman, the chokecherry was the most used food plant and fifth most used medicinal (after yarrow, calamus, sagebrush, and fernleaf biscuitroot). But he devotes more space to its medicinal than to its food use. As a food farmacist, I know the fine line between food and famacy is difficultly drawn. Algonquins took the bark tea, often with calamus, for cough. I have so used the closely related *Prunus serotina*. Blackfoot Indians used the berry juice for diarrhea (the tannin tends to plug one up) and for sore throat (tannins also antiseptic). Members of the La Leche League might be interested in his comments: "Infusion of cambium [inner bark] and saskatoon taken by nursing mothers to pass medicinal qualities to baby." Cherokee used the bark for colds and coughs, chills and fevers, sores and ulcers, agues, measles and "thrash" (possibly thrush or candidiasis). They boiled the fruits for hematochezia. It was also used in steam baths for biliousness, dyspepsia, and jaundice. Cheyenne used fruits, green or ripe, for diarrhea, even in children. Chippewa used the analgesic inner bark for cramps, scrofula and pulmonary bleeding and tuberculosis. Crow used the bark tea for cleaning burns and sores. Flatheads used the resin exuding from cuts in the plant to apply to sore eyes. The bark infusion they used for diarrhea, dysentery, and worms. Lakota made a tea from the leaves during their sun dance festivals. Menominee applied inner bark poultices to galls or wounds on man and beast alike. Mesquaki used a root bark decoction as a rectal douche for hemorrhoids, sort of a poor man's preparation H, clearly with effective tannins. They also made a beverage tea from the bark, no doubt with that familar bitter-almond staste of benzaldehyde. Maine's Micmac made tea of the bark for diarrhea. Navajo Ramah took a cold infusion of dried fruits for stomachache. Ojibwa use the inner bark tea for lung problems and in problems of pregnancy. Maine's Penobscot used bark infusion for diarrhea. Potawatomi used the berries as a tonic, and the bark in collyrium.

I have covered only one species in the preceding paragraph, doubting that ethnobotanists and the Native Americans they write about really know or care which wild cherry they are dealing with. They all have that smell and activity of benzaldehyde and the puckery astringency of tannins.

The black thorn *Prunus spinosa* (I think it is also the sloe berry of the sloe gin fizz I drank in younger days) even made it into the Herbal PDR [[[Fleming, T. et al. 1998. *PDR for Herbal Medicine*. 1st ed. Medical Economics Co., Montvale, NJ. 1244 pp]]] and Commission E [[[Blumenthal, M; Busse, WR; Goldberg, A; Gruenwald, J; Hall, T; Riggins, CW; Rister, RS. (Eds.). 1998. *The Complete German Commission E Monographs*. "Therapeutic guide to herbal medicines." American Botanical Council, Austin, TX and Integrative Medicine Communications, Boston, MA. 684 pp.]]], the fruits getting approval for mild inflammations of the mouth and pharynx. But *Prunus serotina* was listed only as folk medicine by the Herbal PDR. The chokecherry wasn't covered by either of these teutonic books, and not approved by the Commission. I suspect my Maryland wild cherries would do every bit as well for mild inflammations as the European *Prunus spinosa*. The pucker is proportional to the antiseptic tannin. Here's how the PDR said the wild cherry *Prunus serotina* was used folklorically: "as an antitussive, astringent, and sedative, for bronchitis, cough, diarrhea, nerves, and pertussis."

From the caucasian perspective, Facciola notes that the astringent fruits are eaten raw, dried or made into jams, jellies, juices, pies, syrups and wines. Green twigs are stripped of bark and inserted into meats as flavoring skewers. "Nutritious kernels were added to pemmican." Bark, twigs and leaves have been used to make aromatic teas. Facciola notes that the wood of wild cherry, *Prunus serotina*, is particualrly good for smoking thick cuts of meat and fish, imparting a mild fruit tart taste. I might add here that I suspect the barks of our wild cherries might be almost as useful for benign prostatitc hyperplasia (BPH) as the African cherry, *Prunus pygeum africana*. Certainly *Prunus serotina* contains several antiinflammatory phytochemicals, caffeic-acid, copper, kaempferol, magnesium, quercetin, scopoletin, ursolic-acid, and I'll wager it shares many antiprostatitic sterols with Pygeum.

# Cloudberry (*Rubus chamaemorus*)

*The Wild Foods Forum* 11(6):8-9, November/December, 2000

They call it baked-apple berry up in Maine. That's the only place I ever saw it, and there, too, quite rare. In Maine, I see it only in peat bogs, clambering across the cranberries, etc. And the peatbogs themselves are endangered. So we only take field trips in raised walkways through peat bogs, e.g. at Quoddy State Park in Maine, and in Campobello in adjacent Canada. Such peat bogs are a trip in themselves, and a source of many edible berries, bearberries, blueberries, cranberries, choke berries (*Aronia*), choke cherries (*Prunus*), pin cherries, and now this strange one called, most appropriately, baked apple berry. The tan colored fruits smell and taste just like baked apples. But never have I seen enough to make a pie. I think they are endangered anyhow. Confessions are good for the soul. Before we knew it was endangered, we got lost in one of those numerous peat bogs or heaths (haiths) as they are called in Maine, and I ate and enjoyed several.

I'm hoping my friend, horticulturist Dr. Harry Swartz, U. Md., has developed a cultivar so I can grow it here at my **Green Farmacy Garden** (**GFG**). He's working on getting me a bilberry too.

## Food uses

Facciola (1991) suggests that it is more common than my limited experience up north suggests. He notes that cloudberries are eaten preserved, raw, stewed, and in confections, jellies, liqueurs (like lakka) tarts, vinegards, and wines. Laplanders freeze them in snow, a method used by American Indians for many of these berries. Facciola says that fresh frozen berries are available occasionally in large eastern markets, like New York City. And my trusty Moerman (1998) book, *Native American Ethnobotany*, adds that the berries, rich in vitamin C, are stored in seal pokes, kegs or barrels, and buried in the frozen tundra for future use. Alaskans eat the berries straight or with sugar or seal oil or both. Arctic eskimos have their special ice cream, mixing the berries with seal oil and chewed caribou tallow. I think I'd prefer mine mixed with blackberries or blueberries, as some Alaskans mix them. Upper Tanana fry them with grease and/or sugar, sometimes adding dried fish eggs.

## Medicinal uses

Woodland Cree use the root decoction for female problems, especially a difficult labor, much as other tribes use raspberries. Maine's Micmac use the roots for consumption (perhaps tuberculosis), cough, and fever. According to Jonathan Hartwell, formerly with the NCI, the leaf juice and fruit juice were used folklorically for cancerous ulcers. Tannins could help. And that's all the folklore I have on it. While I don't endorse kombucha, I mention that Facciola states that brewing kombucha with raspberry leaves imparts an apple flavor. Maybe baked apple berries would come even closer to that apple flavor.

According to Robbers and Tyler (1999), tannins from several berry bushes (esp. *Rubus* and *Vaccinium*) tend to arrest diarrhea by their astringency which reduces intestinal inflammation by binding to the surface protein layer of the inflamed mucous membranes, causing it to thicken, thereby hindering resorption of toxic materials and restricting secretions. The most widely used astringent herbs include several edible berry plants. Because of similarities, *Rubus* and *Vaccinium* leaves are used similarly. The leaves contain tannin and are consumed as teas, prepared by pouring boiling water over one to two teaspoons of the finely cut leaves. Then they are steeped for 10 to 15 minutes. Material may be mashed in cold water for about two hours and then strained. A cup of tea, up to six a day, may be necessary to effectively control diarrhea. Teas from bilberry leaves may "be used effectively as a mouthwash or gargle for sore mouth and inflammation of the mucous membranes of the throat."

If I were having a baby, or had just had a baby, or were suffering the problems of an uncomfortable monthly episode, I'd probably or possibly crave, as do many American women, a *Rubus* leaf tea. Fortunately I'm not pregnant nor do I have conjunctivitis, so I can just enjoy my raspberry tea. I may go through life without a cloudberry leaf tea, unless Harry comes through. I often add less threatened species of *Rubus* to my antiviral-teas around the house, specifically for the astringent tannins. I am comfortable that I get many of the benefits of the OPC's (Oligomeric Procyanidins) and tannins when I vary my tea routine with *Rubus* leaf. I suppose the same health benefits accrues to OPCS and tannins, whether they come from the common cultivated red, yellow and black raspberries, or the rarer cloudberry.

In an article by Schwitters, author of *OPC in Practice*, we find a quote that supports what I have been saying for years: "OPC is not only found together with the red pigments. It is found in all plants, vegetables and fruits, such as oranges and lemons." Since data on OPC's have rarely been tabulated, I cannot quantify who's the best among them. Since they often co-occur with water-soluble tannins (polymers) and catechins (monomers), one might search for good sources of these and presume that, under certain circumstances, these same sources might be good sources of OPC's. I currently prefer the peanut hulls and the red wines and grape juices to pine bark. A single flavan-3-ol molecule (monomer) is catechin; the pairs and triples (dimers and trimers) are OPC; quadruples (tetramers) and higher polymeric procyanidins are tannin. The whole group is identified as bioflavanols or flavanols.

## References

Schwitters, B."OPC in Practice," Special Advertising Section. *NFM NSN*, October, 1995.

Robbers, JE; Tyler, VE. 1999. Tyler's *Herbs of Choice*. "The therapeutic use of phytomedicinals." The Hawthorn Herbal Press, Binghamton, NY. 287 pp.

# Clubmoss (*Lycopodium lucidulum*)

*The Business of Herbs* 6(6):4-5, January/February, 1989

In the dead of the "temperate zone" winter, those few evergreen herbs in the forests seem so much more conspicuous than in the summer when they have so many other green associates. So it is with the evergreen shining clubmoss, *Lycopodium lucidulum* Michx. Dr. Dave Lellinger, the Smithsonian expert on ferns and fern allies (despite its name, the clubmoss is not a moss but a fern ally); tells me that only recently has he concluded that it should be known scientifically as *Huperzia*, a name completely unknown to me until recently. What's all the hoopla about *Huperzia*?

Huge words sometimes mask the significance of some of the exciting discoveries being reported in our medical journals today. For example, when they speak of "antiretroviral activity," they suggest the herb or compound is showing some activity against the class of viruses known as retroviruses, the type to which the AIDS virus belongs. We'll talk about anti-AIDS activities closer to St. John's Day (June 24th) when the St. Johnswort comes into flower. But here's today's message, cryptically encoded in jargon that would have been meaningless to me a year ago: *Huperzia* shows three times the anticholinesterase activity of eserine.

When the telephone started ringing, I didn't even know what *Huperzia* was. But it didn't take long to discover that it was nothing but the clubmoss, *Lycopodium*, traveling under an alternative scientific name. The species of interest, *Huperzia serrata*, was treated in *Medicinal Plants of China* as *Lycopodium serratum* Thunb., a species rich in biologically active compounds including the alkaloids, huperzine-A and -B. *Huperzia* has been used in Chinese traditional medicine to treat a variety of ailments from pneumonia to hemorrhoids. Its spores were used as a desiccant for abscesses and skin sores.

In their analysis of Chinese herbs, Chen and Lin (Kaohsiung, *J. Med. Sci.* 4:259. 1988) found that one kilogram (2.2 pounds) of *Lycopodium herbage* contained 16,020 parts per million (ppm) calcium or about 16 days' recommended daily allowance (RDA); 2,340 ppm magnesium, 6 days' RDA; 28 ppm zinc, 2 days' RDA; 15,000 ppm potassium, 41 days' RDA; 155 ppm sodium, less than one-tenth RDA; 650 ppm iron, 43 days' RDA; 100 ppm manganese, 25 days' RDA; 5 ppm copper, 4 days' RDA. Traces of arsenic (0.49 ppm) and mercury (0.07 ppm) were also reported. Commenting on the RDA's does not imply that this herb is safe to ingest, only that, like most herbs, it contains significant quantities of minerals. In one study, potassium in amounts far less than the RDA reduced stroke incidence by 40%.

Steven Foster and I share a great interest in similar pairs of species in the eastern and western hemispheres such as the oriental and occidental ginseng. Perhaps our occidental equivalent of the oriental *Lycopodium serratum* is the shining clubmoss, *Lycopodium lucidulum*. When Dr. Lellinger first showed me the oriental *Lycopodium serratum* in the

Smithsonian herbarium, I was impressed at the similarities. Superficially they look alike, but the toothing on the leaves of *L. serratum* is more prominent.

The resemblances between these two species is so great as to lead me to suspect that there might be chemical and medicinal similarities to parallel the similarities in form. Hence I am providing plant materials of our occidental clubmoss to scientists studying the oriental clubmoss.

The huperzine alkaloids isolated from the oriental clubmoss are said to be three times as active as the very active eserine, alias physostigmine, and 30 times as powerful as galanthamine found, for instance, in the daffodil, *Narcissus*. The *Handbook of Medicinal Herbs* (CRC Press, 1985) already hints at potential anti-Alzheimeran activity of the physostigmine from the ordeal bean, *Physostigma venenosum*, reported to improve long-term memory processes in humans. If the scientists are right, huperzine may have three times the promise of physostigmine for the dreaded Alzheimer's.

Chinese studies look very encouraging. As early as 1986, Tang et al. (*Act. PharmO Sin*. 7:507. 1986) reported that huperzine-A had powerful and reversible anticholinesterase activity. Wang et al. (*Act. Pharm. Sin*. 7:110. 1986) suggested this could be clinically useful Zhu and Tang (*Act. Pharm. Sin*. 22:817, 1987) reported initial clinical studies on huperzine-A showing positive results on improving memory. They suggested that huperzine-A and -B might improve cognitive functions in impaired individuals. Xu and Tang (*Act. Pharm. Sin*. 8:18, 1987) ranked the anti-cholinesterase activity of huperzine-A the highest of several drugs tested. Lu, Shou, and Tang (*Act. Pharm. Sin*. 9:11. 1988) concluded that huperzine-A was superior to physostigmine for learning and memory retention (more so in aged than in adult rats). Wang et al (*Act. Pharm. Sin*. 9:193. 1988) reported that clinically, huperzine-A can improve the muscular weakness of myasthenia gravis as well as improve memory in stroke patients with memory impairment. Is there hope for Alzheimer's disease here?

Clubmosses contain several alkaloids, many of which may act synergically, that is, the total effect is greater than the sum of the individual effects, to alleviate certain maladies, maybe even the elusive Alzheimer's disease. The huperzines from *Lycopodium serratum* already show promise. Perhaps similar or even better activities may be found in our occidental *Lycopodium lucidulum*, one of the easiest clubmosses to transplant to the fern garden. Stay tuned!

## Cranberry (*Vaccinium macrocarpon*)

*The Business of Herbs* 10(1):8-9, January/February, 1999

Cranberry is about as American a fruit as there is, used by the American Indians long before the pilgrims arrived. As Harry Smith said on *CBS* November 20, "cranberry is more American than apple pie; cranberries, blueberries, and concord grapes being the only fruits native to America." True, cranberry is more American than apple pie. But there are a lot more American fruits, hundreds of them, that the American Indians ate. Some are relatively obscure and better known to botanists like myself. Along with the cranberry, Indians consumed related bearberries, blueberries, huckleberries and unrelated wild cherries and choke cherries (apparently richer in anthocyanosides than even blueberries, if not bilberries) and wild plums, rosehips, blackberries, dew berries, even baked apple berries up in Maine, and on and on. Most Americans would be better off this Thanksgiving, if instead of turkey and potatoes, dressing and gravy, they upped their fruit/vegetable intake to ten a day, not the three that the average North American tends to consume.

But I'm here to praise the cranberry, both food and medicine. I now have six cranberry plants (down to two now in 2006). Cranberry is featured in the Urinary Tract Inflammation (UTIs like cystitis, urethritis etc.) plot of the garden. Unlike most native American medicinal species, this one has been as well studied in America as in Europe. American Indians did consume cranberry. Maybe that's why you don't find much in the Native American folklore for treating cystitis or UTIs. Like prostatitis, I find no references to these diseases at least by medical name. Surely though, if they existed, the symptoms could have been indicative.

Large quantities of cranberry or concentrated cranberry extracts have been shown time and again, in the United States, to alleviate UTIs. There are more than a dozen compounds in cranberry, unlike a solitary synthetic silver bullet, that can contribute to the relief of UTIs.

Cranberries are rich in "biologically active" substances such as anthocyanin pigments, flavonols, catechins, triterpenoids and organic acids such as chlorogenic acid. The fruits also contain anthocyanosides, the active compounds responsible for increasing sales of the related bilberry extracts in Europe. Administered orally at 100 mg per kg of body weight, anthocyanosides significantly increase prostacyclin-like activity and inhibit blood clotting and ulcer formation. Italian studies confirm nerve-stimulating, anti-ulcer and vasoprotective (vein-protective) activity of these compounds. Like bilberries, cranberries have also been shown to lower blood sugar. Cranberry juice has a reputation, deserved or not, for alleviating or preventing gout, perhaps by acidifying the urine. The fruits also contain quercetin which has quite an array of biological activities. Small wonder the cranberry has such a folk medicinal repertoire.

But let me bring seasonal cheer to those suffering those urogenital problems formerly known as frigidity and impotence. Cranberry might have some viagra-like activity, albeit small, but clearly measureable. In a recent American Chemical Society book, Fitzpatrick at al. (1997) showed that cranberry had more endothelium-dependent vasorelaxing activity, mediated by nitric oxide, than red wine. Translation: cranberries are more active at stimulating the release of nitric acid in the corpus cavernosum than those fruits and veggies studied by Fitzpatrick et al. (1997), maybe even red wine. An article I recently submitted for publication in a food farmacy journal suggested that faba-beans, and garlic, might also recharge the viagroid circuitry. Too much alcohol might be counter-indicated. May I suggest just one glass of red wine or better yet, non-alcoholic grape juice or marmalade or grape-seed extracts with your faba-beans and garlic and cranberry sauce. It just might accentuate the Tom Turkey in foundering males.

## Supporting Document:

Fitzpatrick, D. F.; Coffey, R. G.; Jantzen, P. T. 1997. "Endothelium- dependent vasorelaxing activity of wine, grapes, and other plant products." pp. 237-46 in TR Watkins, Ed. "Wine: nutritional and therapeutic benefits."

## Cranberry for Cystitis

**Multiple Activity Table (with ubiquitous compounds)**

**Analgesic:** ascorbic-acid 75-1,003 ppm; eugenol; selenium; thiamin 0.3 -2.5 ppm;
**Antiinflammatory:** ascorbic-acid 75-1,003 ppm; copper 0.5-4.7 ppm; eugenol; hyperoside; magnesium 50-690 ppm; quercetin 100-250 ppm, quercitrin;
**Antiseptic:** alpha-terpineol; ascorbic-acid 75-1,003 ppm [MIC=3.3-217 mg/ml]; benzaldehyde; benzoic-acid; benzyl-alcohol; eugenol; oxalic-acid; sulfur 65-500 ppm;
**Bactericide:** alpha-terpineol; ascorbic-acid 75-1,003 ppm; benzoic-acid; eugenol; hyperoside; quercetin 100-250 ppm;
**Cyclooxygenase-Inhibitor:** quercetin 100-250 ppm [IC50 (uM) =16];
Diuretic: ascorbic-acid 75-1,003 ppm; hyperoside; quercitrin;
**Lipoxygenase-Inhibitor:** quercetin 100-250 ppm [IC50=3.5uM];
**Uricosuric:** ascorbic-acid 75-1,003 ppm; benzoic-acid; folacin (Fruit) 0.1-0.2 ppm.

# Currant (*Ribes* spp.)

*The Business of Herbs* 3(3):12-13, July/August, 1985

## Currant vs. Evening Primrose

A recent abstract on currants (*Ribes*) may send a chill through the recently stimulated evening primrose (e. p.) planters. North Carolina growers have been offered two thousand dollars a ton for evening primrose seeds. At least two buyers are offering substantial sums for the seeds, and many knowledgeable Carolinians are planting the biennial primrose. Several hundred acres were grown in Oregon last year, and we might expect the same thing in the Carolinas this year.

I too have planted several strains of evening primrose, having recently lost nearly 10% of my obese body weight, with a regimen which included replacing lunch with aerobics and evening primrose seeds or sprouts. I attribute the weight loss to the aerobics, though, and not the evening primrose. Obesity is just one of a long list of diseases reported to be helped by gamma-linolenic acid (GLA), the compound promoted as the active ingredient in the oil of evening primrose. Many claims made about GLA are made by those selling or promoting GLA. I don't frankly know that it does or does not cure or prevent acne, alcoholism, dysmenorrhea, eczema, hypercholestorolemia, obesity, and schizophrenia. I'm quite positive, though, that since I started enjoying the seeds several years ago, I suffered no dysmenorrhea. In these years, I've eaten the seeds, the sprouts, the flowers, the green pods, the leaves, and the roots. Raw tap roots, gathered in fall or spring, are an interestingly pungent treat. In boiling, they smell more like potatoes, then taste a bit closer to turnip. Like so many wild foods, there is nothing really with which to compare the so-called German Rampion, the taproot produced by evening primrose at the end of its first year. In the second year, much energy stored in the taproot moves up for the production of flowers and seeds. A plant may produce hundreds of capsules, each with more than 100 seeds, weighing an average of 3 mg per seed. I enjoyed such seed sprinkled onto "primrose-seed rolls" and herbed goat cheese. If the seeds contain 2% GLA, as I've been told, eight fruits (botanically capsules) with 100 seeds each, would contain 40 mg GLA for free. The 40-cent 500-mg capsule of evening primrose oil at my local herb store also has 40 mg GLA, translating to about $0.01/mg GLA.

Promotion literature states that GLA has normalized malignant cells and reversed cancer growth. My contact in the National Cancer Institute states that the normalization has been effected only in cell cultures, not in experimental animals or humans.

Just when North Carolina is about to be yellowed with evening primrose, we learn that an unrelated northern species may contain as much as 6% GLA. Even evening primrose shows higher GLA percentages in colder climates. Some Nestle workers in Switzerland published in late 1984 that the black currant, *Ribes nigrum*, contains up to 30.5% in oils in the seeds, of which up to 19% may be GLA, which I round off to 6% GLA in the seeds. I quote from *Biological Abstracts*: "This last *Ribes* spp. thus constitutes one of the richest natural sources in GLA yet described. These oils appear promising for critically ill patients who seem unable to convert linoleic (sic) acid into subsequent EFA (essential fatty acid) fractions."

It is on such conversion to more essential compounds that the hullaballo about GLA hinges. GLA is one of the raw materials from which prostaglandins are made. The prostaglandin attracting most attention is PGE1, which is made in the human from linoleic acid, a component of most seeds and some organ meats. Body enzymes first convert the linoleic acids to GLA and then into dihomo-gamma-linolenic acid (DGL), which occurs in the membranes of every living cell, from which they may be withdrawn and converted into PGE1. Both PGE1 and evening primrose oil are antiinflammatory in experimentally-induced arthritic rats. Clearly polyunsaturates, of which GLA is one, can lower blood pressure, cholesterol levels, and the adhesiveness of the blood platelets, at least experimentally. This has led promoters, with some justification, to suggest that a GLA-enriched diet might help prevent high-blood pressure, high cholesterol, and thrombosis and heart attacks.

Regardless of the accuracy of the extrapolations of experimental animal results or even tissue-culture data to humans, there is increasing interest in the nutritional benefits of GLA. The fact that the FDA has sued one firm for making medicinal claims about evening primrose oil will, I predict, stimulate, not hurt, consumer interest in GLA.

Enter the black currant. Even before the discovery of the GLA in the seeds, Europeans had a great interest in the black currant as a health food item. The fruit juice, rich in vitamins A, C, P, and J is said to be viricidal and has been used to treat colds and sore throats. Europeans are using a new medicine, vainoblase, for metrorrhagia, associated with intrauterine devices and/or the pill. Brandies are probably improved nutritionally when the berries are added as we read in Grieve's *A Modern Herbal.* Russians make wine from the berries and the liqueur known as "Cassis" is derived therefrom. Currant juices, jellies, and liqueurs are probably more pleasing but less nutritious if the juices are first strained. Quite probably the seeds are strained off and discarded as useless byproducts of the juices, jelly, and liqueur processors.

Reading all this, Americans might want to plunge headlong into the currant business, selling the juices in one health food market as a vitamin-rich natural fruit juice, the seeds in another market as one of the best sources of GLA. Seeds, of course, could be concocted into confectioneries, even currant seed rolls and cheeses. Perennial, cold-tolerant shrubs, not requiring a great deal of attention, the currant may sound too good to be true. But!!! It is illegal to grow black currants in most of the United States. Call your local Extension Agent to learn the status in your state. Why? Because the black currant is an alternate host of a terrible disease, the white pine blister rust, which can wipe out white pines in short order.

Over half a century ago, Farmer's Bulletin 1398 put the value of the standing white pine timber in the United States at $500 million, in Canada at $600 million. We can probably assume that now, as then, the projected value of the currant is less than the value of the white pine. A 1971 estimate for total U.S. production of currants and gooseberries was 4,000 metric tons, paling in value beside the pine timbers. Many states outlawed all currant and gooseberry bushes, while some targeted specifically only the black currant. Most states have wild species, difficult to control. Many species can serve as alternate hosts for the blister rust. There are species of *Ribes*, for example in India, that are immune to the disease. These could possibly be used to breed a better currant for the United States, healthier for the humans and the white pines around them.

But for now, I predict that byproduct currant seeds from Europe will shortly supplant evening primrose seeds as a source of GLA. But I'll continue to grow my evening primrose. The fluorescent flowers, going from fully closed to open in about 60 seconds, with the day's last rays of light, are probably better for my psyche than the GLA. May I recommend a primrose watching party for the imaginative herbalist seeking inspiration.

# Elder (*Sambucus nigra* ssp. *canadensis*)

*The Wild Foods Forum* 17(1):8-9, Winter, 2006

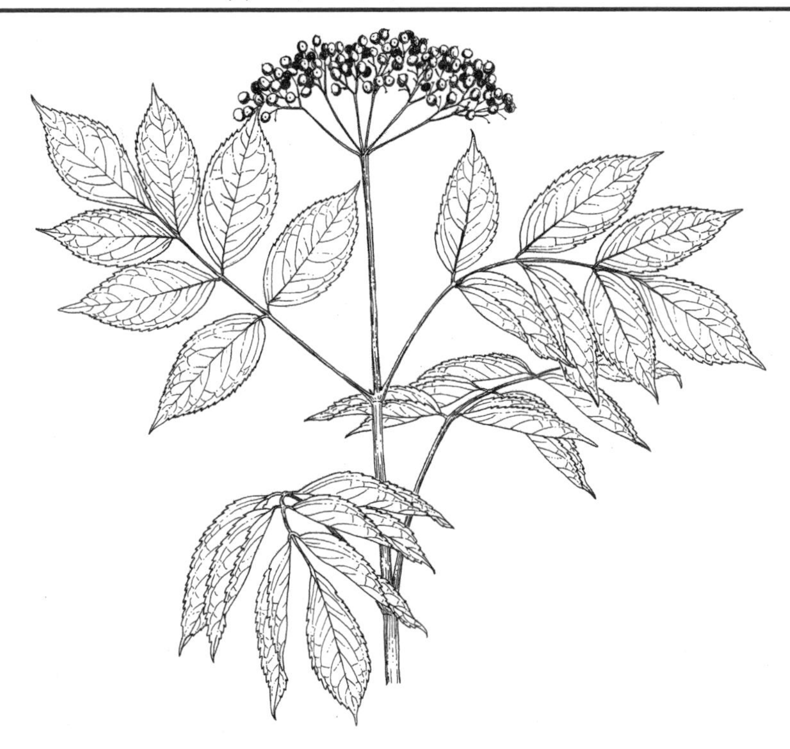

The shadow of bird fever hovers over us as I write this. Some of the herbal societies, elders and juniors, advise us not to talk about herbs for bird flu so I'll just talk about flu. I frankly think elderberry might be as good for influenza as Relenza, and garlic might just do as much as Tamiflu. Many scientists say that if the bird flu evolves to get here, neither of the pharmaceuticals will necessarily be effective. And the flu will evolve resistance to these expensive monochemical drugs. Thank the green farmacy goddess, the polychemical elderberry and garlic will still be here, and will not lead to resistance.

## Notes (American Elder)

Defeated taxonomically, I hereby accept the change in common name to be in accord with the American Herbal Products Association (AH2), so my elderberry becomes the American Elder (AH2). Like Dan Austin (AUS), I accept the Bolli revision and my old scientific name, *Sambucus canadensis* L. becomes *Sambucus nigra* L. ssp. *canadensis* (L.) R. Bolli. And I remove my elderberry from the family Caprifoliaceae, where I learned it more than 50 years ago and follow the cladistic taxonomists and include elderberry in Adoxaceae, as did the USDA. AHPA did not. AHPA recognizes the medicinally important species which they call southern elder (*S. australis*), blue elder (*S. cerulea*), the Chinese elder (*S. chinensis*), the dwarf elder (*S. ebulus*), the European elder (*S. nigra*), and William's elder (*S. williamsii*) while reducing the American elder to a variety of the European elder. The genus is easy to recognize. The species are not! Some are less salubrious than others, so I can't comfortably advocate a generic medicinal approach. I would however resort to any of these species if I had the flu. Since I have a separate account for European elder, I should, to maintain balanced reporting, erect another parallel account for blue elder, as covered well by MPG under the name *Sambucus mexicana*, which the USDA reduces to synonymy under *Sambucus cerulea*. I see that Austin (AUS) used for *Sambucus nigra* ssp. *canadensis* almost all of the Native American names Julia Morton (JFM) used for *Sambucus mexicana* and close cognates to Guatemalan names used by Gupta (MPG) for *S. mexicana*. So frustratedly I suggest that all those colloquial names and indications not included below could be added, and the world would be no worse (nor better) off. And I must confer further with taxonomists, before accounting for *S. cerulea* (*S. mexicana*). Adding to the confusion, JFM and MPG list *S. simpsonii* as a synonym for *C. mexicana* which USN reduces to *C. cerulea*. Meanwhile USN reduces *S. simpsonii* to *S. (nigra) canadensis*. I'll not bother with *S. cerulea* this round. I like Dan Austin's comment in his elegant book *Florida Ethnobotany* – "Europeans and Americans would have understood if you asked which tree was the 'country medicine chest'."

## Dosages (American Elder): FNFF

Fruits widely consumed; flowers dipped in pancake batter to make flower fritters; dried flowers used in herb teas. 2-10 g dry fruit; 2-3 485 mg capsules 2-3x/day; one 485 mg StX capsule, 3x/day; 10-15 g fl; 2-4 g dry flower.

- Algonquins use the bark infusion (scraped upward) as emetic, (scraped downward) as purgative
- Carrier, Cherokee, Gitskan, Iroquois and Ojibwa used bark or root as emetic
- Cherokee used berry tea for rheumatism, the floral tea as diaphoretic, and other parts in decoctions and salves for dermatosis, dropsy, infection, fever, nephrosis
- Chickasaw use branch infusion applied to forehead for headaches
- Choctaw poultice salted leaves onto headache, taking seed and root infusion for liver ailments
- Creek stirred pounded roots in hot water, then tied them on swollen breasts
- Delaware used flower decoction for children's colic, leaves and stems for blood disorders and jaundice; they poulticed bark scrapings to sores, swellings and wounds

- Dominican Caribs use leaf decoction for cold and fever
- Dominicanos use the flora infusion in ocular catarrh ("ceguera")
- Haitians compress the leaves on the head for headache and migraine
- Haitians use diaphoretic flower infusion for chest cold, fever, and sore throat
- Haitians use the leaf infusion for measles, scarlet fever and smallpox
- Houma use pounded roots as antiinflammatory, fermented berries to make a tonic, pounding the bark as an analgesic
- Iroquois use bark or berries as analgesic, antiinflammatory, febrifuge, vulnerary, taking berries for fever, floral tea as laxative .
- Menominee use dried flowers for fever
- Meskwaki use inner bark of young stalks as a purgative, bark infusion as diuretic, expectorant, and for difficult childbirth, and as a fly and insect repellent
- Micmac use bark, berries, and flowers as emetic, purgative and soporific
- Onondaga used the bark as emetic when poisoned by Cicuta
- Penobscot Indians reportedly use the elder for cancer, Georgians using the branches
- Rappahanock used elderberry wine for neuritis and rheumatism, using bark infusion for sores and swelling
- Seminole use root bark decoction as emetic and purgative, for stomachache
- Thompson tamp frayed inner bark in aching tooth
- Yuki use strong dry flower decoction for bruises and sprains

**Extracts (American Elder)**
Most of the clinical studies, proving efficacy in flu, have been on *Sambucus nigra* ssp *nigra*. I have both the European and American growing side by side in the **Green Farmacy Garden**, and suspect they are equally good for flu. Elderberry extracts significantly inhibited Helicobacter pylori and increased its susceptibility to clarithromycin (X15543930).

# Fern, Christmas (*Polystichum acrostichoides*)

*The Wild Foods Forum* 14(4):8-9, Fall, 2003

Why not celebrate Christmas with Christmas fern. I'm sure they call it Christmas fern, but I'm not really sure why. Certainly it's the biggest splash of greenery in winter on the forest floor at my place around Christmas. And some lecturers, really stretching the point, note that the heel-like flange at the base of each leaflet reminds them of Santa's boots. I still remember digging one down in North Carolina and bringing it home to a very appreciative mother, mine, for Christmas. Even replanted in midwinter it took hold. Sixty years later, I still transplant them into bare spots needing a little greenery in midwinter. And my native stock seems more increased than diminished by the process.

In winter, without my St. Johnswort, I get depressed, with mild bouts of S.A.D. or Seasonal Affective Disorder. But if I go for a brisk walk in the sun that seeps through the nude trees in midwinter, I am often cheered by the evergreen ferns around here. Primitive plants, like ferns, horsetails, clubmosses, and ginkgo, all take me back, atavistically, to the days of the dinosaurs.

Christmas Fern is so common around here that collectors ignore it and dig the rarer species. But if you didn't know it was so common, it could hold its own with the prettiest of our ferns. Hundreds came naturally with my Yin Yang Valley. I'd guess it's the most common evergreen fern in Cherokee country. Certainly around here, it outnumbers the evergreen wood ferns (*Dryopteris*), polypodies (*Polypodium*), and spleenworts (*Asplenium*). You don't hear much about ferns as medicinal plants, but many are medicinal. Dr. Dan Moerman has been very kind about sharing his Native American data on plants. I frequently recite some of his contributions on native American species. Many of his comments are available at his website: http://herb.umd.umich.edu.

Here's what he has to say about Cherokee usage: The root decoction is rubbed onto rheumatic areas. Or suggestive of acupuncture, the roots are rubbed onto rheumatoid areas after scratching... The decoction or infusion is also taken for bowel complaints, pneumonia, rheumatism or stomachache. Compounded with other herbs they also take it for chills, fever, and toothache. Iroquois used a decoction of the fern for cramps. They soak their feet in a root decoction for rheumatism in the back and legs. They poultice smashed roots on the back and head of children with convulsions. It's compounded with other herbs for diseased or weak blood. The decoction was used for children and sometimes their mothers to perk them up. For a man unable to talk, they'd inhale the powdered leaf and cough it up. The root infusion was used as an emetic in tuberculosis. Big in pediatric medicine, the plant was used for convulsions, cramps, red spots, sore backs, and spinal problems. For the mothers it was used before and after delivery to clean the womb and often as an internal "female medicine." Farther north, the Micmac used the fern roots to treat hoarseness.

I don't find this species of *Polystichum* listed as an edible fern in my normal bibliographic sources (Facciola, Tanaka, Yanovsky). Too many woodsmen say all fern fiddleheads are edible, but I'm gonna say that not all of them are good and/or good for you. My deer even ignore the marvelous fiddleheads of the often sold commercial fiddlehead, the ostrich fern. Deer do eat the fiddleheads nearly underground, of the midwinter Christmas ferns, maybe even on Christmas day. I have always bitten into any species' fiddleheads I have found and find this one not too repulsive.

I also have almost twenty evergreen fern species (mostly not native to my area) which tend to cheer me as much as the common old ground cedar (*Lycopodium*) from which my mother used to make Christmas wreaths before it was listed as an at-risk species, all but impossible to transplant.

But instead of bringing the ferns and ground cedar to the house on Christmas, I'll visit them on foot, hoping there will be some evergreen ferns (making oxygen by day), sunshine (with its vitamin D), outdoors to remind me that there's beauty even in the cold winter, and that groundhog day's not too far off, and then spring again. I do wish the readers of *The Wild Foods Forum* a happy holiday, hopefully with some holiday greenery.

# Fern, Maidenhair (*Adiantum pedatum*)

*The Wild Foods Forum* 14(1):8-9, Winter, 2003

## Pointer Weed?

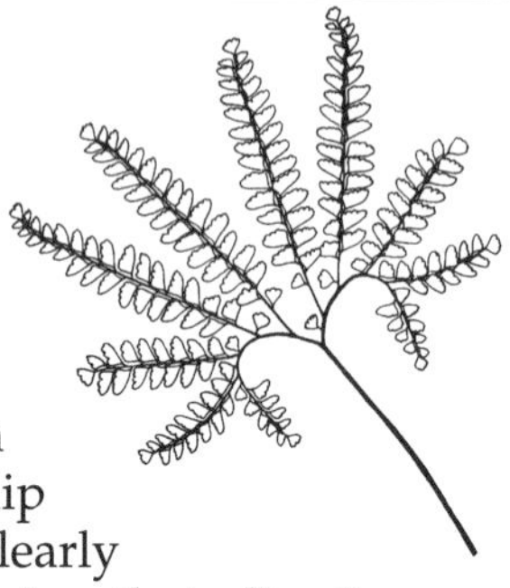

Who'd have guessed that with a name like pointer weed, we are talking about my favorite fern, *Adiantum pedatum,* the maidenhair fern. Sometimes it's called the finger or five-finger fern. Of course I goofed up on its name back in college, when I was teaching botany labs to a bunch of premedical students. A freudian slip indeed, I called it the maidenhead fern when I clearly meant maidenhair fern. The coeds seemed to enjoy that slip. I still make it occasionally. Even Ginkgo has been called maidenhair tree. *Adiantum* is a beautiful shade loving fern that you find occasionally in the moister parts of the eastern deciduous forests (oak/hickory/beech/maple forests as opposed to evergreen forests like pine and hemlock forest or spruce firs father north or at higher altitudes out east.) Why "pointer weed?" Few years back, I spent a few days on a 55-acre spread my son and I bought in wild wonderful West Virginia with some royalty monies from *The Green Pharmacy*. I just escaped my computer chains and drove out all by myself, because it would be my last chance to see all five grandkids in one place in 1999. Nice country, but a long five hour drive from Baltimore. Mostly hillsides or mountain slopes, from 2,300 to 3,000 ft. altitude, with some nice forest, too steep to have been stripped by the lumber companies or the strip miners. And there's a great trout stream down the narrow valley where lies the shack, great spot for all the grandkids, except when the bears get too brazen and/or hungry and/or ornery. Like most of the perennial streams flowing out of the mountains in this limestone country, our creek flows into a sinkhole and goes underground, only to resurface miles away as a bigger stream.

One of the locals, John Alderman, showed me the maidenhair fern noting: "round here we call it the pointer weed or pointer herb" (that pained me less, nomenclatorially), because it grows in the woods where the ginseng grows. But the locals say that the longest finger (pinna of the horseshoe shaped compound leaf) of the fern points to where the ginseng is.

Since locals were growing some healthy ginseng, the pointer weed was certainly pointing properly. West Virginians pick up a lot of spare cash selling wild crafted ginseng roots at this altitude. Alderman laments that too many young folks are illegally digging them before they set seed. He says some of the old folks break off the tops, so the young ones won't find them. They claim that makes it grow better. We don't believe that. Even down at my place in Maryland, the deer often do the same thing to my ginseng, cropping it down to the ground. Done late enough in the season this might not hurt the root too badly, if it has already started storing its winter foods in the root. It's my gut feeling that 2 to 3 back to back premature prunings like this will terminate the plant.

Actually the "pointer weed" itself is worth $10.00 as an ornamental fern for shade gardeners. It's a beautiful fern, I think the handsomest of them all. But I must admit I also like my ostrich, cinnamon, interrupted, all deciduous, and my evergreen Christmas and Shield ferns. Have a lot of all these in my YinYang Valley, most of them doing better on the cooler moister yin slope, like my butter bur, cohosh, ginseng and goldenseal. They tend to dry out too soon too often on the drier and hotter yang slope.

Does maidenhair fern belong in a newsletter on wild foods. Too many people say that any fern fiddlehead is edible. I have not personally eaten a maidenhair, but intend to next spring. I am not afraid to eat any fern fiddlehead here out east, and have sampled most of them. Edible may be overstatement. Most of them are considered survival food, not all that good, raw or cooked.

I'll discuss the ostrich fern, the most popular fiddlehead in another issue. My deer ignore hundreds of their beautiful fiddleheads every spring. Are the deer telling me something? The only fern that I seem to have to protect from the deer in fiddlehead season is the fuzzy cinnamon fern. Matter of fact, the deer are partially responsible for my surging interest in ferns. Except for my cinnamon fern, they seem to be relatively deer proof.

Though now it is too pretty and rare to dig for medicine (or survival food), the maidenhair fern has a great folklore. In Moerman's *Medicinal Plants of Native America*, we read that the Cherokee used the root decoction as a topical for rheumatism. They smoked the leaves for heart trouble, or smoked or snuffed the powdered herb for asthma, nothing I would currently recommend. The whole plant was taken as an emetic for ague and fever. It was also given pediatrically for paralysis and pneumonia. Costanoan Indians used the plant as a depurative and stomach settler. Iroquois used as a diuretic, for dysuria, and as an emetic for the lovelorn. Also they used it for cramps, dysmenorrhea, gonorrhea, rheumatism, snakebite, sores, and venereal diseases. Lummi, Makah and/or Skokomish used it in shampoos and for stomach and chest distress. Menominee used it for dysentery and female ailments. Micmac use it for fits, perhaps epilepsy. Potawatomi take the root infusion for caked breast. In Moerman's super database (www.umd. umich.edu/cgi-bin/herb) we learn that the southwestern Pomo stuck the dark stems in the pierced ear lobe to keep the wound from closing. The Kwakiutl used the leaves to line baskets and cover berry drying racks. Maidu used the dark stalks as decorative overlay twine in the making of baskets. For me, it's too pretty for tea. But – Facciola says that fronds of the capillus-veneris maidenhair fern were dried and used as a tea substitute (in the Arran Islands). There was once a popular British flavoring, capillaire, derived from the European maidenhair by simmering the fronds in water for hours, then thickening further with sugar and orange water. It was then added to fruit juice and water to make soft drinks. It's really too pretty a fern for this hocus pocus. But I thought you should know. The European maiden's hair, *Adiantum capillus-veneris*, bears a pretty impressive array of colloquial names too: five-finger fern, hair of Venus, maiden fern, rock fern, neus hair. e.g. Europeans regard it as demulcent and expectorant. Folklorically, because of the perceived resemblance to maiden's hair, it was used to promote better hair growth, or darker colored hair. The part Abenaki daughter of a Finnish friend of mine grabbed up a handful of dying stalks of *Adiantum pedatum* on a field trip with me in October. I thought at first she was removing the withering tops to prevent diggers from finding them, but no, she was going to use them in an herbal shampoo. The fern is folklorically used for bronchitis, coughs, dysmenorrhea, and pertussis in Europe. It is not approved by Germany's Commission E. According to Moerman, the Mahuna used this species for rheumatism. The Kayenta Navajo used the plant in lotions for bee and centipede stings. They also smoked the plant for insanity.

Though described in teas and syrups, I think of this fern as more ornamental than medicinal and more medicinal than edible. When I want to quote someone as saying a plant was edible, I turn first to Yanovsky, 1936, who listed 1,112 plant species consumed as food by the Native Americans. Neither he nor Moerman list *Adiantum* as food. *Couplan's Encyclopedia of Edible Plants of North America* mentions the European species being used as a pleasant aromatic tea. "In 18th-century Europe, a popular drink ('bavaroise') was made by mixing with milk a syrup made with the European maidenhair fern, *A. capillus-veneris* (m.a.). The five finger fern (*A. pedatum* JAD) can be used in the same way. In America it was often used to make a cough syrup. So even Couplan is not saying it is used as a food, but that it could be used as a tea, and is used to make a cough syrup.

**2007** – and I'll be 78 three days after April Fool's Day. this year. I confess to feeling more senile each year, and that's the way life goes, with or without herbs. I'm convinced the herbs stave off the deterioration. Still I deteriorate. Hope spring eternal, still. In an atavistic childlike exercise, I now have planted down in my wooded valley an artificial circular planting (about 20 feet in diameter) with ostrich and maidenhair ferns on the perimeter, lady ferns and maidenhairs inside my fairy ring circle. Also I have plugged in some mushrooms hoping they too will play my fairy circle game. I'm predicting that if I live until the 17-year cicadas rejoin me (and me, them), that some of my ferns will have, by stoloniferously outgrowing, generate their own green fairy rings. I have observed natural fern fairy rings up along the Patuxent River, downstream from Tai Sophia. Matter of fact, that's what prompted my maidenhair circle. Stay tuned.

# Fern, Male (*Dryopteris filix-mas*)

*The Wild Foods Forum* 14(2): 8-9, Spring, 2006

## A Male Fern Myth

Among the unwelcome spam popping upon my computer is one that talks about herbs for enlarging the penis. I did not request this. It results from mailing lists I suppose. But in 2002, I unearthed one interesting abstract about our fern of the month, the male fern. Here's the way the translated abstract reads:

> **Abstract:** In male mice and rats, one drop of an extract from Dryopteris filix mas, administered orally pure or suspended in sunflower-seed oil, caused a spectacular enlargement of the penis. This unexpected effect cannot be explained so far and will have to be elucidated by further experiments (In German).

Kantemir I; Akder G; Tulunay O. 1976. "Preliminary report on an unexpected effect of an extract from *Dryopteris filix mas*." *Arzneimittelforschung*, 26(2):261-2.

I've never seen it in the original journal and suspect this may be the authors' translation from more than 25 years ago. Strange how I only found it when I got interested in ferns. And it is one of the few ferns covered in my original CRC *Handbook of Medicinal Plants* (1985). I missed that penile-enlargement item in my book. You never get it all in a book. But I do see so many comments under toxicity that I fear that ingesitons of the male fern seems a dangerous way to enlarge the penis, if it really does. And I surely doubt that it does. But there are surprises for me every year, when suspect old folklore proves out. Looking at my quote, I advise against consumption of male fern. Glad I had this quote in my computer. Even I don't have a copy, now that the second edition came out in 2002.

"Hardy ornamental fern, sometimes sold as an herbal drug. Said to serve as a substitute for hops. Rhizomes and stipes contain an oleoresin which paralyzes the intestinal voluntary muscles and the analogous contractile tissue of the tapeworm, which is then easily dislodged by a purgative. Filicin is an active vermifuge, especially effective with tapeworm, to all forms of which it is poisonous. It is administered in capsules, in oil medium, or in pills of 12g doses for adult. Tenia are expelled a few hours later. It is combined with calomel to insure both purgative and vermifugal action. The drug is also used in veterinary practice. Rhizome used as insecticide in Vietnam" (Duke, 1985).

Considered an old folk remedy for cancerous tumors. Known as a vermifuge, especially good for tenia, back to the days of Theophrastus. Said to be aperient, astringent, cyanogenetic, pectoral, poison, tenifuge, as well as vermifuge. Used in China for epistaxis, menorrhagia, puerperium, and wounds. Contains 6.5% oleoresin, with albaspidin, filicic acid, filicin (mostly margaspidin), filix re, filmarone (tenifuge), flavaspidic acids, paraaspidin, deaspidin, resin, aspidinol, phloraspin, and tannin. Attributing most of the medicinal activity to the phloroglucides, *Hager's Handbook* lists and shows the structure for more than two dozen.

Used by the Cherokee as an antirheumatic, emetic. Root infusion used alone or in a compound for rheumatism. Root infusion held in mouth for toothache (Hamel). Main active compounds believed to be flavaspidic acid and desaspidin. The male fern typically used with a saline purgative to expel parasites (PNC).

According to Blumenthal et al. (Commission) the herb is used, at least folklorically, externally for bunion, leg and foot pain, cracked soles of the fee, paresthesia, frostbite, circulatory disturbances, venectasia, minor ulcers, lumbar and cervical syndrome, spondylarthritis, acute and chronic joint inflammation, ischialgia, lumbago, rheumatism, arthritis, cicatricial keloid, scar tissue contraction, neuralgia. It is negatively evaluated for use in rheumatism, sciatica, muscle pain, neuralgia, earache, toothache, teething in infants, sleep disorders, and internally for tapeworms and flukes (KOM).

## Toxicity

In too large doses, male fern is an irritant poison, causing muscular weakness and coma, and has been proven particularly injurious to the eyesight, even causing blindness. Other symptoms include nausea, diarrhea, vertigo, delirium, tremors, confusion, and cardiac or respiratory failure. Rose states: "It has caused allergy reactions in some and can be fatally poisonous if misused. It should be used only by prescription from a doctor" (Duke, 1985).

## Cultivating Male Fern

I have ordered several specimens for my **Green Farmacy Garden**, though I have no plot for purported "penis-enlarging herbs," anymore than I do for "bust-enhancing herbs." Lots of fenugreek has been sold for the latter presumed effect. Fenugreek shows up in at least three bust-enhancing formulae, and of course, Lydia Pinkham's compound.

Speaking generically, Hoshizaki and Moran (HAM, 2001) note that *Dryopteris* is often cultivated for accent, or background, or in borders in temperate gardens. Deciduous fronds may wither in place (marcescent), and may or may not lose their green color. Some 50 species are cultivated in the United States alone, and natural artificial and natural hybrids abound. Shield ferns are relatively easy to transplant and cultivate, but those adapted to cold don't fare well in warm climates. Some require acid soils. Taxonomically difficult, the fronds extremely variable, sometimes on an individual basis. Of the common male fern under discussion, HAM says: "hardy to zone 4(5), this species is reportedly a natural hybrid between *D. caucasica* and *D. oreades*. Fronds deciduous farther north, may be evergreen farther south. Grows in low to medium light, in moist media."

Hoshizaki. B.J. and Moran, R.C. 2001. *Fern Grower's Manual.* Timber Press, Portland Ore. 604 pp.

## Appendix Resources

AHPA, 1997: (Eds. McGuffin, M., Hobbs, C., Upton, R. and Goldberg, A.) *American Herbal Products Association's Botanical Safety Handbook.* CRC Press, Boca Raton. 231 pp.

BDW: Beckstrom-Sternberg, Stephen M., Duke, James A. and Wain, K.K. "The Ethnobotany Database."
http://probe.nalusda.gov:8300/cgi-bin/browse/eth nobotdb.

Duke, J. A. 1985. *CRC Handbook of Medicinal Herbs.* 704 pp. CRC Press, Inc., 2000 Corporate Blvd, NW, Boca Raton, FL 33431. 696 pp. (=CRC).

Duke, J. A. 1986. *Handbook of Northeastern Indian Medicinal Plants.* Quarterman Publications, Inc., P.O. Box 156, Lincoln, Massachusetts 01773. 212 pp.

FAD: Foster, S. and Duke, J. A. 1990. *A Field Guide to Medicinal Plants: Eastern and Central North America.* A Peterson Field Guide. Houghton Mifflin company. 366 pp.

FNF: Duke's *Father Nature's Farmacy* database http://www.ars-grin.gov/duke/

Grieve: *A Modern Herbal* by Mrs. M. Grieve. http://www.botanical.com/botanical/mgmh/c/cel ery45.html

Hamel, Paul B. and Chiltoskey, Mary U. 1975. *Cherokee Plants and Their Uses - A 400 Year History.* Herald Publishing Co. Sylva, N.C. 65 pp. From Dan Moerman http://www-personal. umd.umich.edu-/~dmoerman/

HCD: Brinker, Francid, N.D. 1998. *Herb Contraindications and Drug Interactions.* Eclectic Medical Publications, 14385 S.E. Lusted Road, Sandy, Oregon 97055. 263 pp.

KOM: Blumenthal, M., Busse, W. R., Goldberg, A., Gruenwald, J., Hall, T., Riggins, C. W., Rister, R. S. (Eds.). 1998. *The Complete German Commission E Monographs.* "Therapeutic guide to herbal medicines." American Botanical Council, Austin, TX and Integrative Medicine Communications, Boston, MA. 684 pp.

Moore: Michael. Dosages and Preparations. http://chili.rt66. com/hrb-moore/ManualsMM/MatMed5.txt PHR: Gruenwald, J. et al. 1998. *PDR for Herbal Medicine.* 1st ed. Medical Economics Co., Montvale, NJ. 1244 pp.

PNC: Williamson, E. M. and Evans, F. J., *Potter's New Cyclopaedia of Botanical Drugs and Preparations,* Revised Ed., Saffron Walden, the C. W. Daniel Co., Ltd., Essex UK, 362 pp, 1988, reprint 1989.

# Fern, Rattlesnake (*Botrychium virginianum*)

*The Wild Foods Forum* 14(3):8-9, Summer, 2003

I have at least two species of *Botrychium* on my property, the non-evergreen rattlesnake fern, *Botrychium virginianum*, and the coppery colored semi-evergreen, leathery grapefern, *Botrychium multijugum*. If I sound confident, don't let me fool you. As in most fern genera, the species in this genus are tough to distinguish.

Primitive plants, like ferns, horsetails, clubmosses, and ginkgo, romantically take me back to the days of the dinosaurs. Rattlesnake fern and grape fern are not common around here. But there are a few local and transplanted specimens down in Yin Yang Valley (my copycat Fern Valley Garden, with clonal pairs of ferns on the yin and yang slopes).

You don't hear much about ferns as medicinal plants, but many are medicinal. And if you'll watch Vickie Shufer's *Wild Foods Forum*, you'll see the beginning of my first proposed book for the millennium, *Edible and Medicinal Ferns of the Eastern U.S.* Once we have positively identified 52 of our eastern ferns, Peggy, also a fernophiliac and an artist, will illustrate them in color, and we plan to do a deck of cards. So if you have had some interesting experiences with ferns, or know of good published stories on the use of our temperate ferns, don't hesitate to share them with me, if you want them disseminated.

I covered a few ferns in my book on *Medicinal Plants of Northeastern America* (1986). For the rattlesnake fern, I mentioned that the Abenaki used a decoction of the fern for pediatric ailments. And as the name implies, the roots were boiled by the Cherokee to treat snakebite.

Chippewa poulticed smashed roots of the rattlesnake fern to snakebite also. The Ojibwa used it for pulmonary and respiratory complaints, some suggest tuberculosis. They also applied the smashed roots to bruises, cuts and sores. Dr. Dan Moerman has been very kind about sharing his Native American data on plants, so I'll frequently recite some of his contributions when I write about native American species, from his 1986 book.

There's a swampy backwoods area on the west fourth acre of my 6 acres that always surprises me with an abundance of rattlesnake ferns. (Hence I call it rattlesnake corner, hoping to scare the sometimes vandalistic kids away.) The fact that it is crawling with poison ivy does not seem to scare them. I found so many rattlesnake fern shoots this year I subjected a few to experimental abuse. The rattlesnake fern is a tough one to transplant. It would be as difficult as ginseng to clone, me thinks. Too often the dirt on dug specimens falls way from the roots. And hence a high mortality. This year, I dug and transplanted 6 in my usual haphazard fashion, but a comparable six I dug and bagged up in a small biodegradable paper lunch bag and planted the whole bag of dirt intact with the fern, watering carefully inside the paper bag. After a week all six bagged plants were OK but only two of the 6 unbagged were still standing tall. Two had been decapitated. I assumed deer, who don't normally seem to bother most of my ferns, had done the dastardly deed of decapitation. Deer tend to like my fern trails as an alleyway through the forest underbrush. But I read in Hoshizaki and Moran (2001), henceforth HAM, that slugs have a liking for them. "Guard against slugs and snails, which readily attack the newly emerging fronds. Grape ferns should also be protected from the wind." But whatever decapitated them did not seem to bother nearby non-transplants, just the transplants. Early, perhaps premature conclusion. Bagged plants have twice t ude experimental conditions. I certainly agree with HAM that "This species is difficult to establish." I don't have to establish it. It keeps coming back like a song.

Here's what Moerman (1986) has to say about Cherokee usage. The root decoction is used to induce vomiting. They boiled the roots down to a syrup which they rubbed onto snakebite. The Chickasaw used the plant as a diaphoretic, emetic and expectorant. Chippewa also used the root decoction as a snakebite application, and as a repellent. The Iroquois took the root decoction, cold with liquor, as a cough remedy in tuberculosis. Ojibwa also took it for TB. Potawotami also used it but the purpose was not specified.

I don't find any species of *Botrychium* listed as an edible fern in my favorite bibliographic source (Facciola, 1991) but Tanaka, often quoting Yanovsky, (1936) mentions that the young fronds of *Botrychium virginianum* are edible, and that the fronds of Japanese *Botrychium ternatum* are eaten as a vegetable. Yanovsky covers no *Botrychium*. Too many woodsmen say all fern fiddleheads are edible, but I'm gonna say that not all of them are good and/or good for you.

Technically this rattlesnake fern may not even have a fiddlehead, its leaves not creating the crozier within my experience. My deer even ignore the marvelous fiddleheads of the often sold commercial fiddlehead, the ostrich fern, which I'll discuss after the fiddleheads start emerging this spring. But I have always bitten into any fiddleheads I have found and find the new leaves of rattlesnake fern not too repulsive. Besides, who wants to eat an uncommon, if not endangered, fern that could make you barf?

# Frostflower (*Cunila origanoides*)

*The Wild Foods Forum* 9(1):8-9, January/February, 1998

In the late fall an old botanist's fancy turns to frost flowers. At least this one's does. For almost a decade now, I have had flowers twelve months of the year, Thansgiving, Christmas Day, New Year's Day, etc., at least when the temperatures got well below freezing the night before.

Idling in the woods, one Sunday morning, a week or so after Thanksgiving, I noted a strange white lump on the soil, suggesting in color at least, the plastic "peanuts" they use in filling boxes. Stooping over to pick it up, I noted that it was in fact a hollow white collar, surrounding an old stem. I picked up the collar, soon to see that it was ice. And the old stem smelled like thyme. It was the mountain dittany, *Cunila origanoides* (*C. mariana*), alias dittany, American dittany, mountain dittany, sweet horsemint, stone mint, etc., said to have been used by the Indians and early American settlers as a remedy for colds and fevers. Its oil is said to be a stimulant aromatic. Because of its high content of thymol, it is probably a good antiseptic as well. I like the quote *Organic Gardening* attributes to famed pharmacognoscist Norman Farnsworth in their first issue of the new decade (Jan, 1990, p. 54):

> "Thymol has been found to loosen phlegm in the respiratory tract... It also has been shown to act as an antitussive which will relieve coughing." If I had a backache and a lot of dittany, I'd drink dittany tea and maybe even add a little to my bath water. Thymol is also said to be spasmolytic. And if I had pizza with cheese and tomato, and no spices, I'd add a little dittany in lieu of oregano. *Grieve's Herbal* speaks of 'oil of dittany' – which is stated to contain about 40 per cent of phenols, probably Thymol."

But you can overdo the thymol. Somewhere I read the following:

> "The director of one herb academy
> Learned something about his anatomy.
> Thyme, in bathing tisanes
> Can corrode the membranes,
> Leading to bad bathhouse blasphemy."

Seems the director, after steeping too long in a bath too strong with thymol, had blistered some critical mucous membranes. Even GRAS herbs should be used in moderation. *Cunila*, *Monarda*, and *Thymus* can all be good sources of thymol. It seems that thymol and carvacrol often run in tandem, especially in the mint and umbel families, and both have antiseptic, spasmolytic, and tracheolaxant properties. I thought I was onto something new when I discovered the ice collars, since I had not observed them before in my 60 years. But there's nothing new under the sunspots! My friend Jeff Strachan has observed the ice phenomenon or "frost flowers" in West Virginia. Steyermark reports it in his excellent *Flora of Missouri*. Herbalist Steven Foster describes it well in his splendid *Herbal Bounty*: "During the first chills of autumn frost, dittany produces frost flowers at its base – twisting, white, fluted ribbons of ice, sometimes four inches tall and two inches broad. This phenomena is caused by cell sap rising from the still-alive root into the dead tissues of the leaves and stems. The rising vapors seep through cracks in the stem, crystallizing as they contact the freezing air. Frost flowers have to be seen to be appreciated" (*Herbal Bounty*, Peregrine Smith Books, Salt Lake City, 1984). The frost flowers and the aroma of thyme (which accompanied the icebound dead stems, even in January of 1990) so impressed me that I submitted dittany to Gordon Cragg for the AIDS and cancer screens of the National Cancer Institute. Hopefully it will show as much activity as the more mundane selfheal (*Prunella*) submitted with that same submission, because of selfheal's developing reputation for AIDS, etc. Foster tells me dittany is called feverwort in Arkansas. And he reports its use for headache and snakebite, as does Steyermark, who notes its use, dry or fresh for tea. Jeff tells me that when he brought potted plants he was studying into a class greenhouse, most of the greenhouse whiteflies (*Prialeuroydes vaporianum*) migrated to his dittany, for a few days. Then, after populations built up on the dittany, the whiteflies returned to the other host plants, in even greater numbers. Jeff is hinting, of course, that some of the aromatic compounds in the dittany might lure whiteflies to some fatal trap. An interesting concept which reminds me of another evasive bit of doggerel, suggesting it might lure more than whiteflies:

> I said she musta been kiddin' me,
> When she said she wasn't gittin'any
> 'Til she started drinkin' dittany;
> And she swore she wasn't kiddin' me,
> That now she's a diddlin' plentily.

There are a few preparations used by some women, usually women of herbal inclination, that smell like dittany, or cumin, or thyme, or a mixture of the three. Some men find the aroma, and the herbally inclined, attractive. I also find the dittany attractive, summer or winter, and truly believe that a January tea of the aromatic dead stalks of *Cunila* and *Monarda* helped break up a bad lingering cough. I suspect expectorant and antiseptic properties reside even in the dead stems persisting in the winter. And I find the "frost flowers" uniquely inspiring, and useful in leading you to the sleeping dittany, waiting to be transplanted, and ready to spring back to life, if moved to your winter greenhouse.

One week, I drank the melted water of a "frost flower" and the next week, I inhaled the melted water from one of Ecuador's "snow flowers," Volcan Cayambe. The "frost flowers" of the dead dittany resemble miniature snow-capped volcanoes, with last year's stem in the center of the crater. Both the little and the big piles of ice elicit, and now, the aromas of dittany, "recuerdos del Condor," mystically and magically winging me back to the majestic Andes.

Like snow-capped volcanoes,
Frost flowers' wintry heaves.
Beneath the dit'ny grows,
Nestled amongst the leaves.

Too late did I discover
This lover of the land.
You pick a wintry lover,
She melts right in your hand.

Though not unique! Steyermark mentions that *Helianthemum canadense, Pluchea camphorata,* and *Verbesina virginica,* and a few other species make similar frost flowers.

# Grape, Wild (*Vitis* spp.)

*The Wild Foods Forum* 8(2):8-9, March/April, 1997

> *... and he looked that it should bring forth grapes, and it brought forth wild grapes...* Isaiah 5

You may not think of wild grapes as a weed but many farmers do. Paul Straus with UpS (United Plant Savers) in southern Ohio, thinks of wild grapes as the most destructive weed in his forest preserve, bringing down huge trees under the excess weight of the wild grape. Even the seeds that you spit out of cultivated grapes sometimes germinate and become a nuisance, although most of such seedlings may perish. Even in Biblical times, this reversion of cultivated fruits to wild weedy types was recognized as hinted at in the Biblical quote above.

Most, or at least many people, define a weed as any plant growing where it is not wanted. Vickie and I kinda like to nibble on the young shoots and tendrils of the wild grapes we encounter, especially in spring. But that means it's not a weed anymore, it's a pleasant woodland nibble. So that's a magical way to make your weeds disappear. If it's wanted, it's not a weed. If you want your weeds, all of a sudden, by definition, you have no weeds anymore.

Most wild grapes have small acid fruits with very little juice. But even those wild grapes can be appreciated when you're hungry and/or thirsty. Middle easterners often use the leaves of both cultivated and wild species as food. I have eaten and enjoyed stuffed grape leaves prepared for me by Egyptians, Greeks and Lebanese, but I think they were made from cultivated grape leaves. This year I'm going to substitute some wild grape leaves in the recipe. But I nibble indiscriminately on the weedy grape volunteers in the forest around me, finding more leaves and tendrils astringent, a few more pleasantly tart.

Only in 1997 did we learn that grape leaves are the best reported source of resveratrol, which now proves to be of great anti-cancer and anti-cardiopathy potential. True, the red wines and grape juices (often evoked to explain the French paradox) also contain resveratrol but not as much as the leaves contain. I'll bet but cannot yet prove that wild weedy grape leaves contain even more resveratrol than the "tame" grape leaves. Resveratrol is one of the medicinal compounds that seems to protect plants from their natural enemies, bacteria, funguses, insects and viruses. When we, as agriculturists or as plant breeders, start selecting plants for better taste, we often select against the natural pesticides. And we need to apply more and more of our pesticides to these derived grape varieties or the diseases and pests will demolish them.

I know this from personal experience. I named my farmette **Herbal Vineyard** nearly 35 years ago thinking I was going to grow organic grapes by intercropping grapes with aromatic pesticidal mints. I planted more than 50 varieties of grapes, many of them expensive French hybrids. And disease and bugs wiped me out. Those derived grapes had less "pycnOPCs, (that's my word for oligomeric procyanidins (OPC), like the trademarked OPC pycnogenol, which word, like taxol, I am not supposed to use. And they probably had less resveratrol and viniferins than the wild types. Again I don't know this for fact, a little bug and fungus told me, as they devoured my high-falooting grape varieties, and ignored the weedy grapes at the edge of the woods. Today the only grapes I get are some wild grapes dangling from the trees in the fence row and an off-concord cross that volunteered in the fence row by the woods. They apparently have enough of these natural pesticides to survive. My French hybrids did not. If I try this experiment again, it will be with old fashioned types of grapes intercropped with extremely robust aromatic mints like *Monarda* and *Pycnanthemum*. Matter of fact, if any of you readers out there are into grape-growing, let me know. I am getting too old. I'll trade you a thousand dollars worth of books to set me up a new **Herbal Vineyard** on the north forty, out here in rural Maryland, half way between Baltimore and D.C. I now think the old fashioned grape varieties can be grown organically while those highly derived hybrids are pesticide dependent. Why? Because the old fashioned varieties have enough of the internal (intrinsic) natural pesticides like pycnOPCs, resveratrol and vivniferin while those highly derived varieties no longer have enough of the intrinsic pesticide so that extrinsic pesticides, too often synthetics, must be applied to protect the plant from grazers and disease.

There's a lot breaking on resveratrol. It's been shown to be a natural COX-2-Inhibitor, which might suggest that it is useful in alzheimer's (especially with its newly discovered attribute of reducing beta-plaque tangles in the brain), arthritis, and cancer, especially of the colon. One study demonstrated that resveratrol and quercetin (also in grapes and wine) have NSAID activities useful in inflammatory diseases (X15180920), possibly even avian flu with cytokine bursts. It inhibits some flu and other viruses. Some Lyme disease protocols embrace resveratrol, but possibly in a better container, *Fallopia japonica* (JAD, 2006).

You've already seen pycnOPCs on sale in bottles as the trademarked pycnogenol™. Many "advanced" humans, like advanced or derived grape varieties, no longer get enough pycnOPCs in their derived processed diets so they buy grape seeds extracts, pine bark extracts, tea extracts, or purified OPCs to replace what their ancestors got from an unprocessed diet. I'll wager that all woody plants contain OPC's including the high priced one with the trademarked name. Now with the 1997 cancer-preventing news on resveratrol, I predict that by 2,000 at the latest, they'll have resveratrol in a capsule too, costing ten or twenty dollars or more per month, to replace the resveratrol that we eliminated from our diet in the progress of "mankind." But we wild food grazers won't need to buy any pycnogenol if we graze on various barks, not just the grape or pine, but probably any bark. Ditto for resveratrol; nibbling on wild grape leaves, we will probably consume a hundred or a thousand times more resveratrol than our non-grazing neighbors on their refined processed diets.

What I've said about the edible grape leaves probably also applies to the wild grapes. From August until frost, I crush up a few and add to my lemonade making it light purple, with added resveratrol and pycnogenol™, for free. After frost this year, I'll be heading to the Holy Land, to see tame and wild grape vines, in their Biblical setting.

Now, a generalization. All this leads me to reiterate a far-reaching conclusion. Natural pesticides are natural medicines. Wild grapes then will have more medicinal value than tame grapes. And grazers like Vickie and I get more natural medicines than our non-grazing counterparts. So I'm saying that wild weedy grapes will have even more of most of the biological activities of the tame grape. Here's what I had to say about the grape in my *Medicinal Plants of the Bible*.

"Sap of young branches used as remedy for skin diseases. Leaves astringent, used in diarrhea. Juice of unripe fruit astringent, used in throat affections. Dried fruit cooling, demulcent, laxative, stomachic. Regarded as apertif, astringent, demulcent, diuretic, expectorant, hemostat, laxative, lithontryptic, refrigerant, restorative, stomachic, and tonic, the grape is a folk treatment for cachexia, cancer, cholera, consumption, diarrhea, dropsy, heart, hoarseness, kidney, nausea, ophthalmia, seasickness, skin, smallpox, sore throat, thirst, tuberculosis, and warts. Grapes figure into several anticancer "remedies": cancer, condylomata, corns, fibroids, impostumes, moles, neoplasms, polyps, scirrhus, sclerosis of the liver, testicles, and uterus; tumors of the ear, fauces, neck, testicles, throat, tonsils, uterus, and uvula; and warts. In the Transvaal, grape syrup is used for diptheria. Lebanese have a grape "cure" for fever, liver, nervousness, smallpox and tuberculosis. Small young leaves and/or tendrils are fed to infants to prevent scurvy and iron deficiency; the seeds and roots are ground for an anemia treatment, as is wine itself. The expressed leaf juice is applied to various skin conditions, including "cancer." Wine or its distillate is used by Lebanese for cramps, stomachache, toothache, for any pain for that matter. More recent headlines in the United States proclaim that red wine (perhaps due to tannin) show some viricidal activity against herpes, more so than white wine. Ayurvedics regard the fruits, especially the black fruits, as aphrodisiac, diuretic, laxative, purgative and refrigerant, and use them for asthma, biliousness, blood disorders, burning, eye ailment, fever, hangover, jaundice, sore throat and strangury. Unani use the leaves, or their juice, for bleeding at the mouth, headache, nausea, piles, scabies, splenitis, and syphilis, the ashes of the stem for arthritis, bladder stones, orchitis and piles, the fruit for fever, the seed ash for inflammation. They consider the seeds aphrodisiac, astringent and refrigerant, the fruit as depurative, digestive, expectorant, and stomachic."

## Grape Seeds

Grape, often called vine in the Bible, was one of the more important of more than 100 medicinal plants in the Bible. The green seedless grapes are twice as expensive as the red grapes with seeds. But probably the green seedless lacked many of the health-giving benefits of the red grape which had more polyphenols, and the seeds which were chewed up in my fruits juice blender this morning. Yes, the health food companies are going to great lengths to tell you about and sell you on their grapeseed products. I believe that the grape seeds do contain many phytochemicals that our paleolithic ancestors consumed in larger quantities than does modern man and woman.

Too often American consumers are duped into buying seedless grapes (oftn much more expensive than seeded grapes) and then walking into the health food store next door to buy grapeseed extracts, which admittedly have many health giving attributes. But in the process the consumer is paying twice as much as would have been paid for seeded grapes (which are not quite so pesticide-dependent). So the genetically selected seedless grapes are environmentally and economically more costly, and the seed extract, usually produced in concert with wineries or other grape industries, have their energetic costs as well. I'm saying that the natural seeded grape contains more natural pesticides and hence requires fewer synthetic pesticide. They are then friendlier to your health and that of your environment.

So if you want these paleolithic phytochemicals, you can buy the grapeseed extracts, or you can grind up the seeds in your fruit juice, or go out in autumn and eat those small fox grapes, which probably more closely resemble what your paleolithic ancestors consumed. I sometimes chew up those seed, or like the racoons and possums, swallow them whole, suspecting that I too, like the other animals, pass them whole, and perhaps better prepared to germinate next spring, better fertilized. Or you can, as do I, enjoy eating the young new shoots of grape, raw, or rolled around rice in olive oil in dolmas. That's the best way to get my resveratrol.

I'm such a cheapskate that I'd rather eat my grapeseed if my fillings will tolerate such than pay big bucks for a grapeseed extract, highly praised though they be. E.g. Gabetta et al. (2000) report that one brand of grapeseed (Leucoselect) has 80% (-)-epicatechin-3- O-gallate and its dimers, trimers, tetramers and their gallates. (-)-Epicatechin-3-O-gallate may be the isomer reported synergistically thermogenic by Dulloo et al. Gabetta et al. (2000) also report 9.2% (+)-catechin, the isomer that reportedly has COX-2-Inhibitory activity, possibly implying antialzheimeran, antiarthritic, antiinflammatory, and anticolon-cancer activities, the latter three of especial interest to me. If the leucoselect reflects the whole seeds, then it would fall at 92,000 in the following table (Zero Moisture Basis). But that's a big if! It's for sure though that the capsules would contain up to 92,000 ppms (+)-catechol and lots of (-)-epicatechin-3-O-gallate and its dimers, trimers, tetramers and their gallates, possibly making it more promising for obesity than green tea (and pine bark, and other things pushed for their OPC's ).

What's been said about tea, then, might be said in part about grape, but for the lack of caffeine. *Science News* on New Years Day, 2000, commented on tea as "the brew for a slimmer you" based on the work of Abdul G. Dulloo, U. Fribourg. Switzerland. Like capsaicin, and fish oil, epigallocatechin gallate, a flavonoid in green tea, has a thermogenic effect, speeding the conversion of flabby fat to heat. Men burned some 4% more energy (~80 additional calories) on days they took tea capsules and the tea made the body burn fat preferentially. The *Science News* article (Raloff, 2000) blamed the thermogenic effect on epigallocatechin gallate but a Reuter's *Health Review* stated simply epigallocatechin. Perhaps both are right.

So instead of my morning coffee with fatty cream and sugar, I popped the contents of two of Nature's Herbs' green tea capsules into a cup of water, added some hot pepper sauce, and half a capsule of Stevia. That mix probably contains at least 5 thermogenic compounds with no ephedrine or synephrine. I still think some rich company should challenge the FDA and put the Stevia in more convenient green packets along the blue and pink and white (sugar) and tan (brown sugar) in the restaurant sugar bowls (Raloff, 2000). Already praised as a powerful antioxidant, green tea extract may also help dieters lose wight, say researchers in the *American Journal of Clinical Nutrition* (Dec., 1999). The green tea extract may be a safe improvement on traditional diet pills because its does not generate an increase in heart rate, according toe Dr. Abdul Dulloo, University of Geneva in Switzerland, and his colleagues. In their study, the investigators measured the 24-hour energy expenditure of 10 healthy men receiving daily three doses of caffeine (50 mg), green tea extract (containing 50 mg caffeine and 90 mg epigallocatechin), or a placebo. Compared with placebo, green tea induced significant increases (~ 4%) in energy expenditure. The thermogenesis was not linked to the small quantity of caffeine found in tea (Subjects receiving similar amounts of caffeine derived not from tea displayed no change in daily energy output. Dulloo's team emphasizes that to treat obesity, one must reduce energy intake (i.e., dieting), or increase energy output. Green tea extracts may accomplish the latter function, but mechanisms for the action remain unclear. The extract contains a high amount of catechin polyphenols, which may work with other phytochemicals to speed up fat oxidation and thermogenesis, where the body burns fat fuels to generate heat. This stimulated thermogenesis and fat oxidation did not raise subjects' heart rates, perhaps making green tea better than stimulant diet drugs, which may have adverse cardiac effects, especially in obese subjects with hypertension and other cardiovascular problems, e.g. those associated with syndrome X (*American Journal of Clinical Nutrition* 1999; 70: 1040-1045).

So this morning instead of green tea, I had grape leaf tea. I can grow grape leaves but I'm not so good at growing tea leaves. Not bad. And I ate the "tea" grounds, getting some free resveratrol, catechin, and epigallocatehcin, sans caffeine. Grapeseed extracts show many activities, e.g. antioxidant and antiulcer activities. But grapeseed oil contain 1000-fold more tannins than other conventional seed oils. Additionally, they contain epicatechin and epicatechin-gallate which may underlie the recently reported thermogenic activities of tea. Seed fractions containing campesterol, catechin, 2-trans-4-cis-decadienal, 2- trans-decenal, epicatechin, 2-trans-heptenal, linoleic-acid, linoleic acid ethyl ester, linoleic acid methyl ester, nonanal, oleic-acid, palmitic-acid, palmitic-acid butyl ester, beta-sitosterol, stearic- acid butyl ester, and stigmasterol, were biologically active.

Cranberry (and probably other related berries, rich in anthocyanidins, anthocyanosides, condensed tannins, oligomeric procyanidins [OPCs], alias proanthocyanidins, alias procyanidins, alias tannins), can both prevent and treat P- fimbriated *E. coli* associated with UTIs (*The New England Journal of Medicine*, Oct. 8, 1998). But grapes too contain anthocyanins and many *Escherichia coli* killers. So cutting and sweetening your cranberry juice with grapejuice (with seed macerate) might be even better for those pesky UTI's. Seed fractions containing campesterol, catechin, 2-trans-4-cis-decadienal, 2- trans-decenal, epicatechin, 2-trans-heptenal, linoleic-acid, linoleic acid ethyl ester, linoleic acid methyl ester, nonanal, oleic-acid, palmitic-acid, palmitic-acid butyl ester, beta-sitosterol, stearic-acid butyl ester, and stigmasterol, were active against some gram (+) and (-) bacteria, *Citrobacter freundii* (-), *Escherichi coli* (-), *Escherichia cloaca* (-), *Staphylococcus aureus* (+), *Staphylococcus coagulans*. Catechin showed modest activity against *E coli*. Epicatechin was active against all the bacteria (Palma and Taylor, 1999). As one of the better sources of COX-2-Inhibitor, resveratrol, grape leaves, like grapes, may be important cancer fighters. I don't recommend a straight grape diet. Instead, increase your uptake of grape and grape leaves and seeds (always striving for 7, 7, 7, 7, 7, 7, 7 (beans, culinary herbs, fruits, grains, nuts, spices, veggies) increasing your dietary diversity but not your calorie count. I didn't mention meat, but feel that Jeffersonian use of red meats (as spices) and more generous use of cold water fish and fowl are OK, if not desirable. It may depend on what your ancestors ate millennia ago what's best for you.

There is so much for your good health in the good Biblical grape, that I thought you should see what I had to say about the grape back in 1985:

"In general agricultural selection breeds out some of the natural pesticides, like resveratrol, which also have many interesting biological activities. The recent ACS book, *Wine, Nutritional and Therapeutic Benefits*, heaps praise on resveratrol, failing to tell us that there is 10-100 times more in the leaves, and I suspect seeds, than in the fruit pulp and wines. Ironically, leaves stressed by disease, insects, physical damage ar liable to be richer with resveratrol. The seeds have only recently come to the market and clinical trials are few and far between. On the other hand the fruits contain more than 30 types of anthocyanins. Small wonder that grapejuice has 4 times the antioxidant ORAC score of any other fruits juice studied (JNU). Resveratrol has gotten much press for cancer prevention. E.g. Stewart at al (2003), commenting on resveratrol as a candidate for prostate cancer prevention, comment that it may constitute 5-10% of grapeskin. 'Resveratrol may represent the tip of the iceberg of a broad class of stilbene and related polyphenolic natural products,' possibly safe and effective agents for cancer prevention. They look to resveratrol as a lead agent for prostate cancer prevention since it inhibits each stage of multistage carcinogenesis, and scavenges incipient populations of androgen-dependent and androgen-independent prostate cancer cells (X12840221). Resveratrol protect against colitis, and has antioxidant and apoptotic actvities. At levels of 5-10 mg/kg/day (equivalent to one gram a day if I were the 100 kg rat), resveratrol reduced colonic injury, index of neutrophil infiltration and levels of cytokine (Martin et al., 2204, X15013856). But I like to remind us that it is a cocktail of closely related compounds, piceatannol and pterostilbene deserving almost as much praise as the resveratrol (X15309446). Many other anticancer activities are listed in the USDA database. Pycnogenol in grape seeds (and the patented pycnogenol from pine bark) has received almost as much academic praise as resveratrol. Cesarone et al., report the prevention of edema on long flights with Pycnogenol™ (X16015414). Reading that study, I'd be inclined to chew up and eat my grape seeds on long flights. I've heard the famed pharmacological author, Varro Tyler, was killed by just such edema. Peng et al. (2005) reported antihypertensive activities of grape polyphenols (e.g., proanthocyanidins, which lack appreciable estrogenic receptor binding) in estrogen-depleted, female, spontaneously hypertensive rats, probably via an antioxidant mechanism (X16105821). A study by Fernandez-Pachon et al. (2005) confirms what I had long heard, red wine increases uric acid levels. That can be good in normouricemic humans, but may induce a gout crisis in hyperuricemic individuals. Maximum concentrations of maximum antioxidant capacity (and uric acid) occurred after about an hour. Uric acid, like albumin and bilirubin, is an endogenous antioxidant as well (X15941351)."

And here's what I said more than 2 decades earlier in that first Bible book of mine:

> *...But they shall sit every man under his vine and under his fig tree...* Micah 4

"Cultured for fruit, eaten fresh or processed into wine, raisins, juice, with some cultivars adapted for the canning industry. Even Noah planted the grape after the flood and made wine therefrom. Grape seeds contain 6-20% oil, used for edible purposes, soaps, and as a linseed substitute. The leaves of this and other species are eaten in other cultures. Sap of young branches used as remedy for skin diseases. Leaves astringent, used in diarrhea. Juice of unripe fruit astringent, used in throat affections. Dried fruit cooling, demulcent, laxative, stomachic (31). Regarded as apertif, astringent, demulcent, diuretic, expectorant, hemostat, laxative, lithontryptic, refrigerant, restorative, stomachic, and tonic, the grape is a folk treatment for cachexia, cancer, cholera, consumption, diarrhea, dropsy, heart, hoarseness, kidney, nausea, ophthalmia, seasickness, skin, smallpox, sorethroat, thirst, tuberculosis, and warts. Grapes figure into several anticancer 'remedies': cancer, condylomata, corns, fibroids, impostumes, moles, neoplasms, polyps, scirrhus, sclerosis of the liver, testicles, and uterus; tumors of the ear, fauces, neck, testicles, throat, tonsils, uterus, and uvula; and warts. In the Transvaal, grape syrup is used for diptheria. Lebanese have a grape 'cure' for fever, liver, nervousness, smallpox and tuberculosis. Small young leaves and/or tendrils are fed to infants to prevent scurvy and iron deficiency, (the seeds and roots are ground for an anemia treatment, and wine itself is suggested for anemia). The expressed leaf juice is applied to various skin conditions, including 'cancer.' Wine or its distillate is used by Lebanese for cramps, stomachache, toothache, and for any pain for that matter. More recent headlines in the U.S. proclaim that red wine (perhaps due to tannin) show some viricidal activity against herpes, more so than white wine. Ayurvedics regard the fruits, especially the black fruits, as aphrodisiac, diuretic, laxative, purgative and refrigerant, and use them for asthma, biliousness, blood disorders, burning, eye ailment, fever, hangover, jaundice, sore throat and strangury. Unani use the leaves, or their juice, for bleeding at the mouth, headache, nausea, piles, scabies, splenitis, and syphilis, the ashes of the stem for arthritis, bladder stones, orchitis and piles, the fruit for fever, the seed ash for inflammation. They consider the seeds aphrodisiac, astringent and refrigerant, the fruit as depurative, digestive, expectorant, and stomachic (Duke, *Medicinal Plants of the Bible,* 1985)."

[[There's a lot breaking on resveratrol. It's been shown to be a natural COX-2-Inhibitor, which might suggest that it is useful in alzheimer's (especially with its newly discovered attribute of reducing beta-plaque tangles in the brain), arthritis, and cancer, especially of the colon. One study demonstrated that resveratrol and quercetin (also in grapes and wine) have NSAID activities useful in inflammatory diseases (X15180920), possibly even avian flu with cytokine bursts. It inhibits some flu and other viruses. Some Lyme disease protocols embrace resveratrol, but possibly in a better container, *Fallopia japonica,* which see. JAD, 2006]]

# Groundnut (*Apios americana*)

*The Wild Foods Forum* 13(6):8-9, November/December, 2002

With the energy crisis threatening, I like to remind WFF readers of a little consulted resource. It is *Handbook of Energy Crops* by James A. Duke, 1983, not exactly published, but still available online at http://www.hort.purdue.edu/newcrop/duke_energy/duke index.html.

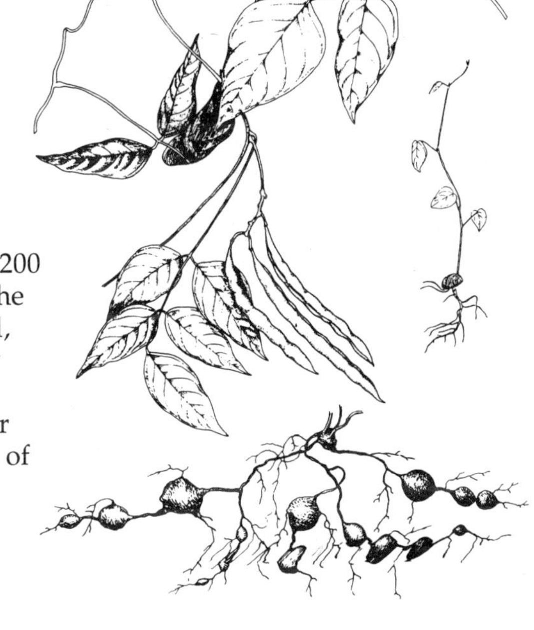


In that are presented 200 species accounts including the following, slightly edited, account of one of my favorite wild foods. I think Americans would be better off if they replaced some of their dietary potato with this protein-rich root crop.

## Uses

An attractively flowered plant, suggestive of Wisteria, *Apios* has been described by the NAS as a "useful, sweet-scented ornamental." I have enjoyed the tubers raw or cooked. During the potato famine of 1845, *Apios* was introduced to Europe (but not for the first time). Its cultivation there as a food crop was abandoned when potato growing again became feasible. The plant was much esteemed by early American settlers, who ate them boiled, fried, or roasted, calling them groundnuts, potato beans, or Indian potatoes. The Pilgrims of New England survived their first few winters thanks to the groundnut. Blackmon presents several groundnut recipes. Erichsen-Brown recounts many of the Indian uses. Menominee preserved the roots by boiling them in maple syrup. Even bread was made from the root. Indians were said to eat the seeds like lentils. I would like to join the ranks of Bill Blackmon, Ed Croom, Janet Seabrook and Noel Vietmeyer, and advocate more studies of the economic potential of this interesting tuber, harvestable all year round. I agree with Blackmon and Reynolds, who, after studying *Apios* intensively stated: "the prognosis for developing *A. americana* as a food crop looks outstanding." Advocates should be aware of its weed potential, at least among uncultivated perennials, e.g., cranberries and azaleas. Mrs. Duke threatens to eradicate my healthiest specimen, climbing to the top of her 15-foot saucer magnolia.

## Folk Medicine

According to Hartwell, the tubers were used in folk remedies for that cancerous condition known as "Proud Flesh" in New England. Nuts were boiled and made into a plaster: "For to eat out the proud flesh they (Indians) take a kind of earth nut boyled and stamped."

## Chemistry

Some describe the plant as having a milky juice. Seabrook suggests that the latex could be used commercially. According to the NAS, the only published analysis records a remarkable protein content of 17.5%. Prompted by the inadequacy of analysts, Duke arranged for new analytical investigations. Sanchez and Duke, based on these analysts provided by Benito de Lumen, report (ZMB): 3.75 crude fat, 5.50% ash, 17.28% crude protein, 28.84% neutral detergent fiber, 44.63% available carbohydrate, and 1.06 nonprotein nitrogen. Subsequently, Walter et al. tabulated the differences in analysts between fresh and dry tubers of *A. americana, A. fortunei*, and the endangered *A. priceana* (Table I). Saponins have been reported in the genus, and the absence of tannins refuted above. Whether or not the plant exports its fixed nitrogen as ureides (allantoin, allantoic acid) as is typical of many of the subtropical Phaseoleae or as the more soluble amides (asparagine and glutamine) as in such temperate legumes as *Lupinus, Pisum, Trifolium*, and *Vicia* remains to be seen. Because it is suggested to have a cowpea-type Rhizobium, I predict it will be a ureide exporter. Some calculations suggest it takes ca. 2.5 times as much water (remember this is an aquaphyte) to export N as ureides. But the ureides are more economical with a C:N ratio ca. 1:1; cf. 1:1 for asparagine, 5:2 for glutamine. Many legume sprouts are rich in allantoin, widely regarded as a vulnerary medicinal compound. According to the Merck Index, allantoin is a product of purine metabolism in animals, while it is prepared synthetically by the oxidation of uric acid with alkaline potassium permanganate. Medical and veterinary use – "Has been used topically in suppurating wounds, resistant ulcers, and to stimulate growth of healthy tissue" (Merck & Co.). *Dorland's Illustrated Medical Dictionary* puts it differently:

> **allantoin** (ah-lan'to-in) – Chemical name: 5-ureidohydantoin. A white crystallizable substance, C4H6N4O3, the diureide of glyoxylic acid, found in allantoic fluid, fetal urine, and many Plants, and as a urinary excretion product of purine metabolism in most mammals but not in man or the higher apes. It is produced synthetically by the oxidation of uric acid, and was once used to encourage epithelial formation in wounds and ulcers and in osteomyelitis. It is the active substance in maggot treatment, being secreted by the maggots as a product of purine metabolism.

The direct role of allantoin in gout, if any, should be of great interest to those American males who have gout, especially if they ingest large quantities of legume sprouts or comfrey. *Apios* produces a complex pterocarpan that appears structurally similar to glyceollin III, a phytoalexin of the cultivated soybean.

## Description

Twining, herbaceous vine, the stems short-pubescent to glabrate, 1 to 3 m long, the rhizomes moniliform, with numerous fleshy tubers 1 to 8 cm thick. (Some plants have fleshy roots only, others both fleshy roots and tubers, and others only tubers.) In winter, the stems have a distinctive brown color and are locally flattened, enabling the experienced collector to distinguish it from honeysuckle. Leaves once-pinnate, 1 to 2 dm long; leaflets 5 to 7, ovate or ovate-lanceolate to lanceolate, ca. 3 to 6 cm long, glabrous to short-pubescent, obscurely stipellate; petioles mostly 2 to 7 cm long; stipules setaceous, soon deciduous, 4 to 6 mm long. Inflorescence 5 to 15 cm long, nodes swollen, flowers I to 2 per node, subtended by linear-subulate bracts 2 to 2.5 mm long; pedicels 1 to 4 mm long with 2 linear-subulate bractlets near apex. Calyx sparsely short-pubescent, broadly campanulate, tube ca. 3 mm long; petals nearly white to brownish purple, the standard obovate or orbicular to obcordate, reflexed, obscurely auricled, 9 to 13 mm long, the wings shorter, slightly auricled, the keel strongly incurved; stamens diadelphous, 1 and 1. Legume linear, 5 to 15 cm long, 4 to 7 mm broad, 2 to 12-seeded, dehiscing by 2 spirally twisted valves. Germination cryptocotylar.

## Germplasm

Reported from the North American Center of Diversity, groundnut, or cvs thereof, is reported to tolerate acid and bog soils, partial shade, slopes, and waterlogging. In 1982, the Plant Introduction Officer of the USDA suggested to me the possibility of mounting a germplasm expedition to collect germplasm of this species, and its endangered relative, *Apios priceana* Robinson, which produces a single large tuber instead of a string of small tubers. NAS speculates that a bush-like mutant may be found in nature. Seedlings from Tennessee had 22 chromosomes, while plants from the northern part of the range were triploid. Blackmon and Reynolds discuss the variation in germplasm they have already assembled. (2n = 22.)

## Distribution

Widely distributed in eastern Canada and the United States (often around ancient Indian campsites) (Florida, Texas, to Nova Scotia, Minnesota, and Colorado). Usually in low damp bottomland or riparian woods and thickets. Seems to be associated with *Alnus* in Rocky Gorge Reservoir, Maryland, as well as on the eastern shore of Maryland. Unfortunately, it can become a serious weed in cranberry plots. Uninfested bogs yielded nearly 14

MT/ha cranberries, whereas herbicide plots yielded only ca. 670 to 2,300 kg/ha cranberry .372 Perhaps the cranberry salesmen could find a market for the groundnuts, since both are Native American food plants.

## Ecology

Ranging from Subtropical Dry through Cool Temperate Forest Life Zones, groundnut is reported to tolerate annual precipitation of 9.7 to 11.7 dm (mean of 2 cases = 10.7), annual temperature of 9.9 to 20.3oC (mean of 2 cases = 15.1), and pH of 4.5 to 7.0 (mean of 2 cases = 5.8). Produces well in south Florida and Louisiana. I have successfully germinated fall harvested seed, after soaking in hot water, room temperature water, or frozen water, seeds that sunk and seeds that floated after soaking. These took 4 months from harvest to germination, whereas their unsoaked counterparts had still not germinated. Fall-harvested seed apparently exhibit no dormancy when planted in spring.

## Cultivation

According to Vilmorin-Andrieux, since seeds do not ripen in France, it is multiplied by division in March and April, or in the latter part of summer. Divisions are planted in good, light, well-drained soil 1 to 1.5 m apart in every direction. Reynolds spaced his seedlings at 2 x 3 feet, tubers at 3 x 3 feet. Stems should be supported by poles or stakes. Ground should be kept free of weeds by an occasional hoeing. Cultivation, if overdone, might discourage the rhizomes and their tubers. Seedlings require at least 2 years growth and a minimum photoperiod of 14 hours to induce flowering. Tuber dormancy can be broken by chilling (several months at 35 to 40°F) or using ethylene.

## Harvesting

According to Vilmorin-Andrieux, the tubers are not large enough to be gathered for use until the second or third year after planting. Blackman's results in Louisiana show this is not true where there is a long growing season. Once large enough, they can be dug at any time of the year when the ground is not frozen. If carefully dug, strings of four score tubers can be achieved.

## Yields and Economics

According to Elliott, Asa Gray once said that if advanced civilization had started in North America instead of the Old World, the groundnut would have been the first tuber to be developed and cultivated. Femald, Kinsey, and Rollins recount an anecdote indicating the economic value of the groundnuts to the pilgrims, "The great value to the colonists of this ready food is further indicated by a reputed town law, which in 1654 ordered that, "if an Indian dug Groundnuts on English land, he was to be set in stocks, and for a second offence, to be whipped." Yields of 30 MT per acre were erroneously reported (should have been 30 MT/ha) for cranberry bog weed populations. Reynolds has attained the equivalent of ca 40 MTlha from tubers in I-year studies in Louisiana. Some of his plants yielded more than 3 kg tubers.

## Energy

Currently, this looks like a poor prospect for biomass production. However, one should at least consider the possibility of developing the crop for marginal habitat (swamp), the tubers as the main crop; the aerial biomass, as residue, might be used for production of rubber, leaf protein, and power alcohol. The nodulated roots fix nitrogen. Around Rocky Gorge Reservoir, in Maryland, the plant is most commonly intertwined in N-fixing *Alnus* species. Nodules were recorded on *A. americana,* but root-nodule location relative to tuber formation was not specified. Root hairs are said to be lacking on secondary roots of mature plants. Four rhizobial strains isolated from *A. americana* nodules were not tested on the host, but since they produced nodules on cowpea plants, the species was considered a member of the cowpea miscellany. The rhizobia are described as monotrichously flagellated rods with cowpea-type, slow cultural growth. H. Keyser suggests conservatively that *Apios* fixes >100 kg N per ha. With no idea of the solubility of N fixed by the groundnut, I recommend it be studied as a potential intercrop for marsh and aquatic plants, especially rice and wild rice. It might also be considered for cultivation around the edges of reservoirs used for irrigation, hence adding a small token of nitrogen to the irrigation waters. Because of their tolerance to both acidity and waterlogging, they might be especially advantageous around impoundments in strip-mine reclamations. Certainly the scorings by Roth et al. do not speak well for the energy potential of *Apios*. They give it a score of 14, in a system whereby only species receiving scores of 11 or less were regarded as potential renewable energy sources.

## Biotic Factors

*Agriculture Handbook No. 1654* lists the following diseases affecting this species: *Alternaria* sp. (leaf spot), *Cercospora tuberosa* (leaf spot), *Erysiphe polygoni* (powdery mildew), *Microsphaera diflusa, Phymatotrichum omnivorum,* and *Puccinia andropogonis* var. *onobrychidis* (rust). Reynolds reported powdery mildew, virus, possibly anthracnose, root-knot nematodes, mealy bugs, spider mites, aphids, white flies, leaf-eating caterpillars, cucumber beetles, grasshoppers, stink bugs, and fire ants. In some cases, the fire ants are responsible for mealy bug infestations. Although most Erythrinae are bird pollinated, *Apios* seems to be mostly bee pollinated.

## *Groundnuts – (Apios americana)*

Selected Song from *Herbalbum* © 1985 by Jim Duke

Whiteman say to the redman "Is this the Promised Land?"
"Groundnuts and wild rice and turkey in the hand!"

Whiteman say to the redman
"Just look what you have got."
"Wild rice and wild thyme and turkey in the pot."

Whiteman say to the redman "I think I envy you."
"Wild rice and artichokes and groundnuts in the stew."

Redman say to the whiteman
"Do you really have to push?"
"Redman and greener land, and turkey to the bush."

Redman say to the whiteman
"Are you really having fun?"
Nuts and bolts and wild, wild oats,
and the turkey on the run!"

Blackman say to the whiteman
"Just look what you have done."
"Played your hand on the redman's land,
and the turkey's on the run."

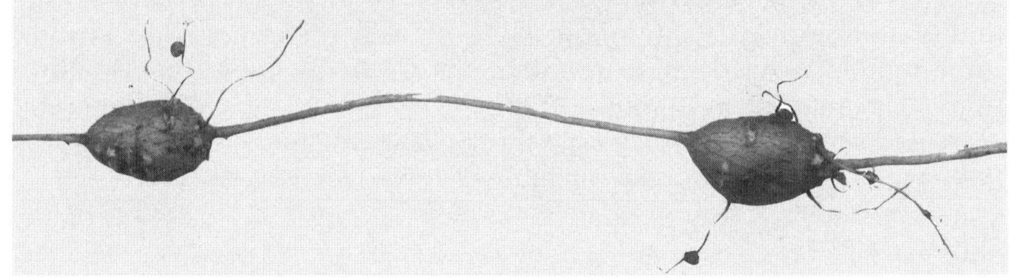

# Horse Balm (*Monarda punctata*)

(circa 1994)

*Science News* in September carried an article entitled "Mossy Memory-Booster For Alzheimer's." I was reading it at the same time CBS' Dan Rather announced the approval of Cognex (Tacrine) for Alzheimer's. *Science News* said that Huperzine A, an alkaloid derivable from a Carolina clubmoss, was more effective, more specific, than THA (tacrine), the FDA approved drug. "Huperzine-A is proving to be one of the most potent and selective acetylcholinesterase inhibitors under study for the treatment of Alzheimer's disease, which damages memory and affects 4 million U.S. residents. Clubmosses also contain nicotine, familiar to our Carolina tobacco growers, which also inhibits cholinesterase (See *Science News* 143:47). Quite possibly nicotine and huperzine would be synergic as insecticides and as acetylcholinesterase inhibitors. But are they safe?

People with Alzheimer's seem to suffer from a lack of acetylcholine in the brain, and from inflammatory and oxidative perturbations of the brain and in the new millennium, beta-plaque fibrils seem to be even more contributory to alzheimer's. The three compounds huperzine, nicotine, and tacrine prevent the breakdown of acetylcholine. We know that nicotine can be absorbed through the skin, because it is sold in expensive skin patches to curb the smoking habit. But there are also several compounds in the food chain that prevent the breakdown of acetylcholine. These seem to be most abundant in mints, which are noteworthy also in their content of antioxidant compounds (rosemary, sage and thyme contain more than a dozen antioxidants). Mint compounds which are known to prevent the breakdown of acetylcholine and/or choline include carvacrol, carvone, cineole, p-cymene, fenchone, limonene and limonene oxide, pulegone and pulegone-oxide, alpha-terpinene, terpinen-4-ol, and thymol. You'll probably find many more on the phytochemical database. Many if not all of these compounds are dermally absorbed and some can cross the blood brain barrier. Thus rosemary shampoo could possibly have acetylcholine saving activity comparable to tacrine. That's why I have been betting my head of hair that rosemary shampoo would have some (maybe more, maybe less) of the activities reported for the approved FDA-drug. Yes, rosemary shampoo contains at least five compounds that share the anti-cholinesterase activity of the famous tacrine.

I might consider nicotine patches along with my rosemary. According to herbal clips (HUC-7-11-6-3), nicotine is being studied for Alzheimer's and Parkinson's. "The more receptors one has in the brain, the more protection one has against getting these diseases...Nicotine seems to increase the number of receptors on brain cells. It acts like the chemical actylcholine, which opens certain receptors like a key...Low doses of nicotine cause "arousal, stimulation, increased heart rate and blood presssure." An ideal medicine, however, would not carry the same dangers with it that nicotine does. Jack Henninglield, a top government pharmacologist, says however, "that nicotine works like a drug; it looks like a drug; it is a drug pure and simple," from a drug delivery system, a blast-furnace like cigarette. "Any product that burns tobacco is almost impossible to have at an acceptable label, "says Henningfield (HUC-7-11-6-3).

There's a wild "balm," in sandy places, sometimes called horse-balm. It contains much more carvacrol, e.g., than rosemary. Matter of fact it was higher in carvacrol than anything else in my database, and used to be the commercial source of thymol, which still shows up in Listerine®. America deserves the best medicine for Alzheimer's. Could it be the horsebalm? Americans deserve to know, not to have the herbal alternative taken away from them by a regulatory agency more inclined to believe the published pharmaceutical literature (they should see what they didn't publish) rather than the empirical wisdom evolved over the millennia.

If herbalists started selling horse balm shampoo claiming that it contained acetylcholinesterase inhibitors, our regulatory agency could either confiscate, destroy or bar such horsebalm shampoo. What they should do (in a society where 25% of us, and more than half of the elderly who are most likely to suffer Alzheimer's, are not covered by insurance to pay for tacrine and/or the doctor to prescribe it) is determine which was safest and more effective, tacrine or horsebalm. Until such trials, we don't know but what horesbalm could be better. It very probably is safer. It surely would be cheaper. Horsebalm is about as well known as tacrine, has been longer known and consumed, and contains many acetylcholinesterase and antioxidant compounds (more than a dozen).

I hereby bet my hair that horsebalm shampoo would do nearly as well as the FDA-approved drug. What next? The price of proving a drug safe and efficacious has risen dramatically, $90 million, to 125, to 231, to 285-300, and finally in May of this year to $359 million ($500 million in 1994, 1.7 billion in 2006). Who would invest a billion to prove that horsebalm shampoo is better than tacrine? You and I could grow our own horsebalm, make our own shampoo, and self medicate. There'd be no way for the mendicant merchant to recoup the $billion. I suspect that, if herbalists started pushing horsebalm shampoo, that our regulatory agency would declare horsebalm a hazard to society (when it is probably less hazardous than what they have approved).

I have for years added horsebalm to my mixed mint teas. American Indians before us used horsebalm as a snuff and as a tea, for cough, constipation, cramps, enteritis, fever, headache, stomachache, but I find no reference to their using horsebalm for Alzheimer's. Maybe they didn't have Alzheimer's or didn't recognize it. Sly Fox Indians placed the leaves near the nostrils to rally persons near death. Ojibwa merely rubbed it in the skin. That's a weird way to apply medicine – but remember the topical capsaicin, nicotine, and scopolamine patches and remember that most of these aromactic antiacetylcholinesterase phytochemcials can be applied transdermally. Horsebalm can contain up to 1.25% carvacrol some of which can be absorbed dermally, and some of which reportedly can cross the blood-brain barrier and which is reported by Austrian scientists to prevent the breakdown of acetylcholine. Horsebalm also contains up to 2.7% thymol which also prevents the breakdown of acetylcholine. Would the FDA get us if we put a little horsebalm in our bath and shampoo? Just horsing around! But I suspect the horsebalm might be as good as what the FDA approved, a little bit safer, and a whole lot cheaper.

# Jerusalem Artichoke (*Helianthus tuberosus*)

*The Wild Foods Forum* 15(2):8-9, Spring, 2004

In Latin it's *Helianthus tuberosus* L. In genteel English it's Jerusalem artichoke. To some of my farming friends, it's more liable to be called Fartychoke, in reference to its gas-generating potential. One 19th Century writer (Coues, 1897) put it this way: "when boiled, the root is tolerably good eating; but when eaten raw, it is of a windy nature and sometimes causes severe colic." It's one of the few native North American food plants, once eaten by American Indians and now eaten occasionally by the Caucasians that supplanted them. It is one of those species for which I find no recorded Amerindian folk medicinal uses, indicating that it, like the groundnut, *Apios americana*, was used exclusively as food, not as medicine. At least, if Indians had medicinal uses, they were not reported in the literature available to me.

I checked with Dan Moerman in 1999. It's hard for me to believe.

Neither Dan Moerman nor I find any reference to medicinal uses of the American Jerusalem artichoke by the American Indians. However, my ethnobotanical database quotes other sources, outside America as citing some folkloric usages: Androgenic; Aperient; Aphrodisiac; Cholagogue; Diabetes; Diuretic; Rheumatism; Spermatogenic; Stomachic and Tonic (Duke and Wain, 1981).

This winter I intend to repeat an experiment I performed with beans in 1990. I did this after learning that a pound of faba beans might contain enough of certain natural chemicals to help Parkinson's disease. For a week, I ate a 16-ounce can of beans each noon. The first, second and third days were of a "windy nature," but by the fourth day, my intestinal flora could handle the beans with ease. If this is true of artichokes, I could eat them all winter long with little or no flatus after the first two or three days.

If any of you readers feel inclined to check this out for yourself, I'd like to hear how you make out. There's no easier rootcrop to grow. I enjoy it raw – it turns too mushy for most North American palates when cooked.

Back (Sep. 20, 1990) when we were on the verge of war with Iraq, we had to rethink our alternative energy sources, and believe it or not artichoke could produce a lot of energy alcohol, in case all Sadam's Arabian buddies cut off our petroleum. Yes artichokes are a cheap source of food, fodder and biomass that can be converted into energy alcohol. So thinking energy, I looked into my Iraqi sources. I was intrigued to find that Jerusalem Artichoke, a native American plant, was reported to be androgenic in a book on the *Medicinal Plants of Iraq* (Al Rawi). That gives this weedy plant the folk reputation of the ginseng, supposedly aphrodisiac. That could sell a lot of artichokes if true. Some other interesting entries showed up in *Steinmetz Codex Vegetabilis*, and I won't even translate these; you'll learn a lot more and possibly stay out of trouble if you look them up: antidiabetic, antirheumatic, aperient, cholagogue, spermatogenic, and stomachic. But there's nothing in my American folklore for this once all-American plant.

What's good about the artichoke is that it is a copious producer of tubers which can be dug all winter when the ground isn't frozen. And these tubers are our second best source of inulin, now newly called a prebiotic. It has long been known as a famous source of inulin, once considered good for diabetics. But 98% of that inulin is indigestible, which led Gerald Seiler (*Econ. Bot.* 44: 322. 1990) to say that "Jerusalem-artichoke tubers provide an excellent low-energy diet food ... Fresh tubers are low in calories (7 cal/100 g) but satisfy hunger." That could start an artichoke fad if it caught on. Seiler's paper gave us new data for the artichoke. The average tuber contains 63% water at flowering time. On a dry weight basis, there's 9.8% protein, 0.45% calcium, 0.12% magnesium, 0.33 % phosphorus, 2.22% potassium, 0.15% sodium, 34 parts per million (ppm) iron, 126 ppm manganese, 37 ppm zinc, and 20 ppm copper. Wild types averaged richer in protein, calcium, sodium, and copper; tamed types richer in magnesium, phosphorus, potassium, iron, manganese, and zinc.

But my enthusiasm for this weed got recharged in 1999 with a new symposium. Granted my weed chicory is a better known source of inulin, but my artichoke is a much more edible root, and probably produces more inulin per hectare.

Recently I have been thinking about chicory as the poor man's echinacea, but I think that many of the following should be investigated, like black-eyed susan, echinacea, and wild quinine for immunostimulant activity, cichoric acid content, and inulin content. My database gives some maximum (incredibly high) figures for potential inulin content. Wouldn't it be interesting if we gave this to the echinaceologists and found that immunostimulation was as much a function of the oliogsaccahride inulin and some of the oligo- and polysacchardies in echinacea. That's partly why I compiled this list of the top seven inulin producers in my database.

Most of the major sources of inulin are foods, but none of them are much consumed by the American consumer. Matter of fact Moshfegh et al. (1999) show that wheat, which contains much lower levels of inulin and oligofructose, is our major source, contributing some 70% of American's dietary inulin (sensu latu), onions contribute 23-24%, banana and garlic 2-3% each. They tell us that the average American diet provides 2.6 g inulin and 2.5 g oligofructose. A hundred gram overdose of fresh artichoke tuber could provide 15 g inulin plus oligofructose, indicating that it would require only ~30 grams fresh artichoke to provide 5 g inulin plus oligofructose. The dry artichoke could contain up to 75 g inulin plus oligofructose, so it would take less than 10 gram (1/3 ounce) dry artichoke to provide that 5 g inulin plus oligofructose.

The original dietary fiber hypothesis (Burkitt and Trowell, 1975) suggested that a deficiency of fiber in modern diet increased colon diseases, colon cancer, constipation, diverticular disease and hemorrhoids.

And I have been a high fiber freak since hearing Burkitt speak, in his usual picturesque fashion (your turds should go splat, like a cow's). Evidence is strong that inulin (and oligofructose henceforth and forever more) increases fecal bulk and fecal nitrogen elimination, promoting the growth of bifidobacteria proportional to other anaerobes. (Bifids appear to displace pathogens.) Inulin from chicory roots and oligofructose at 20 g/day increase fecal bulk (2.0-1.3 g per g fed respectively). Animal studies show that diet with 10% oligofructose (roughly equivalent to 40-60 g in humans) reduces aberrant crypt foci and growth of transplanted tumors.

This is widely accepted, but still controversial, that inulin increases counts and proportions of fecal bifidobacteria. Short chain fatty acids (SCFAs) clearly enhance colonic absorption of calcium. Increased uptake of Ca, Fe, Mg, and Zn seen in lab animals is of great potential if confirmed in humans. Inulin can reduce cholesterol a/o triglyceride concentrations. More clinical studies are needed to confirm (or refute) inulin's potential in colon cancer, compromised immune function, hepatoses, hyperlipidemia, nephroses, osteoporosis, and ulcerative colitis (Jenkins et al., 1999).

Rats fed inulin absorbed more Ca and Mg than control rats despite an increase in total fecal mass. Chronic ingestion of inulin decreased or prevented the loss of bone mass, calcium and phosphorus from the bones of gastrectomized rats and the loss of bone mineral density by ovarectomized rats (Greger, 1999). But don't take that data to the osteoporosis bank yet.

One group found no increased calcium or iron absorption in adult humans but did observe increased calcium absorption in adolescents (early prevention???). Another group reported, following inulin tests, increased calcium absorption but not Fe, Mg and Zn (Greger, 1999).

It is thought that there are 400-500 different bacterial species in the human large intestine (Gibson, 1999), each competing with you for food and nutrients and probably altering your absorption of minerals etc. Certain oligosaccharides that cannot be digested, except by bacteria, are PREBIOTICS. Those oligosaccharides containing fructose can alter the human gut flora towards a bifid-dominated flora, by specific fermentation routes.

In gut homeostasis, the gut flora is central in preventing invasion of pathogens. Additionally they play other important roles, e.g. improved lactose tolerance, supplying SCFA as energy substrate, antitumor properties, neutralizing some toxins, stimulating the intestinal immune system, and maybe lipolytic activities. Feeding 15g inulin in lieu of 15g sucrose markedly increased bifid bacteria while decreasing bacteroides, clostirdia and fisobacteria. On sucrose diet, bacteroides dominated the flora, on oligofructose or inulin, bifids dominated. Bifids and lactobacilli secrete antibiotics. Bifids are antimicrobial to gram-positive and gram-negative pathogens, campylobacters, escherichi coli, and salmonellae (Gibson, 1999). Gibson cites the Scottish outbreak of *E. coli* 0157 that killed 20 people in 1996: "*Bifidiobacterium infantis* and *B. longum* strongly antagonize *E. coli* 0157. And inulin (from chicory or jerusalem artichokes) can probably increase those bifids. But those of us over 55 years old have much fewer fecal bifids compared to the young whippersnappers. While hundreds of people were infected during that Scottish outbreak, all the fatalities were elderly. Prebiotic health foods may have much virtue for the elderly. And artichoke and chicory are weeds at my place, free for the eating" (Gibson, 1999).

## References

Gibson, GR. 1999. "Dietary modulation of the human gut microflora using the prebiotics oligofructose and inulin." pp. 1438s-1441s in Milner, JA and Roberfroid, M. eds.

—— 1999. "Nutritional and Health Benefits of Inulin and Oligofructose."

*The Journal of Nutrition* 129(7S): July (Supplement). pp. 1395-1502.

Greger, J.L. 1999. "Nondigestible carbohydrates and mineral bioavailability." pp. 1434s-1435s in Milner, J.A. and Roberfroid, M., eds. 1999. "Nutritional and Health Benefits of Inulin and Oligofructose." *The Journal of Nutrition*, 129(7S): July (Supplement). pp. 1395-1502.

Jenkins, DJA, Kendall, CWC, and Vuksan, V. 1999. "Inulin, Oligofructose and Intestinal Function." pp. 1431s-1433s in Milner, J.A. and Roberfroid, M. eds. 1999. "Nutritional and Health Benefits of Inulin and Oligofructose." *The Journal of Nutrition* 129(7S): July (Supplement). pp. 1395-1502.

# Jewelweed (*Impatiens capensis, I. pallida*)

(Unpublished, circa 1999)

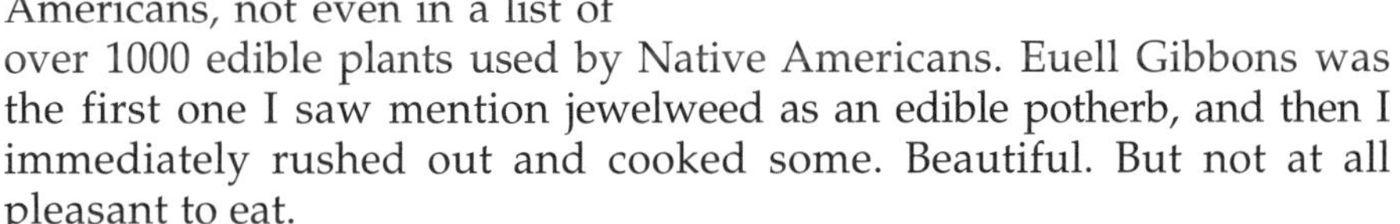

You don't find it in all the medicinal plant books, (certainly not in Commission E and very minor mention in the new Herbal PDR, for digestive problems of all things), but you will find it in the 2nd edition of Foster and Duke. They recount its most famous and long-standing use for the prevention and treatment of poison ivy. Nor will you find it in all the edible plant books, but you will find it in my *Edible Weeds Handbook*. I was sagaciously skeptical about its edibility because I find no record of its having been eaten by the Native Americans, not even in a list of over 1000 edible plants used by Native Americans. Euell Gibbons was the first one I saw mention jewelweed as an edible potherb, and then I immediately rushed out and cooked some. Beautiful. But not at all pleasant to eat.

That's when I learned that most books were partially wrong when they described the leaf arrangement as alternate (one at a node). That's true for the top half of the plant, the half that botanists usually study in the herbarium. But on the bottom half the leaves are opposite (two at the node). Being cautious, I cooked my first jewelweed greens through two changes of water, freezing the water I strained off. Ice cubes made of jewelweed tea, like the foliage itself, are said to be good, either just after contact with poison ivy, or after the rash has already developed. Some even claim that jewelweed, and its ice cubes, are preventive of poison ivy, like drinking the tea. (Some bold souls dangerously eat a little poison ivy believing a little will bolster their immunity; science lends no credibility to such; three have told me of violent reactions following the ingestion of poison ivy; about as many told me of successes with such.) I rub myself down with jewelweed before and after 5-10 minute bouts of uprooting poison ivy down in Yin Yang Yuan (my Chinese name for my **Fern Valley Garden**, formerly called Phenology Valley, as of August 1999, christened Yin Yang Yuan. There's where, about a decade or more ago, I gathered that first batch of jewelweed greens. Even after a second boiling, it retained a beautiful rich green color, but tasted about as bad as spinach to me. (I don't like spinach or chard or lambsquarters of the centrosperm alliance – CENTROSPERMAE, nearly as much as I like cabbage, collards and cress of the mustard alliance – CRUCIFERAE; now BRASSICACEAE.) Matter of fact, I'll now use jewelweed as a medicine, rejecting it as food myself. I have eaten the pod with no displeasure, and have gathered the discharging seeds into a bag, and found them edible in small quantities. They are appropriately described as tasting like butternuts. These same seeds are eaten by mice, grouse, pheasants, and quail. Deer and rabbits graze the foliage and hummingbirds visit the flowers.

I have consulted with Dan Moerman AND his marvelous new book (1998) and database, and still I find no record of the Indian using this common plant for food. Should I view this lack of reported Indian food usage as a red flag? Dan rechecked for me in 1999 and he still has no record of its food use. Here's his response to this drafted idea:

> "Jim, that's fine. I checked again. No food uses at all. 54 drug uses (*I. capensis*, 41; *I pallida*, 13) plus several uses as a yellow or orange dye. Most uses external: poison ivy, rashes generally, cuts and bruises, nettle stings, etc. Only a very few internal uses (to force childbirth, infusion of roots enhances urination – another saw palmetto??). The hint could be the dye uses: dyes are often toxic. I think I wouldn't eat jewelweed, either.

I discuss the jewelweed and enumerate several other presumed edibles that the Amerindians did not eat in *Coltsfoot* 7(6). 1986. It belongs in the medicinal arena. If they didn't eat it maybe I shouldn't. I have the same feeling about my ostrich fern fiddleheads and the deer. If the deer who are wiping out half of my vegetation won't eat that fiddlehead, and will eat poisonous mayapple, tomato and yew leaves, then maybe I'd best not eat the fiddlehead (I still do.)

Recent research by my friend Chemist Bob Rosen, super scientist, finally revealed the secret behind jewelweed's activities against poison ivy. The antihistaminic, antiinflammatory and antipruritic activities are probably due to lawsone, also reported to have many other activities. Lawsone is also used as a sunscreen and with dihydroxyacetone, has been used as an instant-tanning lotion (no sunlight required). A search of the literature showed many patents in both these areas. Lawsone is approved by the FDA for these purposes at about the 1% level in formulations under the cosmetic sections of the USP. Dr. Rosen tells me that lawsone in local jewelweed (*Impatiens capensis*) runs bout 1 - 5 ppm in stalks, up to 50 ppm in orange air roots, but is difficult to determine in the green leaves, where the intense cholorophyll interferes with analysis.

Long a fan of jewelweeds' (*Impatiens capensis* and *pallida*) antipruritic activity as regards poison ivy and stinging nettle, I was delighted to see a

Japanese article on closely related *Impatiens balsamina* (Ishiguro et al., 1998). Shoots have long been used in the orient for arthritis, beriberi, bruises and rheumatism. In Japan, they paint the juice from the white flowers on the skin to alleviate dermatitis, including urticaria. Ishiguro et al. (1998), after finding antianaphylactic, antihistaminic and antipruritic activities, discovered two dinapthofuran-7,12-dione derivatives, balsaminones A and B isolated from the fruit wall, along with 2-methoxy-1,4 napthoquinone. All have significant antipruritic activities. Mice given 10 mg/kg or either balsaminone cut back scratching their noses significantly.

Naturally I copied this to Dr. Rosen, at Rutgers. Bob has kept me advised of his patented work on jewelweed, the native American *Impatiens*. The Rutgers patent "specifically covers napthoquinones and analogs whether synthetic or natural for itching and is assigned to Rutgers University." I don't think that this patent prevents me from continuing to use jewelweed and its lawsone for the prevention and relief of poison ivy, and for antihistaminic activity against nettle stings (which weirdly inject one with neurotransmitters, like acetylcholine, choline, histamine, leukotriene and serotonin). As I interpret patents, this one would prevent me from isolating napthoquinones from jewelweed and selling the chemicals for itch relief. But it doesn't stop my friends from using the succulent plant for the relief of itch, following poison-ivy or stinging nettle encounters.

Many of you have heard me tell the story of trying to dye my beard with the antihistaminic lawsone from the jewelweed (I failed, no mordants and fixatives). You see, lawsone also occurs in the Biblical hair dye henna, which might also then be indicated for itch. I still have only Dr. Rosen's analytical data to support my speculation that napthoquinones might be concentrated in the red prop roots of the jewelweed. Certainly the prop roots are where red coloring is concentrated or at least most obvious, unmasked by chlorophyll. Therefore, I speculate that you will get more antihistaminic activity from the redder aerial roots.

## Jewelweed Seeds

I was surprised to have a jewelweed ejaculate in my hand on June 8, 2004, up at Paul's UpS place in Meig's County, Ohio. They hadn't even started flowering back home yet and, later, Paul said they hadn't really started flowering here either. How could that be? Seed with no flowers.

My question: How can there be seed when there were no flowers? The answer: Thanks to a great three volume series by Eastman: cleistogamous flowers! Sometimes, especially in poor light, as in Paul's **Ramp Hollow**, the jewelweed has cleistogamous flowers – i.e., flowers that don't open, yet set seed. Eastman divulges a lot I had overlooked. Each flower produces ca 2.5 ml nectar a day, with ca 40% sugar. The *Impatiens pallida* may start a few days earlier and hold its flowers 2-3 days, usually a day longer than *Impatiens capensis*. Both species flower until frost. In shadier situations, the plant may produce the green cleistogamous flowers which never open but which do set seed. Eastman suggests that on some plants, there may be more cleistogamous than chasmogamous flowers, producing more seed. He adds that seed from the chasmogamous flowers are ejected further. Seeds require at least 140 days of winter stratification, and they often germinate almost in unison. More than any of my books, Eastman (1995) recounts the major animal and plant associates.

# Jimson Weed (*Datura stramonium*)

*The Business of Herbs*, 8(5):8-9. November/December, 1990

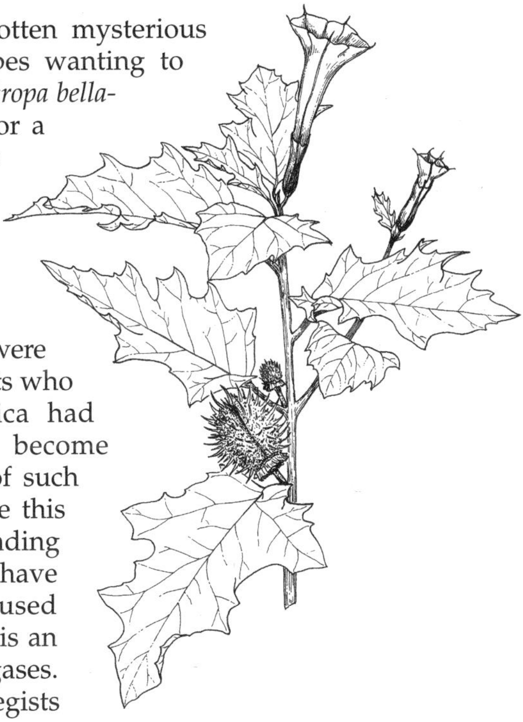

For several years I have gotten mysterious phone calls from Pentagon types wanting to know if we grow belladonna (*Atropa belladonna*) in this country. Except for a few herbalists, there seems to be no overt growers here. It's cheaper to import some herbs, such as belladonna, guar, psyllium and stramonium, than it is to grow our own.

The calls about belladonna were prompted by concerned strategists who wanted to insure that America had enough atropine should we become involved in gas warfare. Fear of such involvement is higher as I write this (August 7, 1990), with troops heading for Saudi Arabia, since Iraq does have nerve gases which may be used against their enemies. Atropine is an antidote to some of these nerve gases. I have always told those strategists something that didn't turn them on. We can get all the atropine we need, with scopolamine as a byproduct, from the soybean fields around Jamestown, Virginia. You see, jimson weed (*Datura stramonium*) is one of the major weeds in our Eastern soybean fields.

## Why it's called jimson

Jimson is a corruption of Jamestown. The story goes that years ago (1676) John Smith was dispatched to Jamestown to quell the Bacon Rebellion. Some of his military men cooked up some jimson weed, perhaps mistaking it for the also-dangerous pokeweed (*Phytolacca americana*). They were made ill, but it doesn't sound too life-threatening in Robert Beverly's *History and Present State of Virginia* (1705, 1855):

> "...they turn'd natural Fools upon it for several Days. One would blow a Feather in the Air; another would dart Straws at it with much Fury; and another stark naked was sitting in a Corner, like a Monkey grinning and making Mows at them; a Fourth would fondly kiss and paw his Companions, and sneer in their Faces, with a Countenance more antik than any in a Dutch Droll. In this frantik Condition they were confined, lest they in

> their Folly should destroy themselves...Indeed they were not very cleanly, for they would have wallow'd in their own Excrement, if they had not been prevented. A Thousand such simple Tricks they play'd, and after Eleven Days, return'd themselves again, not remembring anything that had pass'd."

Is it poison or medicine? Let's not speak lightly of the jimson weed. Many fatalities are attributed to jimson weed intoxication. But one person's poison is another person's medicine. Jimson weed is one of many sources of atropine, a very dangerous alkaloid. But today, that alkaloid is strategically important. It may save some American lives on the Arabian Peninsula. It is the antidote to nerve poison.

Those of you who read *JAMA*, the Journal of the American Medical Association, may have seen ads for SCOP, which seems to be little more than a transdermal patch of scopolamine, another alkaloid derived from jimson weed and other members of the nightshade family. Scopolamine is also a dangerous alkaloid that is being promoted as an alternative to ginger or dramamine, applied as transdermal scopolamine patches, for seasickness and other types of vertigo (dizziness).

## Conflicting research

One study, by an herbalist, showed that ginger in 1,000-mg doses was effective orally at preventing seasickness. Another study, probably sponsored by the pharmaceutical industry, concluded that ginger was ineffective and scopolamine effective. Having written a book on spices, I vote for the ginger. Regrettably, without an unbiased comparative study, we may never know which of these herbal alternatives is safer and more efficacious, ginger itself or scopolamine from the jimson weed. And we won't be sure whether they are better or worse than the conventional dramamine. Unless the government sponsors studies comparing new drugs (synthetic or natural), not only with placebo but with the recognized herbal alternatives, we may not be getting the best medicines.

Jimson weed is a dangerous herb. It contains several poisonous alkaloids. But one of these, scopolamine, may prevent seasickness among landlubbers heading via ship for the Arabian Peninsula. Another, atropine, may be the best antidote to a nerve gas now in the possession of Iraq. Visitors to my garden will see me place a leaf of jimsonweed behind my ear, saying that I am getting transdermal doses of scopolamine, maybe even enough to prevent vertigo. But I tell them to watch my pupils for me. If they get too big, I may be overdosing on transdermal atropine, which optometrists once used in drops to dilate the pupils. Careful with this weed.

## Postscript

Sadam Hussein lit up many of the oilwells in Kuwait as he withdrew, spilling tons of oil on the desert, some burning, some forming lakes of oil. I was invited to visit Kuwait thereafter and see how the desert was recuperating. I saw new seedlings popping through sandy crusts of oils. I even saw young plants of henbane, *Hyoscyamus*, a relative of jimsonweed and alternative source of atropine and scopolamine. Several members of Solanaceae produce both alkaloids. But while there in Kuwait, I also found an arabic-language atropine injection kit. Yes the atropine could have been very important, and it could have come from our jimson weed. And as you hear me say so often, the residues could be converted to energy alcohol after the atropine and scopolamine have been extracted.

# Juniper (*Juniperus communis*)

(Unpublished)

## Jumpin' Juniper, the Gin Berry

Few of you think of the juniper as a Christmas tree, let alone a Biblical herb, and a potent medicine. But I have used species of juniper as a Christmas tree. That was years ago, when I could readily cut a local *Juniperus virginiana*, the red cedar. Peggy doesn't like the idea. Two other species of juniper were mentioned in the Bible. But I'll focus today on what could be called the gin berry, *Juniperus communis*, which has a host of medicinal uses. According to Erichsen-Brown (1989) *Juniperus communis* is a circumboreal species with 3 indistinct varieties, usually recognized in North America on dry, poor, rocky, sterile soils, from the Yukon south to Maine, New Hampshire, Pennsylvania and Illinois, down into Carolina and Georgia. And wherever it occurs it has a strong medicinal reputation. E.g. Maine's Penobscot Indians used the berries for colds Malacite and Micmac use the juniper in shampoos and tonics, and as medicine for consumption, rheumatism, sprains, tuberculosis, ulcers and wounds. Come with me to Maine next summer and I'll teach you some of the medicinal uses of Maine's many conifers. I even tasted the *Juniperus* berries, surprisingly like gin in flavor.

Two great books on Amerindian ethnobotany (Erichsen-Brown, 1989; Moerman, 1998) will be my textbooks for my Maine medical botany and ethnobotany courses, as I introduce you to more than a hundred edible and medicinal plants of Maine. Those texts list a plethora of folk medicinal uses which I have faithfully moved into my Herbal Desk Reference. And there's more than folk medicine. The Bjornnson Icelandic manuscript cited by Erichsen-Brown mentions that juniper is called fire-tree, not fir tree, in Greece, for if the fire is covered with ashes of Juniper, "it will keep alive for almost a whole year."

Even Germany's Commission E, which I like to quote as authoritative, approves some of the former folk uses of juniper. Unfortunately there are nearly a dozen different English translations and interpretations of Commission E floating around here in the United States. So when you say Commission E approves, you almost have to specify which version of Commission E. For example, one scholarly version of Commission E

(Blumenthal et al., 1998) approves juniper only for dyspepsia (its most frequent "endorsement") while another (Gruenwald et al., 1998) adds loss of appetite, bladder and kidney stones and UTI's. Both of these books were intended to help the physicians here in the U.S. get a better handle on herbal ups and downs. Gruenwald's even bears the title *PDR for Herbal Medicine,* PDR being the abbreviation of Physicians Desk Reference. It's enough to drive one to drink, and juniper belongs in my favorite drink, herbal gin tonics. Here's one quaint recipe I'll try some slow day. Juniper berries render pure alcohol orange, and caraway and fennel improve the flavor (CEB). Further, the berries of the juniper are added to spruce beer to improve its flavor. The berries have even been used as a pepper substitute.

Smarter people than me take chloroquine or larium to prevent malaria when they go to the tropics. But they often suffer such side effects as insomnia, nervousness, and yeast overgrowths. On my last trip I took a hydroethanolic extract of juniper and sweet annie (qin hao in TCM, *Artemisia annua*), I sometimes call it "gin-hao." I was taking my cue from a naturopathic physician, Dr. Steve Morris, who had been with me on a Pharmacy Ecotour to Kenya and Tanzania. In the NgoroNgoro Crater of Tanzania, every mosquito carries the malaria parasite. All Steve had was tincture of sweet annie, not even taking chloroquin or larium, and he, like the rest of us on the more rigorous pharmaceuticals, came out unscathed. I've heard of one Mexican botanist who took only tincture of quinine, and he unfortunately did get malaria. I'd like the mix of both myself. And I get a little quinine with each tonic I drink. But what about the juniper; it contains two weak protisticidal compounds (acetic acid and rutin), but some potent lignans, at least two kin to antoplasmodical podophyllotoxin.

Phillipson et al. (1995) studied antimalarial activity of the important antitumor lignan podophyllotoxin which occurs in some junipers, mayapples and chervils and perennial flaxes in the temperate zone, and in *Hernandia* and *Hyptis* in the tropics. Podophyllotoxin is active against *Plasmodium falciparum* (IC50=10.3 ug/ml), slightly more active than the synthetic derivative etoposide (14.8 ug/ml) and much more active than teniposide (inactive at >500 ug/ml) (Phillipson et al., 1995). This lends even more credence to my favorite antimalarial tonic.

Sales of etoposide and teniposide, semisynthetic derivatives of the lignans, are approaching a half billion dollars a year, mostly for lung and testicular cancers. But, at least as far as the malaria parasite is concerned, the natural compound is more poisonous, and that's why they call it podophyllotoxin.

One corollary I often add to my synergy story is that on average semisynthetic derivatives of a natural pesticide (medicine) will be less pesticidal than the natural. Evolution too would have selected the more potent pesticide and nature can do more substitutions than man has even thought of.

Long before podophyllotoxin (modified as etoposide approved for cancer in 1984) and taxol (approved for ovarian cancer in 1992) were approved by the FDA as anticancer medicines, Chippewa were unknowingly getting their podophyllotoxin and taxol by boiling the twigs of red cedar and Canadian yew respectively. They would both take this rather poisonous concoction orally and sprinkle it on hot stones as a sweat for rheumatism. (CEB). I'm actually considering such a poisonous concoction as a possible cancer preventive. I have a weird suspicion that minute doses of poisons are good for our immune systems which protect us from invading cancers and germs. While not understanding homeopathy at all, I might rather take subhomeopathic (low in nannogram levels but still there as a molecule, rather than dilute until no molecule remains) doses of podophyllotoxin or taxol than full doses. They might boost my immune system.

While I don't recommend my putative cancer and malaria preventives to anyone else (as a botanist, I cannot and should not prescribe; it's even dangerous of me to suggest such unproven herbal approaches), I like my antimalarial potpourri. Smells good. Tastes good. And I didn't notice any side effects (could be habit forming). And I've survived forty five scattered weeks in the Amazon where even my shaman suffered a near fatal bout with malaria, and lost his brother to malaria. Juniper has a lot more going for it than gin tonics. If you'd like to see them check out the following entry from my updated Herbal Desk Reference. This is being edited and will soon be published, with nearly 400 illustrations by CRC Press as edition 2 of my CRC *Handbook of Medicinal Herbs* (1985).

# Lupine (*Lupinus perennis*)

*The Business of Herbs*, 12(3):12-13. July/August, 1994

Ironic that a Russian paper (Andreeva et al., 1992) should rekindle my interest in this lovely, locally endangered lupine species, *Lupinus perennis* L. I first met this enchanting wildflower when working on my dissertation, Psammophytes (sand-dwelling plants) of the Carolina Sandhills, way back in the '50s.

Fortunately for me the abstract of the recent Russian paper was in English. It stated that compounds (genistein and luteolin and their glycosides) therein were better than the reference drug papaverine (also a plant-derived drug) at preventing high blood pressure. This was my first indication that genistein had some promise in cardiopathy, helping lower or prevent high blood pressure.

Adding this to my FNF database (Duke 1992), I see published references to the following activities for genistein: abortifacient, antiangiogenic, antifertility, antihypertensive, antileukemic, antimicrobial, cancer-preventive, estrogenic, fungistat; hypotensive; phytoalexin; topoisomerase-II inhibitor; and tyrosin-kinase inhibitor. (It's nearly a full page now on the updated phytochemical database at USDA in 2006.) A Medline search on the keyword "genistein" produced more than 100 references. Genistein and, by inference, lupine show promise both in the prevention and treatment of our worst killers, heart disease and cancer.

I enjoyed just looking at the lupine the Russians call "sundial lupine" in the sunny sand hills of the Carolinas. Here, today, in Maryland, 40 years later, I have located them on only two sites, both on sandy soils on power-line rights of way. So impressed with their beauty was I that I went through all the red tape to get a permit to collect on a special stretch of power line well endowed with several rare plant species that I have seen nowhere else in Maryland. This stretch is mowed only once a year, and not treated with herbicides. The annual mowing, like annual burnings in savanna habitats, tends to favor these sandhill and savanna species which are overgrown with shrubs if not mowed or burned annually. Of course, regular mowing several times a year would eliminate a lot of these rare species. The lupine seems to be holding its own on these sites. It is not yet officially listed but is rather endangered here in Maryland. With handsome flowers, our lupines rival the Texas bluebonnets, but don't seem to be thriving so well.

Until the Russian study, there hadn't been much medicinal interest in this lupine. Duke (1986) mentioned that the Cherokee drank the cold tea for hemorrhage and nausea. Moerman (1986) was more explicit, noting that the Cherokee took the cold infusion and used it as a wash "to check hemorrhage and vomiting." He added some strange Menominee uses as well. They rubbed the plant on the hands or face to give a person the power to control horses. Conversely they used the plant for "fiery" fodder, "to fatten a horse and make him spirited and full of fire."

Ingrid Fordham, USDA; Harry Swartz, University of Maryland; and I are cooperating in an effort to get the plant into tissue culture, hoping (perhaps fearing) that its genistein content might possibly move the plant from the flower, food, and fodder arena to the "farmacy" arena. Genistein is being touted for its perceived ability to lessen the odds for breast and prostate cancer. Many scientists attribute the lesser incidence of breast cancers among Orientals, with their high-soy diets, to the genistein in tofu and other soy foods. There is newer, even more exciting evidence that genistein, by preventing (anti-) vascularization (angiogenesis) of small tumors one millimeter or less in diameter, may stop the growth of young cancers, preventing full-blown tumors. After a visit with one of the leaders in this new "antiangiogenic" research, Dr. Judah Folkman, Children's Hospital, Boston, I was convinced that this compound could help prevent many cases of diabetic blindness here in the U.S. Folkman wants to test it against disfiguring pediatric hemangiomas.

Earlier, anticipating widespread uses for genistein, I sent several food legumes, unfortunately excluding our native lupine, to scientists for analysis. One, a pioneer anticipating the cancer-preventive nature of genistein-containing soy products, had published widely on the potential health benefits of genistein-containing plants. My legume samples were also forwarded to Dr. Adlercreutz, Finnish specialist in angiogenesis. Of those that he analyzed, the Andean lupine proved to be highest in genistein. Swartz and Fordham have both species of lupine in tissue culture and may attempt to hybridize them.

## Leave lupine alone?

In an unusual but not unexpected twist (Anon, 1992), our lupine is only one of two food-plant species for the caterpillar of the frosted elfin butterfly (*Incisalia irus*), a butterfly officially endangered in Maryland. The only other species on which the caterpillar feeds is the wild indigo, *Baptisia tinctoria* (L.) R. Br., which shares the same sandy open habitat with the wild lupine. Perhaps our wild lupine is best left in the ornamental arena, and kept out of the pharmaceutical arena. Or utilized cautiously as a source of wild germplasm to be incorporated into the cultivated food lupines of the world, it might contribute to a breeding program with the more common lupine species, grown elsewhere as fodder crops. It could provide some cold tolerance and sand tolerance as well as the perennial habit for better-developed crop species.

The flowers are much too pretty for anyone to eat those few seeds that mature, escaping predation from seed weevils. Still, it is listed as a food plant. Calling it wild lupin, without the "e," Facciola (1990) says: "The seeds are eaten like peas after proper preparation." Calling it wild lupine or wild pea, Tanaka says: "Pods and seeds are eaten cooked." But Yanovsky (1936) failed to mention it in *Food Plants of the North American Indians*, while he did list 1,112 other North American food plants.

There are lots of dietary sources of genistein, much better tasting than lupines, and perhaps lower in alkaloids. Even though our endangered lupine could contribute genistein genes to other legumes, I think we should leave it to languish in peace, over there under the Beltsville power lines. Just looking at the flowers can lower my blood pressure. Simply walking along the power line can lower my blood pressure (except when I see the trails made by the motorbikes encroaching upon endangered species). Replacing red meat with legumes might reduce hypertension.

And now, genistein is reported to lower the blood pressure. That's the reason for all this hype about a hypotensive herb under a high-tension power line. Lupine, the lovely!

# Maples (*Acer* spp.)

*The Wild Foods Forum,* 13(2):8-9. March/April, 2002

As the sap is beginning to rise and the maple buds are swelling, so are summertime foragers eagerly anticipating the coming season. That partly explains the line in my maple song "Maple sap's arising, my spirit's risin' too." As I drafted this (Feb. 20, 2002), Peggy (Mrs. Duke) called me up from my basement computer room. She spotted the yellow bellied sapsucker drilling in our backdoor maple (not my favorite maple by any means). The sapsucker would leave and return to the freshly drilled holes periodically to consume the sap. But between trips, cardinals would sip some drips. They'd hover over the freshly drilled holes furtively sipping the exudate, then fly away, perhaps weary from the hovering. Wonder who knew first about maple sap, the birds or the humans. I'm betting on the birds.

Over a decade ago, I published other info on the maples. My *Handbook of Edible Weeds* is still available from CRC Press. In it I covered about 100 edible weeds, and yes, maple is considered a weed by some, culinary treasure by others, ornamental by others. Here's the utilitarian part of my maple entry from the CRC *Handbook of Edible Weeds* (Duke, 1992):

## Distribution

Characteristic trees of the Eastern Deciduous Forest, some species in dry forests, more in moist forests, and some in swamp forests, flowering as early as February farther south; on into June in the north or high mountains, fruits ripening in autumn. Can be a weed in woods-grown ginseng or goldenseal. WA-ME-CA-FL. Zones 3-7.

## Utility

Celebrated as the sources of maple syrups, maples have provided their seeds and inner bark as primitive food stuffs. Some people talk about the seeds as food, others as medicine, while one MD considers them toxic. So far, I have not encountered a maple seed I enjoyed – raw, boiled or fried. Facciola mentions what must have been an acquired taste: Indians cooking dewinged seeds in milk and butter. My horses stripped the inner bark off the maples in early spring, attracted by the upward flow of that dilute sugar solution we call maple sap.

At the ripe old age of 55, I tired of not having personally experienced the tapping of the maple. So before the red maple buds had swollen in February, I bored a hole into a trunk, plugged it with a hollow reed tilted to drain into a coffee can hanging off the trunk. On good days (following cold nights), the can would fill up with a sap so watery that it had no hint of sweetness. Hours of boiling reduced it to a thin, slightly sweet solution with which I could make instant coffee, pre-sweetened, by adding the powdered coffee to the "syrup." It takes a long time to boil down 40 quarts of sap to make the one quart of maple syrup. If you have a fixed campsite and permanent outdoor fire, you may find the boiling-down process practical. The sap can be concentrated by leaving it out at night, throwing off the ice (relatively pure water) the next morning, and repeating the process as long as the nights are freezing. WSSA lists only *Acer macrophyllum* Pursh (Bigleaf Maple), *A. rubrum* L. (Red Maple), and *A. saccharum* Marsh (Sugar Maple) as weedy maples. Many people consider silver maple (*A. saccharinum* L.) equally weedy. With shallow wiry surface roots, maples can be serious weeds in woods-grown ginseng, interfering seriously with cultivation.

## Caution

Dr. John Churchill, in a well documented Smithsonian lecture, reported toxic properties from some maple seeds.

Since I published that, Dan Moerman's excellent *Native American Ethnobotany* book appeared, with a lot of new info about the folk medicinal uses of the maples and I have moved some of that in the Herbal Desk Reference format, soon to be published by CRC. And I derived some "new" (for me) old information from that marvelous resource, *Medicinal and Other Uses of North American Plants* by Charlotte Erichsen-Brown (CEB). In her excellent book, one finds such picturesque bits of history, e.g.

> "Lahontan attended (with the Potawatomi) a feast consisting of four courses. The first was whitefish boiled

in water; the second the boiled tongue and breast of deer, the third two woodhens, the hind feet of a bear and the tail of a beaver; the fourth a large quantity of broth made of several sorts of meat. For drink he had maple syrup beaten up with water."

When I am writing up a plant like this, I check abstracts on the PubMed database to see what's new. Found some real strange ones this time. Beavers let their red maple "cuttings" soak for two days before eating them (Muller-Schwarze et al, 2001). Soaking apparently makes them more palatable, perhaps by leeching out those toxic saponins. Yes, there's tentative support for the toxicity. Weber and Miller (1997) hint that eating red maple leaves poisoned some zoo zebras, apparently via hemolysis as is characteristic of saponins. Stair, et al. (1993), reported earlier that horses develop severe and often fatal hemolytic anemia after ingesting dried leaves from red maple trees. They reported how two horses aborted and developed fatal hemolytic anemia after consuming wilted red maple leaves.

There's even the possibility that red maple could be used in curbing the tent caterpillar problem. Ethanolic extracts of red maple leaves reduced feeding by forest tent caterpillar larvae (*Malacosoma disstria*). Of several compounds newly reported from maple: gallic acid, methyl gallate, ethyl gallate, m-digallate, ethylm-digallate, 1-O-galloyl-beta-D-glucose, 1-O-galloyl-alpha-L-rhamnose, kaempferol 3-O-beta-D-glucoside, kaempferol 3-O-beta-D-galactoside, kaempferol 3-O-beta-L-rhamnoside, kaempferol-3-O-rhamnoglucoside, quercetin 3-O-beta-D-glucoside, quercetin 3-O-beta-L-rhamnoside and quercetin 3-O-rhamnoglucoside, (-)-epicatechin, (+)-catechin and ellagic acid) the gallates, (-)-epicatechin, and kaempferol 3-O-beta-L-rhamnoside deterred the feeding. The most effective were the digallates, deterring feeding by 90% (from the PubMed abstract of an artilce by Abou-Zaid et al., 2001).

## *Maple Syrup*

Song from *Herbalbum* © 1985 by Jim Duke

Maple sap's a rising, my spirit's rising too;
It's really tantalizing what sugar does to you.
Springtime in the maple trees, the buds are fleshing out;
I'll have some sugar if you please,
I'll tap it with my spout.

Drilled a hole into the tree, tapped it with bamboo
Busy as a honeybee, my sugar's all for you
Twenty quarts will make a pint, if boiled for thirty hours
Lots of time for peace of mind,
and plucking some wild flow'rs.

Indians knew their sugar good,
knew what they were doing,
Had squaws ascattered thru the woods,
ready for the squeezing.
So the Indian lived out in the woods to boil the syrup down;
Took all his squaws and all their goods,
when springtime rolled around.

Takes a great big iron pot, and half a cord of wood
To boil the sap an awful lot, to make the syrup good.
Watched pot never boils they say,
espec'ly when it's sweet;
So let's leave out pot today, and grab a bite to eat.

### CHORUS

Maple sap is on the rise
Catch a pretty girl by'er eyes
If she blushes, realize
That's what makes the sap to rise.

# Mountain-ash (*Sorbus americana*)

*The Wild Foods Forum* 11(3): 8-9, May/June, 2000

There are many good tasting berries, rich in anthocyanins, in the Maine North Woods, but the mountain ash is not one of them. Though it may be richest in anthocyanins, it is poorest in taste, at least to my jaded palate. I remember sampling a heavily fruiting tree not too far from Eagle Hill (near Steuben) one summer. I was glad I had a water jug nearby. Here's a case where the European mountain ash or rowan berry, *Sorbus aucuparia*, is described as edible, while the American is often described as inedible if not downright poisonous (many members of the rose family do contain cyanide). Authors of my favorite edible plant books (Facciola,1991; Moerman, 1998, and Tanaka, 1976) apparently did not have the bad experience I had. I'll try again next year too, maybe after the frost in September. Don't want to let one sour experience sour me for life. Moerman says of the American: "Fruits are processed into jams, jellies, beverages, wines and marmalades. When mellowed by frost, they become palatable and may be eaten raw." Of the European: "Fruits are processed into preserves, jellies, compotes, wine, bitters, liqueurs, perry, brandy, syrups, added to soups, etc." In Poland they flavor a Vodka known as Jarzebiak. Also used as a substitute for coffee. Leaves and flowers are used to adulterate tea.

Moerman, apparently speaking only of Amerindian food uses says that the Montagnai, Ojibwa and Quebec Algonquin, like bears, used the fruits of the American for food, but does not mention food uses for the introduced European species. Western Indian groups ate the western Mountain-ash, *Sorbus sitchensis*. Tanaka says of the American species, only: "fruit is processed into marmalade" but of the European – "Fruit is processed into preserves, jellies and compotes, also used as a substitute for coffee. It is made into a liqueur."

But in my ethnopharmacy course we stress food farmacy and folk medicines. And the mountain-ash is one of the richest sources of ANTHOCYANINS. In a review of anthocyanins, Mazza and Miniati (1993) and Takeoka et al. (1997) report 211-215 mg/100 g for black beans 2,370 mg in the seed coat or testae), 300-700 mg/100 g fresh fruit for bilberries, 80-325 for blackberries, 725-1050 in black chokeberry (*Aronia melanocarpa*) 160 in boysenberries, 250 in black currants, 7-495 for blueberries, 350-450 in cherries, 75-80 for cranberries, 300-420 in crowberries, 50-400 in hawthorn, 350 in huckleberries, 30-330 in lingonberry, 1,500 in mountain ash, 10-20 in red currants, 30 to 750 for red grapes, 20-60 in red raspberries, 25-180 in saskatoon berry (*Amelanchier alnifolia*), 140-380 in sea buckthorn, 115-256 in whortleberries, (Mazza & Miniati, 1993; Takeoaka et al, 1997) Boik (1995) notes that some anthocyanins, as anticoagulants, might prevent blood clots, even strokes. He reports also that they may protect collagen from degradation by inducing cross-linking of collagen fibers, by promoting collagen synthesis, and by preventing enzymatic cleavage of collagen. Anthocyanins inhibit collagenase. By inhibiting collagenase activity, anthocyanins may inhibit invasions by cancer cells. Boik suggests, for arthritis and capillary permeability, doses of 20 to 40 mg pure anthocyanins thrice daily, or 120 mg/day. Remember that 100 g usually calculates to about half a cup. Consult the table above to see where you can get your daily 120 mg anthocyanins, e.g. ca ½ to 1/12 cup bilberries. But for Maine's mountain ash, highest on the chart (and unfortunately inedible to me), I'll try after frost next year; matter of fact; I'm going to try to get a specimen for my **Green Farmacy Garden**. At 1,500 mg anthocyanin per 100 g fruit, that's only 1/25 of a cup for mountain ash (and for Maine and Marylands chokecherry, only about 1/20 of a cup). So frankly if you wanted to buy American, and if you blame anthocyanins for all the activities of bilberies, you might be better off with mountain-ash which tastes terrible or with black chokeberry, which tastes OK but puckery, than with the bilberries and blueberries which taste good. If I am reading the literature correctly, 120 mg anthocyanins or that fraction of a cup of these berries could help alleviate or prevent worsening of arthritis, cancer, and capillary fragility. Not just these bad tasting mountain ash berries but those pleasant tasting ones too. A half cup of a mix of these can help a lot of us, especially those who don't eat enough fruits. The longer we live the more likely we are to get arthritis, cancers and capillary fragility. So let these fruits enhance your diet, your health, and your future years (Boik, 1995; Mazza & Miniati, 1993).

Moerman lists all the American Indian uses he ever found published on *Sorbus americana*. Quite impressive. Algonquians boiled inner bark and buds for general debility and moral depression. Iroquois took the fruit as a digestive aid. Malecite took the bark tea as an analgesic after parturition and the pains of motherhood. They poulticed burned bark onto boils. They took the root tea for colic, using the plant also as an emetic. Montagnai took the bark decoction to purify the blood and stimulate the appetite. Ojibwa took the root bark for gonorrhea. Maine's Penobscot used the plant as an emetic. Quebec Algonquians used the bark of this, quite appropriately, as they used wild cherry bark, taken in tea for colds and as a tonic. Tete de Boule boiled inner bark and buds for general debility and moral depression. Tlingit used the plant for pleurisy.

And a cyanide warning re the European rowanberry! *The Wealth of India* (WOI), my 11-volume favorite ethnobotany encyclopedia, reports amygdalin (342-617 ppms) and HCN (20-37 ppms) from the frozen fruits. That suggests that these fruits might be an alternative source of laetrile. The WOI suggests that the antiscorbutic, aperient, astringent, depurative, diuretic, emmenagogie fruits are useful in hemorrhoids and strangury. The extract is used for dyspepsia and irritations of the gall-bladder. Europeans use their mountain-ash like we use our mountain-ash (and wild cherry), the laxative leaf tea as a pectoral in bronchitis and cough. The bark tea might be used like that of wild cherry, imparting that rich benzaldehyde taste (due to the amygdalin and cyanide) to your cough syrups. Tannins in the bark tea make [[them]] useful in diarrhea.

The tannins might be as good at antiviral activity as the overhyped $42-a pop- relenza, but I'd bet even more on elderberries than on rowanberries.

Anyone can go to my database and find some of the many activities attributed to the anthocyanins. For ophthalmologic problems a larger dose is indicated (600 mg anthocyanins a day for myopia and nyctalopia). But a half cup of mountain-ash berries could provide that too.

# Mud Plantain (*Alisma plantago, A. plantago-aquatica, A. subcordata*)

*The Business of Herbs* 9(5):10-11, November/December, 1991

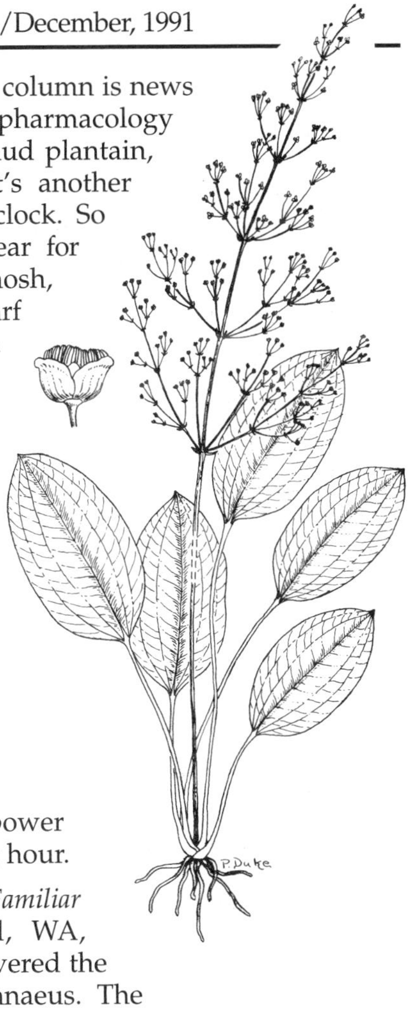

Often the trigger for an Herb a Day column is news breaking on the chemistry, medicine or pharmacology of an herb. But I write today on the mud plantain, *Alisma* spp., for a different reason. It's another white flower I can add to my floral clock. So what? This year was an incredible year for white flowers: blackberries, black cohosh, black locusts, bloodroot, dogwoods, dwarf ginseng (first year I ever saw more than a million in one stand), mayapples, multiflora roses, raspberries, star-of-bethlehem, wineberries – to name just a few.

It was an incredibly floriferous spring, with green and white lining the highways. Brighter colors followed in time, and they too seemed to outdo themselves this year.

## Spring of '91:

Probably never be outdone!
White flowers made their run,
Smiled their hour in the sun.
Somehow white flowers' dour power
Rewound the watcher's waning hour.

Browsing J. T. Fraser's Time, *The Familiar Stranger* (Microsoft Press, Redmond, WA, 1987), I was delighted to see that he covered the floral clock (*Horologium Florae*) of Linnaeus. The Father of Taxonomic Botany, Linnaeus, was also called Karl von Linne, the name, abbreviation (Linn.) or initial (L.) that follows more scientific names of plants than any other.

Floral clocks are nothing more than collections of plants whose flowers tend to open and/or close at certain hours of the day. Linnaeus told us the white water lily opened between 6:00 and 7:00 A.M. My mud plantain in July opened between 8:00 and 9:00, a little bit later than my white (and blue and pink) chicories. My star-of-bethlehems opened closer to 11:00, as implied by its French name, La dame d'onze heures, I translate to "'leven o'clock lady." I didn't plant any white four-o-clocks this year, but they are quite punctual. My white-flowered *Datura meteloides* opens its aromatic throat toward the sky closer to 7:00 to 8:00 P.M., attracting the huge hovering hawkmoths shortly thereafter.

For nearly the tenth year in a row, my yellow, large-flowered evening primrose started its floral display by Father's Day, providing my sedate fireworks on July 4. Evening primrose is the most punctual and charismatic of my floral clock flowers, opening almost explosively at 8:40 P.M., plus or minus 10 minutes, in early July. There are some colorful timepieces, like hawk's-beard, hawkbit, scarlet pimpernel, salsify, spiderwort, morning glory, moonflower, day lily (and there are nocturnal day lilies as there are night-flowering relatives of the morning glories), dayflower, etc. Like my evening primrose, many of these more punctual flowers last only one night, to be replaced by a new one or two the next night. I won't bore you with the complete list of floral clock candidates, but I will save some primrose and *Datura* seed, to exchange with you for seed of any punctual openers you might have that I haven't already obtained for my floral garden.

The mud plantain has small flowers, but I am pleased to add it to the floral clock list. It will also turn up in other lists: of poisonous, medicinal and edible plants. As so often happens, the scientific names of the mud plantain are confused and confusing. Under the names *Alisma plantago, A. plantago-aquatica* or even *A. subcordata*, one reads that the roots of mud plantain are edible, though the uppermost portion may be poisonous. Some books even refer to the plant as an ornamental. Under *A. plantago*, Uphof states that the base of the plant is considered poisonous; when properly prepared it becomes harmless – used as food by the Kalmucks. *The Wealth of India* says merely that the rhizome of *A. plantago* L. is said to be edible. Steinmetz says the roots are eaten as a vegetable in Russia.

The Pakistani *Encyclopedia of Planta Medica* attributes experimental antihepatonic (liver protective), diuretic (stimulating urination), hepatonic (stimulating the liver), hypocholesterolemic (lowering cholesterol), hypoglycemic (lowering blood sugar), lipotropic (burning fat) and natriuretic (increasing the sodium excreted in the urine) activities to *Alisma plantago*. All those big words suggest that "Big Jim Duke" might be better off eating mud plantain than barbecued pig.

Hsu et al. inform us that the Chinese name, Tse-hsieh, means "a flood unleashed from a marsh," in allusion to its rapid diuretic activity. Rats fed 5% powdered *Alisma* did not develop fatty livers and had lower cholesterol levels. In test tubes, *Alisma* inhibits the bacteria that cause tuberculosis, and it is said to lower the blood pressure.

Once highly regarded for dog bite and rabies in Europe, and for snakebite in the U.S., *A. plantago* seems to have fallen out of favor, at least in Occidental medicine. Paradoxically, the Chinese believe that the plant stimulates the female genitalia and promotes conception, while believing that the seed promotes sterility. So far, that information seems to have eluded many of our Herbals for Females. Also reportedly antiscorbutic (scurvy preventing), astringent and sudorific (stimulating sweat), the herb has been suggested for cystitis, dysentery, epilepsy, gravel and kidney stones, some of which might be helped by the proven diuretic activity.

While I don't recommend mud plantain as medicine or food, I see no harm in adding it to the wetter end of your floral clock. There are water lilies for several hours of the day. Floral clock layouts I have seen to date all seem to be circular or semicircular. Adrienne Mayor provided some excellent info on, and layouts for, clock gardens in Number 36 of *The Herb Quarterly*. Lazy, I think it's time to go digital, with a linear layout from dawn to dusk (5:00 A.M. to 9:00 P.M., roughly, at **Herbal Vineyard** in July).

**2006** – and my beautiful circular clock, delightfully encircled by anise hyssops laden with circling swallowtails, is pretty but not punctual. My store bought seeded four-o'clock was three hours late last year. I recommend you have your major clock flower in pots, and once they have made up their individual ornery psyches as to their opening hours, move it where it belongs.

# Osage Orange (*Maclura pomifera*)

(Unpublished)

It's been more than 50 years since I bowled those sticky, round, milky, green fruits down on Mordecai Drive, in Raleigh, North Carolina, where I spent many of my formative years. We thought of them more as green cannon balls or bowling balls than monkey oranges. I never did get bold enough to try eating one, even after I learned it was close kin to mulberry and fig, both of which I ate then and now.

On jury duty at the county seat one day 40 years later, I took long walks at lunch, and couldn't help rolling those osage oranges down the hilly streets of Ellicott City, Maryland. Nostalgia set in. I never really did grow up: still enjoy my walks in the woods and knowing how to live off the land. And I like contemplating natural pesticides and medicines, instead of those synthetic poisons being created by the huge corporations, hurting our ecology and economy, as they try to stay in the black at the expense of our green. That's why I was so interested in the Italian lady's comment, that she was using those crazy fruits to keep cockroaches out of her house. She was on the jury with me, and shared my interest in things natural.

Then more than 10 years later, after I retired, my ex-boss at the USDA was all excited, having heard the same story about the osage orange, that it could repel cockroaches. I never got really thrilled about the insectifugal (insect-repellent) properties of this plant, though it is reportedly a cockroach repellent, like bay leaves. Do they really repel cockroaches? If they do, they should be worth a lot to us, while harmful to the pesticide companies.

When my new boss asked about it, I checked my database at USDA via the Internet (URL address: http://www.ars-grin.gov/duke) to see just which pesticidal compounds it contains. Nothing there. I hadn't yet entered the data on the osage orange.

But I'm a compulsive compiler. So I went through my massive libraries at home and in the office and entered the data. There was one particularly rich source of data. [[Smith, J.L. and J.V. Perino. 1981. "Osage Orange (*Maclura pomifera*): History and Economic Uses." *Economic Botany* 35(1): 24-41.]] Yes, osage orange contains several pesticidal compounds. Perhaps that's why osage orange is one of the healthiest tree species in North America "despite the variety of diseases and pests which can live on the tree." Alvaxanthone and macluraxanthone from the root bark are reportedly highly toxic to goldfish and mosquito larvae.

Following my encounter with the Italian on jury duty, I mentioned the idea to Martin Jacobson, who was in charge of the USDA's natural pesticide program back then. A personal communication from Martin Jacobson, retired chief of USDA Natural Products Laboratory, to the Italian says that the fruit extract is reported to repel bark beetles, dry-wood termites, and Japanese beetles. The wood also repels termites. These pigments probably serve at protecting the roots from decay and pests, like the antifungal compounds found in the wood. According to

*The Wealth of India*, a heat-stable, non-toxic antibiotic, suitable for use as a food preservative, has been extracted from the heartwood and root.

## Cockroach repellent?

While some authors blame the cockroach repellency on aromatic phytochemicals, Dr. David Brunner, Missouri Botanical Garden, suggests that the rubbery latex "gums up the mouthparts of any insect that sticks its beak in there. It's like getting a mouthful of rubber cement." Ann Raver (*New York Times*, Nov. 27, 1994) says she rid her home of cockroaches simply by placing whole osage oranges strategically around her apartment. That beats what I used to do with them as a boy down in Raleigh. We used to have bowling games in the middle of Mordecai Drive, using those bowling green osage oranges.

Although the fruits are sticky and unappealing, most people say they are toxic – with little evidence to support this. Still, Pullar (1939) reported the fruits toxic to sheep. Deaths of cattle and horses blamed on osage orange may be due more to choking than toxicity. Walter Lewis and his wife Memory Elvin Lewis mention that it is suspected of causing livestock loss in Arkansas and Texas, suggesting that it is a poisonous plant. Sensitive to pollen himself, Lewis also mentions it as an aero-allergen, causing allergic rhinitis, bronchial asthma, and/or hypersensitivity pneumonitis.

If the fruits are edible at all, the seeds should be removed; they contain hemagglutinating lectins that are direct hemagglutinins to erythrocytes of various mammals. Since the hemagglutinins are concentrated in the epicotyl, they may serve as a defensive mechanism against predators (Smith and Perino, 1981).

## Mulberry relative

The plant belongs to the mulberry family, and is close enough kin that the leaves can be used to rear the mulberry silkworms. You may have heard the story about the CIA, or some spooky agency, planning to use the trifoliate orange (truly a citrus, *Poncirus trifoliata*) as an impenetrable thorny hedge. The osage orange might be viewed as another slow-growing, impenetrable hedge plant, at least those that are thorny. It was recommended as a hedge to President Thomas Jefferson when hedges were supposed to be "horse-high, bull-strong, and pig-tight." Additionally, a kilometer of old hedges grown into trees can supply 2,500 posts, but it takes 15 to 20 years to grow back to post size. With a decay-resistant, antifungal compound and its great strength, the wood makes the finest railroad ties (Smith and Perino).

Great Plains Indians had bows and clubs made of the strong wood of the osage orange. A Scottish traveler there in 1810 reported that the price for one of the bows was a horse and a blanket.

## Commercial possibilities

I find it exciting that the fruits are higher in pectin (40%) than any other fruit in my USDA database. Could this pectin be worth harvesting, extracting in the process the pesticidal compounds as natural pesticides, proteolytic enzymes from the fruit, and lectins from the seed? I'll predict that an integrated operation could make good use of this hardy tree, capable of growing on land-reclamation projects. Matter of fact, it has weedy tendencies.

The fruits have antioxidant properties, reportedly useful to prevent spoilage in the food industry. *The Wealth of India* tells us that there are four antioxidant isoflavone pigments. Pomiferin is one antioxidant, but there are many more listed in the phytochemical database.

The rather repulsive sticky resin in the fruits may be suitable for adhesives and paints. Water extracts of the root have been used in dyeing and tanning. The wood contains 9-10% tannin. It also contains the same yellow dyes, maclurin and morin, found in fustic (*Chlorophora tinctoria*). A proteolytic enzyme, macin (and maybe another disain), might also be economically viable. *The Wealth of India* says that macin may be used for tenderizing meat and sausage casings. The proteolytic enzyme, ficin, from closely related figs, and bromelain, from pineapples, are figuring more and more in medicine, moving from folk medicine to food pharmacy. Some proteolytic enzymes, like bromelain from pineapple, papain from papaya, and zingibain from ginger, are used in bating skin for leather, chill-proofing beer, making cheese, medicine, shrink-proofing wool, and tenderizing meat. Calculations are that a small fruit (175 g) contains enough enzyme to coagulate 1,000 liters of milk in 30 minutes at 37°C. "These high amounts of enzyme may be large enough to warrant commercial exploitation of osage orange if the market for proteolytic enzymes continues to grow."

According to *The Wealth of India*, the fruit extract is used as a cardiac stimulant. That's more than we find in most American literature about medicinal uses of this multi-purpose tree. But there's not much folklore medicinally about the plant.

# Passionflower (*Passiflora incarnata*)

*The Business of Herbs* 8(2):6-7. May/June, 1990

Even down in the Carolinas, where I took my Ph.D. in Botany (1961), the passion-flower, the so-called maypop, *Passiflora incarnata*, rarely starts flowering as early as May. Once it does start, it will flower and fruit sporadically right up to frost. Nor is the mayapple, *Podophyllum peltatum*, ripe in May, although it may flower in May. Strange, but the unrelated mayapple and maypop have edible fruits with equally indescribable, yet similar, aromas.

Very similar to the maypop is the rarer species, *P. morifolia* (including *P. warmingii*) whose fruits are less than 1½ inches long (those of *P. incarnata* are longer than 1½ inches). These plants have toothed leaflets in contrast with another Carolina species, *P. lutea*, which has toothless leaflets and smaller, purplish fruits that are almost globe-shaped.

*Passiflora* is a large, mostly tropical, American genus, with increasing species diversity toward the equator. The *Flora of Maryland* (Brown and Brown) includes only *P. incarnata* and *P. lutea*, while South Carolina (Radford, Ahles and Bell) adds *P. morifolia*, and Florida (Small) adds four more species:

Leaflets toothless; petals absent; fruits 1-1/2 to 2 inches long, on bracteate stalk; leaf stalks with paired glands ... *P. pallens*

Petals greenish-white; hairy fruit; leaf stalks without paired glands ........................................... *P. sexflora*

Leaflets toothless; petals absent; older stems winged; fruits small, purplish black; leaf stalks with paired glands ........ *P. pallida* or *suberosa*

Leaflets entire; petals white; young stems velvety; older stems winged; leaf stalk with paired glands .......... *P. multiflora*

## Diversity vs. Latitude

South Maryland has two species, South Carolina, three, Florida, six native species, while, reflecting tropical diversity, Latin America has hundreds of species, many with handsome flowers and/or edible fruits. Consequently, many are introduced outside their native range as cultivated plants, sometimes becoming quite weedy. Frost will, of course, kill many of the tropical introductions. Other transplants have failed due to nematodes or a combination of nematodes and fungus, especially *Fusarium*.

## Sedative Properties

*Passiflora incarnata* seems to be the most important medicinal species, and as such it may be adulterated (with *P. coerulea* or *P. edulis* according to *Hager's Handbook*). Aware of such adulterations, Europeans (who buy more of this American species than we Americans do) have been working out methods for detecting adulteration. Lohdefink and Kating (1974) suggest that harman (alias aribin, loturin, methylcarboline or passiflorin) may be the active ingredient. Controversially, of the seven species they tested, they state that none contains harmine, harmaline, harmole, or harmalole, all of which are reported by other authors, as summarized by Leung's *Encyclopedia of Common Natural Ingredients* and as illustrated in "Father Nature's Farmacy." Varro Tyler says, "The plant does contain one or more so-called harmala alkaloids, but their number and identity are disputed. Besides, such alkaloids generally act as stimulants, not depressants." Tyler is referring to the use of the extract as a sedative by Europeans. One Romanian chewing gum containing *Passiflora*, for instance, is patented as a sedative. Following Polish reports of sedative effects of the alkaloid fraction, Japanese scientists found maltol in the alkaloid fraction. The maltol induced depression in mice and had sedative effects, but not enough to explain the total sedative effects of the extract. It looks like synergy is raising her head again.

# Pitcher Plant (*Sarracenia purpurea*)

*The Wild Foods Forum*, 13(3): 8-9, July/August, 2002

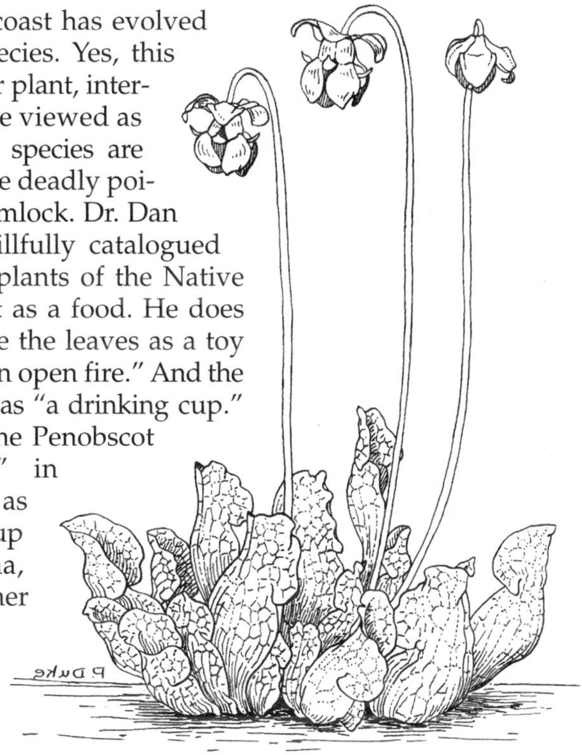

Strange how the east coast has evolved so many insectivorous species. Yes, this one eats insects. But pitcher plant, interesting as it is, should not be viewed as an edible plant, as some species are reported to contain the same deadly poison as occurs in poison hemlock. Dr. Dan Moerman who has so skillfully catalogued the edible and medicinal plants of the Native Americans, does not list it as a food. He does note that Cree children use the leaves as a toy kettle "to cook meat over an open fire." And the Potawatomi use the leaves as "a drinking cup." Shall we call it the "pristine Penobscot or Potawatomi pitcher" in Maine – I think of it more as an insectivorous dixie cup when down in Carolina, where I first met the pitcher plant more than 50 years ago.

Way down east in Washington County Maine, at the Humboldt Field Research Institute, Eagle Hill, Steuben, we have sundew and pitcher plant. We don't have the venus fly trap which is restricted to the Carolinas where I took my botany training. But at Eagle Hill, back in 2000, I did my first Maine CEU "Medical Botany for Pharmacists and the Medical Community." An early version of the syllabus is already online at my USDA database (http://www.ars-grin.gov/duke/). We annually refer to that syllabus in the leisure and tranquility and greenery of the "North Woods," right on the coast of Maine, as far east as you can go in the United States.

Pitcher plants, even more so than sundews, seem to be restricted to peat bogs, and we have many of them in Maine. Be prepared to get wet as we wander with wonder from dry land with such medicinal species as arbutus, bearberry, evening primrose, sarsaparilla, and St. Johnswort to the bog with its strange insectivores, often intertwined with cranberry, another great food and medicinal species.

The pitcher plant is more a curio than a hard core medicinal species, but it has a lot of justified folklore behind it. An essential reference is my cherished *Native American Ethnobotany* (Moerman, 1998). Dr. Moerman goes through tribe after tribe, describing Native American uses of this

American medicinal plant. My USDA phyochemical database shows some chemical rationale behind many of these uses. Iroquois reportedly took the plant to alleviate thirst (strange doctrine of signatures, as the pitcher often holds stagnant water, even breeding mosquitoes while "eating" other insects. They use the leaves in remedies for recurring chills followed by fever, as well as shakiness. Roots are used for liver ailments. A cold decoction is taken for whooping cough and the plant is used for pneumonia. And out of my paradigm, they use the plant as a love and a lacrosse medicine, perhaps also a doctrine of signatures influence. Maine's Malecite may still use the plant for tuberculosis, formerly called consumption (I would add some of Maine's goldthread for its antituberculic berberine). Menominee, also out of my paradigm, use it in sorcery. Maine's Micmac use the plant similarly for spitting of blood. They also use it for nephrosis. Roots used for smallpox, sore throat and tuberculosis. Montagnai use it also for smallpox. Ojibwa use the plant in parturition. Maine's Penobscot use pitcher plant tea for hematoptysis and nephrosis. Potawatomi use it in a squaw remedy (often suggesting menstrual or parturitional difficulties). Quebec Algonquin use a decoction of the root tops for urinary problems and the leaf infusion to facilitate childbirth. Tete de Boule Algonquin use the roots as a diuretic, mixed with beaver kidneys for urinary tract disorders. *Sarracenia flava* strangely may contain the hemlock poison, coniine. I think the *Herbal PDR* may have erred when it said that purple pitcher plant contained coniine. The NAPRALERT database and *Potter's New Cyclopedia* specify that coniine occurs in *Sarracenia flava*, not *S. purpurea* (HDR).

# Pokeweed (*Phytolacca americana*)

*The Business of Herbs* 8(6):10-11. January/February, 1991

## Pokesalad

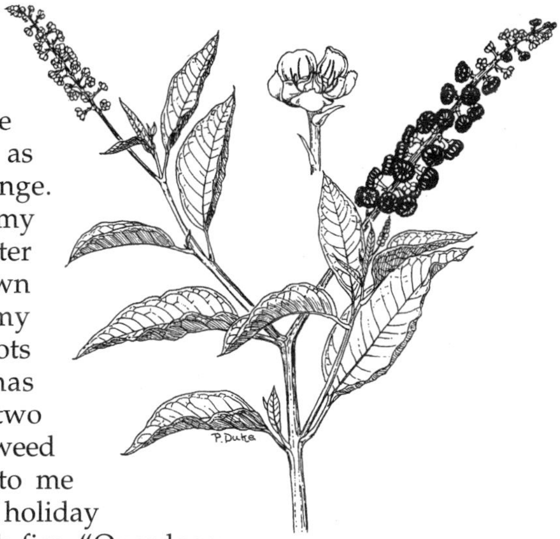

In Appalachia the local gentry tend to think of pokesalad or pokeweed (*Phytolacca americana*) more as food or medicine than as pesticide. That may change. Still, pokesalad is one of my favorite potherbs. Dug after frost in fall, the roots, thrown into a dark corner of my greenhouse, send up shoots in time for the Christmas holidays. Boiled through two changes of water, the pokeweed is much more appealing to me than some of the other holiday fare. But I am playing with fire: "Overdoses have sometimes been fatal. Because poke is mitogenic, handlers should wear gloves. The proteinaceous mitogen PWM may produce blood cell abnormalities when absorbed... Hardin and Arena recall attending to a five-year-old girl who died from ingesting poke berries, crushed and added to water to simulate grape juice" (Duke, 1985, playing it safe, conservative and CYA).

Some Appalachians take a few seeds a day for arthritis. I imagine the AMA would frown more on this than on the NSAIDs (nonsteroidal anti-inflammatory drugs) some doctors recommend for arthritis. NSAIDs cost several thousand American lives a year, largely due to bleeding ulcers. The Appalachian practice may hark back to the Cherokee usage of the berries or the berry wine for rheumatism reported by Moerman (1986). I can't recommend this, either. A cousin of mine once painted her body with pokeberry juice for Halloween. She called desperately a few minutes later. **Recommendation:** Don't do it! Bathe immediately if you do! You see, pokeberries contain mitogens which can upset your cellular physiology. I cannot endorse pokeberry, externally or internally, as a medicine. Still I'll nibble on pokeweed raisins, hoping to stave off worsening arthritis as I age.

Indians were not bashful about using it. Cherokee poulticed it for fevers, nerves, sores, swellings and ulcers and took the root infusion "to build the blood" and for eczema and kidney ailments. Delaware Indians used it for rheumatism, but differently. They used a strong root or twig infusion in herbal steam for rheumatism. Iroquois took a decoction of the stems for chest colds, using the root in salves for bruises and bunions and in infusion for liver ailments. They also used the plant as a cathartic, emetic, expectorant and in witchcraft and love charms. Mahuna, recognizing the plant as poisonous, still used the roots for neuralgic pains and the leaves for skin diseases. Micmac used the leaves for bleeding wounds; Mohegans applied crushed berries to sore breasts; Pamunkey took berry tea for rheumatism; and Rappahannock used the plant for dysentery, piles, poison ivy, rheumatism and warts.

**Antirheumatic**

Note that many of the tribes used poke for rheumatism. Modern medicine still prescribes steroids for rheumatism. The FDA notes that pokeweed "contains an acidic steroid saponin."

**Antiviral**

The Pokeweed Antiviral Proteins (PAP) are being studied as anticancer and anti-AIDS agents (Bonness, 1990). These ribosome-inactivating proteins, popularly called RIPs (two from the leaves, one from the seed), "are potent toxins that kill most cells they are allowed to enter (bacterial cells excluded)." Thus they can kill the bad cells and the good cells. In a complex shearing of the ribosome, indispensable to the cell for manufacturing protein, the RIP prevents the cell from further protein synthesis. "Once the ribosomes are damaged, protein synthesis stops, and the cell dies...A number of one-subunit RIPs (such as trichosanthin and pokeweed antiviral protein) have the uncanny ability to selectively act upon virally infected cells...These RIPs are selectively taken in by virus-infected cells." Translated, that means the RIP aims for the AIDS-infected cell. For more than a decade, NIH has been investigating immunotoxins, toxic proteins like RIPs linked to antibodies, targeting them for carcinomas, leukemias and lymphomas, so that the poison is aimed specifically at the cancer.

So, there's a small chance, at least, that the RIPs from pokeweed can help in the war against AIDS. Bonness (1990) recounts another novel approach, playing upon the Human Immunodeficiency Virus (HIV) affinity for a special molecule, CD4, produced on the surface of healthy cells. The RIP (usually castor bean's ricin rather than pokeweed's PAP) is attached to the CD4 molecule which still attracts HIV-infected cells, which bind to it (with fatal results to the infected cell) instead of the healthy cell.

A molluscicide, too. In a very childish but fun experiment, I proved to myself that pokeweed juice repelled mollusks, even if it didn't kill them. Slugs often feed on the dog food in Shemo's (my dog) platter. I added a shallow film of water to one platter, a shallow film of water with pokeberry juice to another, then added slugs. The slugs were much quicker getting out of the poke water than the pure water. That's not really very scientific. Had I measured the quantity of pokeberry juice and the time it took the slugs to get out, I could have used big words like "relative evacuation time" (R.E.T.) and said that R.E.T. was 50% faster with 50% pokeberry juice, indicating molluscifugal (mollusk-repellent) activity.

The USDA once wanted seeds of an Ethiopian species, *Phytolacca dodecandra*, the endod, which shows great promise as a molluscicide. Heretofore, molluscicidal activity was of greater interest to tropical countries suffering schistosomiasis, transmitted by an aquatic snail. In Adwa, Ethiopia, the incidence of schistosomiasis in one- to five-year-old children dropped from 50% to 7% in five years when crushed endod berries were added to the river water (Adams et al., 1989). Further the endod produces a RIP called dodecandrin, which might also be investigated for medicinal applications, e.g., in AIDS and cancer.

In the U.S. a recently introduced mollusk now clogs filters in American water works, so there is a monied interest in a good molluscicide. The zebra mussel, *Dreissena polymorpha*, introduced less than a decade ago, has fouled water intake pipes at municipal and industrial plants, disrupted municipal water supplies and altered the ecosystem in Lake Erie. For example, biologists at the Detroit Edison plant on western Lake Erie counted 200 zebra mussels per square meter on the intake screen. A year later there were 700,000. Schools were closed in Monroe when a combination of zebra mussels and ice completely shut off water flow. (Roberts, 1990).

Also fungicidal, larvicidal and spermicidal, the endod might contain the answer to the zebra mussel. Unfortunately, a preliminary survey of several species of *Phytolacca* showed that our *P. americana* lacks the all-important lemmatoxin and molluscicidal saponins found in *P. dodecandra* (Parkhurst, 1974). Who'd have thought pokeweed could provide food and kill viruses and even mollusks, maybe even unplugging the water filters around Lake Erie?

# Prickly Ash (*Zanthoxylum clava-herculis*), (*Aralia spinosa*)

(Unpublished)

## Toothache Tree or Toothache Tree

The last time I saw "herbist" Tommie Bass (Dec. 19, 1994) he had some toothache bark and yellowroot on sale out front of his humbly herbal home. We talked long and lively but I failed to quiz him on which toothache bark he had there. (See Photo of Historian and Folklorist Jim Brown with some of that toothache bark.) How embarassing; I may never know which is in the picture. I'm pretty sure it is *Aralia*. There are three major species in the eastern U.S. herbal world, all sharing the common names devil's walking stick, hercules club, prickly ash, and toothache tree.

I have them growing side by side in the **Green Pharmacy Garden**, *Aralia* (ginseng family) alongside the unrelated *Zanthoxylum* (citrus family). And Crellin and Philpott have them grouped side by side in their useful book recounting Tommie's herbal lore. But the strongest clue is in their first paragraph, partially quoted here:

> "Prickly ash is just a shrub with thorns from the ground up. It has white blooms and purple berries." That would make it the *Aralia*, of which, Tommie says, "We have mostly...*Aralia spinosa*" around here. The *Aralia* stem bark is chewed or the berries taken in tea for toothache. It is also used in eardrops for earache. He also recommends it in rheumatism."

Regrettably, Crellin and Philpot, not Tommie, mix the species in their commentary, assigning the citrus relative *Zantho-xylum*, to the Araliaceae (Ginseng Family), and assigning the ginseng relative *Aralia*, to the Citrus Family Rutaceae. Fortunately they retain the scientific name *Aralia* as they recount medicinal lore. I'm convinced that *Aralia* is what Tommie used most, if not exclusively. They mention that the Indians used the *Aralia* bark decoction for persistent coughs and dropsy. They also mention adding the berries to wine for rheumatism.

Photograph by Dr. Bob Stiles December 19, 1994

Jim Brown – Alabama Historian; Tommie Bass – Alabama Herbist; Jim Duke – Alabama Botanist

Historically, before Tommie, interest in *Aralia* waned and *Zanthoxylum*, the citrus relative, assumed relatively more importance. But frankly, I suspect that we cannot prove with which species the accounts and accountants were dealing. I suppose I could harvest samples of the barks of both and learn how to distinguish them, maybe even prove that the pictured toothache bark is *Aralia*. But it would take some hard core research. Few of us can distinguish powdered bark samples, even though both will curb the toothache. And there are no herbarium specimens, to my knowledge, to back up any of the studies I have reviewed.

Though I don't think Tommie was dealing with *Zanthoxylum*, I"ll recite a few tidbits of what Crellin and Philpot related re *Zanthoxylum*, the other toothache bark. Much the same. For rheumatism, syphilis, toothache; diaphoretic and stimulant. They even cited sialogogue (causing salivation or slobbering) activity, reminiscent of jaborandi in the same citrus family. (Wonder if it also helps with glaucoma like sialogogue pilocarpine). They mention a survey back in 1912 where 2,565 physicians reported using *Zanthoxylum*, only 725 using *Aralia*. I suspect there are fewer than a handful of allopaths using either today. Neither are major in the herbalists' pharmacopoeias.

It's easy to tell the *Aralia* toothache tree, with its huge trebly compound leaves, from the simply compound *Zanthoxylums*. To the amateur the trees themselves may be difficult to distinguish. To those not taxonomically challenged, they may be keyed as follows:

a. Leaves doubly or trebly compound ............ *Aralia spinosa*
a. Leaves simply compound
    b. Leaflets glabrous beneath, flowers in large terminal clusters ....................................... *Z. clava-herculis*
    b. Leaflets pubescent beneath, flowers in small axillary clusters ....................................... *Z. americana*

Once upon a time, long, long ago, I received a northern prickly ash (*Zanthoxylum*) from Michigan, and southern prickly ash from Texas. One American species is being used for sickle-cell anemia, but I doubt the users know for sure which species they have. One flowers after the leaves, suggesting it is *clavaherculis*. Mine mostly have 10 or 12 lateral leaflets, on leaf stalks up to 3 mm long, glabrous, with an eccentric midvein. That tells me, if my books are correct, that my big one is *clava-herculis*, my little one *americana*. I'll provide samples of both to anyone capable of analyzing them for antisickling activity.

## Edibility

Before the spines harden, orientals cook (even here in the U.S.) expanding *Aralia* leaves, serving vinegar. I tried cooking our young leaves and cannot recommend it. The 10 leaflets and 2 spines I consumed were too much like turpentine in flavor, more medicinal than edible. The pot liquor remaining was much more pleasing than the potherb.

## Medicinal

*Aralia*, the "overgrown relative of ginseng," was used by the Cherokee: the root bark pounded, as a carminative, diaphoretic, emetic and tonic, for colic, paralysis, rheumatism, toothache and VD. Chippewa gargled the decoction for sore throat; Creek use the root for internal bleeding. Delaware a/o Onondaga used bark and or root decoction to purify the blood. Rappahannock poulticed febrifugal roots on boils, and washed sores with tea.

## Natural History

Joining my pigeons, songbirds, sparrows, thrushes, chipmunks, foxes and skunks, I have eaten the berries, with no pleasure, spitting out rather than chewing the reputedly poisonous seed. Robins frequently nest in the *Aralia* by the gazebo in the **Green Farmacy Garden**, perhaps protected by the spiny trunk. When in flower, there's a constant huge of many varieties of insects in the huge inflorescences. Reportedly, the bark and roots of the *Aralia* may cause dermatitis.

Any spine can have bacteria on it. I would be amazed if all spines did not have copious bacteria on them as do the leaves. But very few species, *Aralia* not among them, actually inject poisons into us botanists. I'm not sure of any tree thorns injecting anything. Hairs of nettle do inject neurotransmitters. Still we hear frightening stories about some of the tropical spiny trees. And puncture wounds in a humid environment often become infected, sometimes seriously.

I once got hyper about *Zamthoxylum clava-herculis* as another example of synergy (data provided by Saqib et al. (1990). From 800 grams of dried berries (from 3,000 g fresh berries) they got 18 g of semisolid residue (F001) and 8 g of a methanolic residue (F005) both of which were biologically active against brine shrimp. F005 was cytotoxic to breast, colon and lung cancer lines. One mixture of cnidilin, imperatorin, isoimperatorin, psoralen and xanthotoxin, was lethal to brine shrimp with an LC50 of only 4.25 ppm. Even the strongest of the five furanocoumarins, psoralen and xanthotoxin, were less active pure, with LC50's of 5.93 and 7.92 respectively. That means it took less of the mixture than it did of individual pure compounds to kill the shrimp, meaning that (1) there was synergy or (2) there were unidentified compounds that were more active than those studied or (3) both (1) and (2) were true. In either interpretation, the whole was more active than the expected sum of its parts.

Extracts of *Z. clava-herculis* and isolated chelerythrine exhibited activity against MRSA (methycillin-resistant *Staphylococcus aureus* [X12672160]). There have been two PubMed articles on an African *Zanthoxylum* (alias *Fagara*) and sickle cell and certainly the African varieties have shown clinical improvement. Following up on that, a local clinical herbalist tried our prickly ash with equally good result. Here's our exchange early in 2006.

"DOC: Any news on prickly ash and sickle cell; I'm updating

> my account on *Zanthoxylum*. I'd like to quote you if you don't mind. Peggy and I took all our kids and grandkids to the Amazon over New Years Eve 2005/6. All my genes in one big pool. Broke my economic bank but enriched our memory banks. . . jim
>
> Hi Jim: Nothing new on sickle cell – still have several patients taking it faithfully for almost a decade and swearing it works super. But, as you know, without dollars, useful folk remedies just get ignored, and no doctors will listen to the poor folk who swear that it works. . . DOC"

Reading between the lines in news reports, one sees that the pharmacophiles are trying to manipulate natural compounds so they can patent it and homophobically make some money, not cure the patient. Zhang et al. (2004) note that vanillin binds with sickle haemoglobin (Hb S) and inhibits cell sickling, potentially benefitting patients with sickle cell disease (SCD). But the widely distributed phytochemical, vanillin, has little or no antisickling effects given orally, rapidly decomposing in the upper digestive tract. So they seek a pro-drug, which is biotransformed to vanillin in vivo. At doses as low as 7 mg/kg (ipr mus) the drug increased survival time (X15180869). The authors say they synthesized the prodrug which converts to vanillin in vivo but did not name it. As far as I know they are keeping the name of their prodrug secret. But there are many natural compounds which are pro-drugs for vanillin, e.g. ferulic acid (X15180869). Perhaps the following from an African species or related compounds in Amazonian or North American species, could serve more cheaply as prodrugs – 3,4-O-divanilloylquinic acid, 3,5-O-divanilloylquinic acid and 4,5-O-divanilloylquinic acid (burkinabins A-C) (X15110696).

Come to the **Green Farmacy Garden** and compare these very different genera, *Aralia* and *Zanthoxylum*, that have often been confused in the literature and quite possibly in practice. Either can help with toothache. As to being sure of the two species of *Zanthoxylum*, I have not yet arrived.

## Phytotherapy Research – 2003 Mar; 17(3): 274-5:

"Activity of *Zanthoxylum clava-herculis* extracts against multi-drug resistant methicillin-resistant *Staphylococcus aureus*" (mdr-MRSA). Gibbons S, Leimkugel J, Oluwatuyi M, Heinrich M. Centre for Pharmacognosy and Phytotherapy, The School of Pharmacy, University of London, London, UK. simon.gibbons @ulsop.ac.uk. In a continuing search for compounds with antibiotic activity against methicillin-resistant *Staphylococcus aureus* (MRSA), possessing multidrug of flux systems, we have demonstrated activity associated with extracts from Southern prickly ash bark, *Zanthoxylum clava-herculis*. Bioassay-guided isolation of an alkaloid extract led to the characterization of the benzocphenanthridine alkaloid chelerythrine as the major active principle. This compound exhibited potent activity against strains of MRSA, which were highly resistant to clinically useful antibiotics via multidrug ef flux mechanisms (X12672160).

*Am J Vet Res*. 1996 Aug; 57(8): 1239-44: "Neuromuscular effects of toxins isolated from southern prickly ash (*Zanthoxylum clava-herculis*) bark." Bowen J.M., Cole R.J., Bedell D, Schabdach D. Department of Physiology and Pharmacology, College of Veterinary Medicine, University of Georgia, Athens 30602, USA.

## Objective

To define the nature and mechanisms of neuromuscular effects of toxic principles in bark of southern prickly ash tree (*Zanthoxylum clava-herculis*) that might contribute to its clinical toxicity in cattle.

## Animals

31 rats, 1 dog, and 4 rabbits.

## Procedures

Extracts were prepared from bark samples, using 2 extraction methods. Contractile responses, resting potentials, miniature end-plate potentials (MEPP), and end-plate potentials of rat phrenic nerve-hemidiaphragm preparations were recorded. Blood pressure and contractile responses of the cranial tibial muscle to nerve stimulation were recorded in an anesthetized dog. Topical anesthetic activity in rabbits was determined by evaluation of the corneal reflex.

## Results

One extract usually stimulated muscle contractile response, whereas the other inhibited this response when evoked by nerve stimulation, but not when evoked by direct muscle stimulation. Inhibitory extract (XI) had a hypotensive effect, but lacked topical anesthetic activity and effect on resting potentials. This extract also reduced amplitude of MEPP and end-plate potentials, but did not affect their time course or the frequency of MEPP. Stimulatory extract was not active in presence of neuromuscular blocking agent tubocurarine.

## Conclusion

Active principles in Southern Prickly Ash extracts appear to exert their action on neuromuscular transmission probably through blockade of postjunctional, end-plate receptors (XI) or enhanced release of neurotransmitter (stimulatory extract).

## Clinical Relevance

Signs of clinical toxicity in cattle were best correlated with effects of XI, which can be antagonized by Ca2+ and neostigmine (X8836382).

## Saw Palmetto (*Serenoa repens*)

*The Business of Herbs* 12(1):12-13, March/April, 1994

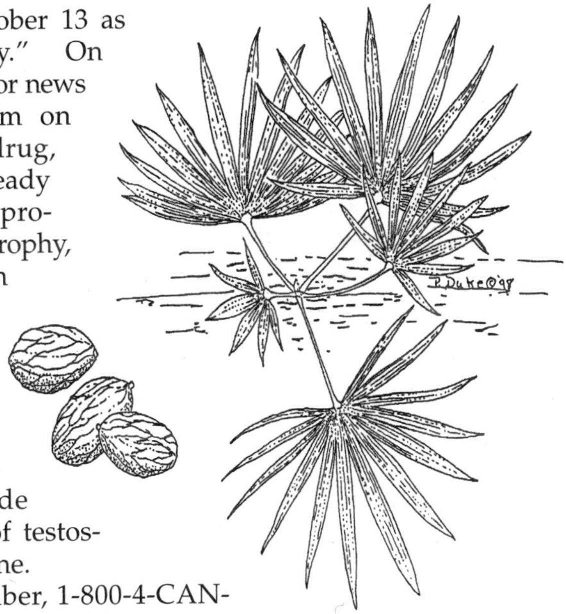

I think I'll declare October 13 as "National Prostate Day." On October 13, 1993, all the major news programs did a news item on Merck's new prostate drug, finasteride or Proscar™, already approved for BPH (benign prostatic hyperplasia or hypertrophy, depending upon to whom you listen). They announced an upcoming $60-million study by NCI to see if it could prevent cancer of the prostate. They suspected this possibility because finasteride prevents the conversion of testosterone to dihydrotestosterone.

They even gave a number, 1-800-4-CANCER, for older males who might like to participate in the study. I called and got a minute-long recording telling me they weren't open until 9:00. After 9:00 I called three times, and my secretary called even more, but we never got through. We followed the binary phone recordings through to the bitter end when the recording said, "Hold and you will be answered in turn." Had we held, though, we would still be holding. First we would get a busy signal on the hold, which would then terminate, leaving us holding a dead phone. I hope the NCI is better with their cancer cures than they are with their phone.

I wanted to volunteer for the Proscar™ study, since 64% of men my age have BPH. But I bet my prostate gland that edible Prosnut[NTM] (NTM = no trademark) butter, made of saw palmetto, pumpkin, and a few other edible seeds would do about as well for BPH as finasteride. In an article entitled "Trick or Treat: Pumpkins or Prostatitis," I made that bet and gave my recipe.

### October 13, 1993

I received my copy of a similar article which a friendly editor had shortened and retitled "The 'Farmaceutical' Alternative: A Seed for All Seasons" (*Raleigh Reporter*, 10/9/93) with a recitation of the "farmaceutical" formula for Prosnut butter, mentioning not only saw palmetto but various cucurbitaceous (cucumber, pumpkin, watermelon) seeds, soybeans, peanuts, almonds, Brazil nuts, walnut, and flax, all food items, plus a little zinc picolinate. I'd ingest two or three Prosnut butter sandwiches a day on zinc-enriched whole-wheat bread if I were worried about my prostate.

## October 13

I received a fax from a correspondent who had invited me to visit with one of the world's experts on the antiangiogenic properties of the compound genistein. That fax had an article from the newsletter *ALTERNATIVES for the Health Conscious Individual* (Vol. 5 No. 3, Sept. 1993) in which Dr. David G. Williams praised the research of Dr. Judah Folkman, an expert on angiogenesis. Dr. Williams said: "In both prostate and breast cancer one can make the reasonable assumption that if shark cartilage therapy can inhibit new blood vessel formation there's a good chance the tumor can be made less aggressive and metastasis can be stopped...If I had a history of either breast or prostate cancer (among others), I'd definitely be taking shark cartilage to help prevent any recurrence."

Never did I even consider the shark cartilage myself, figuring that might hurt the shark race much more than it helped the human race. We now know that we have plenty of antiangiogenic compounds in beans, which aren't endangered.

Yep, there's genistein. Hard-core shark saviors, like hard-core vegetarians, take heart! Unlike Dr. Williams, Dr. Folkman has been praising beans more than sharks. As a matter of fact, it was Folkman's work that prompted an earlier draft of mine called "Tofu or not to fu," extolling tofu as one alternative source of genistein, one of the most promising antiangiogenic compounds. It seems though that genistein is found in most American beans as well as in the oriental soybean. Genistein was recently even reported from chickweed. If I were worried about cancerous BPH and metastases or newly developing small tumorlets, I'd add some genistein to my Prosnut butter.

Look at the biological activities reported for genistein: abortifacient, antiangiogenic, antifertility, antihypertensive, antileukemic, antimicrobial, cancer-preventive, estrogenic, fungistat, phyto-alexin, topoisomerase-II-inhibitor, and tyrosine-kinase(PTK)-inhibitor. (See the database now in 2006; it's nearly a page long.)

## October 13

I got a third call from a man who had read my "Trick or Treat" paper. He had BPH. He was praising the good results he was having with saw palmetto, better than he had with pumpkin seed. And a friend of his, with cancerous BPH, was in remission, thanks apparently to the saw palmetto. Add these anecdotes to those Dr. Jerome Jaffee recounted about his father-in-law, who also went into remission for cancerous BPH on saw palmetto, and I feel safe betting my prostate that saw palmetto will do what finasteride will do.

Most of the problem with BPH is an accumulation of the activated hormone dihydrotestosterone in the prostate with aging. French research has shown that the extract "inhibits up to 90% of the activity of the prostate 5-alpha-reductase responsible for the transformation of the testosterone into (di)hydrotestosterone."

## Unavailable as medicine

But I can't recommend it to anyone else. Especially since the FDA in 1991 declared all OTC treatments for BPH inefficacious. Technically that makes saw palmetto unavailable as a medicine, but we could still make it available as a food. The name Prosnut butter is not intended to signify any medicinal intent but to be a short and catchy contraction for "prosaic nut butter," suggesting a food-grade product like peanut butter, and, like peanut butter, rich in beneficial nutrients. We don't need to recount the studies showing that saw palmetto extract prevents the conversion of testosterone to dihydrotestosterone. Isn't that what the finasteride does?

Is saw palmetto a food plant? Facciola (1990) says, "Fruits are edible. Florida pioneers once made a carbonated soft drink from the juice of the berries and called it 'Metto.' Produces several delicious palm hearts the size of a walnut. All but one can be harvested without killing the tree. Seeds are edible." Tanaka (1976) says, "Fruit and seeds were eaten." Uphof (1968) says, "Seeds were important food of the aborigines. Flowers are source of a good honey. Dried, ripe berries...are collected in August to January, sometimes they are dried to a prune-like substance." Yanovsky (1936) says, "Fruit eaten in Southeastern States." Better yet, Steven Foster (*Health Foods Business*, April 1992) quotes E. M. Hales (1898): "There is no doubt that the aborigines of the Florida peninsula depended largely upon the berries of the Saw Palmetto for food."

## A rumor

There's an anecdotal rumor that saw palmetto was going through the FDA review process and almost made it. Approval was denied, about the same time finasteride was approved. Surely saw palmetto is cheaper! Estimates put saw palmetto at about 70 per day; Proscar, $2.50-2.80 per day. Prosnut butter could be cheaper, and could be contrived to taste as good as peanut butter. Hexane extracts of saw palmetto have anti-androgenic properties rather similar to those of finasteride. Would U.S. consumer interests be served by our regulatory agency if saw palmetto proved better, safer, and/or cheaper than finasteride, yet was rendered unavailable to the consumer by FDA edict? I have bet my prostate that the herbal alternative will do what finasteride will do!

How can I win my bet? Merck's published data on sponsored research might be anticipated to show that finasteride is better than saw palmetto. Recently Indena's monographer Greg Ris put out a fact sheet on saw-palmetto extract. I suspect that monograph might cite data more favorable to the saw palmetto, a product sold by Indena. What we really need is an unbiased head-on competition between saw-palmetto extracts and finasteride, independently conducted by a disinterested party.

If you want to try saw palmetto, you may have to go to Florida and harvest your own, or go to Europe, where it is selling well for treatment of prostatic disorders. Oh well, a relaxing, stress-reducing trip might help prevent prostate cancer and heart disease. Indulge in lots of citrus, as well. So far the FDA has not outlawed it, even though there are claims being made that the limonene in citrus can prevent cancer. And replace your animal fat with genistein-rich beans while they too are still legal.

I must insert this comment, early in 2006. Loudly and frequently reported on the news this week are comments that saw palmetto is not efficacious in serious BPH. Let me loudly say that no American should believe any report like this, unless the herbal alternative is reliably compared also with the competitive pharmaceutical. Watch the scoreboard. Push for a mandatory third arm in all new herbal and all pharmaceutical clinical trials: The pharmaceutical vs. a good competing herbal, vs. placebo. Then we'll know which is better. In the few third arm trials so far, the herb looks good. Insist on third arm clinical trials in the future, so we can finally rest assured that many of these herbs are in fact just as good as the more expensive pharmaceutical.

# Spicebush (*Lindera benzoin*)

*The Wild Foods Forum* 12(3):8-9, May/June, 2001

I was really looking forward to seeing my visiting Amazonian Shaman, Antonio. I wanted to see his reaction to the spicebush, *Lindera benzoin*, because it looked more like coca, *Erythroxylum coca*, than anything growing here at the **Green Farmacy Garden**. Would he think it closer kin to coca, or to the many members of the laurel family Lauraceae, to which it belonged. That's the family to which the Biblical bay leaf belongs, and our North American sassafras. And most members are aromatic.

But Antonio did relate it, not to coca, but to the dangerous family, Apocynaceae, to which belong many genera and species with the Peruvian common names "sanango." As a matter of fact he was so sure (wrongly) of the similarities, that he figured that, like "chiriq sanango," this would be very good for arthritis and boneache. After the smoke had cleared from Antonio's magic visit, I consulted my Foster and Duke *Peterson's Field Guide to Medicinal Plants* (FAD in my Medical Botany syllabus) and found that spicebush does have arthritis as one of its medicinal implications.

Finally retired from the federal government, I am a bit more uninhibited about sounding off on one of my favorite themes, giving the herbal alternative a fair shake. Today, I'll just talk about spicebush (*Lindera benzoin*), its culinary and folk medicinal uses, and its potential as a remedy for yeast (candidiasis), an ailment widely mentioned on TV these days, especially on furtive commercials.

Spicebush is one of the commonest undershrubs in the forest around my **Green Farmacy Garden**. And it has quite a bit of folklore about it. Still I didn't find reports on the chemicals which no doubt contribute to its aromatic, culinary, essential oil, medicinal, and pesticidal properties. We and the Asians have studied their species of *Lindera* while ignoring ours. And some American scientists, while busy studying alien species of *Cocas*, *Cuphea*, and *Umbellularia* as sources of lauric acid, ignore this copious resource in our back yards. Is spicebush a food? Facciola (*Cornucopia*, Kampong Publ. Vista Ca. 1990) says: "Young leaves, twigs, and fruits contain an aromatic oil and make a very fragrant tea. The twigs are best gathered when in flower as the nectar adds considerably to the flavor. Dried and powdered fruits can be used as a substitute for allspice. The new bark is pleasant to chew."

King's *American Dispensatory* (Eclectic Institute, Reprint 1984) says: "The dried berries were used during the American Revolution and in the South during the late Rebellion as a substitute for allspice ... The bark, in decoction, is said to be refrigerant and exhilarating, and exceedingly useful in all kinds of fever, for allaying excessive heat and uneasiness; a warm decoction is employed to produce diaphoresis. The decoction may be drunk freely."

I quote these directly so you, and the FDA, may see that they have served as tea and spice for years. That puts them in the category I abbreviate GRAF, generally recognized as food.

In my *Handbook of Northeastern Indian Medicinal Plants* (Quarterman Publ., Lincoln Mass. 1986), I mention that the Cherokee Indians used spicebush for blood disorders, cold, cough, croup, dysmenorrhea, hives, phthisis and swellings. Cherokee drank spicebush tea as a spring tonic, and steeped the bark with wild cherry and dogwood in corn whiskey to break out measles. Creek Indians used the teas for pains of rheumatism, (anodyne antirheumatic), for purifying the blood (depurative) and making themselves puke and sweat (emetic and diaphoretic). Wisely they added willow to spicebush tea for drinking and using in the sweat lodges for rheumatism. The drug of choice today is still usually based on salicylates derived from willows. Ojibwa took the tea for anemia and that "tired rundown feeling." Rappahannock used the tea for menstrual pain or delayed periods.

To these Moerman (*Medicinal Plants of Native America*, Mus. Anthropology, Tech Rept. 19, 1986), in his more extensive survey adds that the Cherokee also took the tea for hives (sometimes associated with yeast, JAD). Iroquois used it for colds, fevers, gonorrhea, measles, and syphilis. Mohegans chewed the leaves or took the tea for worms.

In their *Peterson Field Guide to Medicinal Plants* (Houghton Miflin, Boston, 1990), Foster and Duke add that the settlers used the berries as a substitute for allspice. It's not bad! Medicinally the berries were used as a carminative for flatulence and colic. The oil from the fruits was applied to bruises and muscles or joints for chronic rheumatism. The tea made from the twigs was popular with the settlers (and available all year) for colds, colic, fevers, gas, and worms. The bark tea was used for various fevers, including typhoid, and to expel worms.

In the new *Big Book of Herbs*, (Interweave Press, 2000) Tucker and DeBaggio, mention that an herbal vinegar made from the twigs and fruits was used to preserve beets. Fruits have been dried and powdered and substituted for allspice. Dried leaves are great in potpourri. As usual, they do not go into medicinal detail. They give us some cultural detail, recommending this spicebush as an excellent background in shaded herb gardens. Hardy to Zone 5, it is endemic to shady situations, but will survive full sun, if adequately watered. It seems to fare best in subacid soils, rich in organic matter, and can be propagated by divisions in spring.

In all that listing of applications, there's not much folklore to anticipate that spicebush might be useful in yeast (candidiasis). But maybe the Indians didn't have yeast??? Apparently the yeast is a normal component of the flora of all human beings. Maybe candidiasis is mostly an iatrogenic ailment, induced by our medicines. Respected naturopaths, Murray and Pizzorno (*Encyclopedia of Natural Medicine*, Prima Publishing, Rocklin CA. 1991) say that when antibiotic use first became widespread, it was noted immediately that yeast infections increased. White man's alcohol, anti-ulcer drugs, corticosteroids, increase in diabetes, oral contraceptives, tights instead of cotton undergarments, and too much sugar in the diet all may have contributed to the emergence of candidiasis as a major ailment, today afflicting half our women folk. The total incidence and relative frequency of vaginal candidiasis have increased more than two-fold since the late 1960s.

There are a lot of synthetic alternatives for yeast, e.g. Nystatin, which is effective in mild cases. But Murray and Pizzorno suggest that garlic is more effective than Nystatin. I'd like to see the results of comparative heads-on trials between garlic, Nystatin and spicebush extracts. I'd like to see spicebush extracts compared also to Terazol, which reportedly leads to recovery of 95% of patients within three days. I'd like to see it compared with butacoconazole (Femstat), clotrimazole (Gyne-Lotrimin), ketoconazole (Nizoral) and miconazole (Monistat), all reportedly with an 80-90% cure rate. But the Graedons, after listing the latter four, reiterate the anecdote of the lady who had wasted $2,000 in office fees and medication, when a GP prescribed douching three times a day with 2 tablespoons vinegar in a quart of water (Graedons, 1991). That solved her $2,000 problem.

Studying 54 plant species for antimicrobial effects, Heisey and Gorham (1992; *Letts. Appl. Microbiol.* 14: 136-9) found that extract of stem bark of *Lindera benzoin* ("spicebush") strongly inhibited yeast (*Candida albicans*), much better than any of the other 53 species. (Walnut husks also showed some activity.) Now if vinegar could have saved that lady $2,000, might not a vinegar extract of spicebush bark, garlic, and walnut be even better.

Spicebush is best of the 54 studied. Garlic is reportedly better than Nystatin. I suspect that our mixture might be as safe and efficacious as any of the drugs named above, but we'll never know.

You've seen the flurry of ads for expensive over-the-counter "remedies" for yeast. "See your doctor if you're not sure. But if you're sure you have yeast, use our brand." Ten years ago, my doctor told me you couldn't be sure without identification of the microorganisms involved. I doubt that has changed. Our FDA has become more relaxed in this regard. But if you started selling spicebush/garlic/vinegar for yeast, you'd be breaking the law, and the FDA might get you. But they won't bother those OTC drugs because they have been proven safe and effective, to the FDA's satisfaction, apparently. Are they more or less safe and efficacious than spicebush /garlic/vinegar? I don't know. You don't know. The FDA doesn't know. The drug companies and physicians don't know.

# Strawberry, Wild (*Fragaria virginiana, F. vesca*)

*The Wild Foods Forum* 10(3):8-9, May/June, 1999

## The Strawberry Defense

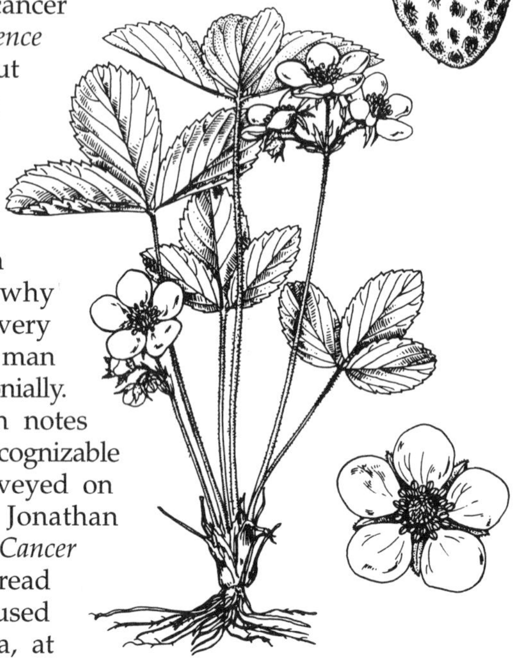

*The Raleigh Reporter*, April 24, 1993

"Berry good and nutty anticancer agent?" That's the question *Science News* (April 2, 1988) asked about ellagic acid, a cancer-preventing compound found in the strawberry (*Fragaria* spp.). The strawberry was all but indispensible to the Indians who preceded us here in America. Is that, perhaps, why Indians seemed to have had very little cancer before the white man came? They smoked, but ceremonially. Anthropologist Dan Moerman notes that cancer was rarely if ever recognizable in the documents he has surveyed on early American health. In Jonathan Hartwell's *Plants Used Against Cancer* (Quarterman Press, 1982), we read that strawberries have been used for laryngeal cancer in Russia, at least folklorically, and for other types of cancers, inflammations, sclerosis of the spleen and liver, and tumors.

Ellagic acid has many proven activities. Among other activities reported in my CRC *Handbook of Biological Active Phytochemicals* (CRC Press, 1992) are activities against cataracts, gout (and strawberries are an old folk remedy for gout), preventive for cancer, gout, and hepatitis. For some of these activities, it need be present only at levels of 3 parts per million (ppm). What would 3 ppm translate to in Jim Duke. I weigh a bit more than 100 kilograms (kg) (100 kg=220 pounds), but we'll round it down to 100 kg. One kilogram is a million milligrams. Three ppms is 3 milligrams (mg) per kilogram (kg). Weighing 100 kg, I would need 300 milligrams ellagic-acid to bring me to 3 ppms. The highest report I have for ellagic acid is ca 8,000 ppms in the dry fruits, 32,000 in the dry leaves, of strawberry. That would translate to 800 ppms in the fresh fruit, 3,200 in the fresh leaf, assuming they were 90% water. I would have to eat almost a pound of fresh strawberries (I could live with that) or a half-cup (100g; no thanks) serving of strawberry leaves to get 300 mg ellagic acid. According to a scientist interviewed for the *Science News* report I mentioned earlier, ellagic acid – prevalent in strawberries, but also in Brazil nuts and grapes – scavenges carcinogenic chemicals like many of our pollutants, thereby preventing normal cells from becoming cancerous. Ellagic acid reduces damage to DNA (the structural material of our chromosomes) 45 to 70%, hinting that at appropriate levels, ellagic acid might halve the incidence of experimental cancers. But strawberries contain several other cancer-preventive compounds: alanine, ascorbic acid, beta-carotene, caffeic acid, catechin, catechol, chlorogenic acid, p-coumaric acid, ellagic acid, epicatechin, fiber, gallic acid, glutamine, glycine, p-hydroxybenzoic acid, linoleic acid, alpha linolenic acid, lycopene, methionine, myricetin, myristic acid, niacin, oleic acid, pantothenic acid, pectin, salicylic acid, selenium, serine, tocopherol, and vanillic acid, in those delicious fruits alone. Other interesting preventive compounds are present in the leaves. I, like the American Indians, rate strawberries as one of the treasures of spring, and enjoyed them immensely, long before I knew of their anti-cancer, anti-cataract, anti-viral, and anti-tartar potential. I have enjoyed my strawberry leaf tea even more, now, knowing that it is rich in ellagic acid and several other cancer-preventive compounds.

Strawberries, a favorite fruit with many, including the Native Americans who even had strawberry festivals, are like most of our berries, rich in many important health-protecting phytochemicals our ancestors got more of. Yes, each berry contains thousands, believe it or not, of phytochemicals, some shared with all living species, some shared with all other plant species, and some unique. Most of these phytochemicals are well known to our genes from the fact that wherever your ancestors evolved there was some edible member of that berry-rich family, the rose family. I could name fifty berries in the rose family, and if you're not careful, I may name fifty before 2000 is over. I think that the greater variety of wholeseome berries you ingest, the healthier you'll be. Yes readers of *The Wild Foods Forum*, more likely to be grazers, are getting so many phytochemicals in their grazing, that they may need less herbal medication. Welcome to the New Millennium, getting back to your paleolithic roots, and berries etc.

Here in Maryland, I get frustrated trying to identify my wild strawberries. My *Brown and Brown Herbaceous Plants of Maryland* (partially illustrated by Mrs. Duke) lists two wild species, the wild strawberry, *Fragaria virginiana*, Duchne. (with umbelloid flowers in flat topped clusters like Queen Anne's lace) and seeds sunken in pits in the strawberry, the berry clusters not reaching beyond the leaves, and the woodland strawberry, *Fragaria vesca* L. (with racemose flowers [in tapered flower clusters] and seeds on the surface of the berry, the berries often extending beyond the leaves). Sounds simple!! But their pictures have the flower clusters differing from their key description. So I turn to my college professors *Flora of the Carolinas*, and find that Radford Ahles and Bell (1968) add that the *virginiana* has petals (the white part of the flower) twice as long as the sepals (the green outer structures shaped rather like the petals but pointed), while the *vesca* petals are no longer than 1.5 times the length of the sepals. Petal splitting, if not hair splitting, I call it. So at age 70, I take the geriatric generic way out and go out and munch on *Fragaria* spp., not really caring which species it is.

Strawberry is one of America's gifts to the world food basket, but my old alma mater, the USDA, has made watery giants instead of the original tasty phytochemical powerhouse that won the Indians' respect. I don't know of any North American food species that has gone downhill nutritionally as much as the American strawberry, thanks to USDA plant breeding and improvement. We won't even talk about genetically modified organisms (GMO's) which should make things even worse. Today, thanks to the USDA, you can find strawberries so big that one weighs an ounce. But who wants to pay a dollar for an ounce of water.

## Native American Uses

If you want some old-fashioned good tasting strawberries, go into some old fields and find some of the wild ones. And that's more like what our early American ancestors ate, rich, and probably better endowed with ellagic acid, that cancer preventive. But for now, there's more ellagitannins in the leaves which make a pleasant tea. According to Dan Moerman, the Coastal Salish and Winnebago did make a tea from the leaves. Blackfoot Indians used the tea for diarrhea and Carrier for stomach bleeding. Cherokee take the tea for diarrhea, dysentery, hepatitis, jaundice, nerves, and scurvy. They held the fruits in the mouth to remove tartar. Chippewa took the root infusion for infantile cholera. Iroquois took the whole plant in tea to regulate the menses, the root tea for bloody diarrhea, chancre sores, to purify the blood and as a collyrium for sties. They also used the plant for colic and teething in children and gonorrhea and stroke in adults. Maine's Malecite and Micmac made tea of strawberry and dwarf raspberry for irregular periods. Navajo consider the whole plant "life medicine." Ojibwa use the tea for stomachache, even in children. Okanagan-Colville applied powdered leaves in deer fat to sores, considering, appropriately, the powdered leaves antiseptic. They dusted the powdered leaves into childrens' mouths to treat sore mouth. Potawatomi used the root for stomach distress. Quileute chewed the leaves and poulticed them onto burns. Ramah, like the Navajo, consider the whole plant "life medicine." Thompson Indians take tea of the root or whole plant for diarrhea and dysentery, even with children. They made underarm deodorant pads from the leaves. Elsewhere we read that they used the berries as a deodorant (Moerman, 1998).

## USDA Study

Since I have retired, they (USDA) have gotten more interested in chemo-prevention of cancer and are studying such things as strawberries' ellagic acid, folate, and lutein. Matter of fact, they now realize that they selectively bred out of soybeans such chemopreventives as Bowman-Birk inhibitors, estrogenic isoflavones, phytic acids, phytosterols, protease inhibitors, and saponins. Here's a strawberry item from the slick USDA monthly journal:

ARS (USDA) fruit scientists John L. Maas, Gene J. Galletta, and Shiow Y. Wang evaluated 36 strawberry varieties for their ellagic acid content. Most was found in leaves, followed by seeds, green immature fruits, and red ripe fruits. So if ellagitannins are your target, you might do better with the leaves (and don't scrape the seeds off the outside of the fruit). Leaves of the varieties "Tribute" and "Delite," both introduced by ARS, had more ellagic acid than other varieties tested. The strawberries could be bred to maximize ellagic acid in the fruits, where it is most needed, from a human dietary point of view. Pure ellagic acid is highly insoluble and biologically unavailable. When ellagic acid is synthesized by plants, it usually occurs combined with glucose as bioavailable water-soluble ellagitannins. Strawberry fruits produce at least 5 different ellagitannins, but their chemical structures and effectiveness as anticarcinogens have yet to be determined. This synergistic mix, speculates Jim Duke, would do much more to prevent cancer than the silver bullet, ellagic acid, insoluble and unavailable (JAD]).

Gary D. Stoner of the Department of Preventive Medicine, Ohio State University in Columbus has shown that natural ellagitannins from dehydrated strawberry fruit protected against some forms of cancer, especially esophageal, if added to the diets of rats. The diet significantly reduced the incidence of chemically induced tumors of the esophagus, and Stoner and colleagues believe that other compounds in the fruit also contributed to the positive results. Ellagic acid also occurs in raspberries, blackberries, cranberries, walnuts, and pecans (Stanley, D. 1997. "Boosting ellagic acid in strawberries." (*Agricultural Research* 45 [August] 16-18).

The moral of this USDA study, as I interpret it is, take a generous serving of a generous variety of berries. Variety is the spice of life. And don't scrape the seeds off your strawberries. Do not take pure ellagic acid, which is biologically unavailable.

Strawberry leaves (*Fragaria vesca* and *F. viridis*) even made it into the Herbal PDR (Fleming, T. et al. 1998. *PDR for Herbal Medicine*. 1st ed. Medical Economics Co., Montvale, NJ. 1244 pp) and Commission E (Blumenthal, M; Busse, WR; Goldberg, A; Gruenwald, J; Hall, T; Riggins, CW; Rister, R.S. [Eds.]. 1998. *The Complete German Commission E Monographs: Therapeutic guide to herbal medicines*. American Botanical Council, Austin, TX and Integrative Medicine Communications, Boston, MA., 684 pp.) But it was listed only as folk medicine, and not approved by the Commission. Here's a quote of their disapproval caveat: "Activity in the indications listed has not been adequately demonstrated." Here's how Commission E and the PDR said the leaf was used folklorically: anemia, arthritis, cardiopathy, catarrh, circulatory disorders, diarrhea, dysmenorrhea, dyspepsia, fever, GI catarrh, gout, gravel, hepatitis, impure blood, intestinal sluggishness, jaundice, kidney ailments, night sweats, obesity, rashes, respiratory catarrh, rheumatism, sluggish metabolism, and stones. I remember people suggesting strawberries, like cherries, when I was suffering gout (before I started taking celery seed as a hypouricemic gout preventive). So I went to my database http://www.ars-grin.gov/duke/ and find that strawberry does contain 4 possible "gout-preventive" xanthine-oxidase inhibitors, ellagic-acid, gallic-acid, pedunculagin, and quercetin. So if my food farmacy preventive (celery seed extracts) should get lost, I might have to resort to the fine folk food farmacy remedies – cherries and strawberries.

## Antioxidant Activity

Heinonen et al. (1998) compared the antioxidant activities of several fruits. Subscribers to the antioxidant hypothesis will interpret this as suggesting that these fruits contribute to the prevention of cancer, cardiopathy, cataracts etc. etc. The amount of total phenolics varied from 617 to 4350 mg/kg in fresh berries as gallic acid equivalents (GAE). In LDL at 10 uM GAE, the extracts inhibited hexanal formation in blackberries, red raspberries, sweet cherries, blueberries, strawberries. In lecithin liposomes – sweet cherries, blueberries, red raspberries, blackberries, strawberries. But red raspberries were more efficient than blueberries at inhibiting hydroperoxide formation in lecithin liposomes. HPLC showed high anthocyanin in blackberries, hydroxycinnamic acid in blueberries and sweet cherries, flavonol in blueberries, and flavan-3-ol in red raspberries. Berries are significant sources of phenolic antioxidants with potential health benefits. Different berries have different phyto-chemicals mostly responsible for their antioxidant activities. A mix of berries gives a mix of antioxidant phytochemicals which gives a mix of modes of anioxidant protection.

Heinonen et al. (1998) state that fresh berries contain up to 100 mg/kg flavan-3-ols, up to 300 mg/kg flavonols (to 550 in strawberries), up to 200 mg/kg hydroxycinnamates, up to 2,110 mg/kg in blueberies, and relatively high amounts of anthocyanins (up to 5,000 mg/kg). Caffeic acid derivatives amount to 17-41% of the total hydroxycinnamates in black currants, 42-48% in red currants, 90-100% in blueberries and 35-87% in sweet cherries. Put variety in your fruit bowl.

### Reference

Heinonen, IM, Meyer, AS, Frankel, EN. 1998. "Antioxidant activity of berry phenolics on human low- density lipoprotein and liposome oxidation." *J. Agric. Food Chem* 46:4107-12.

# Sundew (*Drosera rotundifolia*)

*The Wild Foods Forum*, 16(2):8-9, Spring, 2005

Good name sundew. Writing in midwinter, it brings back lazy days of summer. Come to Maine with me and I'll show you where it got that glistening name. Sundew is a small ground hugging plant frequent in bogs in old gravel pits near our lodge on Eagle Hill. It has a ground-hugging rosette of light green round leaves covered with red-stalked red to purple glands on the tips of which are often dew-like drops, containing proteolytic enzymes. When the sun hits those dew drops right, they glisten like minute diamonds. But they may lure insects to their unwitting death. Those sticky hairy glands function almost like flypaper and may ensnare and slowly digest the unwary damselfly. According to Foster and Duke (2000), the leaf edges curl inwards after a bug is snagged. The proteolytic enzymes gradually break down the insects' bodies into absorbable nutrients. Yes, the sundew, like Maine's pitcher plants and Carolina's venus flytrap, is a partial carnivore. It makes most of its living by photosynthesis, the process by which green leaves turn $CO_2$ and $H_20$ into carbohydrates and oxygen. But like me, partial carnivore, these insectivorous plants take a little meat now and then, subsidizing their nutrition with nutrients derived from the enzymatic breakdown of the trapped insects. Try making a fingerprint of the leaf by pressing it in the sundew page of your book; it will give you a purplish leaf print.

One summer in Maine, I was watching one trapped green bug 6-8 mm long caught in the sundew drops. Alexander King, my right hand **Green Farmacy Garden** volunteer, called from several yards away. He was there on a scholarship provided by Joerg-Henner Lotze, director of the Station. Alex was freeing two small dragonflies, different colored, but probably the same species. We assumed that they might have been tired from mating, contributing to their post copulatory rapture capture by the dreaded dew of the meat-eating sundew. Yes, they can ensnare insects! I refer to them as the fly-paper plant, and they can digest captured insects.

That proteolytic activity of enzymes in the "dew" may underlie the American Indian medicinal uses of the plants reported by anthropologist Dan Moerman (1998), and summarized with others below. The Kwakiutl use the proteolytic plant for bunions, corns and warts. If you have a pair of similar sized bunions, corns and warts, bring them with you to Maine, and you can treat one with my "bunionADE," a mix of renewable hand-picked sundew leaves (unendangered species in the disturbed gravel pit), marigold (Tagetes) flowers, and some willow bark for its salicylic acid. I'll bet if we treat the worst of the pair, twice daily with the mixture, leaving the better of the pair as a control, we can change their relative status. And you will be part of our north woods field laboratory on ethno-botany, medical botany, and natural history. The enzymes that digest an insect might digest your wart. But you experiment on yourself at your own risk! As a botanist I cannot prescribe to anyone else. I'm willing to volunteer some of my warts and fearless valor for self experimentation if you can't bring you own. If I have a likely pair of new growths by class time, I'll volunteer them to the class for experimentation.

The class will, I hope, steer clear of the other Kwakiutl folklore: "Plant used as a 'medicine to make women love-crazy,' a love charm" (Moerman, 1998). The Seminole usage of another species, *Drosera capillaris*, might make a lot of sense, i.e. rubbing the glandular plants on ringworm sores. Plumbagin had fungicidal activity. Erichsen-Brown's book (1989) gives some more American folklore and an interesting array of colloquial names: eyebright (not to be confused with Maine's Euphrasia), lustwort, moor grass, red rot, and Rosa solis. According to Erichsen-Brown, John Gerarde as early as 1633 said that just eating small quantities of sundew will get female cattle "stirred up to lust…because through his sharp and biting qualitie it stirreth up a desire to lust, which before was dulled, and as it were asleepe. It strengthens and nourisheth the body, especially if it be distilled with wine, and that liquor made thereof which the common people call Rosa Solis…lay the leaves of Rosa Solis in the spirit of wine, adding thereto Cinnamon, Cloves, Maces, Ginger, Nutmeg, Sugar and a few grains of Muske, suffering it to stand in a glasse close stopt from the aire and set in the Sun by the space of ten daies, then strain the same and keep it for your use" (Gerarde as quoted by Erichsen Brown, 1989).

I had to put that little recipe in to show you that yes, sundew was a food, in a broad sense of the word. I find it in several of my food books. And we'll tolerate each student excising one leaf from healthy plants to add into the communal wine tincture of Rosa Solis. In his great book *Cornucopia*, Facciola (1998) says "In Italy, the herb is mixed with brandy, raisins and sugar and fermented into a cordial known as Rossolis." He also mentions that the leaves are used to curdle milk, and the curds and whey produced are consumed directly. So there's a wine tincture, a brandy tincture, and a milk extract consumed as food and beverage.

MD Rafinesque, cerca 1830, says the juice destroys warts and corns, and, added to milk, helps freckles and sunburn (but it will serve as a rennet, making sour bonyclabber, as in Sweden. "Deemed pectoral in South America, a sirup used for asthma." Erichsen-Brown, quoting Rafinesque, 1830. Then quoting Maude Grieve a century later: "In America it has been advocated as a cure for old age; the vegetable extract is used together with colloidal silicates in case of arteriosclerosis." Homeopathically it has been suggested for consumption and whooping cough. In Quebec, the tea is used for arteriosclerosis, asthma, bronchitis, catarrh, cough, hypertension, and pertussis (Erichsen-Brown; 1979).

## A word of caution

As a taxonomy-trained conservationist, I must warn you that it is not easy to tell the rare endangered species from the common species. In some states it is illegal to harvest this interesting plant at all. Although *Drosera rotundifolia* is quite common locally in Maine, it has become endangered elsewhere, and is easy to confuse with rare and endangered species. If you must harvest the plant, (and you may be breaking laws if you do), carefully scissor off one, two or three leaves each from several different plants in populations where there are more than 100 plants (And you'll find populations like that by the thousands in Maine). Erichsen-Brown cautions that *Droseras* are endangered in Wisconsin, and rare in Minnesota and Ontario. "They should never be collected as there are many better remedies more easily available. Sphagnum bogs are damaged by being walked on" (Erichsen-Brown; 1979). But my natural history resource, Eastman, rather conflicts that warning about walking on sundew. Eastman says on page 185 that sundew colonies "often thrive in mammal trails or bogs, areas of disturbance where vegetation is matted down from animal runways or human footsteps."

## References

Eastman, John (abbreviated as EAS below). 1992. *The Book of Forest and Thicket.*
———. 1995. *The Book of Swamp and Bog.*
———. 2003. *The Book of Field and Roadside.* Mechanicsburg, PA: Stackpole Books.

Erichsen-Brown, C. (abbreviated as CEB below). 1979. *Use of Plants for the Past 500 Years.* Breezy Creeks Press. Aurora, Canada. 512 pp. (Now available under a new name, *Medicinal and Other Uses of North American Plants,* from Dover Books (Reprints).

Facciola, S. (abbreviated as FAC below). 1998. *Cornucopia - A Source Book of Edible Plants.* Vista CA: Kampong Publications.

Foster, S. and Duke, J. A. (abbreviated as FAD below). *Peterson Field Guide to Eastern/Central Medicinal Plants.* Houghton Mifflin, Boston. 366 pp. 1990

Haines, A and Vining, T. F. 1998. *Flora of Maine.* Bar Harbow ME: V.F. Thomas Co., P.O. Box 281, 04069-0281. 847 pp. $45 plus 8.70 tax and shipping.

Martin, A. C., Zim, H. S., and Nelson, A. L. (abbreviated as MZN below). 1961. *American Wildlife & Plants.* New York: Dover Publications.

Moerman, D. E. (abbreviated as DEM below). 1998. Native American Ethnobotany. Portland Oregon: Timber Press.

**DO NOT HARVEST**

The endangered species are not always easy to distinguish from the common species. PH2 entries below may apply strictly to *Drosera ramentacea,* or also to *D. peltata, D. madagascarensis,* and/or the Euroamerican *D. rotundifolia* covered here. Haines and Vining key the Maine species as follows:

a. Leaf blades broader than long: ...... *Drosera rotundifolia.*
a. Leaf blades longer than wide:
  b. Stipules free from petiole much of their length; blades 4-5 mm broad, 8-20 mm long. ......... *D. intermedia.*
  b. Stipules adnate to petiole much of their length; blades 1.5-4 mm broad, 15-20 mm long:
    c. Leaf blades linear, 1.5-3.0 mm. ........ *D. linearis.*
    c. Leaf blades obovate to long spatulate, 3-4 mm wide. ...................................... *D. anglica*

## Downsides

AHPA Class 2b, 2c (CAN); no contraindications documented. Plumbagin may be irritant (CAN). None reported (KOM;PIP). But listen to BUR: "It has been rejected since it is said to be poisonous...producing shuddering in man, a sense of constriction of the chest rawness in the throat, pains in the bowels, diarrhea, sweat and diminished secretion of the urine. It is poisonous to cattle because of hydrocyanic acid" (BUR).

## Natural History

White to purplish flowers usually insect pollinated; protandry often leads to outcrossing (JUD). Chief flower pollinators are flies, such as mosquito-like fungus gnats (Mycetophilidae), and gall wasps (Cynipidae). The glistening tentacles release an anesthetic that seems to stupefy the prey and digestive enzymes that dissolve internal organs. This dissolved nutrient is then absorbed by the tentacles (may take a week or more) Many insects fall victim to the tentacles (marsh beetles, Helodidae, and crane flies, Tipulidae). Moths often escape capture because of the detachable scales on the wings; however they can be captured by their scale-free legs. Darwin once recorded thirteen insects trapped in a single leaf of *D. rotundifolia.* One moth caterpillar feeds on the tentacles, consuming the end droplet, the glandular bulb, and then the tentacle itself. The plume moth caterpillar, *Trichoptilus parvulvus*, often attaches its cocoon lengthwise on the flower stalk. A greenish noctuid moth caterpillar, *Epipsilia monochromatea*, feeds on leaves early, then changes its diet to cranberry leaves in the summer (EAS).

# Sweetfern (*Comptonia peregrina*)

*The Wild Foods Forum* 16(3): 8-9, Summer, 2005

If you like the foliage of real ferns (one of my favorite things, not to eat but to look at), you might not object to the misleading common name, sweetfern, my subject for today. It's not a fern, but it looks like one to the uninitiated.

## Common Names

The first 8 names I accumulated for this non-fern had the word fern as part of the name, e.g. Fern Bush; Ferngate; Shrubby Fern; Spleen Fern; Spleenwort Fern; Meadow Fern; Sweet Fern. But rather suggestive of ferns from their greenery, they also share with ferns the absence of petals and sepals, in their rather rudimentary or reduced flowers.

## Ethnobotanical Uses

There are a lot of uses for *Comptonia* on my USDA database: http://www.ars-grin.gov/duke/. The first query will list the important chemical, betulin (but I'll wager that if you analyzed it carefully you'd find more than a thousand) and some of its activities: Anticarcinomic; Antifeedant; Antiflu; Anti-HIV; Antiinflammatory; Antitumor; Antiviral; Aphi-difuge; Cytotoxic; Hypolipemic; Prostaglandin-Synthesis-Inhibitor; Topoisomerase-II-Inhibitor.

But I have to confess, my database will lead you to the much more interesting ethnobotanical database of Daniel Moerman. You can access that by going to http://herb.umd.umich.edu/herb/search.pl or you can reach it from my USDA database. Moerman's data collection is a treasure house; e.g. Algonquins inhaled the leaf aroma or took the tea for headache, or Cherokee took the tea for roundworms, etc. etc.; I've transcribed most of these to my USDA database. Dan has done America a great service by computerizing these and making them available, e.g. to the USDA database.

Sweetfern is certainly a marginal food species as far as I am concerned. Yes, the young nutlets are edible. I've nibbled on them, without getting fat, I might add. And yes, the leaves are used as a spice or more commonly to make beverage teas (EAS; FAC). And we read that our sweet fern is used to line baskets to make berries stay fresh longer (CEB). That would certainly be easy enough up in Maine, and we do have plenty of berries to gather up there.

- Algonquins inhaled crushed leaves or drank leaf tea for headache (HNI)
- Cherokee used tea for roundworms (HNI)
- Chippewa drink catnip/sweetfern tea for fever (HNI)
- Delaware took decoction as antiinflammatory, depurative, expectorant, for cystosis, dermatosis and scrofula (HNI)

- Indianans (Americans from Indiana) plastered the leaves onto cancers (JLH)
- Iroquois used the plant for toothache (HNI)
- Maritime and Mohegan used leaf decoction on poison ivy (HNI)
- Menominee use the tonic plant in childbirth (HNI)
- Micmac used the leaf tea as a tonic (HNI)
- Ojibwa used leaf decoction for flux and stomach cramps (HNI)
- Penobscot Indians used leaf decoction for poison ivy (HNI)
- Potawatomi used leaf decoction for itch (HNI)
- Seneca used the tea as a body deodorant (HNI)

## Natural History

Aromatic as it is, it is often infested with caterpillars [*Acrobasis comptoniella*, a minute webbing moth larva, may web the terminal leaves; sweetfern underwing or wayward nymph (*Catocala antinympha*) feed while stretched parallel to foliage and twigs; chain-dotted or chain-spotted geometer (*Cingilia catenaria*); double-lined gray (*Cleoria sublunaria*); rear-horned papaw sphinx (*Dolba hyloeus*); crinkled flannel moth (*Megalope crispata*)]. White tailed deer are the major foliage grazers; rabbits may gnaw the stem; grouse eat a few buds and catkins [EAS].

The Myricaceae is the most ancient actinorhizal family involved in a nitrogen-fixing symbiosis with the actinomycete Frankia. **Translation:** This primitve group of plants, like legumes, takes nitrogen from the air, and fixes it in the soil, but in convert with fungi rather than bacteria, as in most legumes.

# Teaweed (*Sida rhombifolia*)

(Unpublished)

## Tempted by the Teaweed

My ephedra, alias ma huang, source of the medicinal compound ephedrine, isn't doing very well in the garden. Maybe it's aware that the FDA banned it this week. (Tax week, April, 2004) (Though they include, knowingly or unknowingly, both chemical and pharmaceutical ephedrine (more than half synthetic) as well as whole herb ephedra in their statistics. Confusing the naive public, they aggregate the herb ephedra, the natural chemical ephedrine, and the synthetic chemical ephedrine statistics, and blame all the deaths (fewer than 100) on the herb, and ban the herb. This will discourage a lot of Americans with their weight loss successes, who may resume their obese habits and die of obesity. One estimate blames half a million deaths in America on obesity. Or they will resort to more expensive prescription pharmaceuticals, which take ~ 100,000 American lives a year, even when taken as prescribed (*JAMA*). Yes synthetic ephedrine, probably just as dangerous, possibly more so, lacking the co-occurring synergens, will still be available, at greater cost. So has the FDA done Americans a favor? Or did they do their Pharamceutical lobbyists a favor? The herb will be unavailable. More people will be forced to buy the more expensive pharmaceuticals. Pharamceuticals documentably kill a thousand times more Americans than do herbal supplements.

Fortunately for me, I have a great weed, volunteering almost too frequently, another clock flower (ca 10:00 to 4:00 plus or minus 1 hour, depending on humidity, sunshine and the like). And it keeps coming back every year, all by itself, not demanding a lot of my gardener's attention like the ephedra. It's the country mallow, *Sida* spp., maybe *rhombifolia*, also known as teaweed. Where I travel in Latin America it is known as broom – "escobilla/o," and clusters of the wiry plant, bound together, are used as a broom. In Africa, the plant is sown as a fibercrop with the onset of the monsoon and harvested some 130 days later (yields ca 1,300 kg fiber/hectare).

And it is a food plant, at least marginally so. According to Tanaka, the leaves are used for tea in the Canary Islands. They are so used in Mexico as well. So this teaweed, like tea itself, may contain a CNS-stimulant, in this case ephedrine, and might conceivably be mixed with caffeine containing herbs to capitalize on the thermogenic synergy of caffeine and ephedrine, heretofore widely used in weight loss plans, with good results. I made an interesting "Triplethermogenitea" with a tea of the teaweed (with its ephedrine), with instant tea (for caffeine) and hot pepper seeds steeping for the thermogenic capsaicin. With lemon and sugar I found it more pleasant than hot tea, of which I'm not real fond anyhow.

Proper doses of ephedrine with or without caffeine and capsaicin tend to curb the appetite in the obese, like me, but overdoses of ephedrine tend to make you nervous, or high wired. A close friend takes three capsules a day of herbs high in caffeine and ephedrine and she's fine. Give her a fourth and she shakes like a leaf. Hence I've been afraid to take my "Triplethermogenitea" after noon, fearing it might give me insomnia at night. According to *The Wealth of India*, leaves are reported to contain ephedrine. Roots contain 0.054 % (540 ppm) alkaloids, one of which is ephedrine. (Total alkaloid content of *Sida cordifolia* is 0.085% – 850 ppm). Until I get mine analyzed I'll not know how it ranks for ephedrine content.

## A word of caution

Leaves of some species have caused poisoning in cattle. And the ripe capsule, perhaps mechanically, reportedly causes some poultry loss. But I'm gonna boil the leaves in a coffee decoction and see if it gets me wired like speed. No; I can do better than that. I'll use green tea with its caffeine and supposedly get all those benefits for which tea is being overpromoted (all green leaves, site of photosynthesis and oxygen production, are loaded with their own protective antioxidants). If I try *Sida* alone, maybe my body will be telling me that my teaweed *Sida* does contain ephedrine or some CNS stimulant. Ironically it is coming up in the Aphrodisia section of the Green Farmacy Garden, right beside another stimulant, Turnera, the so-called damiana. Turnera too is a clock flower, often not opening until ten or eleven and closing ca 4-6.

One of our guides in Costa Rica, Jorge has an elaborate tale about the "escobillo" involving a blind man who judges the wealth of the terrain by what his guide tied his horse to. This weed is so difficult to pull up (ask any taxonomist) that there is a belief that even the horse could not pull it up. Hence, animals are sometimes tied to this medicinal plant. Leaves, used to treat stomach disorders, are regarded as diuretic and sedative, and, in Mexico, are used as a substitute for Chinese tea. As a vegetable, they contain about 7.4% protein. The seeds are demulcent and emollient. The ephedrine in the "escobillo" might have gotten the blind man's horse so wired that he might uproot the herb had he chewed the leaves. But smart pasture animals have learned to avoid it. That's why there's so much as a weed in overgrazed pastures and rangeland. Even my much more poisonous yew tree, source of the billion dollar a year drug taxol, is an alternative source of ephedrine.

Julia Morton says Cubans take the weed, as an enema, as a bath, and as a decoction for bowel troubles. The decoction is taken for digestive problems. Venezuelans take the leaf tea for gonorrhea, and as an enema for intestinal problems; seed decoction used as a diuretic. Leaf decoction used for fever and hemorrhoids and as a tonic in Brazil. Root decoction given to babies for diarrhea in Costa Rica. Nicaraguans drink a tea made from the whole plant for urinary, bladder, and urethral problems; leaves crushed with vinegar applied topically for dermatitis and liver pain. Leaf poultice, which contains betaine and choline, is used as a lactagogue, and applied hot for dysmenorrhea in Argentina. Crushed leaves applied to tumors and poisonous insect bites. Plant has been used as an expectorant for bronchial catarrh. Used with varying degrees of success in treating tuberculosis of the skin, tuberculosis of the bones, and tuberculosis of the intestines. Breathing was improved in cases of phthisis and pulmonary tuberculosis by inhaling the plant extract. (This really sound like ephedrine activity). Extract taken for alcoholism. According to TRAMIL studies, root or leaf extracts tested as 1 g/ml were active against *Escherichia coli*, *Staphylococcus aureus*, and *S. cerevisiae.*

Ma huang is illegal now, but I suppose, for now, it is still legal for me to grow my own stash. If not, maybe Mormon Tea, a Utah ephedra, will still be legal, because it apparently lacks ephedrine. But who, without chemical analysis, will know whether I have Utah ephedra, or Chinese or Pakistani ephedra. Not the FDA. So they'll probably try to make them all illegal. If so, I'll stealthily sip my teaweed. But surely the FDA will try to take that away from me too, so I'll have to spend more money on less wholesome alternatives. Maybe its time they made tobacco available only by prescription, if they really want to help the country and not just the pharmaceutical firms. Some people smoke the teaweed. I think it's as safe as coffee, much safer than tobacco.

# Wild Yam (*Dioscorea villosa*)

*The Business of Herbs* 13(2):12, May/June, 1995

There are some wild tales out there about the wild yam. These tales are not well supported by the ethnobotanical literature, though. The wildest untruth is that yams (*Dioscorea*) contain natural progesterone, an important female hormone. That's about as untrue as the story that sarsaparilla (*Smilax*) contains testosterone, an important male hormone (both occurring in male and female humans). I have searched the literature and found no evidence that sarsaparilla contains testosterone or that wild yam contains progesterone. Both do contain compounds which could be chemically converted to the androgenic and estrogenic hormones, however.

At **Herbal Vineyard** I have a wild yam twining symbolically about a sarsaparilla. Talk about a clinging vine! While both vines contain precursors to human hormones, they do not contain these hormones, and apparently the precursors are not converted directly to human hormones in the human body. I once gave Dr. Monroe Wall, father of taxol, a potted pair, an intertwining wild yam (*Dioscorea villosa*) and carrion flower (*Smilax herbacea*). Why? Because in addition to the discovery of taxol, Dr. Wall had done pioneering work on diosgenin!

John Lee, MD, author of the book *Natural Progesterone* (1993) told a correspondent that diosgenin, an important ingredient in wild yam, was easily converted to progesterone by the mere addition of hydrochloric acid (HCl). Very good, if true! That means that stomach acid with its HCl could convert ingested diosgenin to progesterone, which could be very significant to aging females. But I find no natural product chemist who accepts this. So sorry Dr. Lee and Dr. Wall are no longer with us. I don't think Dr. Wall would agree with Dr. Lee that thousands of plants produce progesterone.

## The yam revolution

Back around 1940 Russell Marker was able to convert sarsapogenin from *Smilax* and diosgenin from *Dioscorea* to progesterone. For a while the Mexican yam was the major source of diosgenin, which led to the contraceptive pill, which led to the sexual revolution in North America, which led to more liberal and less safe sex, which led to increased AIDS and a resurgence in other venereal diseases, which reversed us to a somewhat less promiscuous generation practicing safer sex. At one time steroids and other substances derived from diosgenin constituted 15 percent of the world pharmaceutical market, which is today estimated at $150 billion. (I don't know what it is now in 2006.)

But converting diosgenin to progesterone is a complicated process, involving at least four chemical steps, according to Steven Dentali, Ph.D., *Pharmaceutical Sciences*: "Our bodies don't produce progesterone from yams, and can't get it from a tincture of wild yam either. The same is true for the adrenal hormone DHEA (dehydroepiandosterone), sometimes also said to be found in wild yam. There are no enzymatic pathways in the body known to be capable of producing these transformations" (*Am. Herb. Assoc.*, 1994).

Keville quotes sources saying that "people who eat wild yams will have some of progesterone's benefit" and that "regular yams...probably contain a fair amount of it too." But these quotes can be traced back to John Lee's book on progesterone. He is selling his book, if not "natural" progesterone. Certainly his book lists "sources of "natural" progesterone supplements in the back. But Lee, after mentioning natural progesterone as a remedy for most cases of PMS, does list several reportedly effective herbs besides wild yam root: burdock, chasteberry, comfrey, dong-quai, fo-ti, ginger, huang qi, licorice, motherwort, nettle, oat straw, raspberry, red clover, squaw-vine, and yellow dock. Lee attributes natural progesterone, topically applied, with the ability to help alleviate or prevent breast cancer, cervical dysplasia, dysmenorrhea, endometrial cancer, endometriosis, hot flashes, meno-pause, metorrhagia, ovarian cysts, PMS, and uterine fibroids. Some of that may well be true.

How well I remember lecturing to a feminist-oriented outdoor herb celebration up in the Catskills, leaving Peggy behind at Mohonk Resort in New York. I told my audience that most of the wild yam creams drawing such good rave reviews are spiked with synthetic progesterone, often labeled as natural because progesterone is a natural hormone. But these were spiked with commercial progesterone, perhaps converted from natural diosgenin. But the liberated ladies in my audience, while not throwing their wild yams at me, did say they were using homemade wild yam creams to which no external progesterone had been added. And they claimed to be getting progesteronic results. Rationalizing, I suspect that diosgenin itself has some transdermal effects, including progesteronic effects.

What does the folklore tell us about the wild yam? *Dioscorea villosa*, the species where the whole yam hormone story started, is the only yam species listed by Moerman in his *Medicinal Plants of Native America* (1986). He tells us that Fox women used the root to relieve the pain of childbirth. In my database (Duke and Wain, 1981) there's mention of uterotonic activity (Krochmal) in parturition, which does hint at estrogenic activity. The fact that slaves here in the U.S. used the wild yam for "rheumatism" may hint of steroid activity.

## The post-silicone era

After the silicone "bust," underendowed women might wish to consume more yams or, better yet, fenugreek. This might actually enlarge the breast. Anecdotally, fenugreek is reported to cause the breasts to enlarge so much that it was fed to harem women to make them more buxom. Diosgenin which occurs in wild yam and fenugreek seed, has been reported to stimulate growth of the mammary glands, at least in mice (Aradhana et al., 1992). Other estrogenic isoflavonoids, such as formononetin, available in clover and clover sprouts, might share in this mastogenic activity. Adding chocolate to the mix will add yet another reportedly mastogenic compound.

As I wrote this column, a food farmacy formula called "Bus-Tea," containing the food items listed above, suggested itself. With four reportedly mastogenic compounds, might it be effective?

Wild yam, mother of the pill,
Changed us more than most herbs will.

# Wintergreen (*Gaultheria procumbens*)

*The Wild Foods Forum* 13(5): 8-9, September/October, 2002

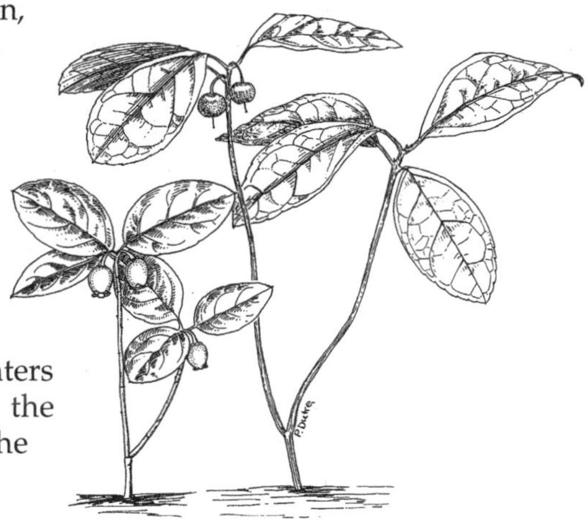

At Vickie's welcome invitation, I excerpt the wintergreen information from my most recent book. Unfortunately that book may be too expensive for many of the readers of *The Wild Foods Forum*. But maybe, if you like what you see, you can induce your local library to get a copy. CRC apparently caters to libraries who can afford the publisher's list price. The **Library of Congress** has all my CRC books, including the latest. [Duke, JA, Bogenschutz-Godwin, MJ, duCellier, J and Duke, PA. 2002. *CRC Handbook of Medicinal Spices*. CRC Press, Boca Raton, FL. $119.95] Wintergreen was one of about 60 species covered in this new book, illustrated by Mrs. Duke.

Oil of Wintergreen has been, and to some extent still is, used as a flavoring agent in beers, beverages, candies, chewing gums (e.g. the now rare Teaberry Gum), soft drinks, and dental preparations, often combined with menthol and eucalyptus. One rootbeer remedy called for 4 drachms wintergreen oil, 2 sassafras oil, 1 clove oil, and ca 120 g alcohol. The red to pinkish spicy fruits are eaten raw, and used in jams, jellies, pies, and syrup. Amerindians ate the berries, even in the snow. Leaves used to make an herbal tea (Mountain Tea), as a condiment, and a nibble. Stronger teas, candies, and wines, are made from the fermented bright-red leaves. Amerindians smoked and chewed the dried leaves. I have steeped the leaves and berries in vodka for my homemade liqueur called "Teaberry Trip," even in midwinter. In summer, I like to add wild ginger and bee-balm. Old timers steeped the leaves in brandy as a tonic liqueur.

No wonder I had little luck with the ladies in college. Musta been my teaberry gum. According to the *Annals on Endocrinology*, and authors Dominic and Pandey (1979), female mice do not return to heat (estrus) following exposure to males perfumed with oil of wintergreen (or a commercial perfume). Male urine may be the source of the pheromone involved in heat induction, ineffective because masked by the potent wintergreen aroma (in experimental rats, that is). Unable to perceive the male pheromone, due to wintergreen oil, females remain out of heat (in anestrus) following exposure to perfumed males. Hmm, negative aromatherapy?

One major active ingredient is methyl salicylate, now made synthetically.

Commercial oil of wintergreen is obtained from distillation of the twigs of black birch. The volatile oil contains 98-99% methyl salicylate. Arbutin, ericolin, gallic acid, gaultherine, gaultherilene, gaultheric acid, mucilage, tannin, wax, an ester, triacontane, and a secondary alcohol are also reported. Other acids reported include O-pyrocatechu-sic-, gentisinic-, salicylic-, p-hydroxybenzoic-, protocatechuic-, vanillic-, syringic-, p-coumaric-, caffeic-, and ferulic-acids. Here are a few of the more notable chemicals found in wintergreen.

In case you wondered, yes the wintergreen in the song here reproduced, represents a lady friend of mine I have known more than 50 years. All my songs are somewhat autobiographical. Witch hazel is about one I didn't know quite so long, just thirty years. Autumn's here, witch hazel flowers and wintergreen fruits persist in the bogs. Can the holiday season be just around the corner?

As the nights get longer, I particularly enjoy the evergreen species that add their greenery to the drab of winter. One fruit which still provides a nibble on New Year's day, a real treasure from Father Nature, is the small wintergreen, *Gaultheria procumbens* (closely rivaled by the tinier partridgeberry, *Mitchella repens*).

Both plants were very important medicinal species to the Amerindians, who no doubt nibbled on the small fruits as they traversed the wintry forest, much as I do on foraging hikes today. Like many Amerindian customs, though, the use of wintergreen is declining, lamentably. A decade ago, I enjoyed lunch with several natural product entrepreneurs, including a representative of one of the major spice companies. The latter confided that he probably had the last reserve of wintergreen in the country, possibly not to be replaced. The lowly wintergreen was early replaced by the stately cherry birch as a source of "wintergreen," both being generously endowed with goodly quantities of methyl-salicylate. A large tree, the cherry birch produces at least a hundredfold more biomass per acre than the diminutive wintergreen. My *Handbook of Northeastern Indian Medicinal Plants* lists over 700 species of plants for which I found published Amerindian uses as medicine. The waning wintergreen is just one of them. Although it had several medicinal applications among various Indian tribes, these may be more or less grouped into those uses that required a painkiller like aspirin, a counter-irritant like mustard, and an antiseptic germ killer like thymol. Looking at the literature, we find that wintergreen does have the forerunner of aspirin, salicylic acid, which has confirmed analgesic, antipyretic, and antirheumatic properties. Translating that, it has properties which make it useful for pain, fever, and rheumatism, three ailments for which the Indians reportedly used them. But the salicylic acid is a minor component of the wintergreen, the major component being methyl salicylate, which, in addition to the above properties, also has anti-inflammatory properties. The penetrating nature of this strong counterirritant is what has led to its presence in many of the topical rubs that Mother used to rub on our chests for colds or aching muscles to reduce both inflammation and pain. What about the antibiotic? Wintergreen contains the compound arbutin, which is both bactericidal and diuretic. So Father Nature's wintergreen combines three ingredients, all of which can be useful when the aches and pains of winter colds and flu set in, lowering the fever, killing the germs, reducing the inflammation and pains of swellings and aches and pains.

From my new spice book, here's my multiple activity menu for wintergreen showing which compounds in it can be helpful in flu. When you give your body an herbal tea, you are giving it a veritable menu of genetically familiar phytochemicals. Your body knows better than your herbalist, pharmacist or physician which, if any, of these phytochemicals the body needs. Through homeostasis, the body selects some of those needed, selectively mining the menu. That's what I mean when I say I prefer the herbal shotgun, with a wide array of medicines, versus the synthetic silver bullet, where the body has no choice.

Children who chew the roots for six weeks each spring reportedly suffer less tooth decay. Wintergreen leaves and/or fruits were used by North American Indians to keep their breath when portaging heavy loads. Algonquin guides chewed the leaves to improve their breathing (and I expect their breath) during hunting. Amerindians smoked and chewed the dried leaves. Quebec Indians rolled the leaves around aching teeth. The Iroquois even took wintergreen for kidney aches.

Once a major drug for cystitis and other infections, arbutin, like wintergreen, has dropped off main stage. For a while arbutin was important, but the pure arbutin was not as important as the plant extract, according to the Merck Index. Not necessarily speaking of wintergreen, Merck probably referred to some other member of the heath family when it said, "Gallotannin prevents enzymes such as beta-glucosidase from splitting arbutin, which explains why crude plant extracts are more effective medicinally than pure arbutin." (Emphasis mine.) No longer do we get arbutin, nor aspirin, nor methyl salicylate, nor even oil of wintergreen from wintergreen, but should I have a cold or urinary tract infection, I would not hesitate to drink wintergreen tea, and were I suffering a chest cold or a muscle ache, I would not hesitate to rub it down with wintergreen extracted into bear grease or hog-lard or even mentholatum. Many of the famous feline balms of the orient owe part of their aroma and effectiveness to methyl salicylate, which, like oil of wintergreen, can be fatally toxic in large doses. But then, all good medicines are toxic in large doses.

I find the aroma of the methyl salicylate, the active main ingredient in wintergreen, very pleasant. I frequently use a boswellin cream with wintergreen when my knee acts up. In Maine, we make wintergreen tea, drinking it and applying it topically for chronic or temporary pain. There are many analgesics in wintergreen. Wintergreen often complements red pepper's capsaicin, and peppermint's menthol in several OTC pain relievers, either these herbs alone, or any one of their constituents, or in various combinations. Methyl salicylate, like wintergreen, has long been employed in baths, liniments, and ointments, for pain relief, e.g. in gout, lumbago, rheumatism, and sciatica.

Strange how wintergreen, like so many powerful aromas, can be a fountain of youth. If the namesake of the song wintergreen were to massage my aching aging back with wintergreen, I'd forget my aches and age. Yes, the beautiful wintergreen persists on some few forest floors where many a moccasin trod centuries ago and too many off-road-recreational vehicles vehemently violate the environment, endangering the environmental treasures like wintergreen. The teaberry green and red signals the approach of the winter solstice.

### *Wintergreen*

*from Herbalbum by Jim Duke, © 1985*

Wintergreen, a breath of spring,
On the wintry forest floor.
It makes a body sing
When the songs don't come no more.

CHORUS
Wintergreen, where you been?
You're the prettiest thing I've seen
Breath of spring, throughout the year
Summers smile, Christmas Cheer.

Trailing nimbly on the ground
Where the sunshine's rarely seen,
What a breath of spring I found,
Taste of April, Wintergreen!

There are others may outshine you
They're more showy for awhile;
But the wintertime won't snow you,
You've still got your springtime smile.

Breath of spring throughout the year
Like the mountain air so clean;
Wear the snowdrop like a tear
Constant lover, wintergreen!

# Part Eight

# Herb A Day…
# North America – Naturalized

# Autumn Olive, Russian Olive (*Elaeagnus* spp.)

(Unpublished, circa 1993)

With the signing of the Israeli and PLO peace pact, there may be a bit more impetus to travel to the Middle East. I must admit that I felt much safer walking at night in Tel-Aviv two years ago than in any other major city of the world. But the hope of peace in the Middle East prompts me to revisit my *Medicinal Plants of the Bible*, now long out of print. I'd like to quote one confusing observation therefrom: "Planted in the wilderness, some of the Biblical oil or olive trees are concluded to be the Russian olive, a common shrub in Palestine...I may have eaten many of the astringent fruits as a boy in Carolina, not realizing I might be sharing a culinary experience with the Children of Israel." In Nehemiah *:15 we are urged to go out to the hills and gather branches of olives and wild olives. I suspect the wild olive may well have been *Elaeagnus angustifolia*. Where I grew up in North Carolina, we used to call them sugarberries. Some of the books today, however, call this weedy, yet useful shrub Russian olive. Other books call it oleaster, silverberry, or wild olive. Making matters worse, there's another silverberry, *Elaeagnus commutata* Bernh. I think I've eaten both of them, out of hand, without a great deal of pleasure.

## Identification tricky

It is easy to recognize the genus *Elaeagnus* because of the silvery scales on the bottom of the leaves and dotting the edible fruit as well. If the descriptions in *Hortus Third* are accurate, the two species reported for Maryland can be distinguished as follows:

Leaves silvery on both surfaces; fruits silvery, on very short stalks; spines, not mentioned; shrub to 12 feet; hardy to Zone 2 . . . . . . . . . . . . . . . . . . . . . . . . . . . . .Silver Berry

Leaves silvery only below; fruits yellow, silvery, on very short stalks; twigs, sometimes spiny; shrub to 20 feet tall; hardy to Zone 3 . . . . . . . . . . . . . . . . . . . . . . .Russian Olive

Unfortunately, the *Elaeagnus* berries I enjoyed on the fall equinox, 1993, were not yellow or silvery; they were red (and I'm down in Zone 5 or 6). So Hortus was no help to me in trying to identify my foraging materials. Hortus does mention *E. latifolia*, *E. macrophylla*, *E. multiflora*, *E. philippense*, and *E. pungens* as having red fruits. So I'll be generic. It might take me two weeks, maybe two years, maybe a lifetime, to figure out positively which species of *Elaeagnus* we collected and enjoyed on the equinox.

Some drupes ("berries") were oblong, some globose. Some of the berries were orange, some deep red, most more or less dotted with silvery scales. Some were terribly astringent, others less so. Some had just two or three berries at the nodes; others had dense clusters of 20 to 30 or more berries.

It seemed to be a super fruiting year in 1993, following a spring in which the odor of the flowers, somewhat like narcissus, permeated the countryside. Tempted by this bounty, we picked a pint each from three different strains and took them home to make what I'll call sugarberry leather-same texture as, and rather similar in flavor and consistency to, guava paste! It's quite a treat and could be effectively and economically extended with apple juice. My friend merely bruised the fruits, heated them gently in boiling water, added sugar, and simmered a few minutes.

## Nutritious fruits

I don't think we would have spent so much time on *Elaeagnus*, had it not been for some new-crop enthusiasts excited about importing the closely related sea buckthorn, *Hippophae rhamnoides* L., to the United States. They are excited because sea buckthorn has very nutritious fruits, with 30 to 40 mg beta-carotene per 100-g serving (half cup). It takes only 50 mg every other day to prevent a second heart attack, at least according to some studies widely reported last year. That same half cup (100 g) could have 50 to 600 mg vitamin C.

Our local *Elaeagnus* did not check out so rich in vitamins C and E, having 50 mg and 10 mg per 100 g, respectively, according to analyses done by USDA's Dr. Helen Norman. Perhaps our *Elaeagnus* may prove to be equally rich in carotenoids. Little by little we learned that it, now best identified as *Elaeagnus unbellata*, is a better source of lycopene than tomato; but because of its invasiveness, the USDA is said to be destroying its plants. Some shrubs can produce 35 pounds of fruit a year, fixing nitrogen at the same time. And they are "low-maintenance" ornamental shrubs.

One California study said that 300 to 400 mg a day of vitamin C could add six years to a man's life, one year to a woman's. And studies in longevity centers in the U.S. seem almost as high on vitamin E. Sea buckthorn is incredibly rich in vitamin E, 160 mg/100 g; that's about 15 times the RDA. Vitamin E probably has as much life-saving utility as vitamins A and C. The administrator of the conservative USDA once said, "Megadoses of vitamin E may help recharge the immune systems of older people." And a Harvard study showed that women who took vitamin E in supplements 10 times the RDA had 40 percent fewer heart attacks than women who did not. Men who took four times their RDA "reduced their chances of developing heart disease by 37 percent, compared to men who took less than 7.5 units [half the RDA]."

Thus, if our weedy silverberry is even half as rich in vitamins as the sea buckthorn, it could still save lives in vitamin-deficient people. But as we'll see, the lycopene and carotenoids in our *Elaeagnus* may outshine the storehouse in Hippophae. Stay tuned!

## Afghan (more properly Autumn, Bohemian, or Russian) Olive (*Elaeagnus* spp.)

If I am late with my newsletter submission, I blame it on the terrorists. They delayed my flight 5 days (and clearly slowed our whole economy), from my KLM/Northwest flights, to the security checks at the airlines etc. Finally home 4 days and 3 thousand dollars shorter, I fear I may be more reluctant to fly as frequently in the future. And I think the airline and travel and ecotour industries will all be hurt. But there could possibly be positive side effects. For too long we have defied gravity with high energetic costs as a consequence. The terrorist's attack on America may get more of us back on the ground where we belong, and stimulate research into self sufficiency, making us more independent of those rogue nations trying to cripple us with petroleum costs. America the green could survive on green alcohol (ethanol produced from renewable biomass) replacing the black gold (petroleum) with farm produced oilseeds and diesels. Wail, Willie, Wail. Then the rogue nations could drink their petroleum on their deserts. Or maybe we could trade them water for the last of their oil. But if we got back into fuel-efficient autos, buses and trains, on the ground, we could decrease our reliance on middle eastern oil significantly, damaging their economies, perhaps as much as they have damaged ours. Without their ill-gained oil-derived billions, they might be dethroned while the resilience of our free society will keep us alive. Starved of oil income, terrorism might self destruct.

After that polemic introduction, triggered by my lost days and dollars in Europe, here's my first attempt to get HAD going again. Ironically it's on another Biblical plant that I wrote up over a decade ago, when tensions were relaxing, not tightening. It's a fast growing weedy low-maintenance shrub that fixes nitrogen (saving us the high energy intensive fertilizer costs), It produces up to 35 pounds of fruits (per tree) which can be converted into food, or lycopene pills with renewable green alcohol as a byproduct. The leaves can be used to feed animals, whose manure might also be gathered for energy production (via methane)

In all the hype we've heard in these weeks following the 9/11 event, economists and politicians urge us to continue consuming as a patriotic effort. "Buy stocks to prop up the market; fly to prop up the airline industry; take a small hotel to prop up the hotel industry, take those trips as though nothing has happened; keep up your wanton and wastrel consumption," our government tells us, not too intelligently me thinks. They fail to realize or admit, that over-consumption of energy is what gets us into this crisis. They should be urging us to conserve and learn to subsist on renewable American sources of energy, not middle eastern petroleum. Today ethanol may be more expensive to produce in the U.S. than petroleum, but that will change when the oil runs out. If we are better prepared for that now with engines that can run on ethanol, transesterified diesels from agricultural oil seeds, as well as petroleum, we could actually lower the costs of our imported petroleums.

You may find amusing (I find it depressing) what I optimistically wrote, almost a decade ago, about this energy species, especially if you compare it to one of the first chapters in my afghan survival manual (currently a very rough draft seeking military sponsorship).

With the signing of the Israeli and PLO peace pact, there may be a bit more impetus to travel to the Middle East. I must admit that I felt much safer walking at night in Tel-Aviv two years ago than in any other major city of the world. But the hope of peace in the Middle East prompts me to revisit my *Medicinal Plants of the Bible*, now long out of print. I'd like to quote one confusing observation therefrom:

"Planted in the wilderness, some of the Biblical oil or olive trees are concluded to be the Russian olive, a common shrub in Palestine...I may have eaten many of the astringent fruits as a boy in Carolina, not realizing I might be sharing a culinary experience with the Children of Israel (Duke, J. 1994. "Russian Olive," *Coltsfoot*).

Sunday, I found myself botanizing with my daughter up near Blind Lake, near Northville Michigan, and we indulged in a few of her local russian olives. You see, we were late getting to Detroit Saturday night, and had to take another hundred dollar room at the Marriott (beat the profiteering $300 rooms that scalped us in Munich). Unable to get a connecting flight home until 3:00 in the P.M., we called my daughter Celia from Detroit. She agreed to pick us up in the morning and take a quick tour of her yard, now decorated with native plants, and then out to the Potawatomi Trail near her summer home on Blind Lake, Michigan. That was the best walk I had enjoyed in over two weeks. So I indulged in several of the afghan olives (my silly name for *Elaeagnus angustifolia*, reserving the more glamorous name autumn olive, for *Elaeagnus umbellata*). And then back to the airport. I've spent most of the German two weeks in public transportation of one kind or another, indulging the german CCCC's: castles, cathedrals, coin-water closets, and consumptive shopping, none of which are my cups of kraut juice.

Back home again, Monday, and cranking up the old computer, I was delighted to read that my friend Ingrid Fordham's research was finally coming to fruition. And the autumn olive was finally being recognized as a better source of lycopene than tomato. I went to the USDA database and took a look at the first species under the genus *Elaeagnus*, *E. angustifolia*. Afghanistan was the first geographic entry under *E. angustifolia*. The more rotund autumn olive was not listed for Afghanistan. But both are weeds here in Maryland, sometimes viewed as noxious, and I'll wager that they both can be found in Afghanistan. Clearly the one being studied by Ms. Fordham is the superior one, *E. umbellata*, with plumper, redder, less acidic, nonmealy fruits, in generous clusters, easier stripped than the inferior Russian or afghan olive, with mealy, narrower, oranger, more acidic fruits, often solitary or paired but rarely in big clusters.

Rich in lycopene and fairly well endowed with ascorbic acid and tocopherol, those tart vitamin "pills," the fruits, even contain some analgesic principles as well. Some shrubs of *E. umbellata*, can produce 35 pounds of fruit a year, fixing nitrogen at the same time. And they are "low-maintenance" ornamental shrubs. And great for reclaiming West Virginia's strip mined soils. My son has a farm up in Green Briar County, West Virginia where the CCC introduced *Elaeagnus*, maybe as early as the thirties, for soil stabilization.

I enjoy seeing what is said of these two species over a hundred years ago in Watt's *Dictionary of the Economic Products of India*, where the Russian olive is also called Bohemian olive, Jerusalem willow, and oleaster. A gum like gum arabic exudes from the wounded bark. The acid berries are largely eaten in Tibet, Baluchistan, and Afghanistan. In Yarkand, an alcoholic liquor is distilled from the berries. The dried berries, called Trebizond dates, are made into cakes by the Arabs. In Baluchistan, the leaves are given as fodder to goats and sheep. In Ladak roots are used as fuses for match locks. Much later we read that the Turkish use the root bark in teas for dysuria (EB49(4):406). Of *E. umbellata*, the seeds and flowers are used as stimulants in cough. The expressed oil of the seed is used for pulmonary ailments. Flowers are considered astringent and cardiac.

But these days, the lycopene is getting all the play, and not just as a cancer preventive. Infertile couples might even benefit from the lycopene so prevalent in the *Elaeagnus*. New Delhi scientists suggest that orally administered lycopene ( 2 mg, twice daily) for 3 months to infertile men aged 23 to 45 can improve sperm activity and shape, statistically significantly. Sperm concentration improved in 20 of 30 patients. Almost three in four displayed improved sperm activity; some 60% showed improved sperm cell shape. Oral lycopene therapy seems to have a role in managing infertility of unknown causes, Nagpur meeting of the Indian Association of Urologists, January, 2001). If these Indian scientists are correct and 4 mg/day lycopene will correct infertility, and the USDA correct in saying there are 15-54 mg/100 g lycopene in *Elaeagnus* fruits, then it would only take 10-25 grams (less than an ounce) fresh fruit to provide that level of lycopene. It would take 12 times more, still managable, to provide the level (60 mg/day) that lowers cholesterol 14%. Autumn olive leather might be a convenient source, even better than tomato paste.

# Burdock, Great Burdock, "Gobo" (*Arctium lappa*)

*The Wild Foods Forum* 17(3):8-9, Summer 2006

## Dec. 20, 1998

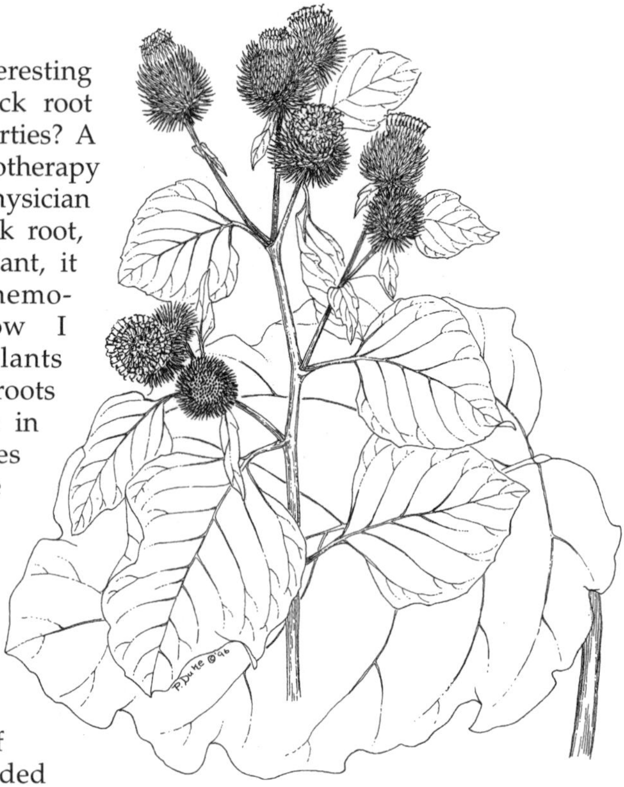

Recently I got an interesting question: "Does burdock root have antioxidant properties? A customer taking chemotherapy needs to know. Her physician said not to use burdock root, because as an antioxidant, it might nullify the chemotherapy." Here's how I answered her. All plants contain antioxidants; roots are not always as rich in antioxidants as leaves (where plants generate all the oxygen we breathe). Burdock is not particularly noteworthy as an antioxidant. Would her physicians tell her not to take green tea or rosemary tea, both of which are better loaded with antioxidants; and all our leafy vegetables contain beta-carotene, ascorbic acid, and tocopherol (all of which have anticancer, antioxidant and chemopreventive and immune boosting chemicals). Would this physician tell her not to use them? It is true. however; antioxidants can interfere with certain types of chemotherapy, in which the pharmaceutical directs oxidative burst against the tumor cells. Well perhaps I shouldn't tell my readers this, but if it were me, I might take the burdock and scrap the doctor and the chemotherapy. I'd find a doctor who wanted to boost my immune system. The pharmaceutical approach damages both tumor and patient. The natural and healthier complementary approach might be to boost the immune system with foods, herbs and spices known to be rich in anticancer compounds and immunostimulants.

Charlton (1998) suggests burdock and blessed thistle provide two important antiretroviral antitumor lignans, arctigenin and trachelogenin. He provided data showing that artcigenin and trachelogenin are antiretroviral at 0.27 and 0.52 uM. Not only did they reduce HIV viral protein production and inhibit reverse transcriptase activity, they also inhibited topoisomerase II00. Elsewhere these have shown activity against leukemia, lymphoma, and various types of tumors.

## Arctigenin

Arctigenin is a lignan in burdock seeds and roots, and I imagine in the petioles which I enjoy in my gobo gumbo. Boik (1996) says that arctigenin has demonstrated potent cytotoxic effects against HL-60 human lymphocytic leukemia (IC50 0.067 ug/ml) close to the levels for the toxic methotrexate and vincristine. Additionally arctigenin was non-toxic to normal lymphocytes. Arctigenin was less potent at inhibiting growth of MOLT-4 human T-lymphocytic leukemia cells (IC50=0.53 ug/ml). Since burdock seeds (or at least the sprouts) are regarded as human foods, I'd not hesitate to ingest the seeds and/or sprouts myself. Burdock seeds induce differentiation in myeloid leukemia cells in mice. Roots contain a mix of tumor inhibitors. One complex polymer in the burdock reduces the rates of tumor-causing mutations. So burdock is both preventive and therapeutic (Crouse 1997).

In the course of screening for pharmacologically active substances from extracts of crude drugs used traditionally in Sino-Japanese herbal medicines, it was found that the 70% ethanol extract from the fruits of *Arctium lappa* L. (Compositae) showed potent antiproliferative activity against B cell hybridoma cell, MH60. By bioassay-guided purification, a new lignan, (+)-7,8-didehydroarctigenin, together with the known lignans (-)-arctigenin and (-)-matairesinol were isolated as the active ingredients from an aqueous ethanolic extract of the fruits of *A. lappa*. Of these active compounds, (-)-arctigenin showed the most potent antiproliferative activity against MH60 cells (IC (50) : 1.0 microM), and the activity was suggested to be due to apoptosis.

My highest score for safety is +++, usually reserved for food plants and wholesome tea constituents. Burdock is a food plant. Under all the activities, I have a lot of f's, the f meaning folkloric, where I have 1, that means there is some next tuber or animal or phytochemical data suggesting a degree of efficacy; 2 would mean approved by Commission E, or strongly supported by my phytochemical database; 3 would mean supported by human clinical trials. Sure we have used big words in this shorthand reporting of the reported activities and indications for the herbs. We don't want to encourage self diagnosis and self medication. If you don't know what all those words mean, they are probably not of much import to you anyhow. And unlike the recently released PDR, we tell you not only where we got the indication, but whether I think it is folkloric or has weak, some, or strong evidence (1, 2, and 3, respectively.) Since burdock is a food, I would not myself be afraid to try it even for those indications that are deemed more folkloric than proven. But believe me I would take burdock, as a food farmaceutical, if I were targeted for cancer, leukemia, lymphoma, or if I had any of those or AIDS. Thus I don't yet find any strong evidence for the folkloric indications like acne and anorexia. If I do, I will upgrade my evaluation on the interactive database.

## GOBO GUMBO (for cancer)

Gobo gumbo is a soup I make from the leaf stalks of gobo, which you may know as the weed burdock (*Arctium lappa*), and I spice it up with turmeric (*Curcuma longa*). I think I lower my chances against the colon cancer that got my dad and two of his brothers.

Can an atavistic reversion to weed-eating prevent, if not cure, cancer? We, who believe our diet has strayed too far from the paleolithic diet with which our genes evolved for hundreds of millenia, belive the answer is yes.

The grim title is attractively alliterative if not alluringly illiterate. But it was spawned a few years back when the senior author was gingerly and grimly approached by a desperate father whose daughter had what appeared to be a terminal glioma. (Dorland's 25 edition defines glioma as a tumor of neuroglial tissue, admitting that the term is sometimes extended to include all cerebral and spinal cord neoplasms.) "Gobo" is the Japanese name for the Japanese vegetable or the American weed that we call burdock. "Gumbo" is an ethnic soup thickened with okra, *Abelmoschus esculentus*, which like cotton contains the antitumor compound gossypol (at 10 ppm). Gossypol is also reported to induce interferon.

After reviewing medline literature and noting associations between blastomas and lymphomas, the senior author reported to the father that he would go for turmeric and burdock, which I think could have prolonged Jackie Onassis' life. Yes, both gobo and turmeric contain antilymphomic lignans. Today, I thicken my gobo with kudzu roots, or other leguminous seeds rich in daidzein a/o genistein, both of which seem indicated for several anticancer activities.

Should he also resort to brain foods, hoping they would help direct the curcumin and lignans to the brain? If so, go for high tryptophan and high serotonin foods. Reading that vitamin $B_6$ is necessary to convert dietary tryptophan to serotonin, I might take 40 or 50 mg pyridoxine a day. That's more than you can get dietarily. Jew's Mallow (*Corchorus olitorius*) is highest in my data base but it would take a dry kilo to give me that 50 mg pyridoxine. Cauliflower and watercress are also good sources, with of course other anticancer compounds. I'd munch on bananas which can contain 25 ppms pyridoxine and 100 mg serotonin.

Charlton sort of dashed water on my hopes for burdock and blessed thistle as anticancer lignan provider. He provided data showing that arctigenin and trachelogenin are antiretroviral at 0.27 and 0.52 uM. Not only did they reduce HIV viral protein production and inhibit reverse transcriptase activity, they also inhibited topoisomerase II00.

## References

Charlton, J.L. 1998. "Antiviral activity of lignans." *J. Nat. Prod.* 61(11):1447-1451.

Crouse, L.V. 1997. "Naturopathic treatment of ovarian cancer." *J Naturopathic Med.* 7(1):51-56.

*Planta Med*. February, 2006. "Antiproliferative and apoptotic effects of butyrolactone lignans from *Arctium lappa* on leukemic cells." 72(3):276-8.

Matsumoto T, Hosono-Nishiyama K, Yamada H. Kitasato Institute for Life Sciences & Graduate School of Infection Control Sciences, Kitasato University and Oriental Medicine Research Center, Tokyo, Japan.

## *Gobo Gumbo Soup*

I don't know but I'll bet you can,
Cancel more than cancer with one lignan
Turmeric and burdock roots,
Genistein from young bean shoots
Onion, garlic, chile, too,
All of them are good for you.

Guess gobo gumbo's worth a try;
Yes! I'd rather eat than dye (freudian slip).

Burdock leaf stalks, and/or diced root, with as much turmeric as possible, whole onions and garlic (for their quercetin), and as available, the following better daidzein and genistein sources, scurfy pea (*Psoralea corylifolia*), kudzu root (*Pueraria lobata*), faba bean sprouts (*Vicia faba*), miso (from soy, *Glycine max*, or other high genistein legume), mungbean sprouts (*Vigna* spp.), clover heads (*Trifolium pratense*), okra for its gossypol (*Abelmoschus esculentus*) and a mixture of edible beans or legume seeds; if available, purslane. Add al gusto, the following antitumor spices, cayenne (the hotter the pepper, the more capsaicin), garlic, ginger, licorice (distasteful to some), mustard, onion (leave the skin on), oregano, rosemary, savory, sesame, thyme, and more TURMERIC.

# Chicory (*Cichorium intybus*)

*The Business of Herbs* 5(3):14, July/August, 1987

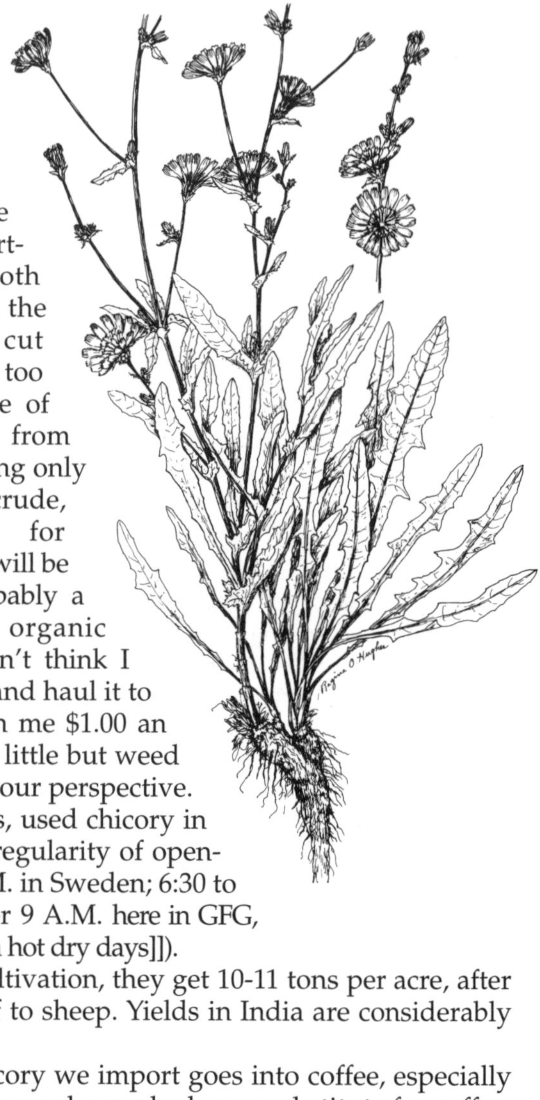

Would you believe we imported nearly 3,000 tons of chicory last year (1986), with ca 1,000 tons of crude chicory (down 500 from 1985) from Poland, and nearly 1,000 tons processed chicory from France. Counting the crude and processed, we imported ca $3 million worth, both years. Some speculate that the Chernobyl incident may cut imports from these countries, too close to Russia and the wave of radioactivity that emanated from Chernobyl. With the U.S. paying only about $0.20 a pound (for crude, compared with $0.50/lb. for processed), I don't think there will be any major shifts. There's probably a ton at **Herbal Vineyard**, organic unradiated chicory. But I don't think I want to dig it, wash it, dry it, and haul it to market for $400. It might earn me $1.00 an hour. Of course, my chicory is little but weed or wildflower, depending on your perspective. The famous botanist, Linnaeus, used chicory in his floral clock because of its regularity of opening and closing (5:00-10:00 A.M. in Sweden; 6:30 to noon in Britain; [[closer to 8 or 9 A.M. here in GFG, and closing by early afternoon on hot dry days]]).

In New Zealand, under cultivation, they get 10-11 tons per acre, after the nutritious foliage is fed off to sheep. Yields in India are considerably lower.

Much, if not all, of the chicory we import goes into coffee, especially Louisiana brands of coffee. It is used, scorched, as a substitute for coffee. But chicory drinking, like coffee drinking, must be an acquired taste. According to *Poisonous and Medicinal Plants of Southern and Eastern Africa*, "the young root is edible, prepared in manner similar to the parsnip or to the carrot." Both roots and shoots are bitter to my taste, but some people eat them after processing. The leaves and roots are suggestive of the related dandelions in both appearance and taste.

From a medicinal point, the roots contain inulin rather than the sugars so bad on some diabetics. Rich in potassium, the ashes of the root could be used as a diuretic (in India the root is highly regarded as a diuretic). Like the dandelion, it has a strong folk reputation for liver ailments. Even the Romans prescribed it for such. Small amounts of harman and norharman also occur in roasted chicory roots. In an emergency, those dependent on quinidine for arrhythmia, might, in desperation, resort to a chicory liqueur. "Alcoholic extracts of chicory root have been demonstrated to exhibit marked depression of amplitude and rate on the isolated heart, simulating the effects of quinidine on the heart" (Leung's *Encyclopedia of Common Natural Ingredients*). Small wonder that Egyptians value the plant for tachycardia. Although the plant is harmless in small doses to animals.

Seeds, containing sterols, oleic- and linoleic-acids, are considered demulcent, refrigerant, and tonic, and are used as a menstrual stimulant (emmenagogue) and to correct "bilious vomiting."

The milky juice (latex) of the plant contains caoutchouc (rubber), and could even serve as an emergency source. Some suspect that, like lettuce, chicory contains sedatives, working like opiates. In his *Honest Herbal*, Tyler mentions an old study concluding that lactucin and lactucopicrin, present in the chicory latex, produce a sedative effect on the central nervous system, capable of antagonizing the stimulant properties of the more arousing caffeine beverages. I share Dr. Tyler's skepticism that the chicory has any serious sedative effect, but were I needing, but lacking, a mild sedative, I'd make me a scorched chicory tea [[sans caffeine]], and curl up with a good soporific book in a warm bed. A good vegetable or herbal "bouillon," to my taste, can be made by steeping flowers of chicory and red clover in a salted decoction of chives, with a dash of dill and a smaller dash of fennel, well peppered.

[[Since I wrote this, inulin has arisen as a superstar among oligosaccharides; chicory is the richest source of inulin in my USDA database. Those wishing to dig deeper (yes chicory goes pretty deep) should consult the newletter, *Active Food Scientific Monitor*, of the ORAFTI Organization (www.orafti.com). ORAFTI produces oligofructose, and fructose from chicory roots. I subscribe, hoping that oligofructans (prebiotics) and *Lactobacillus* (probiotics) might lessen my odds for colon cancer. I actually sought them out after a major gut sepsis in Peru, when I took Peggy, my two children and their children to the Amazon for New Years, 2005/6. They'll remember the good things longer than they will that bug that hit us on the last day of our wonderful week. Inulin and oligofructose are dietary fibers, which, like all dietary fibres, are not digested in the stomach or small intestine. They are fermented in the colon, contributing to better gut function, improving regularity and reducing constipation. I've been a high fiber freak for decades, and continue this passive approach to colon cleansing, even since the authorities told us that fiber did not prevent colon cancer. I still believe that a high fiber diet reduces my odds for the cancer that killed my dad.]]

# Coltsfoot (*Tussilago farfara*)

*The Business of Herbs* 9(4):10-11. September/October, 1991

## Cancer cause or cure?

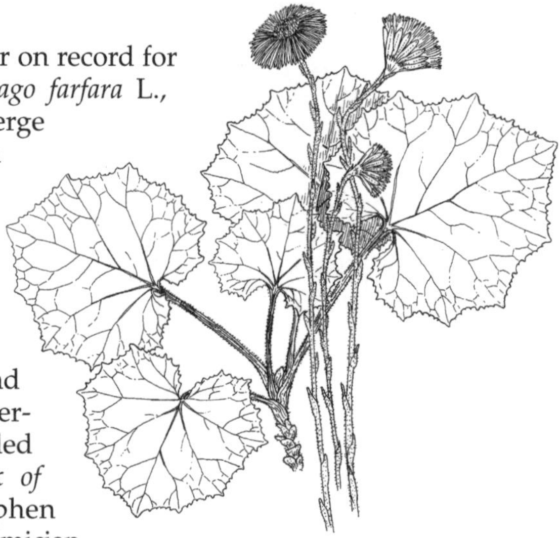

Following the warmest year on record for Maryland, coltsfoot, *Tussilago farfara* L., was the first flower to emerge in my 1991 herb garden (on January 18). It's one of my favorites for inclusion in floral phenology and floral clocks. And it's the namesake of my favorite forager's periodical, *Coltsfoot*.

Readers of *Coltsfoot* and *Business of Herbs* will be interested in a new book called *Cornucopia, A Source Book of Edible Plants*, by Stephen Facciola. As National Academician Noel Vietmeyer says in the introduction, it "records the more than 3,000 (food) species available in the U.S. and abroad."

Vietmeyer gives other numbers of interest to foragers: At least 20,000 species of plants have usefully edible parts, but only 3,000 to 4,000 have been used on a regular basis. Facciola puts it a bit differently: "There are approximately fifteen thousand species of plants recorded in the literature as having been used as food by man. One hundred fifty or more of these have been cultivated on a commercial scale... Yet today, most of the world is fed by approximately twenty crops..."

Rounding off and speculating a bit, this all suggests to me that, of the 250,000 higher plant species of the world, 2,500 could be grown in the U.S. (remember that Yanovsky alone listed 1,112 Amerindian food plants north of Mexico), 250 are of major importance, while 25 provide 90% or more of the world's vegetarian cuisine. This 678-page book has done a good job, efficiently covering more than these 2,500 species.

Working on the CRC *Handbook of Edible Weeds,* I was debating whether or not to include coltsfoot. It's a roadside weed in the northeast and is ingested by many foragers. Here's what Facciola has to say about it: "The young leaves, flower buds and young flowers can be eaten in salads, soups or as a potherb. Fresh or dried leaves and flowers are used for preparing an aromatic tea. The slender rootstock is candied in sugar syrup. A delicious country wine is made from the flowers. Ash from the leaves is used as a salt substitute."

## Alkaloid Alert!

That quote alone would suggest that this is an edible weed worth including in the foraging books. But! There's nothing there about the controversial pyrrolizidine alkaloids (PAs), also found in borage, comfrey, heliotrope (*Heliotropium*), rattlepod (*Crotalaria*), squawroot (*Senecio*) and the closely related butterbur (*Petasites*) [[which blooms even earlier than coltsfoot]]. PAs can induce cancer of the liver and other liver ailments if ingested in large quantities. There's even talk of banning the plants, like comfrey, that contain PAs.

Perhaps you'll remember back in 1987 when we ran a column on basil and the HERP Index, Bruce Ames's controversial method for comparing relative carcinogenicities. In that issue I showed that comfrey leaf tea, while much more carcinogenic for its PA than tap water was for its chloroform, was much less carcinogenic than beer with its ethanol. I did not and do not mean to imply that comfrey leaf is safe. But the cancer risk a daily beer poses is nearly 100 times the risk posed by a daily cup of comfrey leaf tea. Ames's data indicated that nine comfrey root capsules a day might be more than twice as dangerous as the daily beer.

Without quantitative data telling me how much of each PA there is in coltsfoot (and carcinogenicity data for each of the PAs), I can't really tell you whether eating an ounce of coltsfoot is more liable to cause cancer than eating an ounce of peanut butter. [[At age 76, I probably downed another ounce of peanut butter today.]] I frankly feel that federal agencies should give us hard data like that before they ban any minor carcinogens. Perhaps they should give us a risk/benefit analysis as well.

After all, coltsfoot has quite a folk medicinal reputation. Foster and Duke in their *Field Guide to Medicinal Plants* note that smoke from coltsfoot is believed to act as an antihistamine, which tends to explain the use of coltsfoot cigarettes for asthma and coughs. They add that the leaves have spasmolytic activity and that the leaf mucilage soothes inflamed mucous membranes.

## Asthma Alternative?

Does smoking coltsfoot leaves really help asthma? Does it help more or less than the expensive natural or synthetic pharmaceuticals being prescribed for asthma? Should people who can't afford the pharmaceuticals be given more reliable information about herbal alternatives?

I have enjoyed coltsfoot candy, made by boiling down the rootstocks in sugar water. I suspect that it is as good and safe a cough drop as many of the OTC and prescription cough remedies available to us. But I can't imagine a drug company investing $600 million to prove coltsfoot candy safe and efficacious for coughs or coltsfoot cigarettes for asthma. You and I could make our homegrown candy and cigarettes, and they'd have trouble recouping their investment. And, of course, they have proprietary synthetic drugs bringing in billions of dollars for these ailments and iatrogenic (treatment-induced) ailments caused by the synthetics.

Hsu et al. in their *Oriental Materia Medica* suggest doses of 5 to 9 grams (ca π ounce) dried flower buds for asthma, cough, etc. They note that the aqueous root extract reduces or prevents fever. Duke and Ayensu (*Medicinal Plants of China*) add apoplexy, bronchitis, colds, dysphagia, fever, flu, hemoptysis, phthisis and, finally, lung cancer. They note that extracts show antibacterial, antitussive, and CNS-depressant activity.

## Cancer Cause or Cure?

Hartwell's *Plants Used Against Cancer* suggests that, instead of causing liver cancer, the plant is a folk remedy for liver ailments. Just last year we saw that lecithin prevented cirrhosis in chimpanzees. Remember, coltsfoot is close kin to dandelion, and dandelion flowers are twice as high in lecithin as the well-known soybean. I suspect that there is probably lecithin in coltsfoot, too, and that may perhaps lie behind the folk use of the coltsfoot for indurations of the liver.

Concluding, let me pose an unanswered question! Do moderate doses of coltsfoot cause or cure liver problems? Until we have an answer to that question, I can't see the rationale for outlawing another relatively innocuous herb while we drown in alcohol and choke on tobacco smoke. Immoderate rat diets of 4% coltsfoot definitely induce liver ailments! But the 5 to 9 grams recommended by the Chinese in my case would be quite modest, and I would estimate quite safe, if not efficacious. One man's food is another man's poison. One woman's flower is another woman's weed. This is quite a weed, cup of tea, candy, coughdrop, potherb, asthma cigarette, possible cancer cause, possible cancer cure.

# Dandelion (*Taraxacum officinale*)

(Unpublished ca 2000)

Stay! Friend or Foe;
She just won't go
Spray? Yea or Nay;
She's hear to stay

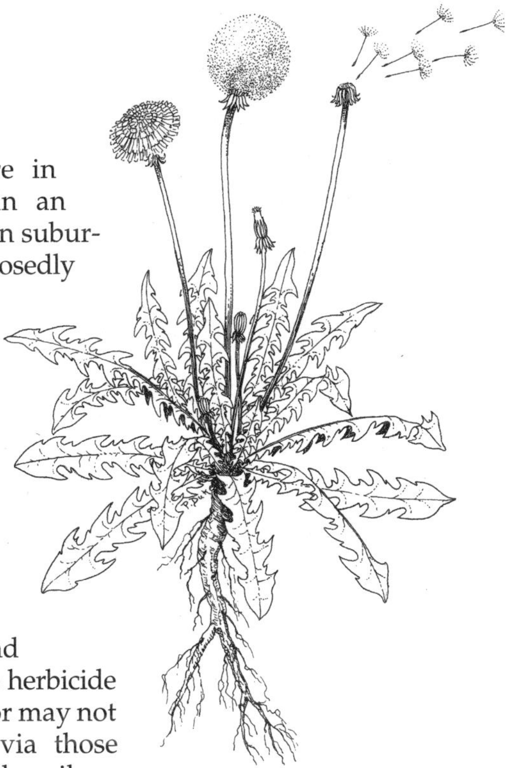

As the lawns green up here in Maryland, I am amused, but in an unpleasant way, by the war between suburbanites and the dandelion, supposedly one of the bitter herbs of the Bible. Too bad the health nuts popping their vitamin pills don't recognize that these bitter herbs of the Bible are Nature's original vitamin pills. Suburban gardeners, among them many health nuts, after an armchair night at the TV, and inspired by TV ads, charge out and spray individual dandelions, actually an attractive combination of green and yellow, with herbicide. And yes, the herbicide can kill the dandelion, which may or may not still set its prodigious progeny via those seeds so easily dispersed with the silvery parachutes. What could be prettier than a bevy of green and gold dandelion being visited by slate and gold goldfinches, eating as many of those seeds as they can before bird and seed fly away. With those parachutes, did dandelions arrive in America before humans? I don't know, but I'll bet they did. I'll also wager that the dandelions are still here after humans and herbicides have moved on to the Great Roundup in the Sky. Cockroaches and dandelions shall survive. The meek shall inherit the earth.

Here's what I said about the lowly dandelion in my *Medicinal Plants of the Bible*:

**Taraxacum officinale** Weber cx Wigg.
**Dandelion**

*...eat it with unleavened bread and bitter herbs...* Numbers 9

Probably the children of Israel learned to eat bitter herbs from the Egyptians. Ancient Egyptians used to place the green herbs on the table, mixed with mustard, and then dunked their bread in the mixture. The Moldenke's (Moldenke & Moldenke, 1952) believed that *Cichorium endivia*,

*Cichorium intybus, Lactuca sativa, Nasturtium officinale, Rumex acetosella,* and *Taraxacum officinale* were among the green herbs of the Bible. Dandelion is sometimes eaten raw in salads, but often blanched like endive and used as a green; frequently cooked with salt pork or bacon to enhance the flavor. Roots are sometimes pickled. Flowers used to make a wine. Ground roasted roots used for dandelion coffee, and sometimes mixed with real coffee. Dried leaves are an ingredient in many digestive or diet drinks and herb beers. Birds like the seeds and pigs devour the whole plant. Goats eat the leaves, but sheep, cattle and horses do not care for it. Dandelion has also been used as a source of latex.

Said to be alterative, aperient, aperitif, bactericidal, cholagogue, depurative, diuretic, intoxicant, lactagogue, laxative, stimulant, stomachic, and tonic, dandelion finds a place in many folk remedies, for abscesses, ague, anemia, arthritis, bad appetite, bilious afflictions, blood, bronchitis, bruises, cancer, caries, catarrh, conjunctivitis, consumption, diabetes, dropsy, dyspepsia, eczema, fever, gallbladder, gallstones, gonorrhea, gout, gravel, heart, heartburn, hemorrhoids, hepatitis, hypochondria, inappetence, indigestion, indurations, insomnia, jaundice, kidney, liver, malaria, nephritis, nerves, piles, rheumatism, scirrhus, sclerosis, scurvy, scrofula, skin, snakebite, splenitis, stones, swelling, tumors, urinary ailments, warts, and wounds (Duke & Wain, 1981; *Quisumbing*, 1951). Hartwell also mentions indurations of the glands, liver, mesentery and spleen, and cancer of the bladder, bowel and breast. The leaves have a higher vitamin A content (14,000 IU/100g) than carrots (11,000 IU/100g). Coumestrol is estrogenic. Dandelion has demonstrated hypoglycemic activity in animals. Dandelion extracts are used in antismoking compounds (Leung, 1980). Species of dandelion have been used in China for breast cancer for over 1,000 years. Widely distributed, beta-sitosterol has shown several types of anti-tumor activity. Roots have been used medicinally as a simple bitter (as in the Lydia M. Pinkham tonic) and mild laxative. Roots, considered aperient, diuretic, and tonic, are used for chronic disorders of kidney and liver, for gallstones, piles, and warts. Lebanese extract the root in wine as a laxative or purgative, depending on the strength. Phillips, noting that "medical usage of dandelion came to western civilization through the Arabs," says that gypsies use the root infusion as a depurative, and laxative, for the liver, rheumatism and sciatica, the raw leaf for a spring tonic, and the leaf tea for heavy breathing and kidney ailments (Philips, 1958) (Duke & Duke, 1983).

## Contraindications, Interactions, and Side Effects (Dandelion): Class 2d (AHPA, 1997)

"No health hazards are known in conjunction with the proper administration of designated therapeutic dosages" (PH2) Commission E reports contra-indications: biliary obstruction, empyema of gall-bladder, ileus; adverse effects: gastric complaints and ulcers (AEHD; CAN; SKY). Other counter-indications reported: biliary inflammation (AEHD). Newall, Anderson, and Phillipson (1996) caution that the sesquiterpene lactones are allergenic and may cause dermatosis. May interefere with diuretic and hypoglycemic therapies (CAN). "(H)erbs with diuretic properties, such as juniper and dandelion, can cause elevations in blood levels of lithium" (D'epiro, 1997). Not for use with acute gallbladder problems (WAM). Use in cholelithiasis only under a doctor's supervision (PIP). Blumenthal et al. (1998) caution that: "As with all drugs containing bitter substances, discomfort due to gastric hyperacidity may occur" (KOM). Do I need to write out this caveat for all the salubrious bitter herbs of the Bible; warning: may cause hyperacidity and gastric distress!?

## Extracts (Dandelion)

LD50 herb 28,800 ipr mus (CAN); LD50 root 36,800 ipr mus (CAN); Diuretic (herb>root). Flavonoids antiinflammatory; increase urine flow. Inulin and mucilage sooth digestive tract, absorb toxins, and regulate intestinal flora help friendly flora thrive and inhibit unfriendly bacteria according to Pedersen (I'd like to see the proof), and relieve muscle spasm (PED). PH2 says the amaroids (bitter compounds) in dandelion are cholagogic (agreed) and secretolytic (disagreed; I think they are secretogogue rather than secretolytic; PH2 also says the drug is "secretion-stimulating").

## References

Duke, J.A. 1983. *Medicinal Plants of the Bible*. Conch Publications. NY. 233 pp.

Duke, J. A. 1999. *Herbs of the Bible: 2000 Years of Plant Medicine*. Interweave Press, Loveland, CO. 256 pp.

# Garlic Mustard (*Alliaria petiolata*)

*The Business of Herbs* 7(6):6-7. January/February, 1990

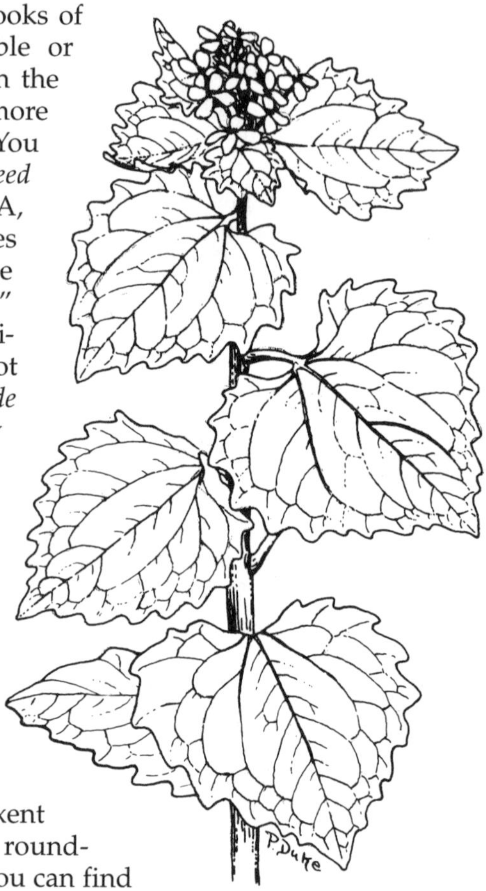

It's not in the major weed books of the U.S., nor most of the edible or medicinal plant books. It's not in the weed books largely because it is more a weed of forest than of farm. You won't even find it in the *Weed Science Society of America* (WSSA, 1984) index of "1,934 weed species of current or potential importance in the United States and Canada." I predict it will be in the next revisions of the weed index. It's not even in the Foster-Duke *Field Guide to Medicinal Plants* due out in early 1990. Still, I know some woodlands where it has taken over the understory as a spring ephemeral, dying back in summer, reappearing as seedlings in fall, followed by large winter leaves which sometimes overwinter in protected alluvial bottoms here in Maryland. It's another in our long list of edible medicinal weeds. [[It grows along the Patuxent near Tai Sophia with another round-leaved herb, *Senecio aureus*, and you can find both in protected places even in midwinter. In midwinter, you don't always get the whiff of allicin when you pick the leaf. Hold it in your closed hand for awhile to speed up the enzymatic conversion to allicin. Then the aroma confirms your identification.]]

I have enjoyed the leaves cooked like spinach on Christmas day, the potherb combining the spicy flavor of mustard greens (it is in the mustard family) and a hint of garlic. For sure, I'm not the only forager eating it. From Great Britain we read (Grieve's *Modern Herbal*, Reprint, 1974): "Country people at one time used the plant in sauces with bread and butter, salted meat and with lettuce in salads, hence it acquired the name 'Sauce Alone.' The herb, when eaten as a salad, warms the stomach and strengthens the digestive faculties." Likewise, we read in *The Wealth of India*, my favorite economic botany encyclopedia: "It is eaten alone as a salad and, mixed with other herbs, it is used for seasoning." I am quoting these sources because I don't want to say it's edible just because I have eaten it. Somewhere, there is someone who will be allergic to it. Therefore, I can't recommend it as a food without qualifications. But what an interesting potherb it is!

## Cancer preventive?

You've heard all the propaganda about the cabbage family as a cancer preventive. And you've probably heard that onion and garlic may help prevent cancer, as well. Well, this strange combo, the garlic mustard, combines chemistries of both the mustard (cabbage) and onion (garlic) families. I sent seed to the late Dr. Herb Pierson of the NCI's (National Cancer Institute) embryonic cancer preventive program. Yes, finally the NCI has a preventive program to join the much older programs looking at the flip side of cancer, looking for cures. From 1977 to 1982 I was involved with the "cure" program, looking for cancer cures in medicinal plants from all over the world in the NCI cancer screening program. Now, I am even more enthusiastic about looking for preventive herbs of which the garlic mustard may be one that so far they, like the weed people and the "grazers" and foragers, have largely overlooked.

## Taxonomy

Like too many weeds, this one suffers the burden of many scientific names, *Alliaria petiolata*, *Alliaria officinalis*, *Arabis petiolata*, *Erysimum alliaria*, and *Sisymbrium alliaria*. Although I've begun this article with one of my favorite common names, garlic mustard, many other picturesque names are used elsewhere: beggarman's oatmeal, English treacle, garlick-wort, hedge garlick, jack-by-the-hedge, leek-cress, penny hedge, poor-man's-mustard, poor-man's-treacle, sauce alone and swarms.

Easily recognized by the large, bluntly heart-shaped, garlic-scented leaves at ground level in fall and winter, and by the bolting stem with many white flowers, each with four petals in April and May, the plant still might be confused with squaw root (*Senecio*), a medicinal plant used by American Indians which may contain dangerous alkaloids. Don't even consider it unless you are sure of the garlic odor.

I'm not positive we can infer the almost magical medicinal properties of garlic and mustard to the lowly garlic mustard. Since the herb certainly merits serious scientific investigation, I am also submitting specimen material to Dr. Lee Wattenberg for analysis. Speaking of the mustard family, in my draft, "Cole Slaw and the Big C (cancer)," Wattenberg says of my purportedly cancer-preventing cole slaw recipe:

> "The preprandial preventive panacea, which shall be referred to in all subsequent communications as PPP, is very impressive. If it doesn't make it in the scientific world, it surely should be included forever in major cookbooks of the world" (Wattenberg, pers. comm., May 15, 1989).

Until I hear more from Pierson or Wattenberg, I'll leave the garlic mustard out of my PPP (cole slaw).

[[Now I add it. Paul Talalay, a major advocate of sulphoraphane for cancer, visited the **Green Farmacy Garden**, and found sulphoraphane in my garlic mustard. It probably occurs in many members of the mustard family. Like many herbs, it contains several different cancer-fighting compounds.]] It is mentioned in Hartwell's classic *Plants Used Against Cancer* as having a folkloric reputation for cancerous or carcinomatous ulcers. According to Grieve's *Modern Herbal* leaves were ingested as a deobstruent (blockage removing) and sudorific (perspiration promoting) and applied topically to gangrene and sores. The leaf juice was taken alone or with honey for dropsy. The small seed, when snuffed, caused sneezing. According to *The Wealth of India*: "The herb is credited with lithontryptic [dissolving stones] properties, and both the leaves and seeds are reported to be diuretic [inducing urination], diaphoretic [inducing sweating], expectorant [helping remove mucus from the throat], stimulant, antiscorbutic [preventing scurvy] and vermifuge [getting rid of worms]. They are applied externally in gangrenous affections and to promote suppuration." Still other adjectives are found in Steinmetz's *Codex Vegetabilis*: antiputrid and detersive.

# Ground Ivy (*Glechoma hederacea*)

(Unpublished, 1991)

## Alehoof As An Antiinflammatory?

What a strange sight! A 61-year old dude walking around in his pajamas on a January morning in his herb garden, with a wad of alehoof (*Glechoma hederacea* L., alias creeping charlie, groundivy, gill-over-the-ground or as I prefer to call it jill-over-the hill) in each hand, and a smaller bolus of alehoof protruding from one nostril. This old man was looking for a winter tonic, not a spring tonic, and was seeking relief from myalgic miseries, i.e. the pains of aching muscles induced by neurological problems.

And this old man, full of big words and little ideas, was also suffering from epistaxis (nosebleed) and ozena (a stench within the nose, better defined by medical dictionaries as "a condition of the nose, of varying etiology, associated with an offensive-smelling discharge"). After a month's relentless assault by such various practitioners as acupuncturist, chiropractor, general practitioner, herbalist, magnetic resonance specialist, masseuse, orthopedist, radiologist and self-urtication (with *Urtica dioica*), the old man, overmedicated, has another painful month to wait until his first encounter with the neurosurgeon. The old man, who for so long skillfully avoided the pill-a-day-for-life syndrome the pharmaceutical industry so appreciates, was now taking daily one allopurinol (gout preventive), two flexerils (muscle relaxant), three motrins (antiinflammatory), and up to four acetominaphens or aspirins (analgesics) and really needed an antibiotic for the sinusitis and cadaverous post-nasal drip causing the ozena. The non-steroidal anti-inflammatory drugs (NSAID's) were at the root of the epistaxis, just as they are reported to be at the root of 10,000-20,000 American deaths a year to bleeding ulcers, largely among arthritics like myself who take the NSAIDs to alleviate the symptoms of arthritis, in my case apparently the herniated disk between vertebrae 5 and 6, impinging on the nerve that goes to the left arm, causing chronic pain in the shoulder, pectoral, tricep, forearm, and chronic numbness of the left hand. How's that for a Faulknerian sentence? People who take too many NSAIDs often have bleeding problems, like my nosebleed, and many clearly die from bleeding ulcers. I didn't have an ulcer last month, but I may by next month. Desperate people in pain take a lot of NSAID's and it is a $2 billion dollar a year market. Matter of fact, there was a relatively new drug (Searle's Cytotec) anticipating a $500 million a year market, being heavily promoted in *JAMA* (*Journal of American Medical Association*) with up to 9 pages of slick advertisement per issue back in 1989 and 1990. (I quit my subscription.) This drug's major function is to prevent the side effects of the NSAIDs. Of course it has some pretty serious side effects of its own. Maybe next year there'll be a new market for a drug to cure the side effects of the drug being sold to prevent the side effects of the NSAIDs. And then the years after that? I call it the Iatrogenic Merry Go Round. And now, chronic neurological pain has me climbing on board, in search of relief.

Still there's herbal help in the alehoof. Instead of the toilet tissue stuffed in my nose, I have the pleasantly aromatic bolus of crushed alehoof leaves. The ozena coupled with the chronic sinusitis and postnasal drip puts the fear of cancer in me, genetically prone to cancer and polyps. So what could I lose by using this old Welsh remedy for epithelial cancers (Hartwell's *Plants Used Against Cancer*) and other types of cancers and tumors. That's why the old man had two wads of alehoof, each consisting of 20 leaves with their stalks, one to make a tea with lemon and sugar, the other to make a potlikker, with oleo, salt and pepper. That's what I mean by winter tonics, a taste of green on the winter scene. Yes, alehoof leaves are available all winter here in Maryland, and probably better for me than coffee or tea.

My illustrious wife Peggy agrees with Paula and Dave Oliver, editors of *Business of Herbs*, where I first published some of these ideas on alehoof, that long lists of folk medicinal attributes are sometimes more depressing than impressing. But here are the adjectives and ailments found for alehoof in my computerized folk medicinal catalog a decade ago:

> Alexeteric, alterative, *anodyne, *antiinflammatory, antilithic, antiscorbutic,*astringent, cardiotonic, diaphoretic, diuretic, pectoral, refrigerant, sudorific and *tonic; folklorically used for *abscesses, *arthritis, *backache, bruises, cancers, *colds, corns, *cough, diabetes, dyspepsia, *epithelioma, fever, *flu, fractures, *headaches, *inflammation, marasmus, *neuroses, *osteosis, renosis, *rheumatism, *sciatica, scurvy, *sores, stones, *swellings, *trauma, tumors and urogenital ailments.

I've asterisked those adjective and nouns that would be useful in my case, not being pessimistic enough to asterisk cancer or tumors, even though I do have polyps and epitheliomas. So, who knows, maybe the alehoof will do as much good as all those specialists I have been consulting? With no controls on this complex personal experiment, we'll never know.

My computer index of a decade ago missed a lot of things. In Leighton's *Early American Gardens*, e.g. we read about alehoof: "Bound in a bundle or chopped like herbs for the pot, it stays the flux in women." This may parallel my use of the herb to stay nosebleed. Natives of Lesotho, perhaps more so than any culture I have read about, tend to stuff several different mint species in the nostrils to treat colds and flu. And many of the mints contain some of the same aromatic compounds found in aromatic over-the-counter (OTC) medicines for such things as colds, flu, and sinusitis. Alehoof juice, honey and pot marigold, boiled together, are said to clean fistulas, ulcers and control the spreading or eating away of cancers and ulcers. Dried leaves or the juice can be snuffed for difficult headaches, like the one that is coming and going with me today. House painters use the tea as a preventive and/or cure for "lead colic." In *Herbalgram,* Yarnel states that alehoof increases lead excretion but he is quoting reference 36 which I have requested.

# Heal All, Self-heal, "Eel Oil" (*Prunella vulgaris*)

*The Business of Herbs* 10(5):12-13. November/December, 1992

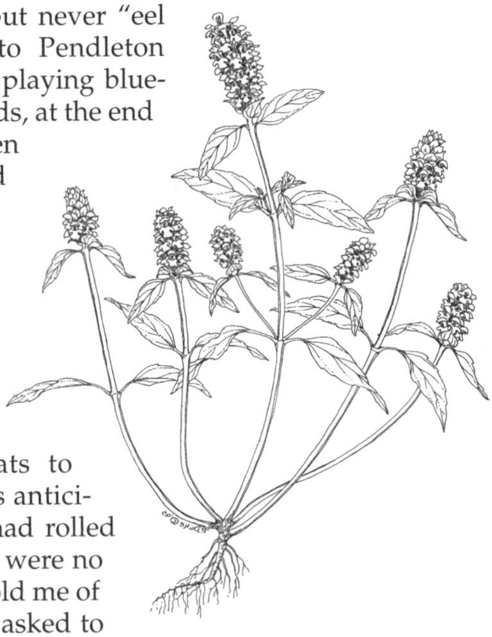

I had heard of "snake oil" but never "eel oil" until a Labor Day visit to Pendleton County, West Virginia. We were playing bluegrass music way back in the woods, at the end of a dirt road, wedged in between two national forests. Deer and turkey almost molested us. We were guests of longtime residents, the Probsts. Following the music, they were telling us some of the old-timers' uses of herbs. For example, they used pennyroyal brooms to sweep away vermin. Once they placed pennyroyal under mattress slats to repel bugs. Mrs. Probst, perhaps anticipating mentholated cigarettes, had rolled her own with pennyroyal. There were no real surprises until Mrs. Probst told me of eating an herb called "eel oil." I asked to see a specimen! She promptly fetched me that wild mint (non-aromatic) better known as heal-all, a name implying panacea.

Scientifically it's *Prunella vulgaris* L., and the name "heal all" has evolved into "eel oil" there in the beautiful backwoods. Add that to quite a long list of names I find here and there: all-heal, blue curls, brownwort, brunel, brunella, bumble-bees, carpenter's herb, carpenterweed, cure-all, dragon's-head, fly-flowers, heal-all, heart-of-the-earth, heart's ease, herb carpenter, hook-heal, hook-weed, London bottles, pick-pocket, pimpernel, prince's feather, proud carpenter, self-heal, sicklewort, slough-heal, small prunel, touch and heal, wild sage and woundwort.

## A potherb?

I didn't remember "eel oil's" use as a potherb. In *Cornucopia* (Facciola 1990) we read that "A refreshing beverage can be made by soaking the leaves, either freshly chopped or dried and powdered, in cold water. Young shoots and leaves are eaten raw in salads, cooked with other greens as a potherb, or added to soups and stews."

## A panacea?

I did know of its medicinal reputation as a panacea with both Chinese and Native Americans. This reputation assumed new significance when

Chinese scientists reported anti-AIDS activity for heal-all extracts, at least in vitro. So much so that I submitted material to Dr. Gordon Cragg for his NCI AIDS screen two years ago. Many of the so-called panaceas and Asian and Indian tonics are speculated to have immune-boosting potential. Wouldn't it be nice if this West Virginia potherb had some immunopotentiating effect? I must confess that I don't find it a pleasing potherb. Even Yanosky (1936) in his survey of 1,112 Amerindian food plants said only: "Cold-water infusion of plant used as beverage in British Columbia."

Writing on self-heal gives me a golden opportunity to mention Kathi Keville's excellent new book, *The Illustrated Herb Encyclopedia* (BBD 1991). In her attractive and fascinating "coffee-table" book, Kathi explains something that puzzled me in China where they still call *Prunella, Brunella.* Here's Kathi's explanation: "Cole tells us in his *Adam in Eden* (1657) that it is called 'Brunella, from brunellen, which is a name given unto it by the Germans, because it cureth that inflammation of the mouth which they call die Braune [quinsy]...'"

## Anti-AIDS Activity

In the same week I received Kathi's color-illustrated book, I received my first copy of a colorfully titled AIDS newsletter, *I Heard It through the Grapevine* (IHITTG #6) (c/o Stephan Korsia, 6721 Romaine St., Los Angeles, CA 90038). There, under an anonymous author, we find "*Prunella vulgaris* a Favorite among Chinese Physicians and American Carpenters." Here we read that in 1989 a California research team isolated prunellin, a polysaccharide that seems "to inhibit Reverse Transcriptase activity in vitro" and "can inhibit in vitro HIV-1 replication in cultured peripheral blood mononuclear cells at a concentration of 12.5 mg/ml," big buzzwords which imply that prunellin might help in AIDS. More recently a Canadian team reported that *Prunella* extract prevents "syncitium formation and cell-to-cell infection," more big words giving another rationale behind self-heal's anti-AIDS potential. Could this really be the anti-AIDS panacea?

## Panacea?

The Iroquois alone used the self-heal in remedies for backache, biliousness, cold, consumption, cough, diarrhea, excessive pediatric crying, nausea, fever, shortness of breath, sickness caused by grief, stiff knees, sore legs, stomachache, stomach cramps, sugar diabetes and venereal disease. Moerman (*Medicinal Plants of Native America* 1986) says: "Infusion of plant taken for any ailment." He adds that Bella Koola took a weak decoction for heart ailments. Cherokee used the root infusion to wash acne, bruises, burns, cuts and diabetic sores. Chippewa used it in a polyherbal cathartic. Cree chewed the herb for sore throat. Delaware used it for fever, Menominee for dysentery, Quileute and Quinault for boils. Thompson Indians took the hot or cold tea as a tonic for general indispositions.

Duke and Ayensu (*Medicinal Plants of China* 1985) report Chinese uses of the self-heal against anxiety, boils, cancer, conjunctivitis, headache, hepatitis, hypertension, opthalmia, scrofula, tinnitus and vertigo. Note that the experimentally antibiotic plant contains biologically active compounds like caffeic acid, camphor, hyperoside, rosmarinic acid, rutin and ursolic acid. Caffeic acid has been suggested as the anti-AIDS component of hyssop (*Hyssopus officinalis*) which I will treat in another issue.

## Rosmarinic acid source

Rosmarinic acid is a well-known antioxidant in rosemary. But self-heal contains more than twice as much rosmarinic acid (6.1%) as rosemary (2.5%). Self-heal was close on the heels of oregano as the mint showing the most antioxidant activity in one French study of 100 herbs. This antioxidant activity may translate into preventive activity against North America's two biggest killers, heart disease and cancer.

All three acids, caffeic, rosmarinic and ursolic, are reported to have liver-protective activities, hinting that the mints in antioxidant teas, maybe even the mint in the mint julep, might have some preventive action against hepatitis and/or cirrhosis. IHITTG #6 adds that Chinese used the flowers to treat jaundice, swollen lymph glands and minor wounds. From IHITTG we read further that *Prunella* extracts also show that eye drops containing *Prunella* help herpetic keratitis. I don't usually get excited about herbal tonics, but if this one stands up against AIDS, a remote possibility, it will bear out the Iroquois panacea, "taken for any ailment."

# Honeysuckle (*Lonicera japonica*)

(Unpublished)

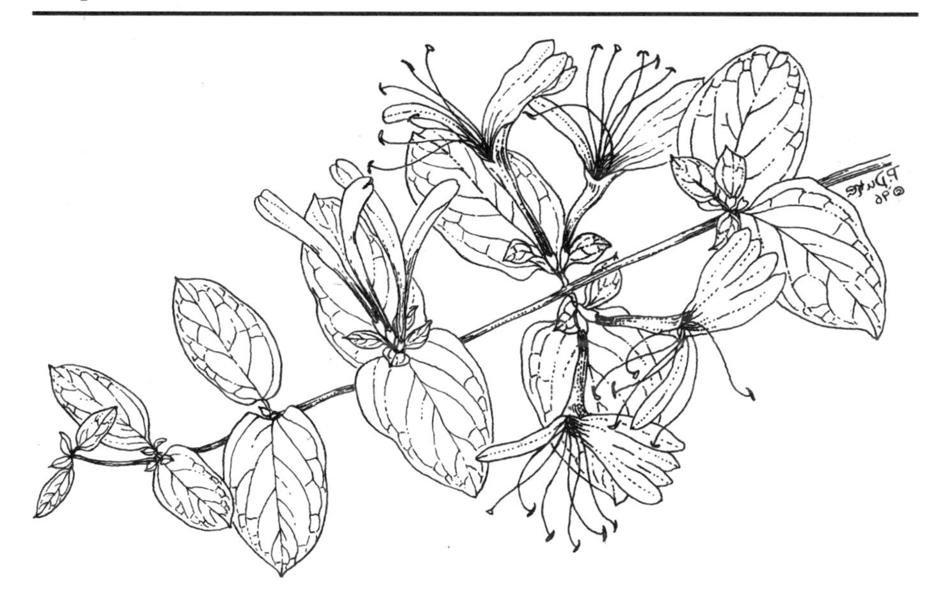

Recently I decided to devote a day to the silver and gold of honeysuckle, a much-maligned weed. Steven Foster called honeysuckle, with good reason, "the most hated alien weed species of the eastern United States." In *Herbal Emissaries* he gives a good account of how it was introduced. In 1806, William Kerr, collecting in Canton for Kew Gardens, took the plant to Britain, via Captain James Pendergrass' ship *Hope*. It arrived in the U.S. that same year as an ornamental. Unfortunately, in 1862, George Hall introduced a more vigorous variety, *Lonicera japonica* 'Halliana.' This variety became the super weed.

I tagged four branches of honeysuckle, so I could time their flowering sequence. Each tagged specimen had four buds at one distal node. I found one that I coded 4-4-4-4, for the four buds, four white flowers, four golden flowers, and four withering golden flowers. I cut another just like it and put it in a vase.

Then life got complicated. I used little "b" for little buds, big "B" for big buds, "S" for silver (white) flowers, and "G" for golden flowers. Without scoring them in advance you can't really tell what's happening. Thus that first specimen became BBBB SSSS GGGG gggg (the latter being the withered golden flowers). Others were even more complex: bbbb bbbb BBBB SSSS GGGG GGGG gggg, for example. But I had to label them so I could watch them transform from day to day. I wanted to see how many days before the white would turn gold, and how many days before the buds would open. And I wanted to investigate its potential as a fresh tea ingredient. That's the beauty of retirement; I can pursue whimsical fantasies like this. Could I make a good tea out of the worst weed in the south?

## Tasting the teas

Experiment one was amazing. I crumpled 100 flower buds into my tea strainer and poured boiling water into a cup with the flowers to steep for 15 minutes. To my surprise I found I could drink it unsweetened, something I can't say for conventional tea and coffee. I may drink five cups of coffee, each with a spoon of sugar and half-and-half, and five glasses of iced tea, each with one or two spoons of sugar. Not good for an obese American. Nor would be those artificial sweeteners. Sure, there's a trace of sugar in the honeysuckle, but at low levels that my Paleolithic ancestors, not my diabetic aunts, would have consumed. And replacing caffeine with chlorogenic and isochlorogenic acids might be smart too, even though chlorogenic acid is just one-sixth as stimulating to the CNS as caffeine.

Experiment two was more mundane. I boiled up an aromatic handful of flowers and flower buds to make a decoction instead of a tea. It was a bit more bitter and considerably darker gray-green. Therefore, I enhanced my decoction by adding some cardamom, the best source of another CNS stimulant, cineole, that I had on hand. This improved both the flavor and perhaps the stimulating activity of my new unsweetened, caffeine-free waker-upper. I can still enjoy it without sugar and caffeine. But I'll bet that if I switched cold turkey to honeysuckle instead of coffee, I would have a withdrawal headache. Think I'll check that out. Honeysuckle is free; coffee is nearly 10 bucks a pound.

Experiment three was informative. I collected into separate porcelain cups, from the same clump of vines, 50 unopened buds, 50 silver flowers, and 50 golden flowers. They had distinctive aromas, which they imparted to the resulting tea. Mrs. Duke, who has a more elegant and refined taste, scored the teas blind, not knowing which was which. She scored the bud tea as best, but with a hay taste. She described the white-flower tea as bitter, and the gold-flower tea as worst, with a fishy (possibly choline or some amine) overtone. Our tastes differed, just as they do in cuisine. I found the bud tea worst due to a bitter overtone, the white flower best, and the hay-scented yellow flowers as next best.

Adding alcohol later in the day created a honeysuckle tincture or liqueur, a bit more pleasing than the teas. Surely the alcohol extracts some chemicals from the flowers that the water had not.

## Where are the bees?

During my long and interesting day with the aromatic honeysuckle flowers, I noted only one insect visitor, a bumblebee, no honey bees. That struck me as strange. So I went to look at various clovers which are the peril of barefoot good ole boys, due to an abundance of honeybees which tend to sting when stood upon. There were no honeybees there either. Cold Spring? Late Spring? Or Silent Spring? Certainly a Stingless Spring! There weren't even any honeybees on my flowering thymes and sages, in years past loaded with bees. I suspect pesticides.

The absence of bees should tell us something. We are crossing the threshold of pesticide tolerance for honeybees. We'll cross our own threshold, maybe in our own "deathtime." I have fewer sperm in my seminal fluid and more pesticides in my fat than did my grandfather. My son and grandson will have even fewer sperm and a bigger pesticide burden. The message is there with the clover and honeysuckle and thyme: fewer bees this year. And that presages even fewer next year; another stingless spring. I fear humanity may feel the sting of xeno-estrogens too late to correct for them.

Meanwhile, the synthetic industry develops new energy-intensive, environmentally unfriendly herbicides to spray such weeds as honeysuckles, and xenoestrogens like paraquat to kill such estrogenic weeds as kudzu and marijuana. Alas, we could extract all the pesticides we need from many of the weeds we instead kill with herbicides.

## Practice what you preach

As I swished the fresh tea through my mouth this morning, I realized that this was not just a beverage, but a mouthwash and a gargle, containing dozens of useful compounds. My flights of fantasy told me that the tea I was enjoying was even more powerful than I had imagined a decade ago, over the Christmas holidays.

There I was jamming data into my computer, drafting my first best seller, *The Green Pharmacy*, when I felt a head cold or flu coming on. The light bulbs went off. Why, Duke, don't you practice what you preach? You just read that the honeysuckle /forsythia combo was the world's most widely used cold/flu medicine. And your yard is full of it. Out I went and stripped the last leaves of the honeysuckle and the young twigs and spring buds, along with a few withered leaves, of the forsythia. Then I made a decoction, added lemon and sugar [[more often than not in those days, I regrettably substituted "crystal lite" for lemon and sugar; I suspect my eyes are some the worse for it]], and enjoyed it as a hot medicinal lemonade. It worked. Instead of three to seven days of misery, sniffing and snorting like the other sufferers around, I kept right on working, having circumvented the villain.

[[We were having what we call a picking paty at my house, members of some of the bluegrass bands I played with, coming over with their instruments to open the New Year with country music and revelery. Some were allopaths, like guitar player, Dr. Les Alstat, and his wife, also a physician who had no respect at all for herbs. More were psychopaths like me, who had come to the psycho conclusions that herbs may be the better medicines. New Year's Eve, guests came over, with many of the psychopaths, but none of the allopaths, taking my anti-viral concoction. Those who did not went on to a full bout of flu. Those who indulged did not. That made a believer of me. Now I use the concoction to thwart colds and flus, if and when the gentler echinacea and garlic fail me.]]

You have probably heard the superstars talk about synergies between AZT and interferon and protease inhibitors improving the life expectancies of HIV sufferers. I'd wager that the synergies from some of the weeds they are spraying with pesticides (further weakening the HIV patient's and the world's immune system) would do as much good at one-thousandth the cost, e.g., a brew of burdock, forsythia, honeysuckle, hypericum, licorice, and self-heal – all free at my place.

Few view the honeysuckle as a major edible vegetable. But read Facciola's *Cornucopia*: "Leaves, buds and flowers are made into a tea. The flowers are sucked for their sweet nectar, used as a vegetable or made into syrup and puddings. Parboiled young leaves are used as a vegetable." Thus, though not exactly GRAS, there's new good evidence to support much of honeysuckle's folklore. I don't even find dishonorable mention in Kingsbury's poisonous plant text. So it is neither GRAP (p for poison) nor GRAS. It has all the qualifications for a Food Farmacy star.

Honeysuckle lowers cholesterol absorption in the rabbit intestine. The flowers activate phagocytosis of leukocytes in mice. (Leung and Foster, 1996). Chlorogenic acid inhibits nitrosation in vitro and in vivo in mice. Further, it inhibits tumor formation in animals. Orally in Nice and rats it has ⅙ the CNS-stimulant activity of caffeine. (I predict it will prove synergic with caffeine and I will add some dried flowers-up to 12% chlorogenic acid-to my coffee tomorrow.) According to Foster and Yue (1992) and Bensky and Barolet (1990) flowers are used for appendicitis, bronchitis, carbuncles, cervicitis, cold, conjunctivitis, cough, dermatoses, dysentery, encephalitis, endometriosis, fever, flu, furuncles, headache, infection, leptospirosis, mastitis, measles, meningitis, parotitis, pneumonia, pulmonosis, rhinosis, and sore throat. The stems, available year-round here at **Herbal Vineyard**, are used in China for appendicitis, flu, furuncles, infectious hepatitis, mumps, pneumonia, pulmonosis, rheumatism, swellings, and urticaria. If it's really good for all those things, small wonder that Stuart (1911) said "prolonged use is said to increase vitality and strengthen life." To your health!

# Japanese Knotweed (*Fallopia japonica*)

(Unpublished, ca 2000)

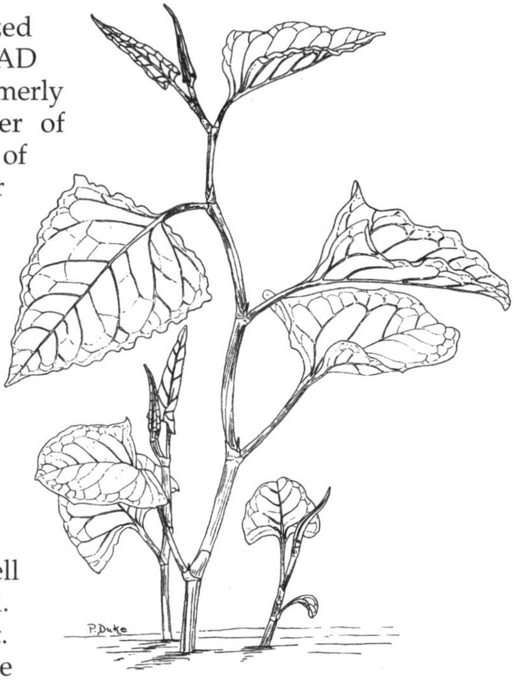

Like Vickie, I was amazed that I had never submitted a HAD column on *Fallopia japonica*, formerly *Polygonum cuspidatum*, another of my favorite weeds with a lot of energy potential. But it's harder to do a column on a plant with a whole lot going for it than it is for an herb just emerging from obscurity.

I wrote about the "Mexican bamboo" not too long ago under the name "Japanese knotweed." If I were to try to market a product made from it, I suspect that the marketers would prefer the name bamboo as it might sell better than the name knotweed. It is a weed, if you don't want it. Yes, that's the way some people define a weed, something growing where it's not wanted. So what is the best and safest weed eradicator. Wanting it! Using it. Because if you want it, it isn't a weed.

## May 12, 2000

I was reeling from Lyme Arthritis (according to my HMO GP's diagnosis) or osteoarthritis (according to my HMO orthopedists diagnosis) or gardener's arthritis (according to my diagnosis; maybe it's time for a fourth opinion). Knee jerk reactor that I am, I really reacted to Emily Senai's program last May (May 12, 2000; *CBS News*, ca 8:00 A.M.) as I rode my stationary bike trying to correct my gardener's arthritis. I suspect it is just plain old geriatric osteoarthritis; the orthopedist was careful to radiographically demonstrate, with new x-rays, the disappearance of the bone-cushioning cartilage (look out shrimp and crab carapaces and beef tracheae alias glucosamine and chondroitin, here I come). Not only did Senai mention the COX- 2 Inhibitor, highly recommended for arthritis, all but endorsing Celebrex for people at risk for colon cancer (like me).

Almost a year later (Mar. 14, 2001), it was Bob Arnott, MD, (*NBC News*, ca 7:45 A.M., EST), rightly or wrongly reiterating that, for preventing cancer, one should take Celebrex, a selective COX-2 Inhibitor, instead of aspirin. He implied that this was FDA advice. That went against what I heard the FDA say recently, "stay away from newly approved drugs."

Celebrex has been with us for two years now! I think I'll go chew on a willow instead. I have familial polyposis which Dr. Arnott said was a good indication for aspirin. I had my scheduled colonoscopy with no new polypectomies April 30, 2001.

It's been a hundred years since the discovery of aspirin. At that time, they said the acetylated synthetic was gentler on the stomach than the natural willow bark (or spiraea according to other stories). I still wonder if that is true. Has anyone seen a clinical comparison of aspirin with willow bark. I've never heard of anyone dying from willow bark. The mortality head count for aspirin and other NSAIDs reportedly runs 10,000-20,000 per year.

So if I can prevent the pain of arthritis and the progressions of polyposis (which I have) to colon cancer with Cox-2-Inhibitors, that's all the more reason for me to go out grazing on my COX-2-inhibiting plant life in the **Green Farmacy Garden**.

Yes Emily Senai, knowingly or unknowingly, furthered the Celebrex campaign to attract more customers to Celebrex. She talked about the promise of COX-2 I's in prevention of FAP (I think that stands for familial polyposis, which I have). She speaks of that pharmaceutical COX-2-Inhibitor, Celebrex, and Tamoxifen (which increases risk of endometrial cancer), as being the NCI approach to cancer prevention. (I think they'd accomplish a lot more with fewer side effects pushing even more their strive for five fruits and vegetables.) Yes, I think you'd do better upping your intake of $500 worth of good COX-2-inhibiting foods rather than $500 worth of Celebrex. Celebrex has only been on the market for a couple years or so now. I anticipate we will learn of more side effects than already appear on the label. On the positive side, we can remind people that many of those five fruits and veggies, herbs and spices, they are striving for contain COX-2 inhibiting phytochemicals which their genes already know. Yes, you polyp-prone-people might want to increase your dietary uptake of natural dietary COX-2-I's.)

There are plenty of natural COX-2 inhibitors out there, contained in well known antiinflammatory food plants or GRAS spices. Suffering from gardeners arthritis today, I'd feel safer indulging in some of these food farmaceutical COX-2 Inhibitors than those expensive brand new drugs that came out in 1999 and will continue to emerge in the new millennium. But if Celebrex promoters are correct and COX-2 Inhibitors can prevent colon cancers, there's an easy way to up your COX-2-I intake.

1. Replace some or all of your coffee with green tea, and/or chamomile tea. Spice them up with clove, lavender, marjoram, rosemary, sage, and thyme
2. Eat more cabbage, celery, chives, currants, rhubarb
3. Use more celery seed, ginger, and turmeric in your teas and cooking.

4. Enjoy grape juice or red wine for their resveratrol, or better yet, enjoy stuffed grape leaves with red wine vinegar.
5. RESVERATRADE: Cheapskate that I am, I'm going to make a ReseveratrADE for free, just adding the ingredients to my fresh orange juice. They are Mexican bamboo (*Polygonum cuspidatum*) and grape (*Vitis* spp). And for one of the few times in my life, I went by a recipe. I took one cup of orange juice, and five shoots of mexican bamboo ("spear" plus 1-2 leaves), and five shoots of wild grape (tip, tendril and 1-2 leaves each), because those tips are tenderer and less fibrous. Blend for 1 minute in Hamilton Beach Blender (about thirty dollars about thirty years ago). Drink before that beautiful green/gold separates out.

I don't know how the activity of this will compare with a celebrex tablet, but figure costs and side effects of the ResveratrADE wil be substantially less. There are cases where every little bit helps, and I suspect that is the case with COX-2-I's your genes know real well. So you can spice your ResveratrADE with COX-2-I spices, enhancing both flavor and inhibitory activity with such COX-2-Is as celeryseed, cloves, ginger, lavender, marjoram, rosemary, sage, thyme and/or turmeric. Yes, grape leaves contain even more resveratrol than the grape fruits, yet grape juice and wine get all the press. And I'll bet that wild grapes will average higher in resveratrol than tame grapes. True, I don't know how much resveratrol is in those grape leaves. But I can and did go out at this time of year and graze the new shoots of Mexican bamboo and the wild grape leaves, thereby ingesting free COX-2-Inhibitors, from widely known edible plants.

## Mexican Bamboozle

I know that my Mexican Bamboo contains a lot of resveratrol, so much so that the Canadian "collaborator" who received my material about 10 years or more ago ceased corresponding with me shortly after reporting back that yes they were rich in resveratrol. They were so rich in resveratrol that I suspect they made him rich too. I provided the materials, but derived no wealth therefrom. Except the wealth of wisdom. That I say, rationalizing, is the true wealth. I can share that with you.

If you are after a COX-2-I mess of potherbs, try my "Mexican BamBoozle": Gather a mess of mexican bamboo (*Fallopia japonica* alias *Polygonum cuspidatum*) shoots and wild grape shoots, and cover with water. Bring slowly to boil, adding salt, black and red pepper, and curry (rich source of COX-2-I curcumin. The piperine in the black pepper makes the curcumin more available to the body). Now to make it taste even better add some onions as the best source of antiinflammatory quercetin. Tastes as good as a good mess of turnip or collard greens. Improved by addition of red wine vinegar (possibly adding a bit more resveratrol) and one glass of red wine as beverage. Aqueous extracts of Mexican bamboo (IC50=38 ug/ml) are 1/38th as potent as allopurinol (IC50=1.08 ug/ml) as a xanthine oxidase inhibitor, making my "Mexican Bamboozle" worth trying in gout prevention. I don't like methanol so I won't recommend the methanol extracts of cassia (*Cinnamomum cassia*) (IC50=18 ug/ml), or Asian Chrysanthemum (*Chrysanthemum indicum*) (IC50=22 ug/ml) or bugle (*Lycopus europeus*) (IC50=26 ug/ml). But maybe an ethanolic or red wine tincture to chase my "Mexican Bamboozle?" Certainly red wine with cassia is delightful, but for arthritis, not gout. Use a white wine tincture for gout (PMID11025157).

Purists might prefer preparing polygonum shoots like asparagus. When they first come up, they look like asparagus and are edible, raw and cooked, according to the books I have on hand. I have certainly enjoyed them raw as a nibble or added to cooked greens, salads and soups. The raw or steamed shoots are good with red wine vinegar.

So instead of racing out and trying to patent and trademark and register my food farmaceutical recipes, so I can make a million selling you things at inflated prices, I give you here my farmaceutical formulae, sometimes called recipes. I know this is the cheapest source of COX-2-I's if in fact COX-2-I's are what you need. And this dietary approach will almost assuredly have less side effects than the average silver bullet pharmaceutical synthetic COX-2 Inhibitor. If somehow, you find my formulas useful, and have more money than you know what to do with, you might consider donating the money you saved to the Amazon Center for Environmental Education and Research (ACEER) where I helped start and they maintain a Botanical Garden in Amazonian Peru, Madre de Dios, or right here to the **Green Farmacy Garden**, where I raise all the important medicinal plants for teaching purposes, only.

But the Mexican Bamboo is no longer a weed, if it prevents cancer, cardiopathy as I predict it will, and its use in Lyme protocols continues. It's a plant we need, not a weed. What an environmentally sound way to attack a weed, learn its use potential.

## Re: Cancer

Sloan Kettering scientists report that resveratrol is a powerful suppressor of COX-2 cancer promotion, inhibiting COX 2 in breast and oral cancer tissues. COX-2 Inhibition is "likely to be important for understanding the anti-cancer and anti-inflammatory properties of resveratrol." It both inhibits the expression of the COX-2 gene, AND inhibits the COX-2 enzyme activities. University Illinois scientists report that resveratrol inhibits COX-2 and restores levels of the cancer detoxicant, glutathione. Resveratrol also is a powerful radicle scavenger. There are several other anticancer compounds in Japanese knotweed: emodin, isoquercitrin, quercitrin, and rutin, but resveratrol may be the most important. The protein tyrosine kinase inhibitory activity of resveratrol may be as important as its COX-2 Inhibition. Both trans and cis isomers possess comparable protein-tyrosine kinase inhibitory activity. Comparison of the IC50 values of resveratrol for protein-tyrosine kinase inhibitory activity with those of piceid (resveratrol-O3-beta-glucoside), also in Japanese knotweed, and resveratrol-O4′-beta-glucoside indicate a requirement for free hydroxyl groups on both phenyl rings for the protein-tyrosine kinase inhibition. Protein kinase C inhibitory analysis suggests requirements for two free hydroxyl groups on one phenyl ring only (Jayatilake et al., 1993).

# Lesser Celandine, Pilewort (*Ranunculus ficaria*)

*The Business of Herbs* 10(2):7. May/June, 1992

First attracted to this herb by the yellowing leaves in early summer, I was drawn back to it when I heard it was also a floral-clock species. Grieve notes that its "blossoms shut up before rain, and even in fine weather do not open before nine o'clock, and by 5 P.M. have already closed for the night."

On my second visit in July, I found only bare ground where the pilewort had been, in deep shade north of Ellicott City, Maryland. But in the bare ground I found hundreds of its bulbs. Perhaps the plant could have herbicidal potential. Grainge and Ahmed (*Handbook of Plants with Pest-Control Properties*) note that its underground parts reportedly worked against the fungus, *Venturia inaequalis*. But the bare ground suggested to me that the plant or its "bulbs" just might have herbicidal properties as well. There were no herbaceous plants associated with the dormant bed of pilewort, even though honeysuckle, poison ivy and virginia creeper were greening up. Still I suspect that pilewort contains an herbaceous herbicide.

There's nothing new under the sun! Nearly 250 years ago, Linnaeus advised farmers to eradicate this weed because it was unattractive to cattle-and also because of its injurious effects on other herbs. (Treating with coal ash or wood ash was said to destroy the plant.) On my third visit in November, I found that the bulbils were germinating and expanding, just as though it were spring.

## First flower of spring

Maude Grieve (*A Modern Herbal*) tells us it was Wordsworth's favorite flower; its blossoms are reputedly carved onto his tomb. In England it is one of the first flowers, bursting into bloom about the middle of February, shortly after leafing out. So it will be a good plant for the phenological calendar as well as the floral clock.

According to Grieve, Swedes sometimes even boiled and ate the leaves as a potherb. Stephen Facciola's *Cornucopia* is even more flattering to the plant: "Young leaves are eaten raw in salads and sandwiches or cooked as a potherb. The bleached stems are cooked and eaten. Both the bulbils which form in the leaf axils and the roots can be cooked and served with meat. Flower buds make a good substitute for capers." I put that in quotes because I personally am reluctant to recommend any member of the buttercup family for food, though others may do so. I will try this one myself, but cautiously.

## Traditional uses

Hartwell (*Plants Used Against Cancer*) mentions that the roots have been used for "hard tumors," cancers of the mouth and corroding ulcers of the breast, warts and even venereal warts (*Condylomata acuminata*). Mitchell and

Rook (*Botanical Dermatology*) indicate that the sap, like so many saps in the buttercup family, is an irritant, leaving me disinclined to try is as an antihemorrhoidal. Nonetheless it has been applied in ointments for piles. Early writers believed this to be useful for piles because of the "Doctrine of Signatures." As Weiss (*Herbal Medicine*) puts it, the tubers were thought to resemble varices (hemorrhoids), and hemorrhoidal treatment seems to have been the major use of this herb for millennia, both internally and externally. Dr. Weiss concludes, "But alas, it is not true…in my own trials and observations, this failed completely, both internally and as an ointment." Hoffman (1985) is a bit more positive: "The herb to choose is Pilewort (Of course!)." Steinmetz (*Codex Vegetabilis*) describes the plant as toxic, stressing its use for piles as external only, in ointments. He adds that the plant is antiscorbutic and the roots, diuretic.

## Planta non grata

Ending rather ominously, not recommending *Ranunculus ficaria* for food or medicine, I must think twice before I introduce it to my floral clock or phenology gardens. Though it is not yet listed as a weed by the Weed Science Society of America, I predict it will be a major woodland weed in low shaded woods once it gets established, just as it is in some shaded valleys north of Ellicott City, Maryland. It makes both aerial and subterranean bulblets, apparently by the hundreds, each of which may start a new plant in some new place where rain water might carry it. In spite of my current interest in floral clocks, I think I'll pass on this one. Maybe it will prove out as a natural herbicide, as alluded to by Linnaeus, and we can use this potential weed to help control others.

# Milk Thistle (*Silybum marianum*)

*The Wild Foods Forum* 8(1):8-9, January/February, 1997

[[New Years Day, 2007; what a start! An Aptos California family, aged 17 to 83, picked several varieties of mushrooms in Wilder Ranch State Park near Santa Cruz. One of them seems to have been the death cap *Amanita*, according to Jondi Gomz of the Santa Cruz Sentinel. And they made tacos with their mushrooms. Mushroom poisoning is not necessarily common, but California has its share. Moral of today's story. Don't dress your taquitas with death cap amanitas.

Ten years ago, in Santa Cruz County and in Sonoma County, death cap mushrooms killed two, one in each county, according to Gomz. Five years ago, a couple visiting Watsonville ended up spending weeks in the hospital after another intoxication. Though only a small percentage of mushrooms are poisonous, mushroom poisoning sent nearly 400 people to the hospital in California last year. But 6 for the New Year's Day poisoning; that's off to a pretty traumatic start.

When the Aptos family entered the hospital January 2, their liver enzymes were at near normal levels but within six hours, numbers jumped into the 100s, and started doubling about every six hours, confirming the presence of "amatoxin." After searching the databases, the physicians in attendance learned that extracts of the Biblical milk thistle (*Silybum marianum*), whose seeds contain silymarin, have been used in Europe to treat various liver ailments. *Amanita* poisoning is deadly for the liver. While waiting for injectable silibinin, one of the 3 flavonolignans in milk thistle seed that are collectively called silymarin, the patients started taking oral milk thistle, the injectable being reserved for the most serious of the patients. Five of the six survived, presumably due to the Biblical milk thistle. I know of no pharmaceutical that could have saved those Californians from amanita poisonings. But apparently the milk thistle, unapproved for that indication, did the trick.

The Biblical milk thistle is a frequent weed in California, and its California distribution is neatly mapped on the website: http://ucjeps.berkeley.edu/cgi-bin/get_cpn.pl?4918. Ironically, I heard about the New Year's poisoning while I was preparing a lecture and a book on Biblical medicinal plants, to be mentioned in San Diego, farther south than Santa Cruz. And milk thistle was one of the herbs I had submitted with my potential handouts. The handouts were not reproduced in San Diego so I take the opportunity to reproduce a few of them here, with milk thistle first and foremost, that Biblical thistle having saved five lives already this year. It could probably save many others from non-mushroom hepatitis. Both interferon, the pharmaceutical, and milk thistle, the herb, have proven useful against various types of hepatitis. I have long urged that they be compared with each other and placebo in three-arm trials. Until we have such an unbiassed third-arm trial, America does not know which is better for hepatitis, the Biblical milk thistle or the pharmaceutical interferon. America deserves to know.

The San Diego symposium was on evidence-based supplements. My surprising conclusion, following an intensive round of talks there. Herbs and supplemnts seem to have at least as strong an evidence base as the pharmaceutcials, many of which seem to be reversing themselves in flip flops, e.g. as with the HRT evidence base collapsing under it in 2002, costing billions of dollars, and thousands of cancer deaths. My San Diego handouts evaluated the evidence base for important Biblical medicinal plants that were grown in California, cultivated, or as weeds. I was so pleased that the milk thistle had saved some lives that I updated a song first published in my *Green Pharmacy Herbal Handbook* (Rodale, 2000).

> And if you're overliving,
> there's one herb you should choose
> Milk Thistle saves the liver;
> From the mushrooms and the booze.
> Did you hear the New Year's News,
> from sunny Santa Cruz
> Some local taco eaters, ingested amanitas
> Milk Thistle saved some five, five of six are still alive
> But the sixth one is past tense, blame the "lack of evidence" (could the thistle have saved her, had it gotten to her sooner;
> I'd have eaten it right away,
> sure it might have saved my day)
> Some evidence-based California food farmaceuticals.

Evidence Level f = folklore; Evidence Level 1 = phytochemical, in vitro or animal rationale; Evidence Level 2 = extracts clinically proven or approved by Commission E; Evidence Level 3 = herb itself clinically proven or approved by Commission E. Recent PubMed Serial Citation Numbers represented by an X followed by the 8 digit number.

MILK THISTLE (*Silybum marianum* (L.) Gaertn.) +++
Anorexia (2); Cholecocystosis (2); Cirrhosis (1, 2); Dyspepsia (f, 1, 2); Hepatosis (f, 1, 2); Mushroom Poisoning (1, 2); Nephrosis (f, 1, 2). One must remember that one half of all newly approved pharmaceuticals will be recalled within their first decade, even after surviving the 1.7 billion dollar trials that prove them "safe and efficacious." Some are recalled permanently. Others only to relabel to point out new side effects not

anticipated in the $1.7 billion dollar trials. Since two Parkinsonian drugs were getting relabelled because of cardiac problems, I pointed out that the Biblical faba bean with its natural l-dopa had been favorably compared with pharmacological l-dopa as an antiparkinsonian food or drug. So I scored the efficacies of four ingredients of a tasty faba beean soup. All told, the four food farmaceuticals, faba-bean, garlic, olive oil and onion, had good evidence bases for over 30 indications.]]

> *Thorns also and thistles shall it bring forth to thee; and thou shalt eat the herb of the field ...* ................Genesis 3

It's appropriate to start the New Year with the Biblical milk thistle, now recognized as the best possible herb, food, and probably pharmaceutical for preventing damage to the liver. Those who over-indulge over the holidays may spare themselves the liver damage by eating milk thistle seeds or, easier, by taking milk thistle capsules. I frequently take my capsules with me on the road, but happily, at home, milk thistle now volunteers as a weed. I have eaten the flowers and seeds, and this year plan to sample the pith of the stems. Now as I write this on December 15th, I still have seven volunteers [[seedling rosettes]] outside in the garden, and two inside in the greenhouse, for lecture purposes.

Some people don't think of milk thistle as food. But here's what I had to say back in 1983 when my *Medicinal Plants of the Bible* was first published:

"The stalks, like those of most thistles, are said to be quite edible and nutritious. Still they are reported to have caused fatalities in cattle. The young leaves are often eaten as salad ingredients. The roots also are eaten like salsify. Birds like the seeds, which might also serve as a famine food for humans. The heads were once eaten like artichokes. The seeds have served as coffee substitutes, and the seed cake is used for cattle fodder, the seed oil being used for food or lubrication."

It's nice to line up all that historical data about medicinal plants being foods. That way the federal agencies aren't as likely to harass us. They view feeding ourselves more favorably than self medicating. The milk thistle is not a GRAS drug, but it is GRAF ( generally recognized as food). To remind the FDA that it is a food, perhaps we should call it the Biblical, Holy or Milk Artichoke instead of milk thistle. With no axe to grind, Uphof's *Dictionary of Economic Plants* leads off with "Annual or perennial herb. Mediterranean region. Cultivated. Very young leaves are sometimes used in salads. Roasted seeds are employed as substitute for coffee."

Cirrhosiphobes would do well to substitute milk thistle seeds for coffee. Clearly money could be made selling BEER BEANS™ (a mixture of twenty parts milk-thistle, ten parts soybean (for its daidzin), and one part ginkgo, by weight) to nervous cirrhosiphobes who continue to drink. Clearly this food should be uppermost in the cirrhiphobe's diet. As Rob McCaleb, Presidential Commission on Alternative Medicine, puts it

"Since the effective dose of milk thistle seed is only 12-15 grams (~one half ounce), its development as a food crop could contribute to better liver health in Mali and perhaps throughout West Africa" (HG37: p. 9. 1996).

I have actually given milk thistle capsules to friends and family inclined to indulge in too much alcohol. However, I think the milk thistle might be a good general recommendation to those of us living in polluted areas, because we are increasingly assaulted by more and more liver toxins. Here is a short summary of what I'll have to say in my *Green Pharmacy* (Rodale, cerca Sept. 1997):

Extracts of the seeds, used as a liver remedy for at least 2,000 years, protect against liver damage and even help regenerate liver cells damaged by toxins like alcohol and diseases like cirrhosis and hepatitis. The effective ingredient, silymarin, will protect the liver from insult by many industrial toxins, e.g., carbon tetrachloride. After the insult, silymarin can even help acute and chronic hepatitis, even cirrhosis. It seems to be a drug of choice for fatty liver. As ABC (1994) observes, milk thistle has a long folk reputation as a liver tonic. The extract is used to improve liver function, protect against liver damage and enhance regeneration of damaged liver cells. Commission E approved milk thistle as supportive treatment for cirrhosis and chronic inflammatory liver conditions. Clinical studies confirm the efficacy of standardized milk thistle extracts in cirrhosis, toxic liver and other chronic liver conditions. Silymarin from milk thistle is protective against many types of chemical toxins, including alcohol. Weiss suggests Legalon tablets (each with 35 mg silymarin): "Initially 2-4 tablets are given three times daily after meals, for a period of 4-6 weeks," cutting back to 3 pills a day after meals. "There are no toxic effects" (Weiss, p. 83). There is a great deal of alcohol-pertinent experimental data on silymarin in vitro or in animals: (1) Radical scavenging (2) Increasing glutathione (3) Inhibiting lipid peroxidation (4) Necrosis Prevention (5)Stabilization of Cell Membranes (6) Stimulation of Protein Synthesis (7) Acceleration of liver regeneration (8) Inhibition of fibrosis. In human clinical trials, extracts have been shown to (1) Decrease transaminases and gamma-GM in serum (remission of necrosis) (2) Reduce serum triglyceride (3) Normalize serum bilirubin and BSP retention (improve liver functionality) (4) Reduce serum malondialdehyde (decline in lipid peroxidation) (5) Increase SOD activity (more antioxidant activity) (6) Reduce cytotoxic lymphocytes (Immunomodulation) (7) Reduce serum procollagen-III peptide (Antifibrotic effect), and (8) Increase survival rate (Deceleration of Cirrhosis).

# Mustard (*Brassica* spp.)

(Unpublished)

## Mustard Musings

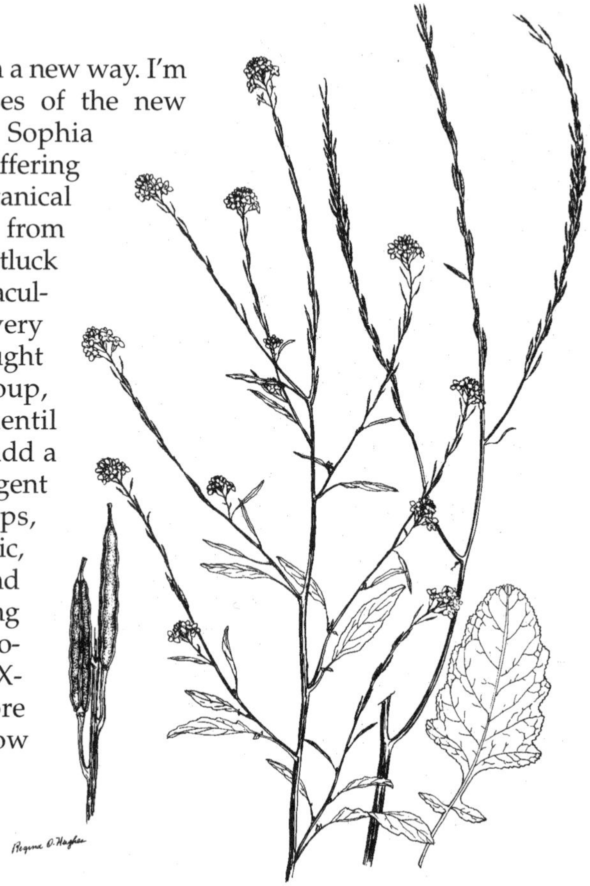

I'm starting the New Year in a new way. I'm auditing the opening classes of the new school in town, The Tai Sophia Institute, Columbia MD, offering an Advanced Degree in Botanical Healing. Got back in town from Peru in time to attend a potluck dinner welcoming the new faculty and the first crop of ten very promising students. I brought my vegetarian lentil soup, described in an earlier lentil newletter. I almost always add a dash of several of the pungent spices to most of my soups, black pepper, capsicum, garlic, ginger, mustard, onion, and turmeric, in a sense making many of the antiarthritic phytochemicals including the COX-2-Inhibitor curcumin more readily available. Yes, now that I am no longer employed by the herb industry, I am leaning more and more towards food farmacy, at the same time as the press is scaring the pants off the public with frightening stories of herb/drug interactions. They fail to tell us that herbs kill fewer than 100 Americans a year (usually those who are abusing the herb) while prescribed pharmaceuticals kill more than 100,000 Americans a year (*JAMA*, 1997). And they fail to tell us, as did *NBC News* January 29, 2002, that 9 million Americans, including one of the President's close relatives, are abusing prescription pharmaceuticals.

I'm auditing these classes because I am very keen that this first Master's Degree Program in Botanical Healing succeed. I'm auditing so that when my classes come up, I can relate my lectures to the lectures the students have already heard or will be hearing, from such luminaries as 7-Song, Soaring Bear, Kerry Bone, Steve Dentali, Mary Enig, Kathy Koumoutsias, Jacqueline Krikorian, Kathleen Maier, Simon Mills, Rachel Pritzker, Aviva Romm, Lynn Schumake, James Snow, Kevin Spelman,

Claudia Wingo, David Winston, and Tom Wolfe. It's been a great pleasure listening to Simon Mills pivotal opening lectures on the "Six Tastes," in which he first covered the pungent compounds, which have triggered this issue of my newsletter.

In their book, *Principles and Practice of Phytotherapy*, used as a text in the Tai Sophia Program, Mills and Bone (2000) note that most, if not all, members of the mustard family contain glucosinolates (sulfur and nitrogen-containing compounds, which though not pungent in themselves are responsible for the pungency). When a glucosinolate comes in contact with the enzyme myrosinase, located in different parts of the cells of most mustard relatives, the glucosinolate is enzymatically converted into the pungent (and corrosive) isothiocyanate. Mustard compresses are still widely used in Europe for bronchial troubles and chronic inflammatory diseases. The mucolytic activities of the hot compounds could be useful in many inflammatory conditions. Glucosinolates and/or their breakdown products have long been known for their allelopathic, bactericidal, fungicidal, and nematicidal properties and lately cancer chemoprevention.

## Glucosinolate:

Anticancer PC56:5; Antiseptic PC56:5; Antithyroid NIG; Bactericide PC56:5; Chemopreventive PC56:5; Fungicide PC56:5; Nematicide PC56:5;

And here's what my database says about isothiocyanates, not surprising since the glucosinolates, when enzymatically altered by myrosinase, form isothiocyanates:

## *Isothiocyanate:

Anticancer PC56:5; Antiseptic MAB; Antithyroid NIG; Antitumor MAB; Bactericide MAB; Chemopreventive MAB; Fungicide MAB; Hypotensive; Goitrogenic MAB; 450-Inhibitor X11506821; Mucolytic MAB; Nematicide PC56:5; Respiradepressant; LD50=120

Most interesting to me in Mill's lecture was his description of a British mustard handbath for digital arthritis or arthritis of the hand. Simply put some dry powdered mustard into a pan of hot water. Then immerse your hands for a few minute. Deep penetrating action detoxifies, apparently. It's certainly worth a try. How well I remember my mother's last ten years. Both of her hands were almost locked into the curved position by what I assume was arthritis. And every time my hands lock up due to too much garden work, I fear that I'll suffer the same fate. But, taking command, I get on my exercise bike, get those dumbells, pedaling as I exercise the very muscles that are tending to cramp up. I believe the rheumatologists when they say that one of the best things for arthritis is exercise. And if I find my muscles locking up on me rheumatically, I may use some powdered mustard in a handbath. Or maybe I'll cook up a big batch of mustard greens, with black pepper, capsaicin, curry, garlic, and onion, and drink half the potlikker and steep my hands in the other half (making it even more potent by spiking it with horseradish or wasabi).

But now, let me warn you, as Simon Mill skillfully warned his audience. Appropriately used, these can be very good phytomedicines. But overdo it, and you're in trouble. These compounds are corrosive and will cause blisters (sometimes desired by some healers, if not their patients). And while normal doses will prevent cancer, this does not mean that you should eat broccoli, cabbage, cauliflower, collards, horseradish, kohlrabi, mustard greens, radish, wasabi, watercress, etc, by the ton. Almost all cancer preventive compounds can actually aggravate cancer in unreasonably high doses, say 10 to 100 times the chemopreventive dose. And yes, too much can mess up your thyroid, even cause goiter, while a little is good.

Here I go again, repeating myself too frequently: all things in moderation, except perhaps variety. Eat some mustard greens, some cabbage, some broccoli, especially those that you enjoy. But I advise my friends against taking up a monofood diet, like mustard greens, broccoli, or cabbage; eating tons of that one boring crucifer every day. It's not natural. Eat a natural diet, closer to what our ancestors ate, with a wide variety of blue, green, orange, purple, red and yellow fruits and vegetables. Enjoy a few 100 g servings of various crucifers each week. I'm convinced it will help prevent cancer, as will moderate doses of members of the garlic family (chives, garlic, leek, onion, ramp). Mix and match. Good diet, good exercise and positive thinking may be your best allies against cancer and other major maladies, cardiopathy, diabetes and several of the other big killers, like pharmaceuticals. The better your diet, exercise, and stress control, the less likely you are to need pharmaceuticals, one of the top ten killers of North Americans.

Even the groundhog won't overdo these mustards. On Ground Hog's Day, Feb. 2, 2002, I said, "Groundhogs will be coming up (dare I say germinating) with the first of the wild mustard seeds. I suspect the groundhogs will take a few bites of wild mustard sprouts and then move on, not overdosing on any one pungent species. Like my deer, they avoid the wild mustard species heavily laden with the pungent defensive compounds that prevent cancer. And like my deer, the groundhogs are more likely, like humans, to eat the less bitter, less pungent cultivated relatives, broccoli, cabbage, etc., which are not any longer so well endowed with those pungent compounds that deter the feeding of the bugs (and bacteria and fungi) as well as the mammals. Up in West Virginia, my son's country consorts eat the groundhog. I hope they serve it with a mess of wild mustard greens, to complement that greasy groundhog. Too much tame meat, (less so wild game like groundhog), can increase your chances of many of those same diseases the cabbage and onion relatives will prevent. Happy Ground Hog Day."

Here's what I said about mustard in my *Medicinal Plants of the Bible,*

~twenty years earlier:

> *...The kingdom of heaven is like to a grain of mustard seed, which a man took, and sowed in his field: Which indeed is the least of all seeds: but when it is grown, it is the greatest among herbs...* ..................................Matthew 13

Black mustard is cultivated for its seeds, the source of commercial table mustard, used as a condiment and medicine. Seeds also contain both a fixed and an essential oil, used as a condiment, lubricant, and soap constituent. Black mustard is mixed with while mustard (*Sinapis alba*) to make mustard flour, used in various condiments as "English Mustard" when mixed with water and "Continental Mustard" with vinegar. The leaves are eaten as a potherb. Mustard flowers are good honey producers. In agriculture mustard is also used as a cover crop. Smoke from burning mustard is said to repel flies and mosquitoes (Kirtikar & Basu, 1975).

Mustard is considered anodyne, apertif, carminative, diuretic, emetic, laxative, rubefacient, stimulant, stomachic, and vesicant (Duke & Wain, 1981). Mustard plaster is used externally for many afflictions, like arthritis and rheumatism. A liquid prepared from the seed, when gargled, is said to be a folk remedy for tumors of the "sinax." In Ethiopia alone, the seed is used for amebiasis, abscesses, bloat, constipation, dysentery, rheumatism, and stomachache as well as for abortion (Jansen, 1981). A decoction or plaster of the seed used in a cataplasm is used for hardness of the liver and spleen. Seeds are also said to help carcinoma and throat tumors. Lately mustards have been shown to contain at least five compounds which inhibit neoplasias induced by polycyclic aromatic hydrocarbons. Mustard relieves congestion by drawing the blood to the surface as in head afflictions, neuralgia, spasms. Hot water poured on bruised seeds makes a stimulant foot bath, good for colds and headaches. Old herbals suggested mustard for alopecia, epilepsy, snakebite, and toothache. Mustard oil is said to stimulate hair growth. Mustard is also recommended as an aperient ingredient of tea, useful in hiccup. Mustard flour is considered antiseptic. The oil is considered useful in pleurisy and pneumonia. Ayurvedics value the leaves for throat complaints and worms, the seeds for cough, external parasites, fever, itch, megalospleny skin ailments, tumors, and worms. Unani also recommend the seeds for boils, ear, eye and nose problems, edema, inflammation, rheumatism and toothache.

# Nettle (*Urtica dioica*)

*The Wild Foods Forum* 17(2):8-9, Spring, 2006

## Needing Nettle

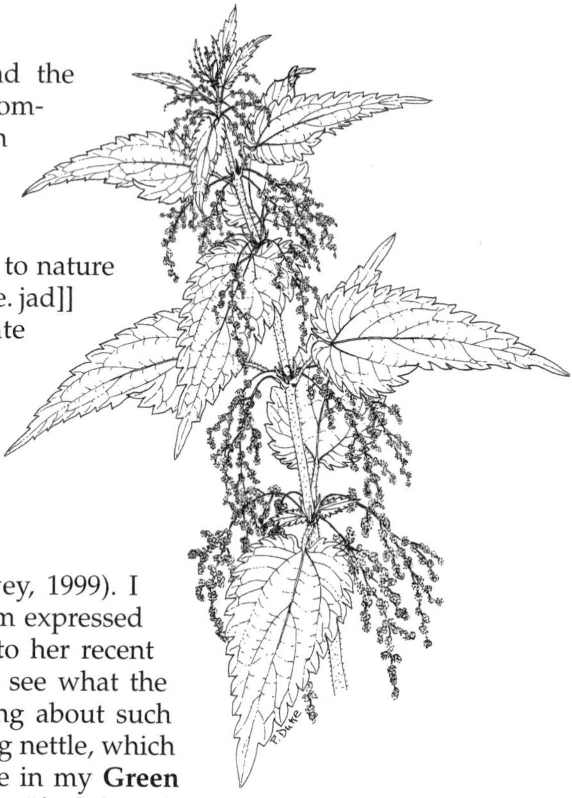

The fact that scientists had the nerve to say that isolated compounds "were better than the whole, synergistic miracle that nature created was a tremendous disservice to the public. [[And to nature and to their own intelligence. jad]] Plants in their whole state adapt to the body's need at that specific time and then work with the body to cleanse, nourish and rebuild whatever needs to be restored" (Laurel Dewey, May 1999).

Laurels to Laurel (Dewey, 1999). I like the sentiments of holism expressed in Laurel's "Introduction" to her recent book. And I always like to see what the western herbalists are saying about such familiar herbs as the stinging nettle, which occupies an important place in my **Green Farmacy Garden** and in my "faith-based" *Herbs of the Bible*, and in Laurel's interesting new book. Maybe Bush should line his rose garden with stinging nettles as a Faith-Based Biblical Medicinal Garden. Nettle is just one of more than a hundred species mentioned in the Bible.

The last sentence in the quote above is what I want to underscore. When a person ingests an herb or a food farmaceutical, that herb or food provides a whole menu of phytochemicals from which the body (I think strongly) homeostatically selects what it needs. This stands opposed to the simplistic synthetic silver bullet, which allows the body no choice: Just one synthetic compound your genes don't know! Scientists may have studied it for long enough to learn its major effects but not its side effects. Stinging nettle is loaded with minerals, phytochemicals, and vitamins, some long familiar to your genes. Reread that last sentence in the quote above, as you contemplate a mess of nettle greens and potlikker, loaded with phytochemicals, in some of which you may be marginally deficient.

Some of my neighbors, attuned to what Laurel is saying about hay fever, often visit in spring to get a new stash of nettle. "Anyone who suffers from seasonal allergies, including hay fever and pollen related concerns, might want to try a daily dose of nettle tea. In one study, more than half of patients taking three cups/day nettle tea, or three to five 500 mg capsules per day, reduced symptoms significantly. Hay fever sufferers who start drinking one or two cups of nettle tea daily (or take two to four 500 milligram capsules a day) in November and continue through April when the pollen arrives have been happily rewarded with an allergy-free springtime...Thanks to the naturally occurring histamine in the plant, those who suffer from minor allergies to lobster, shellfish and strawberries and develop hives may find relief from the root extract." Laurel recommends adding it to your diet when it is in season. Here at the **Green Farmacy Garden**, it is in season almost all year 'round, sometimes on even New Year's Day, on the south side of the barn. Goes good with my New Year's black-eyed peas, though I prefer the taste of turnip greens or collards.

I have so much nettle that I could easily try her rheumatism remedy, steeping in a nettle bath (it doesn't sting once the plant is dried or steamed). Laurel mentions one Godiva-like woman who "rolled naked in the nettles to keep the arthritis pain at bay." Don't think I'll try that one.

Laurel recommends 2-3 cups tea/day starting at the beginning of ovulation until the menstrual cycle begins. "When you take herbs to clean out the liver, you release stored 'anger' along with stored estrogen." And the tea can be taken to "reduce flooding during their menstrual cycle...Nettle tea helps to increase breast milk...Supposedly, it helps women develop a more 'ample' breast over time" (Hardy, 1999).

She mentions the German studies show that it helps with BPH (benign prostatic hyperplasia) as well. "Studies with 67 men over the age of 60 showed that two or three teaspoons of the root extract taken each day reduced their need to urinate at night." There's even more to this than meets the eye. Polar extracts of the nettle roots contain (+)-neoolivil, (-)-secoisolariciresinol, dehydrodiconiferyl alcohol, isolariciresinol, pinoresinol, and 3,4-divanillyltetrahydrofuran, all but the pinoresinol, binding to the human sex hormone binding globulin (SHBG) in an in vitro assay. The affinity of (-)-3,4-divanillyltetrahydrofuran was outstandingly high, with potential beneficial effects of plant lignans on BPH (Schoettner, Gansser, and Spiteller 1997).

Now after visiting Germany, just before and during 9/11, where I saw the Biblical nettle growing along the Rhine, I have more to add to the nettle story. I was replacing the late Varro Tyler who was supposed to lecture the tour group. I called it the Rhine Wine tour. I had a strange new malady myself this spring, which I first termed "incontinence of the nose" (later I found it more clinically named "rhinorrhea"). That's just one manifestation of hay fever which affects so many of us in the spring. For weeks, I had been on my hands and knees in the dusty undergrowth of my yin-yang valley, pulling bittersweet, blackberry, honeysuckle, multiflora rose, and poison ivy, trying to liberate the great collection of ferns I have growing in yin-yang valley. You see, I'm building a deck of cards with pictures of 52 Maryland and Maine ferns. I am too often puzzled by hybrid ferns in the field with my ethnobotany classes in Maine.

In taking care of my ferns, I developed rhinorrhea. And stinging nettle (or serendipidty) cleared it up. I could have taken one of those expensive medications, like Benadryl (two types of which were recalled in the first week of June, 2001, for causing phenylketonuria). But no, I went with the stinging nettle.

*NBC News*, May 29 and 30, 2001 (TV and radio respectively) were pushing their news story that 65% of the more than 4 billion dollars spent on prescription antiallergic drugs was wasted. It was spent on people who did not truly have allergy, partly because the patients demanded, and partly because the doctors acquiesed to those demands, for the over-promoted allergy prescription drugs (allegra, claritin and the like). Colds and sinusitis can trigger the symptoms. Only skin tests can prove that those investing their money, often $80 a month, truly have allergy.

Wouldn't it be ironic if the other one-third, the truly allergic third, as identified by patch tests, would be better off with the Biblical stinging nettle. Could stinging nettle tea (pot likker) and greens be as effective for allergy and hay fever as Allegra? I have no proof that the stinging nettle would help as much as those billion dollar drugs. Clearly Andy Weil feels that freeze dried nettle is proven for hay fever. So I now add *Urtica* to those herbs that should be clinically compared with the competing pharmaceutical, in this case, e.g. Allegra vs *Urtica*. Which is better for allergic rhinitis? Believe me, nobody knows until they are clinically compared. If you believe in prayer, and in the Bible, and in Andy Weil, and maybe even in Jim Duke, then this faith-based Biblical botanical may indeed help you. Believing is often more than half the cure. I don't think the deserved clinical comparisons will ensue. That would help the American public and hurt the pharmaceutical industry. To which do you think the FDA is attuned. Money talks. Herbs only talk to herbal believers. Who would benefit (other than the American public) if stinging nettle proved as safe and efficacious and cheaper than allegra, or claritin, or any other pharmaceutical? Who would lose? Come on Uncle Sam – say Uncle.

In August, 2001, friends from the lab I worked with at the USDA took a long lunch and toured the **Green Farmacy Garden**. One's allergies were also newly worse this year. I recommended she try some nettle. I got an e-mail the following morning:

> "Dear Jim: Thank you so much for the spectacular day. It was an unbelievable pleasure to walk through your garden and learn so many things... I have to tell you that I bought some Stinging Nettle last night for my allergies and they seemed to do better right away. Thank you so much for everything! It was a very special trip."

Another on that tour had once demonstrated for me, xerographically, that urtication with the nettle reduced the size of her arthriticly swollen knuckle. Now there are British clinical trials showing that self urtication with stinging nettle helps arthritic as compared to a placebo lashing with dead nettle (X10911825). That was in 2000. Now two more trials (X11962753; X11950004) reveal different mechanisms by which the antiarthritic activities may be rationalized. I've not seen all the articles but doubt that they suggest as do I that additionally, getting a microinjection of histamine (each hair is ca 0.2% histamine – HH3) might lead your body to mount an antihistaminic reaction, some of which goes to the sting, some of which goes to the arthritis.

When I queried PubMed for *Urtica* AND BPH (benign prostatic hypertrophy), I got 13 abstracts. Roots of the stinging nettle have proven useful in BPH. My HMO physician, after my annual physical with the manual or should I say digital probe and, this year, my third colonoscopy, said "keep up whatever you are doing (High fiber, high fruit, high herb, high nut, high spice, high veggies, high whole grain) to prevent polyps and colon cancer, high genistein, high selenium, high sitosterol diet to prevent BPH. So there are many reasons to add stinging nettles to my soups and green veggie dishes.

Only the botanically inclined are aware of the close relationships of three medicinal plants, all weedy cousins, loaded with biological activities. I speak of (1) hops – major contributor to beers, and very estrogenic; (2) marijuana, illegal but widely used recreational AND medicinal drug, maybe even estrogenic and reportedly mastogenic; and (3) now the Biblical stinging nettle, loaded with neurotransmitting chemical messengers, and also reportedly lactogenic and mastogenic. Even more than marijuana and hops, nettle can make you itch on contact. And like marijuana it's a fiber source, cannabis being the name sake of canvas. And like marijuana, it has a host of proven biological activities and medicinal applications.

Like bee stings, nettle stings have evolved in the antiarthritic folklore of every continent where they occur. Intermission at a folk festival in the Arkansas Ozarks, a nurse, excited about the histamine connection, said she worked with an MD who used nutritional approaches along with histamine injections for athritis and rheumatism. Here in the **Green Farmacy Garden**, the nettle gives you the histamine injection. Nettle shows up in several plots in my **Green Farmacy Garden** (allergy, arthritis, asthma, BPH, bronchitis, HIV, impotence. multiple sclerosis, osteoporosis, and PMS) indicating that I find it very useful for those ailments. Regrettably, it is aggressive and tries to move into adjacent plots. One of the volunteer workers in the garden is a registered nurse (RN). She had the not-so-rare opportunity to evaluate the sting of the nettle for an arthritic knuckle. While coping with a nest of yellow jackets, she got stung, and accidentally evaluated the folkloric sting for arthritis as well. She ranked the yellow jacket more alleviative of the arthritis than the stinging nettle (but the nettles are easier to keep in the window, like my secretary Judi used to do, for arthritic knuckles). Here are the nurses comments:

> "Thanks for suggesting the screen for the yellow jacket holocaust. (That is just as expression, we did not light the gasoline.) We would have been in BIG trouble without it. However, as we were inspecting things, after we got the screen secured with bricks, we both got stung. In fact, I was tickled to get stung while having an arthritic knuckle, in order to test that idea that 'bee keepers never get arthritis.' For the record, it does seem the knuckle is more relaxed after the y.j. sting than after the nettle sting. I may just have to overdose on the nettle stings to get the desired effect."

On the day that I got a call from Jean Carper's researcher, asking about my case histories of nettle for rheumatism, I received an abstract of a German study (Obertreis et al., 1996), undertaken to study the antirheumatic activities of *Urtica dioica*, and showing that nettle extracts inhibit both detrimental eicosanoid and cytokine metabolism. Tumor necrosis factor-a and interleukin-1B are cytokines both suspect in pathogenesis of osteo- and rheumatoid arthritis. Concentrations of nettle extracts from 1.25-5 mg/ml inhibited their secretion dose-dependently and significantly, 5 mg/ml 51% and 100% respectively, after 24 hours. Since none of the flavonoids tested alone inhibited, other factors or synergy must be involved. The nettle extract also stimulated the production of interleukin-6, potentially useful for inhibiting interleukin-1B's deleterious effects (Obertreis et al., 1996).

You might find another explanation more interesting. An allopathic physician who accompanied me to the Peruvian rainforest was more interested in the beer's biological activities than those of the stinging nettle. After several beers he did come up with an interesting explanation for the fact that arthritics among many native people often sting themselves with the stinging nettle.

There's some science behind the nettle. No, its not because it hurts so bad that you forget your arthritis. It's because, following the injection of these histaminic compounds, the body mounts an antihistaminic attack. And some of these defensive natural antihistamines go to the arthritic joint while others go to the nettle sting. Asthma and hay fever are not the same thing but histamines seem to be involved in both. We read in *American Health* (July, 1988): Asthma isn't just a childhood disease, there are millions of adult asthmatics in the U.S. If you are one of millions with allergies (like hay fever), there is 1 chance in 4 that you also have asthma.

According to Andy Weil, MD (*Whole Earth* No. 64, 1989), a hay-fever suffering naturopathic experimenter swallowed capsules of freeze-dried nettle and her hay-fever symptoms went away rapidly. Since then, many victims allergic to seasonal pollen have learned that this harmless remedy enables them to do away with antihistamines, drugs with significant toxicity and such undesirable side effects as sedation, depression, and interference with mental activity. I still have frozen nettle in my refrigerator. That freeze-dried *Urtica* can diminish hayfever symptoms has been confirmed in one controlled clinical trial. That doesn't automatically make nettle the herb of choice. Ironically a histaminic drug may help spare us the antihistamines. Those people who visit my nettle patch every spring, are taking nettle potlikker and eating the greens as a food farmaceutical approach to asthma and hayfever, both of which seem to be increasing here in the good old USA.

Spring is here, and the incredible edible medical nettle is up. A University of Maryland CAM class is due by tomorrow, so I'll teach them the stinging perils of the stinging nettles, as part of my review of the *PDR for Herbal Medicine* [Gruenwald, J; et al. 2000]. I'd give them good grades on most of what they have to say about the stinging nettle, and since it is an edible potherb, I recommend the herbal alternative as the first thing to try, before the competing pharmaceuticals. You see, if your roots are European, your genes probably already know most of the compounds in the Biblical stinging nettle.

According to Gruenwald et al. (2000), fresh leaves of stinging nettle contain acetylcholine, serotonin, and histamine. My *Hager's Handbuch* (ed. 3) adds choline. noting that at 8 ug liquid weight per hair, the hairs contain 1% acetylcholine, 0.2% histamine, and 0.05% 5-hydroxytryptamine. Pressed juice (with scopoletin, beta-sitosterol, and caffeoyl malic acid) is diuretic with sufficient fluid intake. Local anesthetic and analgesic effects have been observed. Caffeoyl acid, in vitro, inhibits 5-lipoxygenase-dependent leukotriene synthesis. Antirheumatic and anti-arthritic effects are demonstrated. A leaf extract inhibits the biosynthesis of arachidonic acid metabolites in vitro. IDS 23, a leaf extract, dose-dependently inhibited cyclooxygenase. A phenolic-acid isolate inhibited synthesis of leukotriene B4 (dose-dependently). The combination of these activities may explain the antiinflammatory effects.

The root causes increased volume of urine, increased maximum urinary flow, and reduced residual urine, all useful markers in BPH. The aqueous root extract was most effective in BPH (benign prostatic hyperplasia). Nettle extracts dose-dependently inhibited the binding of sex hormone-binding globulin (SHBG) to its receptor on human prostatic membranes. Inhibition was partial at 0.6 mg/ml; complete at 10 mg/ml. Most tested lignans had an affinity for SHBG, (-)-3,4-divanillytetrahydrofuran in particular. An N-acetylglucosamine n-specific lectin from nettle was inhibitory to HIV-1, HIV-2, CMV, RSV and influenza A virus [in-vitro EC-50 = 0.3 to 0.9 ug/ml. *Urtica dioica* agglutinin (UDA) protected mice from developing signs, suggestive of clinical signs, of lupus and nephritis. One randomized, reference-controlled, multicenter double blind clinical trial compared efficacy of saw palmetto /nettle extract (PRO 160/120) with finasteride in BPH (Aiken stages I to II). The study involved 543 patients treated 48 weeks with PRO 160/120 extract or finasteride double blind. The primary marker was change of maximum urinary flow after 24 weeks of therapy. Secondary markers included average urinary flow, micturition volume and micturition time. Urinary symptoms were scored on the International-Prostate-Symptom-Score (I-PSS). Differences between the groups most noted were in the lower adverse events categories where the PRO 160/120 group reported less events, esp. diminished ejaculation volume, erectile dysfunction, and headache. Leaf extracts, when used with diclofenac, enhance the anti-inflammatory effect of diclofenac. "No health hazards or side effects are known in conjunction with the proper administration of designated therapeutic dosage" (Gruenwald et al., 2000).

I mention today some news about an old plant, the Biblical stinging nettle. Here's what I had to say more than 15 years ago, in my *Medicinal Plants of the Bible.*

**Stinging Nettle, Common Nettle, Greater Nettle**

*...and thorns shall come up in her palaces, nettles and brambles in the fortresses thereof...* Isaiah 34

"Young tops, gathered when about 15 cm high, can be used as a spring green vegetable, ususally in the form of a purée, but their rather earthy flavor is not liked by some. In Scotland, nettles are combined with leeks or onions, broccoli or cabbage, and rice, boiled in a muslin bag and served with butter or gravy. Nettle beer and nettle tea are made by some people. Dried nettles can be fed to livestock and poultry, but few animals will eat the living plants. I have eaten our species, raw and cooked. In Sweden and Russia, nettles are sometimes cultivated as a fodder plant. Alcoholic extracts of nettle, chamomile, thyme, and burdock have been used in hair and scalp preparations (2). In Russia, the nettle has been used for a green pigment in confectionary. Nettle fiber can be used for making textiles and paper, as has been done during war-time or when other fibers are not available. The fiber is similar to hemp or flax and can be used for fine or coarse materials.

"Nettle is cited as a folk remedy for cacoethes, cancerous ulcers, carcinomata, endothelioma, epithelioma, polyps, sarcoma, and cancers, indurations and/or tumors of the breast, ear, face, feet, joints, liver, lungs, mouth, nostrils, parotids, ribs, spleen, stomach, and swellings of the womb, etc. In Algeria, nettles are powdered and mixed with powdered jasmine for gonorrhea. In Russia, the leaves are used in the preparation of 'Alcohol,' used for chronic hepatitis, cholengitis, cholecystitis, and habitual constipation. Roots and seed are prescribed as a vermifuge. Clinical experiments are said to have confirmed the utility of the herb as a hemostatic. It is also used in ague, anemia, asthma, bronchitis, catarrh, constipation, consumption, cough, diabetes, diarrhea, dropsy, dysentery, dysmenorrhea, dyspnea, epilepsy, epistaxis, gastritis, gout, gravel, headache, hemoptysis, jaundice, malaria, menorrhea, nephritis, neuralgia, palsy, paralysis, pertussis, piles, rheumatism, sciatica, and tuberculosis, and as a hair tonic. Roots are diuretic. Juice of the plants is used as an external irritant. Decoction of plant is anthelmintic, antiseptic, astringent, depurative, diuretic, emmenagogue, rubefacient, and vasoconstrictor. Homeopaths prescribe a tincture of the flowering plant for alactia, beestings, burns, colic, dysentery, erysipelas, erythema, gout, gravel, hemorrhage, intermittents, lactation, leucorrhea, menorrhagia, phlegmasia, preventing calculus, renitis, rheumatism, sore throat, splenitis, uremia, ria, vertigo, whooping cough and worms."

And here's the updated entry from my *Herbal Desk Reference*. Great food, great medicine, faith-based Biblical botanical, with a powerful sting. Give it the respect it deserves.

## Updated April 1, 2005 – Notes (Nettle):

Allen and Hatfield say that no plants, except perhaps dandelion, dock, and elder, are as important medicinally as the nettle in the British Isles. Such feelings may underline the rhyme: "three nettles in May keeps all diseases away" (AAH). MAD entries may apply as well to *Urtica urens*, the smaller dog nettle. Ditto for EFS entries.

- Algerians mix powdered nettles with powdered jasmine for gonorrhea (BIB)
- Carolinans suggest the root for consumption, diarrhea, dysentery, gravel, hemorrhoids, jaundice, nephrosis and pain (BUR)
- Czechs poultice the herb onto cancers (JLH)
- Devonshire locals use nettle top tea for urticaria (KAB)
- French use nettle roots steeped in vinegar for tumors of the feet and spleen, stampoed in honey for tumors in lungs or ribs (JLH)
- Irish drink nettle tea to clear measle rash (AAH)
- Russians self urticate to energize tired muscles (KAB)
- Russians use the leaves in "Alochol," for chronic hepatitis, cholengitis, cholecystitis, and habitual constipation
- Herb decoction taken for cold, cough, rheumatism, stomachache (EB51:195)
- Nettle roots crushed with vinegar for swellings of the feet or spleen (CEB)
- Nettle juice as a mouthwash for swollen uvula (CEB)
- Nettle juice boiled lightly with sugar; two ounces taken orally for bleeding piles (CEB)
- Nettle seed w honey (or nettle juice) for cold, cough, gastrosis, orchosis, swellings (CEB)
- One tbsp seeds with jam or honey for impotence (CEB, where we read that nettle seeds in wine excite to games of love.)

- Seed (and flower) tincture 1 tsp 3-4x/day for ague and malaria (CEB);
- Seeds boiled in wine for orchosis (CEB)
- Seeds crushed in honey for pustules on the lung, sideache, swellings of the ribs, (CEB)
- Seed of Nettle stirreth up lust, especially drunk with Cute (thickened must)...(Gerarde as quoted in CEB)
- 12-15 seed, 3x/dayfor goitre (or bigneck) (CEB)

# Plantain (*Plantago major*)

*The Business of Herbs* 6(3):7-8, July/August, 1988

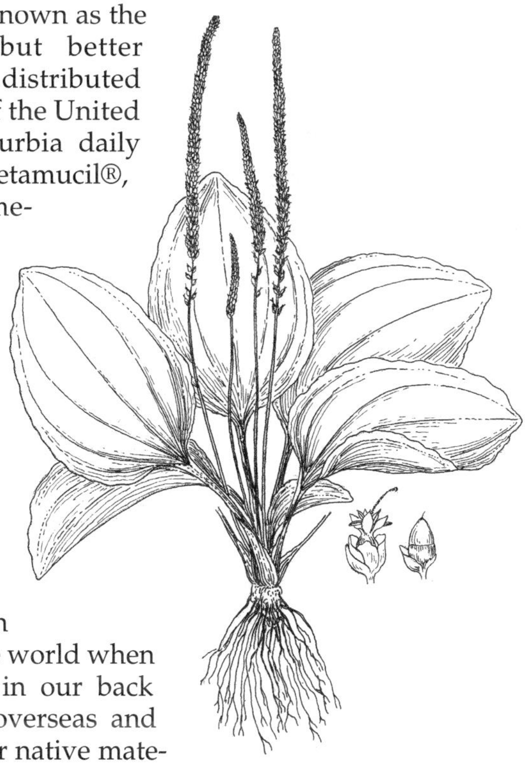

*Plantago major*, once also known as the "white man's footprint," but better known as plantain, is widely distributed in the constipated suburbia of the United States. Many people in suburbia daily take the laxative known as Metamucil®, no "johnny-on-the-spot-come-lately" on the over-the-counter medicinal scene. I grace it with the appellation "rich man's psyllium" because instead of using our common plantain, we import tons and tons of the Indian psyllium, *Plantago ovata*, usually these days from India, at the rate of more than $2,000,000 a month. This is another example of the United States importing an herb from half way around the world when we have the weed growing in our back yard. It's cheaper to buy it overseas and ship it here than to harvest our native material. In 1984 the U.S. imported more than 8,000 tons with a value of nearly $28 million.

I'm not prepared to say that *Plantago major* is as good as *Plantago ovata*. I am saying that it is sometimes used instead of *P. ovata*, or even as an adulterant. One of the better source books on Ayurvedic medicine, Kirtikar and Basu's *Indian Medicinal Plants* says seeds of *Plantago major* are used "as a good substitute for those of *P. ovata*." I predict that markets will grow for Indian psyllium, another old established medicinal plant, recently proving out with new pharmaceutical applications.

Recent studies (Gupta, 1982) from India, which "commands a near monopoly in production and export of the seed and husk to the world market," note that India has 40,000 acres yielding about 3200 tons of processed seed husk. *Plantago ovata* is the main source. Another minor source is *P. psyllium*. Besides these, *P. major*, *P. lanceolata*, *P. pumila*, *P. coronopus*, *P. argentea*, and *P. lagopus*, also produce smaller quantities of mucilage." Remember that it is mostly the husks finding their way into the western over-the-counter market. Husks constitute about 30% of the fruits, the seed about 70%.

Psyllium may represent a double-barrelled shotgun for cholesterol. The fiber (glamorously called "psyllium hydro-philic mucilloid") in the husks, like many dietary fibers, can reduce cholesterol. Seeds also contain an oil reported to reduce blood serum cholesterol levels, at least in rabbits. Wall Street analysts say, "There could be a $5 billion market for anti-cholesterol remedies in a few years" (*Wall Street Journal,* March 12, 1987).

In a double blind placebo controlled study, Dr. James Anderson, of the VA hospital in Lexington put patients on eight-week Metamucil® diets. Total cholesterol levels promptly dropped 14.8%. Anderson says Metamucil® is easier to tolerate than other fiber supplements; still he hopes people will move on to eating more oatmeal and beans as well. Anderson suggests that the 14.8% reduction in serum cholesterol may lower the risk for coronary heart disease by 28% in middle-aged hyper-cholesterolemic men.

In another study (Andersen and Menta, 1983), rats were fed for 22 weeks a diet containing no fiber, or with cellulose, or with psyllium husk. During the study, half of each group were given cancer inductions. At the end of the study 100% of the no-fiber rats had tumors, 70% of those on cellulose had tumors, while only 50% of the rats on psyllium had tumors, showing that psyllium reduced tumor incidence by half.

In a study of Asian Indians with menorrhagia (profuse menstrual bleeding), 3 grams (ca ⅛ oz) seeds a day, given orally, checked the bleeding in 2 to 3 days with no toxic or untoward effects noted (Fazal, 1979). The cholinergic alcoholic extracts of the seeds lower blood pressure in experimental animals.

I can see natural ice cream manufacturers taking up Procter and Gamble's (owners of Metamucil®) banner, suggesting the use of psyllium husks as a wholesome and natural thickener for ice cream. Would that not pit the cholesterol lowering effects of the psyllium against the cholesterol raising effects of the cream? One might even hint at anti-ulcer activity of mucilage as do Kirtikar and Basu: "During its passage through the gut it coats the inflamed and ulcerated mucosa and protects it from being irritated by the fluids and gases, the products of gastrointestinal and bacterial digestion."

Genetically targeted by colon cancer, I'm particularly intrigued by Anderson's comment (*Cont. Nut.* 11(9): 1986): "Fiber may bind or dilute carcinogens or alter bile acid metabolism to help reduce the risk of colon cancer." Equally encouraging words are applied to the psyllium mucilage in *The Wealth of India* (WOI): "The toxins present in the gut are absorbed by the gel of the mucilage and thus are prevented from absorption into the system." WOI cautions that the husk is preferred since a large amount of seed might cause intestinal obstruction.

The leaves of the plant, known in Latin America as "llanten," have quite a folk reputation. Bacteriostatic, they are poulticed onto cuts and sores. Containing allantoin, they are used as a cicatrizant. Containing choline, the leaves are applied to stings, etc. In her *Atlas of Medicinal Plants,* Morton (1981) notes that young leaves are sometimes cooked and eaten or dried and steeped to make tea. "The seeds have been parched and ground into meal."

[[While it's not my favorite food, it's certainly abundant. None need starve, or be constipated. Twice, when getting lax with my normal laxative diets, I have purchased Metamucil®, at bout ten dollars a tube. Now I just strip off the old seeding spikes and save it 'til needed, saving ten bucks in the process, and ridding my lawn of several thousand seeds.]]

[[Today (Johnston, 1997): "The FDA has proposed a rule that would amend the regulation permitting food labeling bearing a health claim on soluble fiber for a lower risk of coronary heart disease (CHD) to include soluble fiber from psyllium husks (*Plantago asiatica* L.)." Kellogg petitioned citing data from 57 clinical studies (1965-1996 – including 21 human studies) on psyllium's ability to lower cholesterol and CHD risk. FASEB has determined that psyllium is safe at levels up to 25 g/day. FDA counters that high levels of psyllium husk "may enhance epithelial cell proliferation in the GI tract or cause allergies in some people" (Johnston, B.J. 1997. "FDA proposes health claim for psyllium." *Herbalgram* 41: 28).]]

THE BATTLE OF BATTLE CREEK
anonpoet (JAD)

Was the FDA getting weak?
Was it turning the other cheek?
Who would have been most balleyhooed,
If psyllium were called a food,
In the battle at Battle Creek?

# Purslane (*Portulaca oleracea*)

*The Wild Foods Forum* 15(3):8-9, Summer, 2004

## Pondering Purslane

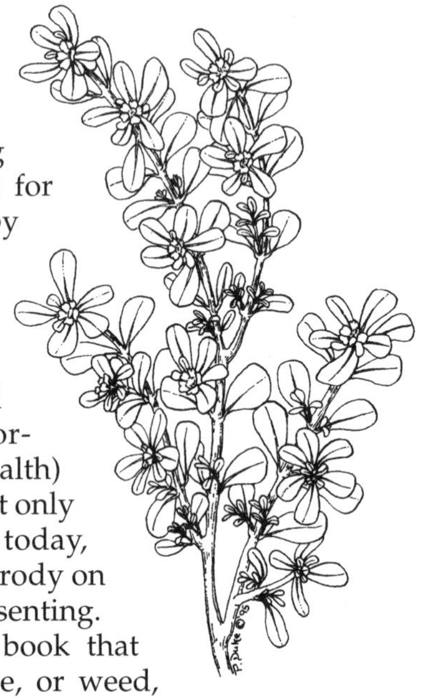

In the first week of June, 2004, the TV's were buzzing about a government- (not pharmaceutical-) sponsored trial suggesting that Prozac with talk therapy was best for depression in teenagers (ca 70%), followed by Prozac alone (ca 60%), followed by talk alone (ca 50%), which was little better than placebo. Unfortunately the study did not look at Omega-3 fatty acids (or fish oil) for depression. I've often heard Dr. Jerry Cott, now with the FDA, and formerly with NIMH (Nat. Inst. Mental Health) say that Omega-3's are very promising, not only for depression but also for mania. And today, Feb. 19, 2006, I am scheduled to sing a parody on Omega-3s at a lecture Dr. Cott will be presenting.

Yes I read in Artemis Simopolous' book that Omega's 3's, that purslane, the vegetable, or weed, depending on your point of view, can contain up to 4,000 ppm of the omega-3-fatty acid, alpha linolenic acid (ALA). That's fresh purslane. That would calculate 80,000 ppm or 0.8% on a ZMB assuming fresh purslane is 95% water. Purslane is also a good vegetarian source of l-dopa and dopamine. And it is one of my favorite wild foods, and the best leafy (as contrasted to certain seeds like cannabis, flax, perilla, walnut, which can be up to ten times richer yet) source of omega-3-fatty acids, in this case, ALA. Could a purslane salad drenched in walnut oil and adorned with flowers of St. Johnswort, all three wild foods, be better and cheaper for teen-age depression than Prozac. Add 7 stigmata (ca 30 mg) of the right crocus (saffron) and you'll be adding what Iranians have calculated to be the equal of 100 mg imipramine as an andidepressant.

I mentioned the St. Johnswort earlier this year. And will be singing about it to Congress at a special luncheon this month trying to insure that in the future herbal alternatives be introduced as a third arm in trials like this Prozac Trial, so that promising herbal alternatives are compared clinically with the pharmaceutical and placebo. Too bad, they should be serving an antidepressant salad to Congress to emphasize my point. Until clinically compared we don't know but what purslane and omega-3-oils, even fish oils for non-vegetarians, might be better than Prozac for teenage depression. I hinted at this more than a decade ago.

Back in 1992, I first published my **Father Nature's Farmacy** database, under the foreboding title CRC *Handbook of Phytochemical Constituents of*

## *OMEGA-3*

Please put my mind at ease,
I don't want no heart disease
Yet everyone expects some Syndrome X
Can I really defy it, with exercise and diet
And omega three, can nix the X for me
Omega-3; Omega-3;
Can you really make a new man out of me
Scour my sclerosis, negate my necrosis,
And leave some CoQ10 with me
Omega-3; Omega-3s;
Can you really make a new man out of me
Just like my artichoke, prevent impending stroke,
And clear my clogged arteries
I thought he was bull shooting,
when I first read Dr. Rudin
But gradually it all made sense to me
Like Doctora Artemis, it was his basic premise
That most of us still need omega 3

**Chorus:**
Omega-3; Omega-3-;
Can you really make a new man out of me;
Lower my depression, lower my blood pressure,
And mute my manic misery

**Chorus:**
Omega-3; Omega-3-;
Can you really make a new man out of me;
Both Roundtree and Cott, mentioned everything
I've got, Fish oil may be the thing for me.

*GRAS Herbs and Other Economic Plants* (1992. 654 pp. CRC Press, Boca Raton, FL 33431). Pretty dull reading, it tabulates all of the ingredients I had seen listed for more than 1,000 species of plants. It also listed, in ppm, the quantities of those ingredients for which I found published quantitative data. Intrigued when I saw that the database could be interrogated with all sorts of weird queries, I had my postdoc, Dr. Steven Beckstrom-Sternberg, make a run to show which species therein were reported to contain the most reportedly "antidepressant" compounds. Purslane was in the top five, at up to a hypothetical 135,000 ppm or 13.5% (on a dry-matter basis¸divide by 10 or 20 to get a very rough idea of the fresh-weight basis), compared to lettuce at 160,310 ppm or 16.0%, amaranth at 15.3%, lamb's-quarters at 13.4%, and watercress at 12.3%. Looks like a good antidepressant salad to me, topped off with some omega-3-fatty acids and those happy flowers of St. Johnswort, and crocus stigmata. On a dry basis, purslane can contain as much as 20,800 ppm calcium, 18,700 ppm magnesium, 11,500 ppm phenylalanine, 81,200 ppm potassium, and 3,400 ppm tryptophan, ubiquitous compounds all reportedly of some use in depression. Add that to the 80,000 ppm omega-3-fatty acid and up to 2,500 ppm adrenaline, noradrenaline, norepinephrine a/o l-dopa. See the MAM for depression in section C. Purslane presents your body a menu of natural chemicals, not a single artificial chemical like Prozac. Given such a menu, your body homeostatically tries to get you closer to norm, says Jim Duke, geriatric flake. This does not necessarily mean that purslane is antidepressant. It means only that it contains significant quantities of phytochemicals that are reported to have antidepressant activities. If your depression is due to a chemical imbalance, these chemicals may help restore balance. Is that why "grazers" run around looking so damned happy? Purslane is great, raw in the garden, even the stems pickled in a pickle vinegar from which the pickles have already been consumed, and in soups and salads.

In *Omega Plan*, Simopoulos (1998) indicates that Americans normally get 14-20 times more omega-6 than omega-3 fats, way out of line with our paleolithic ratios (which she estimates at closer to 1:1). Getting closer to our paleolithic omega-3:omega-6 ratio might eliminate many of the diseases that increase dramatically when one assumes our western diet: ADHD, Alzheimer's, arthritis, asthma, depression, diabetes, heart attack, insulin resistance, lupus, obesity, postpartum depression, schizophrenia, and stroke. If you read this fascinating book, you'll get the feeling, that these ailments might often be helped by eating more fish and ALA, the latter generously provided by one of the weeds our ancestors ate. Dr. Simopoulos found that purslane she collected near her NIH office contained 4,000 ppm ALA, such that a 100 gram serving provided 400 mg ALA. Greek in derivation herself, Artemis also noted that purslane seeds were found in a cave in Greece that was inhabited 16,000 years ago. Chickens are fond of purslane, and the eggs that purslane-fed chickens lay have 20 times more omega-3s than the run-of-the-mill supermarket egg. Historically, she says, early humans got their Omega-3s in seafoods, sea vegetables, nuts, seeds, and green plant leaves. She says the Omega-6s are concentrated in grains and seeds which didn't increase in our diet until the development of agriculture ca 10 millennia ago. Artemis, like me, has come to the conclusion that one serving of purslane fulfills the daily requirement for vit. E (usually difficult to do dietarily), while providing significant quantities of ascorbic acid, beta-carotenes, and glutathione. According to Dr. Simopoulos, Theophrastus (372-287 BC), the father of botany, recommended purslane for dry skin, earache, heart failure, scurvy, sorethroat, and swollen joints. His recommendations for heart patients may have been better than the American Heart Association's. Some 600 French patients recovering from heart attacks were put on the AHA "prudent diet" high in omega-6 diet, or on a modified Cretan diet, with canola oil as a major source of omega-3 ALA. Dietary ALA was clearly diverted into cardioprotective EPA and DHA. Four months into the trial, there were already significantly fewer side deaths in those on the Cretan diet than on the AHA diet. (NO OTHER HEART DIET OR DRUG HAS SHOWN A LIFE-SAVING EFFECT EARLIER THAN 6 MONTHS.) Two years into the study, it was discontinued because it seemed unethical to expose patients to the AHA recommended diet when the Cretan diet was so much better. The Cretan diet resulted in a 76% lower risk of dying from cardiovascular disease or suffering heart failure, heart attack, or stroke. The new diet was more effective at saving lives than anything ever studied (Simopoulos, 1998).

Fatty acids can talk to our genes, Simopoulos says, recounting a study showing that oils high in Omega-6 tell the genes to produce more ras p21, a cancer promoting protein. In contrast, omega-3s inactivate this protein, possibly lowering the cancer risk. As I was first reviewing Simopoulos' book five years ago, Mrs. Duke bought our first tub of canola oil spread, for our 4th of July corn on the cob. [[I am not pro canola, just pro-omega-3's; most if not all canola is genetically modified "frankenfood."]] Peggy is more liable to profit from heartwise Omega-3 choices, since her genes render her more liable than me to heart attack. Maybe tomorrow I can talk her into puree of purslane. That might slow both our osteoporotic (her) and anky losing spondylitic (mine) tendencies. *Prevention* Magazine (June 1995) ran an ad hinting that ca 72% of us don't get enough magnesium. And skillfully the ad notes that magnesium deficiency has been found in patients with asthma, debility, diabetes, headache, hypertension, hypocalcemia, hypokalemia, irregular heartbeat, migraine, osteoporosis, pallor, and tremors. Purslane was then the best source of magnesium {2% on a dry weight basis}, in my USDA phytochemical database, followed by greenbean, poppy seed, oats, cowpea and spinach. An RDA of 450 mg would require only 25 g dry purslane (ZMB).

*The Wild Foods Forum* is more about food than medicine, but the more I read, the more I think wild foods, by getting our genes back in touch with our historically ingested phytochemicals, are medicine, what I call food farmaceuticals, a menu of phytochemicals from which your genes select those it needs, rejecting the unneeded. I am not here to prescribe herbal medicine, but some of our foraging readers may just find themselves lost in the forest without medicine or doctor. It has happened to me in Panama and in Peru. Here's some of the folk medicinal lore and, more importantly, some of the proven pharmacological activities of purslane. Two proven pharmaceuticals, l-nor-adrenaline (2,500 ppm in the fresh plant, roughly 25,000 ppm or 2.5% in a carefully dried plant) and dopa, occur in the plant. Dopa has been widely used in Parkinson's Disease. Noradrenaline, better known as norepinephrine, can stimulate the adrenals, and has been used, at least veterinarily, for low blood pressure and shock. Just last night, I heard about a Tasmanian ant that killed more Tasmanians than several of the competing natural killers, like lightning, sharks, snakes etc, causing death by anaphylactic shock. A little purslane chewed and wadded up under the tongue might possibly supply enough sublingual noradrenaline to stave off terminal anaphylaxis. How many times on my tours have I seen hyperallergenic people enter the forest without their anti-anaphylactic injection kit. Purslane just might save their lives.

Because of high potassium levels (ca 5,000-75,000 ppm) the plant is diuretic (stimulates urination). Experimental rabbits fed purslane experience a drop in blood sugar, suggesting that purslane might be useful to diabetics. Containing dopa, mucilage and sitosterol, the herb might conceivably be pushed by unscrupulous herbalists as an aphrodisiac. Without even defining them for you (you'll learn a lot looking them up), I list some of the folk attributes, real or imagined, of the purslane: aperient, astringent, bactericidal*, cardiotonic, demulcent*, diuretic*, emollient, fungicidal, hemostatic, hypertensive*, hypoglycemic*, hypotensive*, lactagogue, refrigerant, sedative, stimulant*, tonic*, vermifuge, viricide, and vulnerary. (The * signifies that the purslane contains a phytochemical known to possess this activity.) Do you detect a contradiction in hypertensive and hypotensive? The norepinephrine might raise the blood pressure, the potassium lower it! And I'm flake enough to believe that the homeostatic (striving for physiological equilibrium) human body might have mechanisms to grab the activity it needs. Each herb, like purslane, contains dozens, ye hundreds, of biologically active compounds, some synergic (acting in the same direction with augmentive effects), some antagonistic (acting in opposing directions, thus partially or completely nullifying each other.) Thus, herbs, like purslane, constitute a veritable medicinal menu of biologically active compounds from which the body just may select those it needs the most. Again, I offer you a long list of ailments for which purslane has a folk or proven reputation, without defining them for you (if you have the ailment, you probably know what it is): bladder ailments, blennorrhagia, burns, diarrhea, dyspepsia, dysuria, edema, enterorrhagia, fever, gonorrhea, gravel, hematuria, hemoptysis, hyperglycemia, hypertension, hypotension, inflammation, insomnia, leuocrrhea, palpitations, scald, scurvy, sores, strangury, swellings, toothache, urogenital disorders, warts and wounds.

In his scholarly *Plants Used Against Cancer*, the NCI's (National Cancer Institute's) Jonathan Hartwell notes that the purslane has also been applied to cancers or tumors of the eyes, feet, genitals, urethra and uterus, but strictly as folk remedies. Lost in the bush without medicine, I would not hesitate to apply the crushed plant to corns, sores, warts, whitlows or wounds, nor would I hesitate to express the juice onto an earache or toothache as has been reported in the folklore. A recent paper (Rashed, Afifi and Disi, 2003) proved the healing or vulnerary properties of topical purslane. Purslane accelerated the wound healing process by decreasing the surface area of the wound and increasing the tensile strength. In the famed Ayurvedic tradition of India, purslane is also used for asthma, leprosy and piles. Indians also apply the juice of the plant to prickly heat and to the hands and feet, if with a burning sensation. Thirsty hikers might experiment with one recommendation from *Culpepper's Herbal*, placing the herb under the tongue to allay thirst. Juice of the plant was recommended to secure loose teeth as well as to alleviate sore mouths and swollen gums.

Check out my USDA database – you can see the veritable menu of useful phytochemicals reported from this food farmaceutical. Your body knows, even better than you or your physician or quack knows, which phytochemicals it needs. You enjoy grazing the purslane as a food and allow your body to grab those chemicals, without your needing to know how to spell or diagram such dreadful names as alpha-linolenic-acid, l-dopa, noradrenaline.

Purslane is good and chock full of useful minerals and vitamins. I have never known it to induce suicide as some pharmaceutical anti-depressants are reputed to do. I would warn you of one down side, that it is high in oxalic acid. Those with oxalic-acid stones and kidney ailments, might wish to avoid many members of the Centrospermae, like amaranth, beets, buckwheat, chard, dock, lambsquarter, purslane, rhubarb, sheep sorrel, sorrel, spinach, all rather high in oxalic acid. I am not at all sure that *The Wealth of India* is correct. It says (under Spinach): "The oxalates can be eliminated by boiling the vegetable for 15 minutes and rejecting the water (with a lot of the valuable minerals)" (WOI). I would suggest also adding sources of calcium like bones, or ashes, or even milk, to the new water. Suphakarn et al. (1987) investigated the effect of pumpkin-seed supplementation on oxalcrystalluria and urinary composition in 20 Thai boys age 2-7 years. The longer the supplementation with pumpkin seeds, the better the results. Pumpkin seeds lowered calcium-oxalate crystal occurrence and calcium level but increased phosphorus, pyrophosphate, glycosaminoglycans, and potassium values in urine as compared with orthophosphate supplementation. Pumpkin seeds, providing high phosphorus levels, can be used to lower risk of bladder-stone disease (X 3799495).

A Thai study (X3799495) hints that pumpkin seed might somehow neutralize crystals of calcium oxalate. Might this also be of interest in endometriosis, as well as vulvar vestibulitis, and several other disorders when oxalates tend to be a problem. Might it even be taken with some of the oxalic acid rich herbs, purslane, rhubarb, sheep sorrel sorrell, spinach, e.g., which otherwise are quite nutritious.

You may have seen the television ads spurring you on to eat seafood twice a week, implying that there are many health benefits to derive therefrom. Some vegetarians, not inclined to eat seafoods of animal origin, find themselves in a quandary. Probably overdosed with propaganda for the health benefits attributed to the so-called Omega-3 fatty acids, vegetarians have been actively seeking vegetable sources of these health-promoting acids. Writing in the prestigious *New England Journal of Medicine*, NIH scientists Artemis P. Simopoulos and Norman Salem (1986) say "Purslane is the richest source of Omega-3 fatty acids of any vegetable yet examined." Let me insert the word leafy before the word vegetable to make the above sentence more accurate.

Oils of wild walnuts and butternuts are magnitudes higher than purslane, the wild vegetable, in Omega-3 fatty acids, recently suggested to lower our risks for heart diseases, perhaps even cancer. While Rudin's book *The Omega-3 Phenomenon* hints at more than 50 ailments alleviated by omega-3's, our FDA states: "In summary, there is no general recognition of the therapeutic role of omega-3 fatty acids in human nutrition and health at this time." Elsewhere after a cursory study of the claims for omega-3's, I concluded: "As with most other compounds, too little or too much of a given fatty acid can probably be harmful. Be modest...consuming a variety of wholesome oils, or better yet, the seeds from which they are expressed. Variety is the spice of life, perhaps the fountain of youth, with the wide array of antioxidants in a varied unprocessed diet of natural seeds" (*Organica*, 1989).

While not outstanding as an Omega-3 source when compared to seeds, the wild vegetable purslane is a forager's treasure in the dead heat of summer, and can be dried, pickled, or canned for later use in winter. I dry it like I do my culinary herbs, slowly, out of direct sunlight. Then I crumple the dried herb into my winter dried bean soups. The mucilaginous purslane is almost as good as okra or filé (dried sassafras leaf) as a soup thickener. We do not want to prescribe herbal medicine, but some of our foraging readers may just find themselves lost in the forest without medicine or doctor. Maybe we could substitute a mess of purslane greens for popeye's spinach, bringing him out of his slump. Each plant contains hundreds of biologically active compounds, some synergic (acting in the same direction with augmentive effects), some antagonistic (acting in opposing directions, thus partially or completely nullifying each other). Thus herbs, like purslane, constitute a veritable medicinal menu of biologically active compounds.

From my CRC *Handbook of Proximate Analyses*, I have extracted Table 1, a comparison of the nutritional value of five wild greens, on a fresh or wet weight basis. Note that purslane is the "wettest," containing 92.5% to 95% or 925,000 to 950,000 ppm water. Hence, its nutrients are more dilute, on the whole, than those of the other four edible weeds. Hence, it is no superstar from a nutritional point of view. On a dry basis, though, the purslane contains 176,000-442,000 ppm (17.6-44.2%) protein; 24,000- 53,000 ppm (2.4-5.3%) fat; 355,000-632,000 ppm (35.5-63.2%) total carbohydrate; 85,000-120,000 ppm (8.5-12.0%) fiber; 8,977-20,780 ppm calcium; 3,200-7,740 ppm phosphorus; 112-467 ppm iron; 550 ppm sodium; 5,050-31,200 ppm potassium; 105-200 ppm beta-carotene (precursor of vitamin A); 2.3-4.8 ppm thiamine; 11-16 ppm riboflavin; 57-67 ppm niacin; and 1,680-6,170 ppm ascorbic acid (vitamin C). Since the purslane, like most succulent leaves is ca 90-95% water, you may roughly convert to a fresh weight basis by just dividing by 10 (for 90%) or 20 (for 95%). For example, the fresh plant would contain closer to 200-600 ppm ascorbic acid, the carefully dried plant could contain 10-20 times more on a calculated Zero Moisture Basis (ZMB).

You've probably heard Garrison Keeler on *Prairie Home Companion* talking about all the Lake Wobegon children being above average. I have been guilty, over the years, of talking about some of our plants being high in certain nutrients without defining the word high. But in our new nutritional tables, we have finally incorporated a baseline average, averaging various plant foods, specifically 5 aerial vegetables, 5 cultivated leafy vegetables, 5 wild leafy vegetables (like purslane), 5 shoots (like asparagus), 10 fruits, 5 subterranean vegetables, 10 root crops, 10 cereals, 10 pulses and 10 nuts, for a total of 75 foods, representing most types of plant foods. On a dry matter basis, alias zero moisture basis (ZMB), the average plant food has 188,000 ppm (18.8%) protein; 98,000 ppm (9.8%) fat; 644,000 ppm (64.4%) total carbohydrates; 67,000 ppm (6.7%) fiber; 72,000 ppm (7.2%) ash (roughly equivalent to total mineral content); 4,100 ppm calcium, 4,030 ppm phosphorus; 96 ppm iron; 1,660 ppm sodium; 21,640 ppm (2.2%) potassium; 113 ppm beta-carotene; 7.4 ppm thiamine; 8.3 ppm riboflavin; 52 ppm niacin; and 2,450 ppm ascorbic acid.

## Sensitive Plant, "Mimosa," "Chami" (*Mimosa pudica*)

(Unpublished)

Several small and shrubby herbaceous species of the big genus *Mimosa* are most impressive because of their thigmotropy, a big word that means responding to touch. Kids love them. Touch them and instantaneously the plant folds up and closes its leaves. Latins also call them "dormilóon," meaning the big sleeper, because they often go to sleep (not so rapidly as when responding to touch); there's a big word for that nyctinastic, which means moving at night. Many legumes (and the sensitive mimosa is a legume), fold up their leaves at night before or after the sun goes down. It's that rapid folding of the leaves in response to touch that is so impressive. Plants can move, plants can communicate with each other via chemicals (related *Acacia* trees in Africa tell another *Acacia* tree that a giraffe is nibbling on it, and the second *Acacia* generates some giraffe repellent compounds), and some plants, not this one, even having swimming sperm. (Ginkgo has swimming sperm), and many legumes increase the levels of fungicidal compounds they contain when a fungus attacks them. Just as our pet animals are smarter than we credit them, plants are also alive, can communicate, fight off their enemies with natural pesticides, and reproduce. They too deserve a lot of respect. Additionally the green plants make the foods that feed the world, the oxygen that the thankless animals breathe, and most of the medicines used by the third world, and 25% of the pharmaceuticals used in the United States. Thank you green plants.

But the sensitive plant is more than just a curio, it is also a very important folk medicinal plant. If it really contains, as reported, norepinephrine or noradrenalin, compounds active in human nerve transmission, we have to wonder if that compound might be involved in the rapid closing of the leaves, in response to touch. We might even call it the nervous plant.

In a super book, the late Julia Morton, whom I today designate as the grand dame of Latin American ethnobotany, at least here in North America, had many interesting comments on the plant (Morton, 1981). Following the "Doctrine of Signatures," Guatemalans make a tea from the sleeping leaves and bathe their babies in the lukewarm tea, hoping they too will go to sleep. In Trinidad, even the adults take the leaves to promote sleep and to treat urinary infections. And that's exactly one use for it around our Peruvian ACEER camp, for insomnia. Garifuna, in Nicaragua at least, use the tea orally for aches and pains, fever, digestive disorders, and as an abortifacient, for worms and intestinal parasites, and for menstrual disorders and associated hemorrhage.

On our Mayan tours to Belize, we often meet with Rosita Arvigo. In her neck of the woods, as elsewhere it is used as an anodyne (pain-reliever), antispasmodic (relaxes cramps), and diuretic (stimulate utinating; matter of fact one of the Belize names is pissabed). In her area, the dried leaves are often smoked in pipes to alleviate muscle spasms and backache.

Even the Indians of Asia have come out with many interesting uses. Juice expressed from the plant is dropped onto piles and sores. And it is more dangerously perhaps used as a nose drop for sinusitis.The leaves are mashed up and applied as a paste to glandular swelling. They use the root tea for gravel (stones) and other urinary complaints. They claim that cattle readily eat the plant, in spite of its spines, and the meat of the cattle is firmer and they give more milk. They further report in *The Wealth of India*, that it contains mimosine, a compound which is being studied as an herbal sheep defleecer. Mimosine given to sheep may cause their hair to fall out.

Yes, Antonio's "chami" may take the hair off your chest, if *The Wealth of India* is correct.

***MIMOSINE:** Antimelanomic 526; Antispasmodic 20-50 mg/L 526; Depilatory JBH; DNA-Inhibitor JBH; Goitrogenic JBH; Herbicide (IC100=5 mM) 438; Motor-Depressant 1,000 orl mus 526; Teratogenic JBH.

According to the late Dr. Morton, Cubans take the root tea topically for eczema, and internally for fever (and hint that the plant is abortifacient). Other West Indians use it for kidney problems, lumbago, nervousness (like the nervous leaf).

You may have heard our ACEER Shaman, Antonio Montero Pisco, and his story about another legume, the "hicoja," *Bauhinia* spp. bark of which he says was used as tea to prevent conception if consumed during the menses. If consumed during 6 menses, said tea is supposed to prevent conception forever. The same story he tells about the "chami." And because the leaf wilts so rapidly, suggestive of certain organs of the body, shriveled up after intercourse, Antonio seems to follow a reverse "Doctrine of Signatures," suggesting that this same tea, used as a contraceptive or sterilant, might also serve as an aphrodisiac. So far, I doubt this story about the "chami," but almost every time when I have doubted Antonio, some fact emerges to hint that there is method to his madness, a chemical in the plant that might explain its folklore.

## Shepherd's Purse (*Capsella bursa-pastoris*)

*The Business of Herbs* 11(4):12-13, September/October, 1993

Shepherd's purse is an inconspicuous cruciferous weed with a basal winter rosette. The leaves of the rosette are two to five inches long, toothed or pinnately lobed (cut to the midrib leaving a feather-like display of lobes), and relatively long-stalked. The stem leaves are smaller, with proportionately smaller stalks and shallower lobes; the uppermost leaves have their bases nearly surrounding the stem, sometimes with star-shaped (stellate) hairs. But it is the fruits from which the common name derives. They are triangular or notched at the tip with a few small seeds (coins to the imaginative) in each flattened half of the triangle (Duke's CRC *Handbook of Edible Weeds*, 1992).

### Definitely edible

Like many other members of the mustard family, shepherd's purse is a spicy potherb, which may double as a spring tonic, perhaps with some cancer-preventive activity as well. Tender plant parts of the crucifer family are pleasantly peppery when eaten raw (also cancer-preventive according to the NCI); older plants are tough enough to warrant a pinch of bicarbonate of soda to tenderize the fibers. Indians ground the minute seeds to make a nutritious flour. Had I gone to the trouble to gather the seeds, I think I would use them for sprouts, perhaps getting proportionately more vitamin, fiber, and protein and less fat that way. Storage fats in seeds are often mobilized in germinating. Japanese are big on sprouts of the radish, also in the mustard family (which also includes cabbage, cauliflower, broccoli, etc.).

Japanese consider shepherd's purse an essential condiment in their barley-rice gruel, a ceremonial dish on January 7 (Facciola, 1990). Several foraging books suggest the use of the fruits (and/or seeds) as a pepper substitute for addition to soups and stews. Facciola (1990) comments that the fresh or dried roots are used as a ginger substitute. Reducing the plant to ashes by burning in an enclosed container yields a gray substitute for salt. In ashing, almost everything combustible is driven off, leaving the minerals in the ash, including sodium, potassium, etc. Such ashes might also function as a substitute for bicarbonate in tenderizing fibrous plant parts. In a camping situation, I don't hesitate to add ashes from the campfire to a stew for salt and tenderizer. I recite all this to convince you that this is what I call GRAF (Generally Recognized as Food).

## Choline source

There are some interesting compounds found in the shepherd's purse, over and beyond the antioxidant, cancer-preventing sulfur compounds, ascorbic acid, beta-carotene, tocopherol, and glutathione. High in choline, shepherd's purse is one of the top three plants in my "Father Nature's Farmacy" (FNF) database. Martindale's *Extra Pharmacopoeia* hints that choline (5-16 grams per person per day) might have anti-Alzheimeran activity. However, that is considerably more choline than one would normally get in a serving of shepherd's purse, which may contain only 0.2%-1% choline, on a dry-weight basis. That means a dry kilogram could contain 2 to 10 grams choline if it did not dissipate during drying. That also means a wet kilogram would contain only 0.2 to 1 gram, if shepherd's purse is 90% water. Several other activities are reported for choline in FNF, for chorea, cirrhosis (6 g/person/day), cystinuria, diabetes, dyskinesia, high blood pressure, even mania. Based on LD50 data for rats, there's a nice therapeutic window; it takes 10 to 100 times as much choline to kill as to cure.

I won't suggest trying to cure with shepherd's purse, but you might consider adding it to your bean soups. It seems that most, if not all, legumes are high in choline; black-eyed pea (cowpea), fenugreek, lentil, mung bean, pea, and soybean being among the higher. Most of these legumes can be purchased dry at your grocery, soaked overnight, and combined to make a delicious bean soup.

There are few, if any, reasons to believe that choline will prevent Alzheimer's, but anti-Alzheimeran activity is reported, rightly or wrongly. There is one good reason not to try to market anything called "Anti-Alzheimeran Soup." That would be illegal, constituting medicinal labeling. The FDA interprets a label like that as making a medical claim, meaning that the soup mix would have to be proved safe and efficacious for Alzheimer's Disease. That now takes an average $231 million [[1.7 billion by 2003]], pretty expensive for a soup mix. I suppose, but don't know, that it would be legal to call it "High-Choline Soup Mix," leaving it to science to prove whether orally ingested choline is or is not good at preventing or alleviating any diseases.

## Fumaric acid

Shepherd's purse is one of the few herbs for which I have quantitative data on fumaric acid. If I interpret *Hager's Handbook* correctly, the herbage contains 0.14% (1,400 ppm) fumaric acid (usually the report in dry weight percentages), probably meaning only about 140 ppm on a fresh basis. A richer source is the carambola, a tropical fruit, which may contain 310 mg fumaric acid, on a wet basis. Japanese researchers in 1990 reported that fumaric acid experimentally prevented liver cancer, at least in mice fed several different carcinogens.

Could a mixture of high-choline, high-fumaric acid, high-lecithin, and high-silymarin plants prevent cirrhosis and liver cancer? We don't know, and we won't know under the present economic and regulatory climate. Who could afford those millions to prove that these dietary liver-saving compounds work in foods, as they work alone?

The pharmaceutical industry won't do it! The government won't do it! The herb, natural-food, and food-supplement industries can hardly afford millions to do it. But it should be investigated.

I personally think heavy drinkers would do well to entertain the dietary or nutritional approach to sparing their livers. Shepherd's purse is high in two of the liver-saving compounds. And it is high in several antioxidant cancer-preventives. Can eating a weed containing small quantities of several liver-sparing compounds save the liver?

Can we not disburse
Food Farmacy verse?
Can shepherd's purse
Delay the hearse?
There's the FDA curse!

NLEA makes it worse!
Seems kinda perverse
To curse shepherd's purse
What makes it worse
'Tis a federal curse (anon poet)

# Sweet Annie (*Artemisia annua*)

(Unpublished)

## A Bitter Medicine

I just took a swig of sweet annie tincture. No I don't have malaria. I have chronic lyme disease, probably with one or two co-infections, almost certainly *Borrellia burgsdorfii* (Bb) and possibly even babesiosis. But the herb is much better proven for malaria. Matter of fact, in my book, sweet annie alias sweet wormwood, alias Qing Hao is the herb of choice (closely followed by Latin American *Cinchona* and African *Cryptolepils*. I am actively campaigning that a third arm be mandated for any future clinical trials of artemisinin or cocktails containing artemisinin, also to include carefully prepared whole herb extracts. On an LD 50 basis, (oral administration in rats) *Artemisia annua* extracts are less than 1/25 as toxic as caffeine. I have on many occasions taken qinghao tincture as a malaria prophylactic, not positive that it works. I do know that one naturopathic physician, on ecotour with about thirty of us in the NgoraNgora Crater of Tanzania where all mosquitoes are malarial, took tincture of *Artemisia annua* instead of chloroquine or larium, like the rest of us were taking for malaria prevention. None of us got malaria. Subsequently that's what I have taken as preventive in Amazonian Peru, where even my "shaman" caught malaria. That's why we need these clinical trials. A field herbal extract could conceivably be 90% as efficacious as artemisinin and orders of magnitude cheaper, and much less likely to lead to artemisinin-

*Photo Courtesy of Roon Frost*

resistant malaria. Until the cheap extracts have been clinically compared with the expensive artemisinin or pharmaceutical cocktails containing artemisinin, we don't really know which is better. I have identified in the literature a suite of >10 phytochemicials which probably work synergically as a cocktail against malaria. As a strong believer in synergy, I like to quote others, like Buhner in his book *Healing Lyme*: "The whole herb has a much broader range of actions than artemisinin, the isolated constituent." (LYM) Bill Gates has funded one group of California scientists to genetically engineer artemisinin, the major active ingredient, and another group of Caifornia scientist to make ethanol from celluloic residues. His scientists are well aware that use of a monochemical drug like artemisinin will lead to resistance as I predicted in my CRC *Handbook of Edible Weeds* (1992): "Sweet Annie"...is a welcome weed at my place. ... {T}he secondary metabolite is an endoperoxide called artemisinin, and it will kill the chloroquine-resistant malarial strain (today). If [artemisinin] passes clinical trials and becomes widely used for malaria as it already is in China, I predict that the malaria organism will develop a tolerance for it within ten years."Recognizing this tendency for monochemcials to lead to drug resistance, Gates and malarial advisers propose pharmaceutical cocktails mixing the GMO artemisinin with other expensive pharmaceutical antimalarials. That seems to be the big strategy approved by the big pharma thinkers, thinking green (dollars to the pharmnaceutial manufacturers). But we green farmers at the **Green Farmacy Garden** think much smaller and greener (environmentally green). We like the Gates et al. idea of artemisinin in a cocktail of antimalarial chemicals, but we're thinking phytochemicals. In the abstracts of the 2006 Gaia symposium in North Carolina, I saw a great idea which was espoused, as I recall, by Jonathan Treasure. Mix the pure artemisinin, with a concentrated extract including all the important antimalarial compounds in the invasive weed. And all those cellulosic residues could be converted to power alcohol, as also Gates has proposed. Remember that if we extract the antimalarials and synergens, we'll still have ~ 90-95% in the extracting vats, ready to convert that biomass to energy alcohol. Apply this concept to most of our medicinal needs, extracting valuable chemicals from invasive weeds, and we'll contribute to the solution of a lot of problems: malaria and a host of other diseases, maybe most diseases; the high cost of medicines; the high cost of petroleum; the high cost of containing invasive weeds. Maybe we could start selling water to the middle east and quit importing so much petrol. So Gates et al. propose an expensive pharmaceutical cocktail containing artemisinin and other expensive pharmaceuticals. I propose the green herbal alternative, plant derived artemisnin and concentrates of other synergens and antimalarials from the invasive weed. Here's my cocktail; to your health and the health of malarials everywhere and the health of the planet.

## Antimalarial components of *Artemisia annua*

An Evidence-Based Cocktail of Phytochemicals
http://www.ars-grin.gov /duke/dev/all.html.
**Antimalarial agents:** Artemetin; artemisinin; ascaridole; casticin; chrysosplenetin; chrysosplenol-d; cirsilineol; eupatorin; oleanolic-acid; quercetin
**Antiplasmodial agents:** Chrysosplenetin; chrysosplenol-d; oleanolic-acid; quercetinAntipyretics: Alpha-bisabolol; borneol; menthol
**Antiseptics:** 1,8-Cineole; alpha-bisabolol; alpha-terpineol; arteannuin-b; beta-pinene; camphor;carvacrol; carvone; geraniol; kaempferol; limonene; linalool; menthol; oleanolic-acid; rhamnocitrin; scopoletin; terpinen-4-ol; thymol
**Hepatoprotective agents:** Borneol; isorhamnetin; kaempferol; luteolin; oleanolic-acid; quercetin; rhamnetin; scoparone; scopoletin
**Immunostimulants:** Astragalin; coumarin; eupatorin
**Larvicides:** Cuminaldehyde; linalool; thymol
**MDR-inhibitors:** Artemisinin; chrysosplenetin; chrysosplenol-d
**Parasiticides:** Artemetin; casticin; chrysosplenetin; chrysosplenol-d; cirsilineol; eupatorin
**Protisticides:** Alpha-bisabolol; artemetin; casticin; chrysosplenetin; kaempferol
[Source: Phytochemical Database, USDA (http://www.ars-grin.gov/duke) and updates]

## Dosages (Sweet Wormwood):

Plant used as medium to grow brewer's *Aspergillus* in Kangtung (TAN) General dosages; 4.5 - 9 g pl in decoction (FAY). For malaria, 3 g pl juice/day (FAY); 30 g plant (dry lf) or decoction (FAY) 10-20 g/day dry herb or 20-40 ml fluid extract (1:2) (for all KEB's Chinese posologies, these ratios apply) (KEB); higher doses suggested for malaria and lupus (KEB); 50 mg/kg artemisinin for 3 days (KEB); 300 mg/day artemisinin for 50 days for SLE or 30-54 g herb/day for malaria; 500-1,000 mg artemisinin (on first day, 500 mg day for 4 more days (LYM); for Babesia, 300 mg/day artemisinin. A quart infusion of 9 g flowering tops contains 95 mg artemisinin (LYM), a gin tincture of the same amount of crushed herb should contain the same amount of artemisinin, a bit tastier and better extracted with lemon juice and tonic water.

Part Nine

# Herb A Day…

# Polynesia

# Kava Kava (*Piper methysticum*)

(Unpublished)

## Kravin' Kava – One of Duke's Geriatric Dozen

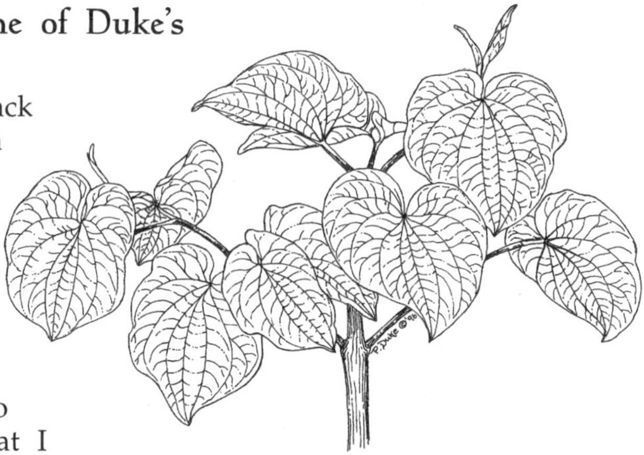

Maybe I got too laid back in Hawaii, going to a kava bar instead of a wine and cheese reception following my lecture there at the University of Hawaii. And I'm almost a week late with this newsletter. So it is only natural that I should write about kava kava, having consumed a whole mug of "Molokai Mud" in mid-March, a special brand "nene" from the island of Molokai. I have no vested interest in kava but fear it will fall victim to another herbal witch hunt, like ephedra and St. Johnswort, great herbs when used traditionally, but with slight potential for abuse or interactions. I know of no deaths yet due to St. Johnswort, one is being suggested (but not confirmed) for kava. But ephedra, or the synthetic-silver-bullet derived therefrom, ephedrine, may have killed a few who abused it. Here's what I submitted in the introduction to edition 2 of my CRC *Handbook of Medicinal Herbs* (2002): "Meanwhile, pharmaceuticals will kill more than 100,000 Americans a year, as per *JAMA*, a pro pharmaceutical journal, while herbs will kill fewer than 100, as per the conservative Washington Post in an anti-herb article, coordinated with the FDA and FDA database (Gugliotta, Mar. 19, 2000)."

Unlike the popular press, the FDA, most allopathic physicians, and the pharmaceutical industry and their lackies, I consider herbs as friend, rather than foe. Used intelligently they could decimate several big killers, including even the pharmaceutical industry. Herbs help reduce mortality, not increase it. Herbs are your preventive and curative friends, like good diet and exercise. They can diminish many mortality figures. Hawthorn could prevent a lot of cardiopathy; echinacea and garlic, et al., cancer; garlic and willow, et al., cerebral strokes; echinacea, elderberry and garlic, et al., flu and pneumonia; beans and onion and fenugreek, et al., diabetes mellitus; magnolia vine and milk thistle, et al., hepatosis; garlic and onions, et al., atherosclerosis; and java tea and restharrow, et al., may help nephrosis. But the bad press on herbs in this millennium is driving Americans from the safer herbs to the more dangerous pharmaceuticals. Remember this figure: pharmaceuticals documentably kill more than

| Killer | American Fatalities/Source | Year |
|---|---|---|
| **Sepsis:** | 225,000 – *Reuters* | Feb. 9, 2001 |
| **Pharmaceuticals:** | 140,000 – *JAMA* | 1997 |
| **Rollover Crashes:** | 100,000 – *NBC News* | Jan 9, 2001 |
| **Medical Errors:** | 98,000 – *Washington Post* | Nov. 30, 1999 |
| **Firearms:** | 35,000 – *CBS* | July 16, 1999 |
| **Drowning:** | 1,500 – TV news | ca. 2001 |
| **Road Rage:** | 1,500 – TV news | ca. 2001 |
| **College Binge Drinking:** | 200 – *CBS AM News* | July 16, 1999 |
| **Nuts:** | 125 – *Science News* | 155:213 |
| **Huffing:** | 100 – *Fox* Channel 5 | Mar 21, 2002 |
| **Herbs:** | ~50 – *Washington Post* | Mar 19, 2000 |
| **Skiing Accident:** | 30 – Chan. 4 NBC | Jan 3, 2001 |
| **Dogbite Deaths:** | 15-20 – *NBC News* | Feb. 2, 2000 |

100,000 Americans a year, while herbs do not documentably kill 100. Yes, these statistics tell us more Americans are killed by sniffing, huffing or snuffing freon in a paper bag, than are killed by herbs.

There is one death questionably reported for kava. I'm slow to believe that one. It's hard to keep up with all the conflicting reports on kava. ABC's Mark Blumenthal has published several interesting running commentaries (Blumenthal 2002). Mark notes that kava has enjoyed safe use for centuries in Polynesia. And he notes that Polynesians blame the European extracts (sometimes acetone, sometimes ethanol), saying that the traditional kava beverages do not produce liver problems. (Michael Balick announced in a January symposium attended by Blumenthal and also by me, that Polynesians may consume a pound at a setting, with so far no evidence of liver toxicity.) For the latest on the kava saga from Mark Blumenthal, see www.herbalgram.org. For an excellent account on kava, well referenced, see Soaring Bear's great website at http://www.herbmed.org/Herbs. Bear lists 35 accounts of clinical trials and 19 for adverse effects and contraindications.

I just received, since drinking my kava in Hawaii, a nice review from Paul Thomas (2002). He says, "In Germany and Switzerland kava use has been linked to about 30 cases of hepatotoxicity in the past few years, including hepatitis, cirrhosis and liver failure; one affected individual was reported to have died and at last one other required a liver transplant." Germany may ban kava, France and Switzerland banned it, and the UK agreed to remove it from shelves. Still, "there are no published reports of kava-induced liver damage in U.S. medical journals." It is of course, Germany's Commission E (abbreviated KOM in my table below), who approved kava (preparations with 60-120 mg/day kavapyrones) little more than a decade ago for treating "nervous anxiety, stress and restlessness." Of course our FDA is watching kava, like ephedra and comfrey with anticipation. Annual United States kava sales run 30 to 60 million dollars, but the kava scare will bring them down, just as bad press on St. Johnswort reduced its sales, OFTEN driving people to more expensive hepatotoxic and/or addictive pharmaceuticals. What we need and deserve, but will not get, is an NIH-sponsored, FDA-reviewed, unbiased comparison of the comparative hepatotoxicity of kava and the pharmaceuticals sold OTC or prescribed for the same indications. Which are most hepatotoxic? Which are more addictive? Which have more side effects? Which can stressed Americans afford? Come on, investigative reporters, dig in!!! Does kava injure more people per consuming capita than pharmaceutical anxiolytics like alprazolam (Xanax), amitriptyline (Elavil, Limbitrol), buspirone (Buspar), chlordiazepoxide (Librium), clonazepam (Klonipin), diazepam (Valium), dozepin (Adapin, Sinequan), fluoxetine (Prozac), fluvoxamine (Luvox), impramine (Tofranil); paroxetine (Paxil), proponolol (Inderal) and sertraline (Zoloft)?

"Unlike most pharmaceuticals used to treat anxiety, kava does not cause addiction or tolerance over time" (White et al., 2000). Wu et al. (2002) milled and extracted kava roots sequentially with hot water and methanol, and found bornyl esters of 3,4-methylenedioxy cinnamic acid and cinnamic acid, pinostrobin, flavokawain B, and 5,7-dimethoxyflavanone. All gave good COX-I and moderate COX-II enzyme inhibitory activities at 100 ug/ml. Wu et al. compared the 5 compounds with 5 pharmaceutical NSAIDs. Flavokawain was most impressive, at 100 ug/ml inhibiting COX-I by 77%, comparable to aspirin at 180 ug/ml, it inhibiting COX-2 by only 16%, roughly comparable to aspirin at 180 ug/ml, but only about ¼ as potent as Vioxx, and one-sixth as potent as Celebrex at 1.67 ug/ml. The authors concluded that a combination of the five compounds and the kavalactones may account for the traditional use of kava for the inflammatory pain of arthritis and gout. I see that as beneficial in dysmenorrhea. And if every little bit of COX-2-Inhibition helps, these might even help prevent Alzheimer's and colon cancer as well.

Yes, I still think, but do not know, that kava is as good as the pharmaceuticals. We'll never know until they are clinically compared. Until such clinical comparisons are performed, I would take the kava preferentially, if exercise, meditation and walks in the woods fail to serve me as anxiolytics. Like so many herbs, kava contains compounds that have been proven synergic.

According to British Pharmacologist, Williamson (2001), *Piper methysticum* "has a well-established place in herbal medicine for the treatment of mild anxiety states as an alternative to the benzodiazepines." The anticonvulsant activity of yangonin and desmethosyyangonin seems superior when these isolated chemicals are given in concert with other kava chemicals. The mix of individual kava constituents is synergetically superior to the most potent single component, dihydromethysticin. And there seems to be synergy between kava and valerian, the combination superior to either herb given alone, at least for stress-induced insomnia (Williamson, 2001).

Hawaiians may be even more frightened by the potential legal maneuvers on kava. Here's some wisdom Will McClatchey attributes to the locals: "Few wine experts would judge a wine based upon alcohol content. Likewise few Polynesian kava experts judge kava based upon lactone levels. It turns out that Polynesians are selecting kava for a lot of different reasons, including flavor, effect, and aroma. This is lost in the literature that focuses upon this as a drug instead of a cultural drink with many varieties and nuances. Americans could go a long way if they could understand this basic fact. Perhaps if Germans took shots of pure ethanol they would have liver problems, but a little wine is unlikely to kill them. The same is probably true for kava, "the misunderstood beverage," not the "abused drug" (Will McClatchey, pers. comm. Mar. 2002).

Yes, I think, but am not sure, the "Molokai Mud" I enjoyed in Hawaii is about as safe as a cup of coffee, and more a CNS-relaxant than a CNS-stimulant, like coffee. I think kava may be good as Xanax for anxiety's Prozac, for menstrual cramps; and Ritalin, for ADHD. That's why I penned the following parody and sang it on TV in Hawaii when I was working with kava growers on the Big Island.

### Kava in the Evening (*A piperaceous parody*)

**The MR. Verse**

Kona in the mornin' kava in the evenin'
Kava when the blue moon's round
Kava when the stress make an uptight mess
Kava kinda kalms me down

**The MRS. Verse**

Kona wakes me up, and kava ease me down.
Alleviates my monthly pain.
Kava's surely the best thing 'round
When hyper Harry's up again.

**The HYPER HARRY Verse**

Kona in the AM, Kava in the PM
If Harry hyperactivates
Yes, kava klearly kinda kalms him
When he hyperagitates.

# Plant Index

# General Index

## Q



## R



## S

# About the Author

James A. "Jim" Duke, Ph.D, Economic Botanist and Ethnobotanist, retired after a full career with the United States Department of Agriculture (USDA, Beltsville MD) in 1995. After "retiring" he served 5 years as senior science adviser with Nature's Herbs. Though he has been retired more than a decade, the USDA still maintains his Phytochemical Data Base online at http://www.ars-grin.gov/cgi-bin/duke. He has more than 25 books dealing with herbs, economic botany and ethnobotany. Currently he teaches Medical Botany as adjunct professor with the Master of Sciences Program in Herbal Medicine at the Tai Sophia Institute, Laurel MD. With an aggregate of 6 years in Latin America, he still leads ethnobotanical trips to the Amazonian Rainforest, accompanied by his *Amazonian Ethnobotanical Dictionary* (Duke, J.A. and Vasquez Martinez, R. 1994. CRC Press, Inc., Boca Raton, FL). He often hosts tours of his own **Green Farmacy Garden** in suburban Maryland, with some 300 medicinal herbs. He was appointed honorary president of the Herb Society of America for 2007.